Biochemistry of Exercise VI

INTERNATIONAL SERIES
ON SPORT SCIENCES

VOLUME 16

Biochemistry of Exercise VI

Editor
Bengt Saltin

Human Kinetics Publishers
Champaign, Illinois

Library of Congress Cataloging-in-Publication Data

Biochemistry of exercise VI.

(International series on sport sciences ; v. 16)
Proceedings of the Sixth International Symposium on the Biochemistry of Exercise, held June 1985 in Copenhagen and organized by the research group on biochemistry and exercise of the International Council of Sports and Physical Education.
Includes bibliographies.
1. Exercise—Physiological aspects—Congresses.
2. Metabolism—Regulation—Congresses. I. Saltin, Bength, 1935- . II. International Symposium on Biochemistry of Exercise (6th : 1985 : Copenhagen, Demark) III. International Council of Sport and Physical Education. IV. Series. [DNLM: 1. Biochemistry—congresses. 2. Exertion—congresses. 3. Metabolism—congresses. Wl IN916BH 1985b / WE 103 B6135 1985]
QP301.B47 1986 612'.04 86-7192
ISBN 0-87322-052-8

These proceedings are from the sixth international symposium on the Biochemistry of Exercise held June 12-15, 1985 in Copenhagen, Denmark.

Managing Editor: Ann Morris-Bruehler
Production Director: Ernest Noa
Copy Editor: Ann Morris-Bruehler
Typesetters: Brad Colson, Theresa Bear, & Sandra Meier
Text Design: Julie Szamocki
Text Layout: Denise Mueller
Printed By: Braun-Brumfield, Inc.

ISBN: 0-87322-052-8
ISSN: 0-160-0559

Printed in the United States of America

10 9 8 7 6 5 4 3 2 1

Human Kinetics Publishers, Inc.
Box 5076, Champaign, IL 61820

Contents

Part I *Control of gene expression and protein synthesis in skeletal muscle.*

Part II *Recent development on receptors: Importance in exercise metabolism.*

Part III *Regulation of metabolism during exercise*

Section A *Nucleotides.*

Section B *Glucose metabolism.*

Section C *Training response.*

Section D *Various factors influencing the metabolism during exercise.*

Part V *Comparative physiology.*

Part VI *Metabolic capacity and response of the performing horse.*

Part VII *Muscle mechanics and adaptation with use and disuse.*

Acknowledgments

Benefactors

Major financial support for the symposium was provided by:

The Danish Medical Research Council
The Danish Natural Science Research Council
The Danish Heart Foundation
The Danish Rheumatism Association
The Danish Sports Assocation
The Ministry for Cultural Affairs
The Novo Foundation
The Tuborg Foundation

The organizing committee also wishes to acknowledge the contributions of the following:

Adidas
Astra-Syntex ApS
Den Danske Bank of 1871 A/S
Pfizer A/S
Privatbanken
Radiometer A/S

Editorial staff

Peter Farrell
Gabrielle Savard
Sören Strange
Inge Holm
Gregory Fox
Erik A. Richter

Secretarial assistance and coordination

Inge Holm

Preface

This symposium is the sixth in a series of international meetings pertaining to the biochemistry of muscular exercise, organized by the research group on biochemistry of exercise of the International Council of Sports and Physical Education. The objectives of the research group are to reach a better understanding of the basic biological mechanisms involved in exercise and to provide practical information to scientists, physicians, and educators interested in the role of exercise in health maintenance.

Held in Copenhagen, this symposium marks the first time a Nordic country has had the opportunity to host a meeting of this kind. It is hoped that one outcome of the meeting will be that research in the area of metabolic response to exercise, which has a long tradition in the Scandinavian countries, will be further strengthened.

The scientific sessions were held at the Panum Institute, and personnel from this institute and the August Krogh Institute of the University of Copenhagen gave generous help in the organization of the conference. The format of the meeting included invited lectures, panel discussions, and poster sessions. These proceedings include the lectures and the panel discussions, whereas the abstracts from the poster sessions are published separately (*Clinical Physiology*, Vol. 5, Supplement 4, 1985). With these publications, the research group and the organizing committee hope to present the current state of knowledge and understanding of the metabolic regulations in exercise and its practical significance.

Jacques R. Poortmans
Bruxelles, Belgium

Bengt Saltin
Copenhagen, Denmark

List of Speakers and Discussion-Chairmen at the 6th International Symposium on Biochemistry of Exercise:

Göran Andersson
Department of Pathology
Karolinska Institute
Huddinge University Hospital F69
S-141 86 Huddinge
Sweden

Robert B. Armstrong
Department of Physiology
Oral Roberts University
7777 South Lewis
USA-Tulsa, Oklahoma 74171

Warwick M. Bayly
Department of Veterinary
Clinical Medicine and Surgery
Washington State University
USA-Pullman, Washington 99164

Michael Berger
Medizinische Klinik E
Universität Düsseldorf
Moorenstrasse 5
D-4000 Düsseldorf 1
West Germany

Brenda Bigland-Ritchie
John B. Pierce Foundation
Laboratory
290 Congress Avenue
USA-New Haven, Connecticut
06519

Frank W. Booth
Department of Physiology and
Cell Biology
The University of Texas
Health Science Center at Houston
P.O. Box 20708
USA-Houston, Texas 77225

Claude Bouchard
Physical Activity Sciences Laboratory
Université Laval
Cité Universitaire
CDN-Québec, G1K 7P4
Canada

Ji Di Chen
Institute of Sports Medicine
Beijing Medical College
PRC-Beijing 100083
China

Michael G. Clark
Department of Biochemistry
University of Tasmania
G.P.O. Box 252C
AUS-Hobart, 7001 Tasmania
Australia

V. Reggie Edgerton
Department of Kinesiology
University of California
2877 Slichter Hall
USA-Los Angeles, CA 90024

Birgitta Essén-Gustavsson
Department of Medicine
Swedish University of
Agricultural Sciences
S-750 07 Uppsala
Sweden

Henrik Galbo
Department of Medical Physiology B
The Panum Institute
University of Copenhagen
Blegdamsvej 3C
DK-2200 Copenhagen N.
Denmark

Philip D. Gollnick
Department of Veterinary and Comparative Anatomy
Washington State University
USA-Pullman, Washington 99164

James M. Hagberg
Department of Internal Medicine
Washington University School of Medicine
4566 Scott Avenue—Box 8113
USA-St. Louis, Missouri 63110

Jens Halkjær-Kristensen
Department of Rheumatology
Rigshospitalet
University of Copenhagen
Blegdamsvej 9
DK-2100 Copenhagen Ø
Denmark

Poul Henckel
Laboratory for the Theory of Gymnastics
August Krogh Institute
University of Copenhagen
Universitetsparken 13
DK-2100 Copenhagen Ø
Denmark

Jan Henriksson
Department of Physiology III
Karolinska Institute
Lidingövägen 1
S-114 33 Stockholm
Sweden

Pavel Hník
Institute of Physiology
Czechoslovak Academy of Sciences
Vídenská 1083
142 20 Prague 4—Krc
Czechoslovakia

David R. Hodgson
College of Veterinary Medicine
Washington State University
USA-Pullman, Washington 99164

John O. Holloszy
Department of Internal Medicine
Washington University School of Medicine
4566 Scott Avenue—Box 8113
USA-St. Louis, Missouri 63110

Hans Hoppeler
Department of Anatomy
Universität Bern
Bühlstrasse 26, P.O. Box 139
CH-3000 Bern 9
Switzerland

Michael E. Houston
Department of Kinesiology
University of Waterloo
CDN-Waterloo, Ontario N2L 3G1
Canada

Thorsten Ingemann-Hansen
Department of Rheumatology
Orthopaedic and Municipal Hospital
University of Aarhus
DK-8000 Aarhus C.
Denmark

Paavo V. Komi
Department of Biology of Physical Activity
University of Jyväskylä
SF-40100 Jyväskylä
Finland

Stanislaw Kozlowski
Department of Applied Physiology
Polish Academy of Sciences
17 Jazgarzewska Str.
00-730 Warsaw
Poland

Steven F. Lewis
Department of Physiology
University of Texas
Health Science Center
5323 Harry Hines Blvd.
USA-Dallas, Texas 75235

Arne Lindholm
Department of Medicine
Swedish University of
Agricultural Sciences
S-750 07 Uppsala
Sweden

Hans O. L. Lithell
Department of Geriatrics
Uppsala University
P.O. Box 12042
S-750 12 Uppsala
Sweden

Terje Lømo
Institute of Neurophysiology
University of Oslo
Karl Johansgate 47
N-0162 Oslo 1
Norway

J. Duncan MacDougall
School of Physical Education
and Athletics
McMaster University
1280 Main Street West
CND-Hamilton, Ontario L8S 4K1
Canada

Oluf Pedersen
Division of Endocrinology and
Metabolism
University Clinic of Internal
Medicine
Aarhus Amtssygehus
Tage Hansensvej
DK-8000 Aarhus C.
Denmark

Dirk Pette
Faculty of Biology
University of Konstanz
P.O. Box 5560
D-7750 Konstanz
West Germany

Erik A. Richter
Laboratory for the Theory
of Gymnastics
August Krogh Institute
University of Copenhagen
Universitetsparken 13
DK-2100 Copenhagen Ø
Denmark

Reuben J. Rose
Department of Veterinary
Clinical Studies
The University of Sydney
AUS-Sydney, N.S.W. 2006
Australia

Loring B. Rowell
Department of Physiology
and Biophysics
SJ-40., School of Medicine
University of Washington
USA-Seattle, WA 98195

Neil B. Ruderman
Diabetes and Metabolism Unit
University Hospital at Boston
University Medical Center
75 East Newton Street
USA-Boston, Massachusetts 02118

Kent Sahlin
Department of Clinical Physiology
Karolinska Institute
Huddinge Sjukhus
S-141 86 Huddinge
Sweden

Gisela Sjøgaard
Danish National Institution of Occupational Health
Baunegårdsvej 73
DK-2900 Hellerup
Denmark

Marek Snochowski
Institute of Animal Physiology and Nutrition
Polish Academy of Sciences
05-110 Jablonna near Warsaw
Poland

David H. Snow
Physiology Unit
Animal Health Trust
P.O. Box 5
Balaton Lodge, Snailwell Road
GB-Newmarket, Suffolk CB8 7DW
England

Albert W. Taylor
Faculty of Physical Education
The University of Western Ontario
Thames Hall
CDN-London N6A 3K7
Canada

C. Richard Taylor
Concord Field Station
Harvard University
Old Causeway Road
USA-Bedford, Massachusetts 01730

Ronald L. Terjung
Department of Physiology
Upstate Medical Center
State University of New York
766 Irving Avenue
USA-Syracuse, New York 13210

Andrus Viidik
Department of Connective Tissue Biology
Institute of Anatomy
University of Aarhus
DK-8000 Aarhus C.
Denmark

Mladen Vranic
Department of Physiology
University of Toronto
Medical Sciences Bldg., room 3358
Kings College Circle
CDN-Toronto, M5S 1A8
Canada

R. Sanders Williams
Department of Medicine and Physiology
Duke University Medical Center
Box 3945
Durham, North Carolina 27710
U.S.A.

Archie Young
The Royal Free Hospital
New End Hospital
New End
GB-Hampstead NW3 1JB
England

Bernard Zinman
Toronto General Hospital
101 College Street
CDN-Toronto, Ontario M5G 1L7
Canada

Symposium Organization

Research Group on the Biochemistry of Exercise

Jacques R. Poortmans,
(Chairman),
Brussels, Belgium

Pietro diPrampero,
Geneva, Switzerland

Philip D. Gollnick
Pullman, U.S.A.

Jan Henriksson,
Stockholm, Sweden

John O. Holloszy,
St. Louis, U.S.A.

Hans Howald,
Macolin, Switzerland

Nikol N. Jakovlev,
Leningrad, U.S.S.R.

Joseph Keul,
Freiburg, W. Germany

Howard G. Knuttgen,
Boston, U.S.A.

Guy Metivier, Ottowa, Canada

Eric A. Newsholme,
Oxford, England

Bengt Saltin,
Copenhagen, Denmark

Albert W. Taylor,
London, Canada

Androus Tsopanakis,
Athens, Greece

Local Organizers

Bengt Saltin
Copenhagen University

Henrik Galbo
Copenhagen University

Jens Halkjær-Kristensen
Rigshospitalet, Copenhagen

Thorsten Ingemann-Hansen
Aarhus Hospital

Erik A. Richter
Copenhagen University

Gisela Sjøgaard
National Occupational and
Safety Commission, Copenhagen

Part I

Control of Gene Expression and Protein Synthesis in Skeletal Muscle

Regulation of Phenotype Expression in Skeletal Muscle Fibers by Increased Contractile Activity

Dirk Pette
University of Konstanz
Konstanz, Federal Republic of Germany

The existence of structurally and functionally defined fiber types or fiber populations and their assembly in various proportions are the basis of the pronounced heterogeneity found between skeletal muscles. Moreover, skeletal muscle fibers can be envisaged as dynamic structures because they are capable of changing certain properties in response to altered functional demands. It has been known for some time that increased contractile activity, as in endurance training, evokes a set of metabolic adaptations that make muscle fibers more suitable to meet the energetic demands of sustained activity (for reviews see Holloszy & Coyle, 1984; Saltin & Gollnick, 1983). In addition, several studies on the human have indicated that increased contractile activity, as in prolonged endurance training, might cause an increase in slow-twitch fibers (Andersen & Henriksson, 1977; Green, Thomson, Daub, Houston, & Ranney, 1979; Howald, 1982; Ingjer, 1979; Jansson, Sjödin, & Tesch, 1978; Schantz, Billeter, Henriksson, & Jansson, 1982; Schantz, Henriksson, & Jansson, 1983). Histochemical evidence for fast-to-slow fiber transitions by endurance training has also been presented for the rat by Luginbuhl, Dudley, and Staron (1984). Time course studies on the influence of prolonged endurance training in the rat have shown graded, sequential changes of all major functional parts of the muscle fiber, that is, its Ca^{2+} regulatory system, its energy metabolism, and its contractile apparatus (Green, et al., 1984; Green, Reichmann, & Pette, 1983). Thus, prolonged endurance training produces alterations indicative of fast-to-slow fiber conversions. These observations point to the importance of activity as a major control for the expression of fiber type-specific properties (Pette, 1984; Pette & Vrbová, 1985).

The important role of activity in the control of phenotype expression is emphasized by the chronic stimulation experiment of Salmons and Vrbová (1969). They showed that chronic, indirect stimulation of fast-twitch muscles with a frequency resembling that normally delivered to a slow-twitch muscle, has pronounced slowing effects on the time courses of both contraction and relaxation. Chronic nerve stimulation of fast-twitch muscle has since been used in many laboratories as a suitable model for studying activity-induced adaptations and their underlying mechanisms (for reviews see Jolesz & Sréter, 1981; Pette, 1984; Pette & Vrbová, 1985; Salmons & Henriksson, 1981).

One advantage of the stimulation model for the study of activity as a regulatory mechanism in phenotype expression is that responses are limited to the target and are independent of fatigue reactions other than within the stimulated muscle. Therefore, stimulation allows the application of higher work loads and, consequently, the study of dose-response relationships within a much wider range. Also, training experiments involve the whole organism and evoke secondary reactions; for example, alterations in food uptake, interorgan metabolism, the endocrine system, and so forth. The role of such secondary effects upon muscle is difficult to separate from purely activity-dependent responses. Moreover, training experiments rely on work loads that must be increased in a stepwise manner to acclimate the animal. Therefore, time course studies on the effects of increased activity are difficult to interpret with training. This problem is alleviated with stimulation, because increased activity can be at maximum from the onset. The following elaboration on the role of activity in regulating phenotype expression will, therefore, exclusively relate to results obtained from chronic stimulation of fast-twitch muscles.

FAST TO SLOW TRANSITIONS BY LOW FREQUENCY STIMULATION

Chronic low frequency (10 Hz) nerve stimulation of rabbit fast-twitch muscles (m.tibialis anterior, m.extensor digitorum longus) elicits a set of remodeling processes that ultimately result in the conversion of a ''white,'' fatigable, fast-twitch muscle into a ''red,'' fatigue-resistant, slow-twitch muscle. The conversion of phenotypic properties involves both structural and functional changes and occurs in an orderly time sequence that depends on the daily amount and total duration of stimulation.

Among the earliest changes are those affecting the Ca^{2+} dynamics of the muscle fiber and those rearranging the enzyme apparatus for energy supply. The remodeling of the myofibrillar apparatus occurs later. Therefore, the changes in contractile properties follow a biphasic time course (Figure 1). An initial steep increase in the time to peak of isometric twitch contraction (1 - 2 d of stimulation) is related with early changes in the Ca^{2+} sequestering system (Heilmann & Pette, 1979). Prolonged stimulation leads to more gradual increases in time to peak and these appear to be related with fast-to-slow transitions in the isomyosin pattern. As judged from changes in the myosin light chain pattern, alterations in the myosin composition occur after 20 d with 24 h/d stimulation (Pette, Müller,

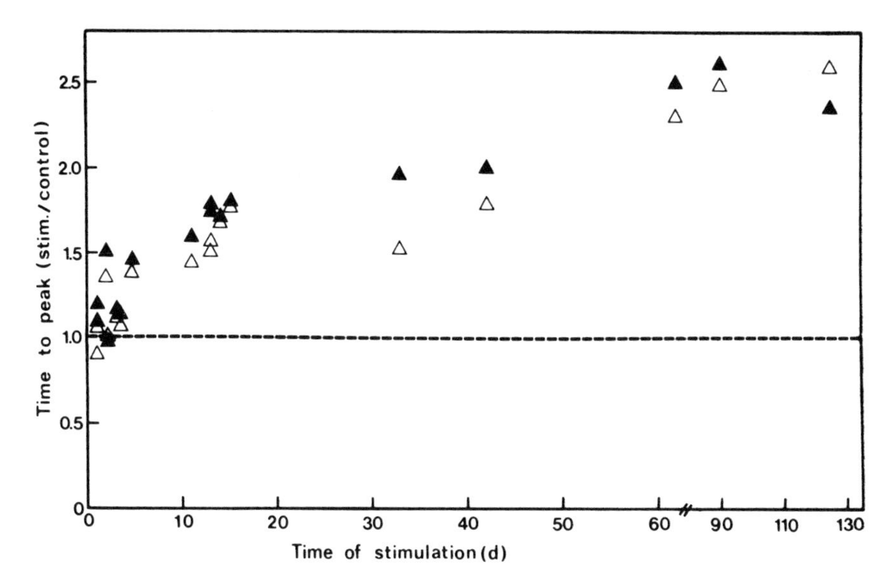

Figure 1 Time course of stimulation-induced changes in the time to peak of isometric twitch contraction of tibialis anterior (▲) and extensor digitorum longus (△) muscles of the rabbit. Values determined in the stimulated (24 h/d) muscles have been referred to those of the unstimulated, contralateral muscles. From "Molecular Transformations in Sarcoplasmic Reticulum of Fast-twitch Muscle by Electrostimulation" by C. Heilmann and D. Pette, 1979, *European Journal of Biochemistry,* **93**, p. 439. Adapted by permission.

Leisner, & Vrbová, 1976; Sréter, Gergely, Salmons, & Romanul, 1973). However, changes in myosin composition are not seen in muscles stimulated 8 h/d up to 35-40 d (Pette et al., 1976). Under these conditions, altered contractile properties reflect primarily changes in Ca^{2+} dynamics.

Changes in Ca^{2+} Sequestration

Studies on isolated sarcoplasmic reticulum (SR) preparations have revealed significant decreases in the maximum capacity and the initial rate of Ca^{2+} uptake after only 1 to 2 d of stimulation (Heilmann & Pette, 1979). These decreases are progressive with the duration of stimulation and correlate with the reduced activity of the Ca^{2+}, Mg^{2+} ATPase, and with reductions in the amounts of the 115 000 M_r-protomer of this Ca^{2+} pumping ATPase and its Ca^{2+} dependent phosphorylated intermediate. The time course of these changes correlate with reductions in the 7 to 9 nm intramembranous particles of the concave (A) faces of freeze-fractured SR vesicles (Heilmann, Müller, & Pette, 1981) and agree with morphometrically determined decreases in the fractional volumes of T-tubules, terminal cisternae and longitudinal SR (Eisenberg & Salmons, 1981). As judged from electrophoretic analyses, the peptide pattern of isolated microsomal preparations is transformed and, after 30 d stimulation, becomes nearly indistinguishable from microsomes isolated from slow-twitch soleus muscle (Pette, Heilig, et al., 1985; Sarzala, Szymanska, Wiehrer, & Pette, 1982; Wiehrer & Pette, 1983). Additionally, some changes in the phospholipid matrix of the SR membranes point to a fast-to-slow transition (Sarzala et al., 1982).

A recent study (Leberer, Härtner, & Pette, 1986), measuring Ca^{2+} uptake with a Ca^{2+} sensitive electrode in muscle homogenates, revealed an almost 50% decrease in both maximum uptake and initial rate after 2 d of stimulation. This dramatic change was restricted to the initial phase of stimulation, because only slight decreases occurred thereafter (Figure 2).

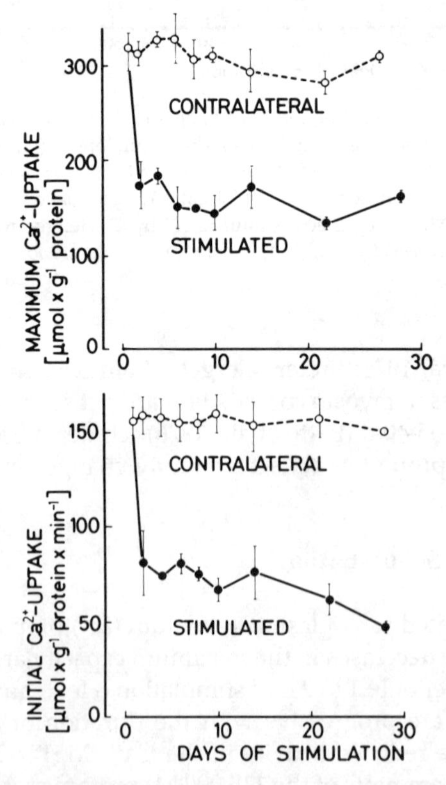

Figure 2 Time course of changes in initial rate and maximum Ca^{2+} uptake of sarcoplasmic reticulum. Ca^{2+} uptake was measured with a Ca^{2+} sensitive electrode in homogenates of chronically stimulated (12 h/d) and contralateral, unstimulated rabbit extensor digitorum longus muscles. The values represent means ± S.D. from 3 to 4 animals at each time point (Leberer, Härtner, & Pette, 1986).

No reduction in the protein concentration of the Ca^{2+}, Mg^{2+} ATPase was detectable by specific immunochemical analysis during this time. It appears likely, therefore, that the initial reduction in Ca^{2+} uptake is caused by a modification of the catalytic activity of the Ca^{2+} transport ATPase.

It is interesting that the reduced capacity of Ca^{2+} sequestration by the SR is followed by a decrease in Ca^{2+} binding in the sarcoplasm. It has been shown that parvalbumin, the major Ca^{2+} binding protein in the sarcoplasm (Heizmann, 1984), starts to decrease drastically after 4 d stimulation and is reduced by 50% in 11 d stimulated muscles (Klug, Wiehrer, Reichmann, Leberer, & Pette, 1983), decreasing to 5% to 10% of its original value in muscles stimulated for more than 21 d (Leberer, Seedorf, Klug, & Pette, 1985).

Changes in Energy Metabolism

Similar to endurance training, chronic stimulation increases the capacity for aerobic-oxidative metabolism. However, the extent of metabolic changes in chronically stimulated fast-twitch muscle exceeds that observed in training studies (Pette, Smith, Staudte, & Vrbová, 1973). A moderate rise in myoglobin (Pette, et al., 1973) and a pronounced increase in capillarization (Brown, Cotter, Hudlická, & Vrbová, 1976; Hudlická, Dodd, Renkin, & Gray, 1982) turn chronically stimulated fast-twitch muscles red. The changes in metabolic capacities are best illustrated by the alterations in the enzyme activity pattern. Collectively, there is a decrease in enzyme activities of glycogenolysis and glycolysis and an increase in enzyme activities involved in aerobic substrate oxidations; that is, activation and β-oxidation of fatty acids, ketone body utilization, amino acid oxidation, citric acid cycle, and respiratory chain (Buchegger, Nemeth, Pette, & Reichmann, 1984; Heilig & Pette, 1980; Klug et al., 1983; Pette et al., 1973; Pette et al., 1976; Pette, Staudte, & Vrbová, 1972; Reichmann, Hoppeler, Mathieu-Costello, von Bergen, & Pette, 1985).

The increases in enzyme activites of terminal substrate oxidation (the citric acid cycle, fatty acid oxidation, respiratory chain) occur in parallel maintaining the constant proportions of these enzymes (Pette, 1966). Their absolute tissue levels reach values that exceed by far those found in a slow-twitch muscle, such as the soleus (Buchegger et al., 1984). As seen in Figure 3, the 5- to 6-fold rise of these enzyme activities correlates with the approximately 7-fold increase in the volume density of total mitochondria (Reichmann et al., 1985). However, other mitochondrial enzymes, especially those involved in extra-intramitochondrial exchange reactions, change in a different manner and, therefore, alter their proportions with regard to the enzymes of terminal substrate oxidation. Thus, β-hydroxybutyrate dehydrogenase increases 28-fold, whereas the activity of mitochondrial glycerolphosphate oxidase is unaltered or decreases

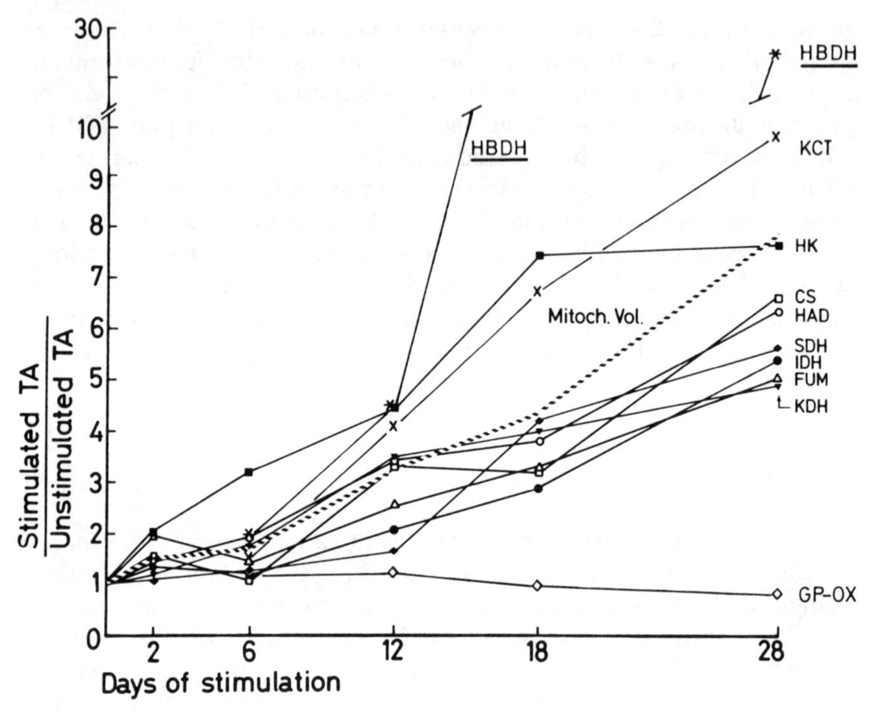

Figure 3 Time course of changes in volume density of total mitochondria (dashed line) and in enzyme activities of the superficial portion of rabbit tibialis anterior muscle in response to chronic stimulation (12 h/d). Volume density of mitochondria and enzyme activities are given as ratios of stimulated versus unstimulated control (with implanted electrodes) tibialis anterior. From "Biochemical and Ultrastructural Changes of Skeletal Muscle Mitochondria After Chronic Electrical Stimulation in Rabbits" by H. Reichman, H. Hoppeler, O. Mathieu-Costello, F. von Bergen, and D. Pette, 1985, *Pflügers Archiv*, **104**, p. 7. Adapted by permission. Abbreviations: CS, citrate synthetase; FUM, fumarase; GP-OX, glycerolphosphate oxidase; HAD, 3-hydroxyacyl-CoA dehydrogenase; HBDH, β-hydroxybutyrate dehydrogenase; HK, hexokinase; IDH, NADP-isocitrate dehydrogenase; KCT, 3-ketoacid-CoA transferase; KDH, ketoglutarate dehydrogenase; SDH, succinate dehydrogenase.

slightly after prolonged stimulation (Figure 3). The changes in the proportions of glycerolphosphate dehydrogenase and β-hydroxybutyrate dehydrogenase (Figure 4) clearly indicate that the increased mitochondrial population is qualitatively altered.

Mitochondrial glycerolphosphate oxidase maintains its constant proportion with the glycolytic enzyme activities (Figure 5). Conversely, hexokinase is inversely proportional to the glycolytic enzymes and maintains a constant proportion with the mitochondrial enzyme activities of terminal substrate oxidation. This rise of hexokinase (Figure 3) indicates that glucose phosphorylation is preferentially linked to ATP from oxidative phosphorylation. The enhancement of glucose uptake by increased con-

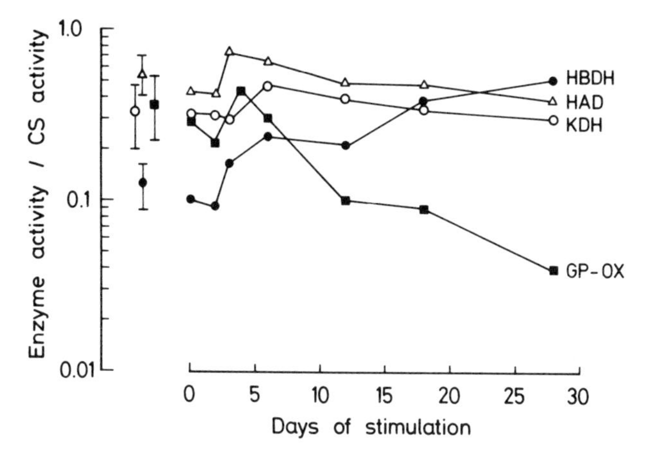

Figure 4 Relative activities of selected mitochondrial enzymes in the superficial portion of rabbit tibialis anterior muscles stimulated (12 h/d) for different time periods. Enzyme activities were referred to the activity of citrate synthetase in each muscle. Mean values ± S.D. (n = 6) from contralateral, unstimulated muscles are given in the left panel. Abbreviations: CS, citrate synthetase; GP-OX, glycerolphosphate oxidase; HAD, 3-hydroxyacyl-CoA dehydrogenase; HBDH, β-hydroxybutyrate dehydrogenase; KDH, ketoglutarate dehydrogenase. Plotted from data of Reichmann, Hoppeler, Mathieu-Costello, von Bergen, & Pette, 1985.

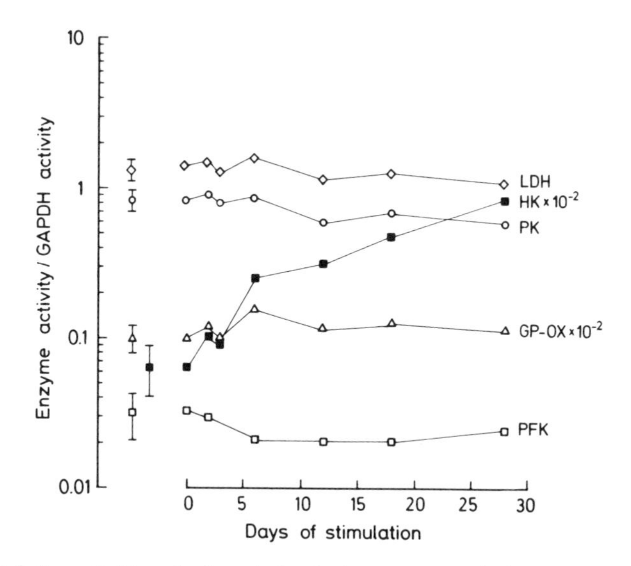

Figure 5 Relative activities of selected glycolytic enzymes and of mitochondrial glycerolphosphate oxidase in the superficial portion of rabbit tibialis anterior muscles stimulated (12 h/d) for different time periods. Enzyme activities were referred to the activity of glyceraldehydephosphate dehydrogenase (GAPHD) in each muscle. Mean values ± S.D. (n = 6) from contralateral, unstimulated muscles are given in the left panel. Abbreviations: GP-OX, glycerolphosphate oxidase; HK, hexokinase; LDH, lactate dehydrogenase; PFK, phosphofructokinase; PK, pyruvate kinase. Plotted from data of Reichmann, Hoppeler, Mathieu-Costello, von Bergen, & Pette, 1985.

tractile activity (see Richter et al., 1986), might be a trigger for hexokinase induction. Time course studies (Heilig & Pette, 1980; Pette et al., 1973; Reichmann et al., 1985) indicate that the increase in hexokinase activity precedes that of the mitochondrial enzymes. Therefore, the increasing drain of mitochondrial ATP into glucose phosphorylation might represent an important trigger for an elevation in the capacity of oxidative phosphorylation, that is, an increase in mitochondrial volume.

An important metabolic adaptation occurs in creatine kinase activity (Figure 6). Confirming our initial findings (Pette et al., 1973), the total activity of creatine kinase decreases in chronically stimulated muscle. This is due to a reduction of its major isozyme, MM-creatine kinase. However, this decrease is partially compensated by a steep rise (4- to 5-fold) of the mitochondrial isozyme (Schmitt & Pette, 1985). The mitochondrial isozyme, which amounts to approximately 2.5% of total creatine kinase activity in normal fast-twitch muscle, increases to 13% to 14% in long-

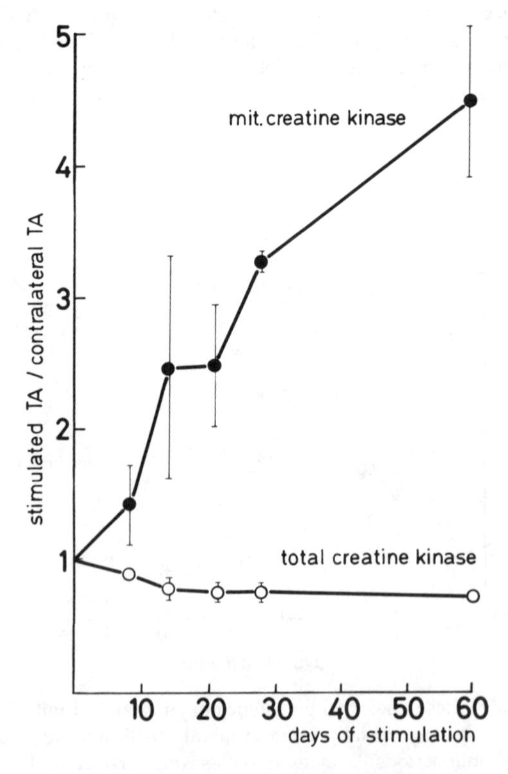

Figure 6 Time course of changes in total and mitochondrial creatine kinase in chronically stimulated (12 h/d) rabbit tibialis anterior muscles. Mitochondrial creatine kinase was determined by fractional extraction (Pette, 1966) and identified electrophoretically. All values are expressed as the quotient between stimulated versus contralateral, unstimulated muscles. Plotted from data of Schmitt & Pette, 1985.

term (60 d) stimulated muscle. Although this fractional increase is partly due to the decrease of cytosolic (MM) creatine kinase, the main increase is due to an absolute rise of the mitochondrial isozyme. In view of the suggested function of the creatinephosphate shuttle for mitochondrial ATP export, an elevated level of mitochondrial creatine kinase points to the reliance of respiratory chain phosphorylation in ATP-supply for contraction in chronically stimulated fast-twitch muscle. This metabolic change correlates with the progressively reduced capacity of glycolytic substrate level phosphorylation (Pette et al., 1973).

The increases in enzyme activities of aerobic substrate oxidation combined with the decrease in glycolytic enzyme activities result in markedly altered ratios between the capacities of the main aerobic and anaerobic metabolic pathways. These metabolic transformations are detectable at the single fiber level (Figure 7). Fibers from normal and long-term stimulated rabbit tibialis anterior muscles form two separate populations using the highly discriminative activity ratio, citrate synthetase/lactate dehydrogenase (Pette, 1985).

In addition to these shifts in absolute and relative enzyme activities, metabolic transformation is reflected by qualitative changes in the isozyme pattern of lactate dehydrogenase (Heilig & Pette, 1980; Klug et al., 1983; Pette et al., 1973). In chronically stimulated muscle, M-type isozymes

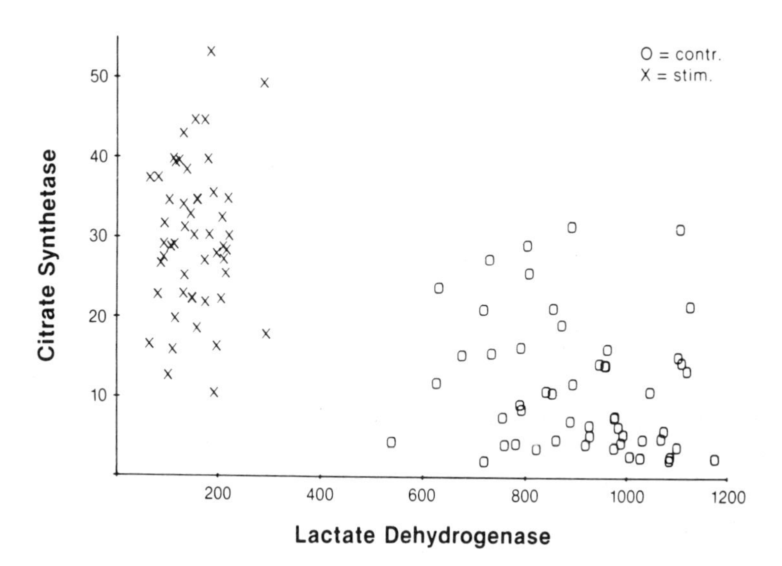

Figure 7 Activity plot citrate synthetase versus lactate dehydrogenase in dissected, single fibers of 84 d stimulated (24 h/d) and contralateral, unstimulated rabbit tibialis anterior muscles. Enzyme activities were determined in the same fibers and are given as μmoles $\times$ min^{-1} $\times$ g^{-1} muscle. O, contralateral, unstimulated; X, stimulated. Plotted from data of Buchegger, Nemeth, Pette, & Reichmann, 1984.

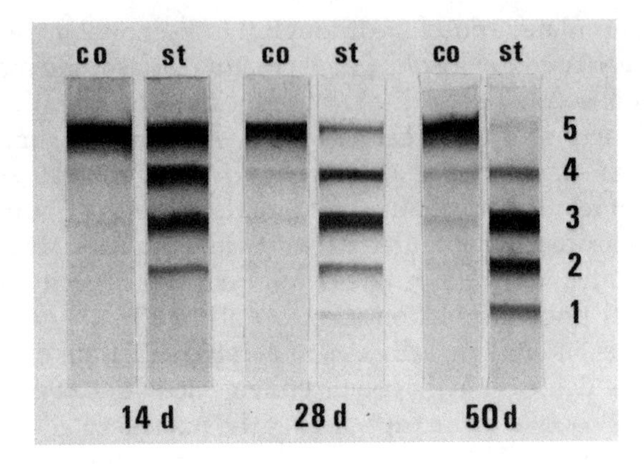

Figure 8 Electrophoreses of lactate dehydrogenase isozymes 1-5 in rabbit tibialis anterior muscles stimulated (12 h/d) for different time periods. Co, unstimulated, contralateral; st, stimulated.

LDH-5 and LDH-4, which are predominant in rabbit fast-twitch fibers (Leberer & Pette, 1984), are progressively replaced by H-type isozymes LDH-3, LDH-2, and LDH-1. The LDH isozyme pattern of 14 d stimulated muscle begins to resemble the pattern typical of a slow-twitch muscle. Prolonged stimulation leads to an almost complete transformation with extremely low concentrations of LDH-5 and a predominance of LDH-3 (Figure 8).

Conversions Within the Myofibrillar Apparatus

The transformation of the myofibrillar apparatus occurs later than changes in Ca^{2+} sequestration or metabolism. Therefore, earlier changes in contractile properties (increases in time to peak of isometric twitch contraction and in half relaxation time) are due to changes in Ca^{2+} dynamics (Heilmann & Pette, 1979). Histochemical assays for myfibrillar actomyosin ATPase activity reveal a progressive increase in slow-twitch (type I) fibers at the cost of fast-twitch (type II) fibers in chronically stimulated fast-twitch muscle (Kwong & Vrbová, 1981; Mabuchi, Szvetko, Pintér, & Sréter, 1982; Pette, et al., 1976). Long-term (2 to 3 months) stimulated muscles appear to be composed entirely of (histochemically defined) type I fibers (Buchegger et al., 1984). Although only selected items have been investigated so far, it seems that long-term stimulation leads to a thorough rearrangement of the myofibrillar proteins with an exchange of fast by slow isomorphs and a corresponding conversion of the sarcomeres. Changes at the ultrastructural level consist of a pronounced increase in the Z-band width (Eisenberg, Brown, & Salmons, 1984; Eisenberg & Salmons, 1981; Salmons, Gale, & Sréter, 1978).

Stimulation-induced changes in myosin composition were first detected by alterations in the myosin light chain pattern (Pette et al., 1976; Salmons & Sréter, 1976; Sréter et al., 1973). Although "fast" isotypes are symmetrically exchanged with their "slow" counterparts, the DTNB (phosphorylatable) and the alkali light chains follow different time courses (Brown, Salmons, & Whalen, 1983; Seedorf, Seedorf, & Pette, 1983). For example, in a long-term stimulated tibialis anterior muscle (Figure 9) the fast type DTNB light chain is replaced by its slow isotype (LC2s), the amount of fast alkali light chain 1 (LC1f) is reduced but still present, being partially replaced by its slow counterpart (LC1s) and the fast alkali light chain 2 (LC3f) is still detectable. This atypical light chain pattern cannot be explained by assuming a simple mixture of type I and type II fibers. On the contrary, it reflects the transition of the whole fiber population with the existence of atypical combinations between fast and slow light and heavy chains. The coexistence of fast and slow light chains has been shown by electrophoretic single fiber analyses (Mabuchi et al., 1982; Pette & Schnez, 1977).

Stimulation-induced alterations also occur in the myosin heavy chain complement (Mabuchi et al., 1982; Sréter, Elzinga, Mabuchi, Salmons,

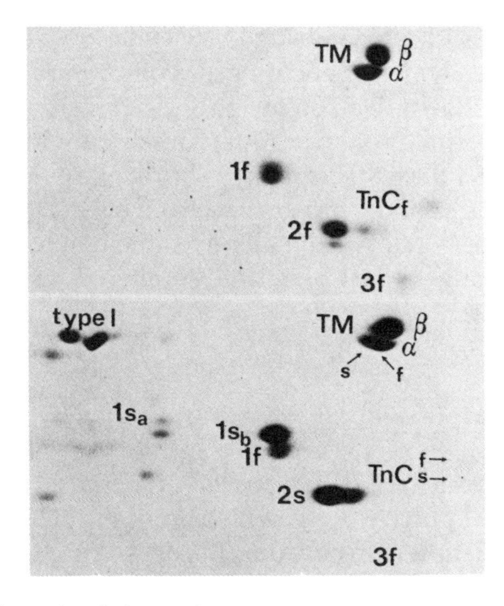

Figure 9 Two-dimensional electrophoresis of a myofibrillar extract from unstimulated, contralateral (upper panel) and 90 d stimulated (24 h/d) rabbit tibialis anterior muscle (lower panel). Abbreviations: type I, type I protein; TM, tropomyosin; TnC, troponin C; 1f, 3f, fast type myosin light chains; 1sa, 1sb, 2s, slow type myosin light chains; f, fast; s, slow.

& Luff, 1975) and may precede those of the light chains (Brown et al., 1983). It appears, therefore, that the protein components of the myofibrillar apparatus are exchanged asynchronously. In addition to the remodeling of the myosin molecule, there is a change in its phosphorylation. Klug, Houston, Stull, and Pette (1985) found a progressive decrease in myosin light chain kinase activity and a rapid reduction in the phosphorylation of the DTNB light chain.

Changes have also been observed for regulatory proteins of the thin filament. Roy, Mabuchi, Sarkar, Mis, and Sréter (1979) described changes in the α/β subunit ratio of tropomyosin in chronically stimulated fast-twitch rabbit muscle. In addition, chronic stimulation induces the expression of the slow isotype of the α-subunit of tropomyosin and fast-to-slow isotype transitions in troponin-C (Figure 9). Another protein associated with the thin filament, type I protein, has been observed only in slow-twitch (type I) fibers (Heizmann, Celio, & Billeter, 1983). The appearance of type I protein in chronically stimulated fast-twitch muscle (Figure 9) is an additional example of an unambiguous change in gene expression.

MECHANISMS OF ALTERED GENE EXPRESSION

During steady state conditions in muscle, the amount of a given protein is regulated by the balance between protein synthesis and degradation (Millward, Garlick, Nnanyelugo, & Waterlow, 1976). Turnover studies on several enzymes of energy metabolism in rabbit skeletal and heart muscle have shown (Dölken & Pette, 1974; Illg & Pette, 1979) that cellular levels of specific proteins can be correlated with their apparent rate constants for synthesis (Figure 10). This suggests that quantitative and qualitative changes in the protein spectrum of chronically stimulated muscle fibers primarily result from altered protein synthesis rates. Furthermore, these changes must be related to altered transcriptional and translational activities.

Changes in Transcription

Quantitative analyses have demonstrated pronounced elevations (maximum 3-fold) in total poly(A)$^+$RNA with significant increases appearing after 6 to 8 d stimulation (Kirschbaum, Seedorf, & Pette, 1986). Experiments using in vitro translation of total RNA or poly(A)$^+$RNA isolated from chronically stimulated fast-twitch muscle have shown that both decreases and increases of fiber type-specific proteins correlate with changes in specific mRNA species. Thus, the appearance of slow type

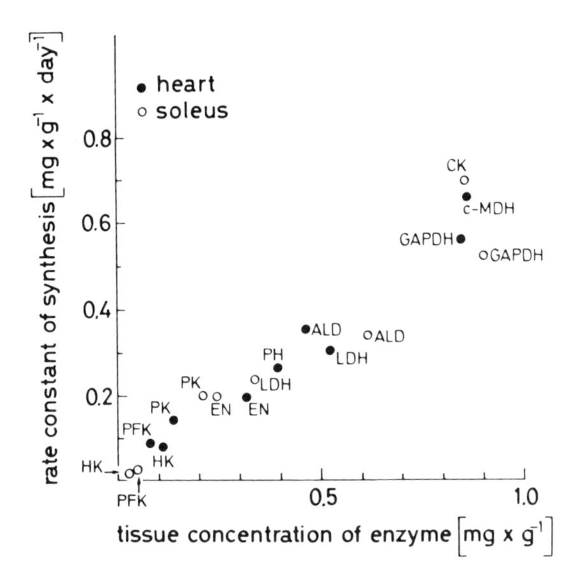

Figure 10 Correlations between concentrations and apparent rate constants of synthesis of individual enzymes in rabbit heart and soleus muscle. From "Turnover Rates of Hexokinase I, Phosphofructokinase, Pyruvate Kinase and Creatine Kinase in Slow-Twitch Soleus Muscle and Heart of the Rabbit" by D. Illg and D. Pette, 1979, *European Journal of Biochemistry*, **97**, p. 272. Adapted by permission. Abbreviations: ALD, fructose 1,6-bisphosphate aldolase; CK, creatine kinease; EN, enolase; GAPDH, glyceraldehydephosphate dehydrogenase; HK, hexokinase I; LDH, lactate dehydrogenase; c-MDH, cytosolic malate dehydrogenase; PFK, phosphofructokinase; PH, glycogen phosphorylase; PK, pyruvate kinease.

myosin light chains in chronically stimulated fast-twitch muscle correlates with the appearance of the respective, in vitro translatable mRNAs (Heilig & Pette, 1983; Heilig, Seedorf, Seedorf, & Pette, 1984; Pluskal & Sréter, 1983). Conversely, the reduction in parvalbumin that precedes the changes in myosin light chains is correlated with a decrease of its in vitro translatable mRNA (Leberer et al., 1985; Pette et al., 1985).

The time course changes in specific mRNAs can be analyzed by immunochemical methods for the isolation and quantitation of in vitro translated proteins. Such studies reveal that changes in tissue levels of parvalbumin, citrate synthetase, M- and H-subunits of lactate dehydrogenase are preceded by changes in the amounts of their in vitro translatable mRNA. Thus, mRNA coding for parvalbumin is reduced 50% after 6 d stimulation, whereas the parvalbumin concentration reaches half of its original value after 11 d stimulation (Leberer et al., 1985). This "precursor-product" relationship also exists for mRNA coding for the M-subunit of lactate dehydrogenase, but at slower decay rates (Seedorf, Leberer, & Pette, 1985).

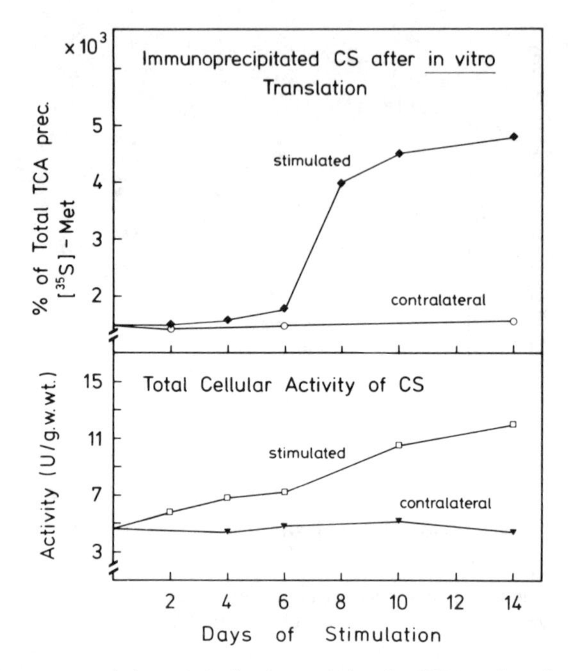

Figure 11 Time course of changes in *in vitro* translated mRNA coding for citrate synthetase, and of citrate synthetase activity in chronically stimulated (12 h/d) and contralateral, unstimulated rabbit extensor digitorum longus muscles. Measurements of enzyme activity and extraction of mRNA were performed on the same muscles. *In vitro* translated ^{35}S-met labelled citrate synthetase was immunoprecipitated and measured for radioactivity. Plotted from data of Seedorf, Leberer, & Pette, 1985.

The increases in both the H-subunit of lactate dehydrogenase and citrate synthetase correlate with increases of their in vitro translatable mRNAs (Seedorf et al., 1985). A slight increase in citrate synthetase activity precedes the steep rise in mRNA (Figure 11). This biphasic increase, which also occurs for other mitochondrial enzyme activities, appears to result from an initial increase in translational activity followed by an increase in transcriptional activity (Heilig & Pette, 1980).

Changes in Translational Capacity

Changes in translational efficiency and capacity apparently precede detectable alterations in transcription. Pronounced increases in total RNA (Heilig & Pette, 1983; Pette, 1984; Pluskal & Sréter, 1983), which is composed mainly of ribosomal RNA, point to severe changes in the translational apparatus. A study of ribosome concentrations and profiles has shown drastic changes induced by chronic stimulation of fast-twitch

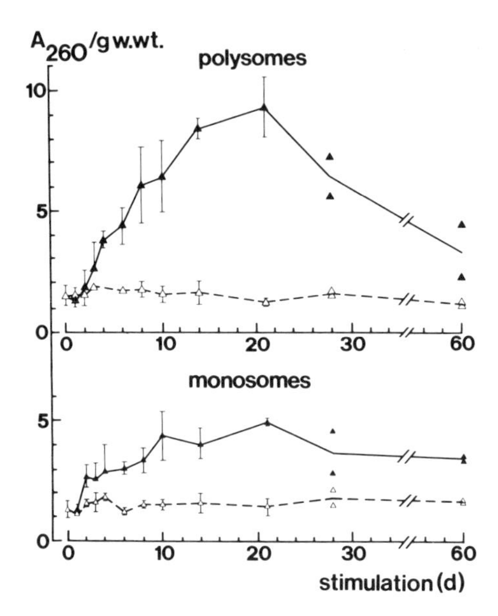

Figure 12 Time course of changes in monosome and polysome concentrations in chronically stimulated (12 h/d) and contralateral, unstimulated rabbit tibialis anterior muscles. Except for 28 and 60 d where only two animals were investigated, the values represent means ± S.D. from 3 to 6 animals at each time point. Plotted from data of Kirschbaum, Seedorf, & Pette, 1986.

muscle (Kirschbaum et al., 1986). Stimulation for 1 to 2 d greatly enhances the assembly of monosomes (Figure 12). At this time, no increases are detectable in either total or ribosomal RNA. It appears, therefore, that monosomes are formed at this early stage from existing precursors. However, stimulation after 4 d causes pronounced increases in total RNA and ribosome concentration (Figure 12), attaining maxima between 14 and 21 d (4-fold increase in monosomes, 6-fold in polysomes). Subsequently, total RNA and ribosome concentration decrease but are still elevated 2-fold in long-term stimulated muscles (52 d) and are, therefore, in the range of normal slow-twitch soleus.

The pronounced effects of chronic stimulation on both the assembly and synthesis of ribosomes support earlier observations of Mastri, Salmons, and Thomas (1982) who described drastic effects of chronic stimulation upon polyamine metabolism. These authors used a 24 h/d stimulation protocol, and, therefore, the time courses of their changes cannot be compared directly with those of the above described alterations. They found pronounced increases in ornithine decarboxylase activity between 18 and 48 h after stimulation onset. This increase was followed by marked, phasic elevations of putrescine, spermidine and spermine.

Ornithine decarboxylase, together with these polyamines, is thought to enhance the synthesis of robosomal RNA (Russel, 1983; Tabor & Tabor, 1984).

MECHANISM OF REGULATION

The preceding discussion clearly indicates that fast-to-slow conversions in chronically stimulated fast-twitch muscle involve events at the translational and transcriptional levels of gene expression. A similar sequence of changes has been observed by Watson, Stein, and Booth (1984) who studied the influence of muscle disuse by immobilization upon the synthesis of muscle-specific actin. They showed that a reduction in α-actin is initially brought about by a decrease in the synthesis rate that is then followed by a decrease in the transcription of the specific muscle RNA.

The question arises as to how changes in contractile activity translate into cellular signals that elicit and control such a sequence of events. Because the fast-to-slow transitions are brought about by nerve stimulation, the possible role of neurotrophic factors must be considered. Chronic stimulation of denervated fast- and slow-twitch muscles (Lømo, Westgaard, & Dahl, 1974; Lømo, Westgaard, & Engebretsen, 1980) and of embryonic muscle cell cultures (Düsterhöft & Pette, 1985; Srihari & Pette, 1981) indicates that innervation is not a prerequisite. The studies of Lømo et al. (1974, 1980) and of Hennig and Lømo (1985) have emphasized the importance of amount and frequency of impulse activity in the control of fast and slow contractile properties.

In addition, humoral factors, such as hormones or growth factors may also be causally related to the stimulation-induced events. Specific effects of different hormones upon the expression of phenotype-specific isomyosins in muscle have recently become evident (Ianuzzo, Patel, Chen, O'Brien, & Williams, 1977; Rutschmann, Dahlmann, & Reinauer, 1984). In this context, the regulatory function of activity upon exposition and/or coupling of hormone receptors could be of primary importance. However, no such studies have yet been undertaken in chronically stimulated muscle.

Considering the sequence of transformational events, the decrease in Ca^{2+} uptake by the sarcoplasmic reticulum appears to be among the first intracellular changes. An increase in free sarcoplasmic Ca^{2+} might, therefore, represent a trigger signal. Pronounced, transient increases in total Ca^{2+} have previously been observed in chronically stimulated fast-twitch muscle (Sréter et al., 1980). Furthermore, it has recently been shown that free Ca^{2+} increases approximately 5-fold during the first 10 d of stimulation and, thereafter, declines to values which, after 30 d, are still elevated 2-fold above normal (Sréter et al., 1985). These changes correlate with the drastic fall in Ca^{2+} sequestration initiating 1 to 2 d after stimulation onset (Figure 2). The subsequent steep decrease in parvalbumin content might intensify the initial effect and lead to a permanent elevation of the free Ca^{2+} concentration.

To date, the cause of the transient overshoot in total Ca^{2+} remains unclear (Sréter et al., 1980). A possible explanation could be that this elevation is at least partially due to fiber damage. Damage of a significant fraction of the fast-glycolytic fiber population has been observed in chronic stimulation after 2 to 3 d (Gambke, Maier, & Pette, 1985; Maier, Gambke, & Pette, 1986). The metabolism of the fast-glycolytic fibers is not programmed for sustained activity. It appears likely, therefore, that their ion pumps collapse when glycogen, the primary fuel for energy supply in these fibers, has been used up by the sustained activity imposed upon them.

However, fiber damage cannot explain the 50% decrease in Ca^{2+} uptake seen as early as 1 to 2 d after the onset of stimulation. Moreover, this decrease persists (Figure 2), whereas the degenerative and regenerative events reach their maximum approximately after 6 to 8 d stimulation and are low after 3 to 4 weeks (Gambke et al., 1985; Maier et al., 1986). Therefore, this steep decrease in Ca^{2+} sequestering capacity, which occurs in a single step and obviously precedes the fiber damage, must be caused by a change of the sarcoplasmic reticulum. Such changes could be brought about by a modification of the Ca^{2+}, Mg^{2+} ATPase or by specific alterations in the phospholipid matrix that affect its catalytic activity. Immunochemical analyses have demonstrated that the amount of Ca^{2+} transport ATPase is unchanged during this time (Leberer, Härtner, & Pette, 1986). Thus, a decrease in Ca^{2+}, Mg^{2+} ATPase specific activity is responsible for the reduction in Ca^{2+} uptake.

The role of Ca^{2+} in regulating protein synthesis and degradation in muscle is generally accepted (e.g., Lewis, Anderson, & Goldspink, 1982; Martonosi, 1982), but the mechanism of a change in gene expression by an increase in sarcoplasmic free Ca^{2+} remains obscure. It is possible that Ca^{2+} acts directly upon transcription and translation but it is also conceivable that its action is indirect and occurs through a chain of metabolic or other cellular events. In addition, perhaps increased activity evokes intracellular signals of different thresholds that act independently and control the expression of specific genes. Therefore, changes in Ca^{2+} concentration may be important but other signals, for example, changes in metabolites such as in glucose, may be of equal importance.

CONCLUSIONS

It is now evident that contractile activity plays a major role in determining and maintaining phenotype-specific properties of skeletal muscle fibers. Increased contractile activity in fast-twitch muscle elicits a time-ordered sequence of fast-to-slow transitions. These events involve all functional components of the muscle fiber and result from alterations of transcription as well as of translation. The initial events related to altered gene expression appear to occur at the translational level. There is an enhanced ribosome assembly followed by an increase in ribosomal RNA and polysomes. These increases in translational efficiency and capacity occur earlier than detectable changes in the amounts of specific mRNAs. In all cases studied to date, changes in specific proteins are preceded by changes in amounts of their in vitro translatable mRNAs.

As yet, it is still uncertain if indeed low frequency stimulation of fast-twitch muscle is able to accomplish a complete fast-to-slow transformation. All variables point toward this type of transformation. Nevertheless, it is evident that long-term stimulated fast-twitch muscles do not entirely resemble slow-twitch muscles; for example, incomplete transformation of the myofibrillar proteins and metabolic changes exceeding normal slow-twitch muscle characteristics. The stimulation model, however, does reflect the plasticity of skeletal muscle fibers. Consequently, the changes induced by long-term low frequency stimulation may represent a state of optimal adaptation to the imposed functional demands. These may vary from those that control the expression of a typical slow-twitch muscle.

Acknowledgements

These studies were supported by Deutsche Forschungsgemeinschaft, Sonderforschungsbereiche 138 and 156. I express my gratitude to all my collaborators for their contributions to this work. I also thank Dr. Robert S. Staron for his help in preparing this manuscript.

REFERENCES

Andersen, P., & Henriksson, J. (1977). Training induced changes in the subgroups of human type II skeletal muscle fibers. *Acta Physiologica Scandinavica,* **99**, 123-125.

Brown, M.D., Cotter, M.A., Hudlická, O., & Vrbová, G. (1976). The effects of different patterns of muscle activity on capillary density, mechanical properties and structure of slow and fast rabbit muscles. *Archiv,* **361**, 241-250.

Brown, W.E., Salmons, S., & Whalen, R.G. (1983). The sequential replacement of myosin subunit isoforms during muscle type transformation induced by long-term electrical stimulation. *Journal of Biological Chemistry,* **258**, 14686-14692.

Buchegger, A., Nemeth, P.M., Pette, D., & Reichmann, H. (1984). Effects of chronic stimulation on the metabolic heterogeneity of the fibre population in rabbit tibialis anterior muscle. *The Journal of Physiology* (London), **350**, 109-119.

Dölken, G., & Pette, D. (1974). Turnover of several glycolytic enzymes in rabbit heart, soleus muscle and liver. *Hoppe-Seyler's Zeitschrift für Physiologische Chemie,* **355**, 289-299.

Düsterhöft, S., & Pette, D. (1985). Changes in myosin light chains by chronic stimulation of myotubes in culture. *The Journal of Physiology* (London), **361**, 33P.

Eisenberg, B.R., Brown, J.M.C., & Salmons, S. (1984). Restoration of fast muscle characteristics following cessation of chronic stimulation. *Cell and Tissue Research,* **238**, 221-230.

Eisenberg, B.R., & Salmons, S. (1981). The reorganization of subcellular structure in muscle undergoing fast-to-slow type transformation: a stereological study. *Cell and Tissue Research,* **220**, 449-471.

Gambke, B., Maier, A., & Pette, D. (1985). Transformation and/or replacement of fibres in chronically stimulated fast-twitch rabbit muscle. *The Journal of Physiology* (London), **361**, 34P.

Green, H.J., Klug, G.A., Reichmann, H., Seedorf, U., Wiehrer, W., & Pette, D. (1984). Exercise-induced fibre type transitions with regard to myosin, parvalbumin, and sarcoplasmic reticulum in muscles of the rat. *Pflügers Archiv,* **400**, 432-438.

Green, H.J., Reichmann, H., & Pette, D. (1983). Fibre type specific transformations in the enzyme activity pattern of rat vastus lateralis muscle by prolonged endurance training. *Pflügers Archiv,* **399**, 216-222.

Green, H.J., Thomson, J.A., Daub, W.D., Houston, M.E., & Ranney, D.A. (1979). Fiber composition, fiber size and enzyme activities in vastus lateralis of elite athletes involved in high intensity exercise. *European Journal of Applied Physiology and Occupational Physiology,* **41**, 109-117.

Heilig, A., & Pette, D. (1980). Changes induced in the enzyme activity pattern by electrical stimulation of fast-twitch muscles. In D. Pette (Ed.), *Plasticity of muscle* (pp. 409-420). Berlin, New-York: W. de Gruyter.

Heilig, A., & Pette, D. (1983). Changes in transcriptional activity of chronically stimulated fast twitch muscle. *Federation of the European Biochemistry Society Letters,* **151**, 211-214.

Heilig, A., Seedorf, K., Seedorf, U., & Pette, D. (1984). Transcriptional and translational control of myosin light chain expression in adult muscle. In H.M. Eppenberger & J.-J. Perriard (Eds.), *Developmental processes in normal and diseased muscle* (pp. 182-186). Basel, Switzerland: S. Karger.

Heilmann, C., Müller, W., & Pette, D. (1981). Correlation between ultrastructural and functional changes in sarcoplasmic reticulum during chronic stimulation of fast muscle. *The Journal of Membrane Biology,* **59**, 143-149.

Heilmann, C., & Pette, D. (1979). Molecular transformations in sarcoplasmic reticulum of fast-twitch muscle by electrostimulation. *European Journal of Biochemistry,* **93**, 437-446.

Heizmann, C.W. (1984). Parvalbumin, an intracellular calcium-binding protein; distribution, properties, and possible roles in mammalian cells. *Experientia,* **40**, 910-921.

Heizmann, C.W., Celio, M.R., & Billeter, R. (1983). A new myofibrillar protein characteristic of type I human skeletal muscle fibres. *European Journal of Biochemistry,* **132**, 657-662.

Hennig, R., & Lømo, T. (1985). Firing patterns of motor units in normal rats. *Nature* (London), **314**, 164-166.

Holloszy, J.O., & Coyle, E.F. (1984). Adaptations of skeletal muscles to endurance exercise and their metabolic consequences. *Journal of Applied Physiology,* **56**, 831-838.

Howald, H. (1982). Training-induced morphological and functional changes in skeletal muscle. *International Journal of Sports Medicine,* **3**, 1-12.

Hudlická, O., Dodd, L., Renkin, E.M., & Gray, S.D. (1982). Early changes in fiber profile and capillary density in long-term stimulated muscle. *American Journal of Physiology,* **243**, H528-H535.

Ianuzzo, D., Patel, P., Chen, V., O'Brien, P., & Williams, C. (1977). Thyroidal trophic influence on skeletal muscle myosin. *Nature* (London), **270**, 74-76.

Illg, D., & Pette, D. (1979). Turnover rates of hexokinase I, phosphofructokinase, pyruvate kinase and creatine kinase in slow-twitch soleus muscle and heart of the rabbit. *European Journal of Biochemistry,* **97**, 267-273.

Ingjer, F. (1979). Effects of endurance training on muscle fibre ATPase activity, capillary supply and mitochondrial content in man. *The Journal of Physiology* (London), **294**, 419-432.

Jansson, E., Sjödin, B., & Tesch, P. (1978). Changes in muscle fibre type distribution in man after physical training—a sign of fibre type transformation? *Acta Physiologica Scandinavica,* **104**, 235-237.

Jolesz, F., & Sréter, F.A. (1981). Development, innervation, and activity pattern induced changes in skeletal muscle. *Annual Review of Physiology,* **43**, 531-552.

Kirschbaum, B., Seedorf, U., & Pette, D. (1986). Changes of the translational apparatus in chronically stimulated rabbit fast-twitch muscle. *Journal of Muscle Research and Cell Motility,* **7**, 60.

Klug, G.A., Houston, M., Stull, J.T., & Pette, D. (1985). Effect of chronic stimulation upon myosin phosphorylation and twitch potentiation in fast muscle. *Medicine and Science in Sports and Exercise,* **17**, 234.

Klug, G., Wiehrer, W., Reichmann, H., Leberer, E., & Pette, D. (1983). Relationships between early alterations in parvalbumins, sarcoplasmic reticulum and metabolic enzymes in chronically stimulated fast twitch muscle. *Pflügers Archiv*, **399**, 280-284.

Kwong, W.H., & Vrbová, G. (1981). Effects of low-frequency electrical stimulation on fast and slow muscles of the rat. *Pflügers Archiv*, **391**, 200-207.

Leberer, E., Härtner, K.T., & Pette, D. (1986). Reduced specific activity in sarcoplasmic reticulum Ca^{2+} ATPase in stimulated rabbit muscle. *The Journal of Muscle Research and Cell Motility*, **7**, 90.

Leberer, E., & Pette, D., (1984). Lactate dehydrogenase isozymes in type I, IIA and IIB fibres of rabbit skeletal muscles. *Histochemistry*, **80**, 295-298.

Leberer, E., Seedorf, U., Klug, G., & Pette, D. (1985). Parvalbumin levels and *in vitro* translation of its mRNA in chronically stimulated rabbit muscle. *The Journal of Muscle Research and Cell Motility*, **6**, 84.

Lewis, S.E.M., Anderson, P., & Goldspink, D.F. (1982). The effects of calcium on protein turnover in skeletal muscles of the rat. *The Biochemical Journal*, **204**, 257-264.

Lømo, T., Westgaard, R.H., & Dahl, H.A. (1974). Contractile properties of muscle: Control by pattern of muscle activity in the rat. *Proceedings of the Royal Society of London, Series B—Biological Sciences*, **187**, 99-103.

Lømo, T., Westgaard, R.H., & Engebretsen, L. (1980). Different stimulation patterns affect contractile properties of denervated rat soleus muscles. In D. Pette (Ed.), *Plasticity of muscle* (pp. 297-309). Berlin, New York: W. de Gruyter.

Luginbuhl, A.J., Dudley, G.A., & Staron, R.S. (1984). Fiber type changes in rat skeletal muscle after intense interval training. *Histochemistry*, **81**, 55-58.

Mabuchi, K., Szvetko, D., Pintér, K., & Sréter, F.A. (1982). Type IIB to IIA fiber transformation in intermittently stimulated rabbit muscles. *American Journal of Physiology*, **242**, C373-C381.

Martonosi, A. (1982). The development of sarcoplasmic reticulum membranes. *Annual Review of Physiology*, **44**, 337-355.

Mastri, C., Salmons, S., & Thomas, G.H. (1982). Early events in the response of fast skeletal muscle to chronic low-frequency stimulation. Polyamine biosynthesis and protein phosphorylation. *The Biochemical Journal*, **206**, 211-219.

Millward, D.J., Garlick, P.J., Nnanyelugo, D.O., & Waterlow, J.C. (1976). The relative importance of muscle protein synthesis and breakdown in the regulation of muscle mass. *The Biochemical Journal*, **156**, 185-188.

Pette, D. (1966). Mitochondrial enzyme activities. In J.M. Tager, S. Papa, E. Quagliariello, & E.C. Slater (Eds.), *Regulation of metabolic processes in mitochondria* (pp. 28-50). Amsterdam, London, New York: Elsevier Publishing Company.

Pette, D. (1984). Activity-induced fast to slow transitions in mammalian muscle. *Medicine and Science in Sports and Exercise,* **16**, 517-528.

Pette, D. (1985). Metabolic heterogeneity of muscle fibres. *Journal of Experimental Biology,* **115**, 179-189.

Pette, D., Heilig, A., Klug, G., Reichmann, H., Seedorf, U., & Wiehrer, W. (1985). Alterations in phenotype expression of muscle by chronic nerve stimulation. In R.C. Strohman & S. Wolf (Eds.), *Gene expression in muscle* (pp. 169-178). New York: Plenum Press.

Pette, D., Müller, W., Leisner, E., & Vrbová, G. (1976). Time dependent effects on contractile properties, fibre population, myosin light-chains and enzymes of energy metabolism in intermittently and continuously stimulated fast-twitch muscles of the rabbit. *Pflügers Archiv,* **364**, 103-112.

Pette, D., & Schnez, U. (1977). Coexistence of fast and slow type myosin light chains in single muscle fibres during transformation as induced by long term stimulation. *Federation of the European Biochemistry Society Letters,* **83**, 128-130.

Pette, D., Smith, M.E., Staudte, H.W., & Vrbová, G. (1973). Effects of long-term electrical stimulation on some contractile and metabolic characteristics of fast rabbit muscles. *Pflügers Archiv,* **338**, 257-272.

Pette, D., Staudte, H.W., & Vrbová, G. (1972). Physiological and biochemical changes induced by long-term stimulation of fast muscle. *Die Naturwissenschaften,* **59**, 469-470.

Pette, D., & Vrbová, G. (1985). Neural control of phenotype expression in mammalian muscle fibers. *Muscle & Nerve,* **8**, 676-689.

Pluskal, M.G., & Sréter, F.A. (1983). Correlation between protein phenotype and gene expression in adult rabbit fast twitch muscles undergoing a fast to slow fiber transformation in response to electrical stimulation in vivo. *Biochemical and Biophysical Research Communications,* **113**, 325-331.

Reichmann, H., Hoppeler, H., Mathieu-Costello, O., von Bergen, F., & Pette, D. (1985). Biochemical and ultrastructural changes of skeletal muscle mitochondria after chronic electrical stimulation in rabbits. *Pflügers Archiv,* **404**, 1-9.

Richter, E.A., Sonne, B., Ploug, T., Kjær, M., Mikines, K., & Galbo, H. (1986). Regulation of carbohydrate metabolism during exercise. In B. Saltin (Ed.), *Biochemistry of exercise Vol. 14* (pp. 151-166). Champaign, IL: Human Kinetics.

Roy, R.K., Mabuchi, K., Sarkar, S., Mis, C., & Sréter, F.A. (1979). Changes in tropomyosin subunit pattern in chronic electrically stimulated rabbit fast muscles. *Biochemical and Biophysical Research Communications,* **89**, 181-187.

Russel, D.H. (1983). Microinjection of purified ornithine decarboxylase into xenopus oocytes selectively stimulates ribosomal RNA synthesis.

Proceedings of the National Academy of Sciences of the United States of America, **80**, 1318-1321.

Rutschmann, M., Dahlmann, B., & Reinauer, H. (1984). Loss of fast-twitch isomyosins in skeletal muscles of the diabetic rat. *The Biochemical Journal*, **221**, 645-650.

Salmons, S., Gale, D.R., & Sréter, F.A. (1978). Ultrastructural aspects of the transformation of muscle fibre type by long term stimulation: Changes in Z discs and mitochondria. *Journal of Anatomy*, **127**, 17-31.

Salmons, S., & Henriksson, J. (1981). The adaptive response of skeletal muscle to increased use. *Muscle & Nerve*, **4**, 94-105.

Salmons, S., & Sréter, F.A. (1976). Significance of impulse activity in the transformation of skeletal muscle type. *Nature* (London), **263**, 30-34.

Salmons, S., & Vrbová, G. (1969). The influence of activity on some contractile characteristics of mammalian fast and slow muscles. *The Journal of Physiology* (London), **210**, 535-549.

Saltin, B., & Gollnick, P.D. (1983). Skeletal muscle adaptability: Significance for metabolism and performance. In L.D. Peachy, R.H. Adrian, & S.R. Geiger (Eds.), *Handbook of physiology, skeletal muscle* (pp. 555-631). Baltimore: Williams & Wilkins.

Sarzala, M.G., Szymanska, G., Wiehrer, W., & Pette, D. (1982). Effects of chronic stimulation at low frequency on the lipid phase of sarcoplasmic reticulum in rabbit fast-twitch muscle. *European Journal of Biochemistry*, **123**, 241-245.

Schantz, P., Billeter, R., Henriksson, J., & Jansson, E. (1982). Training-induced increase in myofibrillar ATPase intermediate fibers in human skeletal muscle. *Muscle & Nerve*, **5**, 628-636.

Schantz, P., Henriksson, J., & Jansson, E. (1983). Adaptation of human skeletal muscle to endurance training of long duration. *Clinical Physiology*, **3**, 141-151.

Schmitt, T., & Pette, D. (1985). Increased mitochondrial creatine kinase in chronically stimulated fast-twitch rabbit muscle. *Federation of the European Biochemistry Society Letters*, **188**, 341-344.

Seedorf, U., Leberer, E., & Pette, D. (1985). In vitro translation of mRNAs coding for citrate synthetase and lactate dehydrogenase isozymes in chronically stimulated rabbit muscle. *The Journal of Muscle Research and Cell Motility*, **6**, 85.

Seedorf, K., Seedorf, U., & Pette, D. (1983). Coordinate expression of alkali and DTNB myosin light chains during transformation of rabbit fast muscle by chronic stimulation. *Federation of the European Biochemistry Society Letters*, **158**, 321-324.

Sréter, F.A., Elzinga, M., Mabuchi, K., Salmons, S., & Luff, A.R. (1975). The N-methylhistidine content of myosin in stimulated and cross-reinnervated skeletal muscles of the rabbit. *Federation of the European Biochemistry Society Letters,* **57**, 107-111.

Sréter, F.A., Gergely, J., Salmons, S., & Romanul, F.C.A. (1973). Synthesis by fast muscle of myosin characteristic of slow muscle in response to long term stimulation. *Nature New Biology* (London), **241**, 17-19.

Sréter, F.A., Lopez, J.R., Alamo, L., Papp, L., Mabuchi, K., & Gergely, J. (1985). Changes in ionized calcium concentration in stimulated muscle. *Biophysical Journal,* **47**, 314a.

Sréter, F.A., Mabuchi, K., Köver, A., Gesztelyi, I., Nagy, Z., & Furka, I. (1980). Effect of chronic stimulation on cation distribution and membrane potential in fast-twitch muscles of rabbit. In D. Pette (Ed.), *Plasticity of muscle* (pp. 441-451). Berlin, New York: W. de Gruyter.

Srihari, T., & Pette, D. (1981). Myosin light chains in normal and electrostimulated cultures of embryonic chicken breast muscle. *Federation of the European Biochemistry Society Letters,* **123**, 312-314.

Tabor, C.W., & Tabor, H. (1984). Polyamines. *Annual Review of Biochemistry,* **53**, 749-790.

Watson, P.A., Stein, J.P., & Booth, F.W. (1984). Changes in actin synthesis and α-actin-mRNA content in rat muscle during immobilization. *American Journal of Physiology,* **247**, C39-C44.

Wiehrer, W., & Pette, D. (1983). The ratio between intrinsic 115 kDa and 30 kDa peptides as a marker of fibre type-specific sarcoplasmic reticulum in mammalian muscles. *Federation of the European Biochemistry Society Letters,* **158**, 317-320.

Neural Regulation of Membrane and Contractile Properties of Rat Skeletal Muscles

Terje Lømo
University of Oslo
Oslo, Norway

An important aim in nerve and muscle physiology is to understand the mechanisms underlying the neural control of muscle properties. The devastating effects of denervation, the restoration of normal properties by reinnervation, and the transformation of contraction speed by cross-reinnervation illustrate particularly well the importance of neural influences and the plasticity of muscle (Close, 1972; Purves, 1976). Motoneurones may regulate the properties of muscle either by evoked muscle activity or neurotrophic influences. In their classical paper on the effects of cross reinnervation, Buller, Eccles, and Eccles (1960) noted that impulse activity might provide a simple control mechanism, yet they concluded that neurotrophic substances were more likely to be involved because the activity hypothesis did not appear to explain the effects of spinal cord section or cross reinnervation.

Since then, chronic stimulation experiments have clearly revealed the importance of nerve impulse activity (Eerbeek, Kernell, & Verhey, 1984; Pette, Smith, Staudte, & Vrbová, 1973; Salmons & Sréter, 1974; Salmons & Vrbová, 1969). The presence of an intact nerve in these experiments, however, makes it difficult to separate the effects of evoked muscle activity and putative neurotrophic substances because changes in nerve impulse activity may change the amount and type of the trophic substances. To overcome this problem, muscles have been denervated and stimulated directly via implanted electrodes (Lømo, Westgaard, & Dahl, 1974). With this approach it is possible to study the effects of evoked muscle activity per se and to test an important preduction of the neurotrophic hypothesis; namely, that if neurotrophic influences, acting independently of activity, are essential for the maintenance of normal muscle properties, then denervated muscles should become abnormal even when they are stimulated electrically with patterns comparable to the normal firing patterns of slow and fast motoneurones (Hennig & Lømo, 1985).

It is helpful to distinguish junctional properties from nonjunctional properties of either the extrajunctional membrane or the contractile apparatus. As discussed elsewhere, formation of neuromuscular junctions requires both evoked muscle activity and activity-independent neural influences (Lømo & Gundersen, in press). Whether activity-independent influences also act along the muscle fiber to neurotrophically regulate nonjunctional properties is much less clear, with some workers proposing the existence of such regulation (Bray, Hubbard, & Mills, 1979; Drachman, Stanley, Pestronk, Griffin, & Price, 1982; Guth, Kemerer, Samaras, Warnick, & Albuquerque, 1981; Thesleff & Sellin, 1980) and other workers (Brown, Hopkins, & Keynes, 1982; Cangiano, 1985; Cangiano & Lutzemberger, 1977; Lømo & Westgaard, 1976) questioning the existence of such regulation. In the following I consider only extrajunctional membrane properties and contractile properties, and conclude that these are primarily controlled by neurally evoked muscle activity, while activity-independent neurotrophic influences do not appear to play an essential role.

METHODS

Young, adult, male, Wistar rats, weighing 250 to 350 g, were used. The operations were done under barbiturate or ether anaesthesia. Soleus and extensor digitorum longus (edl) muscles were denervated by cutting and reflecting the sciatic nerve in the thigh. The insulation was removed from the distal ends of a pair of teflon coated multistranded steel wires. The ends were then placed across the edl or the soleus muscle, one on each side, and the wires run under the skin, through an attachment by screws and dental cement on the skull, to a stimulator above the rat. The rat was kept in a large bucket, where it could move freely. Stimulation started 1 day to 9 months after denervation, lasted from 1 day to 9 months, and consisted of different patterns of trains of stimuli (Table 1). Each stimulus pulse was bipolar. The duration was 0.2 msec in each direction and the intensity 5 to 10 mA. In one series of experiments the muscles were removed from the rat and placed in a chamber superfused with oxygenated Ringer's solution at room temperature. Conventional micropipettes, filled with 4 M K-acetate or 3 M acetylcholinechloride (AChCl), were then used to record resting membrane potentials (RMP) and sensitivity to ACh (Lømo & Westgaard, 1975). In another series the leg was inserted into a Perspex chamber containing oxygenated Ringer's solution at 35° C. The distal part of the soleus or edl was dissected free and connected to a force transducer, while the main blood supply was kept intact. Twitch and tetanic contractions, evoked by direct supramaximal stimuli from large platinum electrodes, were then measured under isometric conditions and at optimal length. Lack of reinnervation was confirmed by stimulating the nerve just outside the muscle and looking for muscle contractions through the dissection microscope.

RESULTS AND INTERPRETATIONS

Regulation of Extrajunctional Membrane Properties

Effects of evoked muscle activity. Figure 1 illustrates the effect of denervation on the sensitivity of muscle to acetylcholine (ACh). In a normally innervated rat soleus mucle fiber the sensitivity was restricted to the endplate region (A). Denervation caused a striking increase in sensitivity along the fiber, which was prevented when the muscle was stimulated directly (B). Figure 2 shows the timecourse for the rise in extrajunctional ACh sensitivity (A) and for the fall in resting membrane potential (RMP, B) after denervation. Stimulation, starting 5 days after denervation, abolished the ACh supersensitivity and restored normal RMP, while stopping the stimulation after 15 days caused the supersensitivity to reappear. Similar results have been obtained in the edl (Lømo & Rosenthal, 1972; Lømo & Gundersen, in press). Thus, in rat muscles, evoked muscle activity restores normal extrajunctional membrane properties in the absence of neural influences from intramuscular nerves.

Effects of nerve degeneration. Two types of experiments show that lack of activity cannot account for all the effects of denervation. First, the ef-

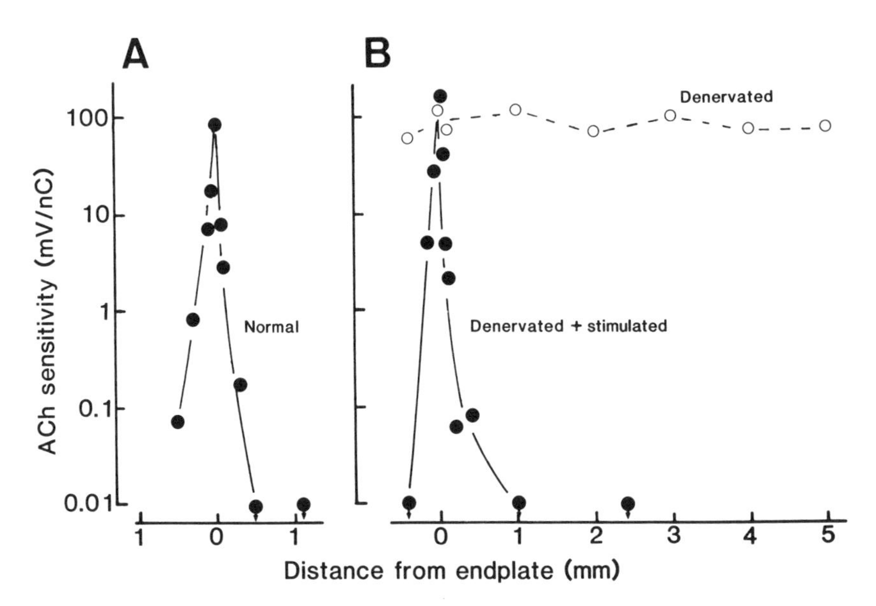

Figure 1 Sensitivity to ACh along single soleus muscle fibers. The muscle containing the fiber in A was normally innervated. The muscle containing the fiber represented by ∘∘∘ in B had been denervated for 5 days, while the muscle containing the fiber represented by ••• in B had been denervated and stimulated electrically for 5 days.

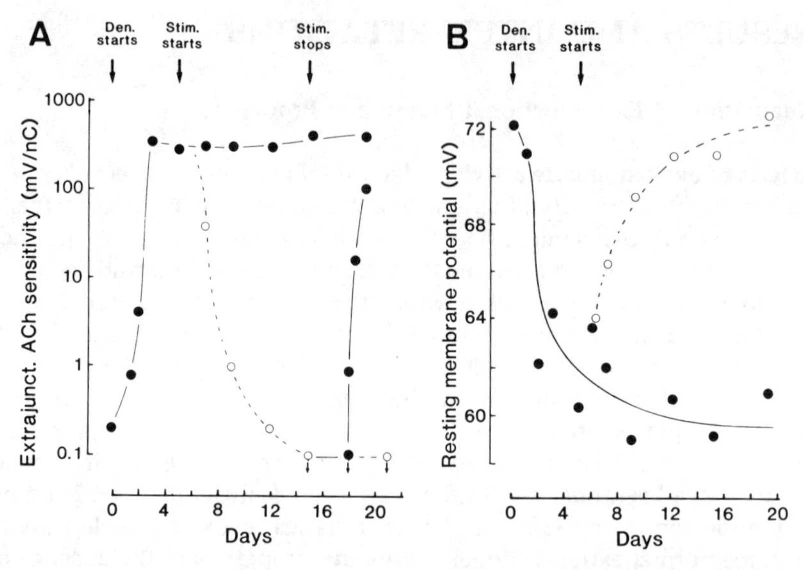

Figure 2 Extrajunctional ACh sensitivity measured 2 mm from the tendon (A), and resting membrane potential (B) of soleus muscle fibers. The muscles were either denervated (•••), or denervated and stimulated from day 5 after denervation (°°°, stimulation consisted of 100 pulses at 100 Hz every 100 sec), or denervated and stimulated from day 5 to day 15 (•••, see arrows). Symbols represent mean values from many fibers in several muscles. Adapted from "Further Studies on the Control of ACh Sensitivity by Muscle Activity in the Rat" by T. Lømo and R.H. Westgaard, 1975, *Journal of Physiology*, **252** and "Control of ACh sensitivity in Rat Muscle Fibres" by T. Lømo and R.H. Westgaard, 1976, *Cold Spring Harbor Symposia on Quantitative Biology*.

fects of denervation develop later when the nerve is cut far from the muscle rather than close to the muscle (Harris & Thesleff, 1972; Luco & Eyzaguirre, 1955). Since the terminals also degenerate later (Miledi & Slater, 1969), the effect could be due to neurotrophic substances disappearing later from the long nerve stump. Second, the muscle responds later, and to a lesser degree, when the nerve is blocked by tetrodotoxin (TTX) than when it is cut (Cangiano, Lutzemberger, & Nicotra, 1977; Drachman et al., 1982). This could be due to continued release of neurotrophic substances from the TTX blocked nerve because TTX does not appear to block axonal transport (Drachman et al., 1982; Grafstein & Edwards, 1982). However, the results could also be accounted for by substances appearing, rather than disappearing, in the muscle when nerves degenerate. Such "products of nerve degeneration" (Brown, Holland, & Ironton, 1978; Cangiano & Lutzemberger, 1977; Cangiano, Magherini, Pasino, Pelegrino, & Risaliti, 1985; Jones & Vrbová, 1974; Lømo & Westgaard, 1976) could act directly on the muscle fibers, or indirectly via substances released by nonmuscle and nonnerve cells, which accumulate transiently and in large numbers after denervation (Murray & Robbins, 1982), in part because nerve breakdown causes the appearance of potent mitogens (Yachnis & Mescher, 1982).

Substantial evidence supports the view that nerve degeneration causes substances to appear which induce ACh supersensitivity and other denervation-like changes, particularly in inactive muscle fibers. Cangiano and collaborators have partially denervated rat skeletal muscles and found that not only the denervated but also the remaining innervated fibers become more sensitive to ACh in extrajunctional regions. Indeed, when the remaining axons are blocked by TTX, the denervated and the innervated muscle fibers become equally supersensitive to ACH (Cangiano & Lutzemberger, (1980). This result is inconsistent with the view that neurotrophic substances, carried by axonal transport and released independently of activity from motor nerve terminals, are responsible for maintaining normal membrane properties in extrajuctional regions. In that case the muscle fibers innervated by the TTX blocked axons would have been expected to have a lower ACh sensitivity than the denervated fibers. Brown and colleagues reached a similar conclusion when they found that destruction of sensory fibers caused a small increase in ACh sensitivity (Brown et al., 1978), and also that paralysis by botulinum toxin eventually caused the same increase in ACh sensitivity as denervation after a larger increase in the denervated muscle initially, which they attributed to products of nerve degeneration (Brown et al., 1982). In our own experiments we have found that supersensitivity may develop locally and transiently around degenerating endplates in preparations where the muscle fibers are kept active either by direct stimulation (slow pattern), or by another (slow) nerve (Lømo & Westgaard, 1976). If absence of neurotrophic substances were responsible for this supersensitivity, then it would have been expected to develop permanently along the entire length of the muscle fibers.

Search for neurotrophic substances. Neurotrophic substances have been searched for by extracting proteins from motor nerves and applying them to noninnervated muscles in vivo or in vitro (Davis & Kiernan, 1984; Max & Markelonis, 1983; Younkin, Brett, Davey, & Younkin, 1978). These substances, however, lead to an increased number of ACh receptors and not to the decrease expected if they were responsible for the low extrajunctional ACh sensitivity of normally innervated fibers. These substances also affect muscle AChesterase activity but apparently only in the endplate region (Younkin et al., 1978). These findings, therefore, provide evidence for neurotrophic control of junctional but not for extrajunctional membrane properties.

One of the proteins extracted from the sciatic nerves, named sciatin, not only induces synthesis of AChRs and AChE, but also promotes maturation and long-term survival of muscle cells in vitro. Sciatin, however, is similar or identical to transferrin (Max & Markelonis, 1983), a normal constituent of blood, which is taken up, but not synthesized, by some adult muscles (Matsuda, Spector, & Strohman, 1984). It is therefore possible that both nerves and muscles take up transferrin and other substances from the blood to serve their own trophic needs, and that a myotrophic effect of such substances is unrelated to their presence in the nerve. It is also possible that these substances normally act only on junctional receptors, which may spread, as AChRs do, to extrajunctional regions after denervation. In that case bath application or intramuscular injection of these substances might have a generalized effect on noninervated fibers that is unrelated to their normal action on innervated fibers.

In conclusion, it has so far been impossible to provide unequivocal evidence that neurotrophic substances are essential for neural control of extrajunctional membrane properties. Some results, often taken as evidence of such control, may be interpreted as due to products of nerve degeneration rather than absence of neurotrophic substances. This issue, however, which is discussed in more detail elsewhere (Lømo & Gundersen, in press), is far from resolved. It appears that a substance should be considered to have an essential neurotrophic effect on skeletal muscles only when it can be demonstrated: (a) that it is released from motor nerve endings; (b) that it cannot be supplied by the blood or nonneural cells; and (c) that the muscles develop abnormal properties in its absence despite appropriate electrical stimulation. Since electrical stimulation apparently is able to substitute for the nerve in maintaining normal extrajunctional properties, I favor the view that neurotrophic substances do not play an essential role in the regulation of these properties. Instead, extrajunctional membrane properties appear to be controlled primarily by evoked activity with substances carried in the blood probably playing modulatory roles.

Regulation of Contractile Properties

Muscle atrophy. Denervated skeletal muscles atrophy rapidly (Figure 3) and show a striking reduction in maximum tetanic force output (Figure 4). Can these effects of denervation be fully counteracted by direct stimulation? If so, then it may be possible in the future to maintain and perhaps make some use of denervated human muscles by suitable electrical stimulation. If, on the other hand, maintaining the muscle also requires neurotrophic substances, then such prospects seem less likely.

Figures 3 and 4 show that muscle size and force output were largely, but not completely, maintained or restored by direct stimulation, even in muscles that had been denervated for many months before the stimu-

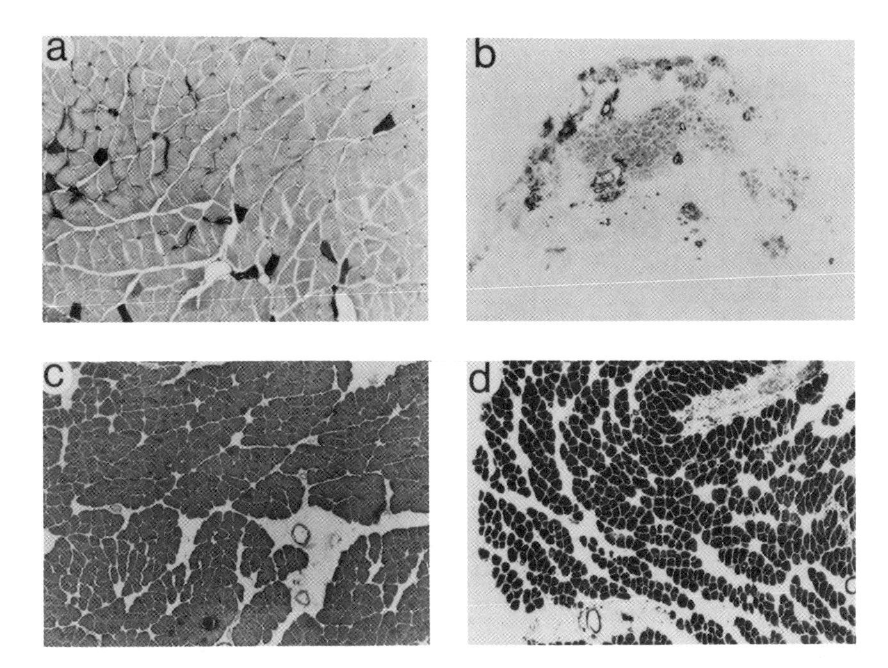

Figure 3 Representative sections of soleus muscles stained for myosin ATPase activity after alkaline (pH 10.4) preincubation. The muscle was normal in a, denervated for 198 days in b, denervated for 236 days and stimulated intermittently at 100 Hz (one train of 60 pulses every 60 sec) for 235 days in c, and denervated for 341 days and stimulated (same pattern as above) for the last 75 days in d. Note the marked atrophy in b (entire cross section of the muscle), the substantial but not complete maintenance or recovery of fiber size in c and d, and the overall dark, type II like staining in c and d (the section in c was several months old and had faded somewhat). From unpublished observations by Hennig and Lømo.

lation started. The incomplete recovery might reflect that neurotrophic influences were lacking. Probably, however, the explanation is more trivial. First, muscle stretch, which is known to affect muscle fiber size (Frankeny, Holly, & Ashmore, 1983; Simrad, Spector, & Edgerton, 1982; Stewart, 1972), was certainly inadequate in these experiments, since all the muscles of the limb, including the antagonists, were denervated and since the working mode was atypical. Second, the electrodes might have damaged or failed to activate part of the muscle. Third, some atrophy usually occurs in innervated muscles during long-term electrical stimulation (Figure 4, Eerbeek et al., 1984; Salmons & Sréter, 1974), although, under such conditions, putative neurotrophic substances should be present. Fourth, properties that do not depend on fiber size, such as extrajunctional ACh sensitivity, are completely restored to normal by stimulation. Given these considerations, and the striking effects of stimulation even on long-

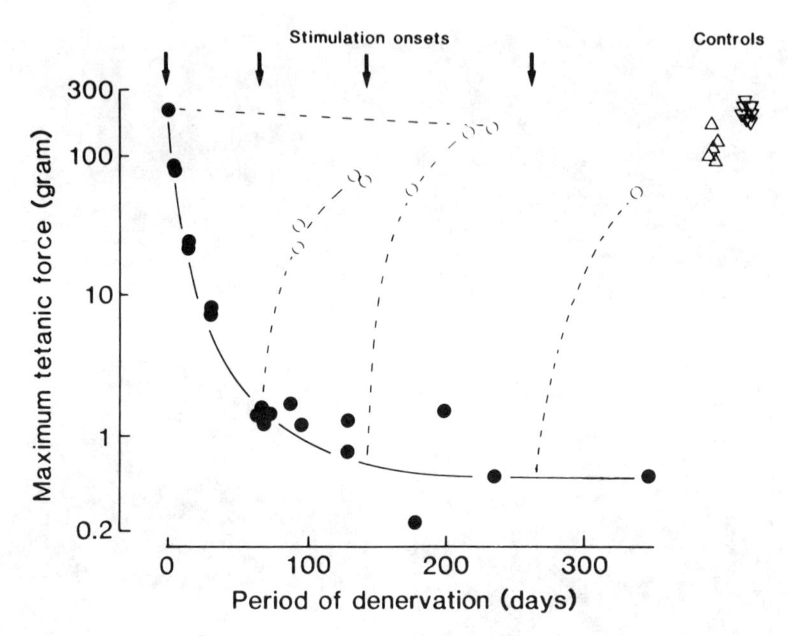

Figure 4 Maximum tetanic force output of soleus muscles at different times after denervation (•••), or denervation and intermittent 100 Hz stimulation (°°°, one train of 60 pulses every 60 sec). The stimulation started at the times indicated by the arrows and continued until the acute experiment. ∇ represents normal soleus muscles from intact rats. Δ represents innervated soleus muscles stimulated for about 3 months in the same way as the denervated muscles. From unpublished observations by Hennig & Lømo.

term denervated muscles (Figures 3 and 4), it seems likely that neurotrophic substances are not essential for the maintenance of muscle size and force output.

Contraction speed—dependence on both frequency and amount of impulse activity. Figure 5 shows that denervated rat soleus muscles maintain a slow twitch and a high fatigue resistance during tonic low frequency stimulation (Figure 5 A), whereas the twitch becomes fast during intermittent high frequency stimulation (Figure 5 B and C), and either fatigue sensitive (B) or fatigue resistant (C) depending on the amount of such stimulation. Figure 6 shows the timecourse for the decrease in isometric twitch contraction time during intermittent 100 Hz stimulation (fast pattern), and the maintenance of a slow twitch during tonic low frequency stimulation (slow pattern), or after denervation and implantation of sham electrodes. Figure 7 shows the twitch contraction time of soleus muscles after about 2 months of denervation and stimulation with the stimulus patterns indicated in Table 1. The slowest contraction time (∿45 msec) was obtained during tonic, low frequency stimu-

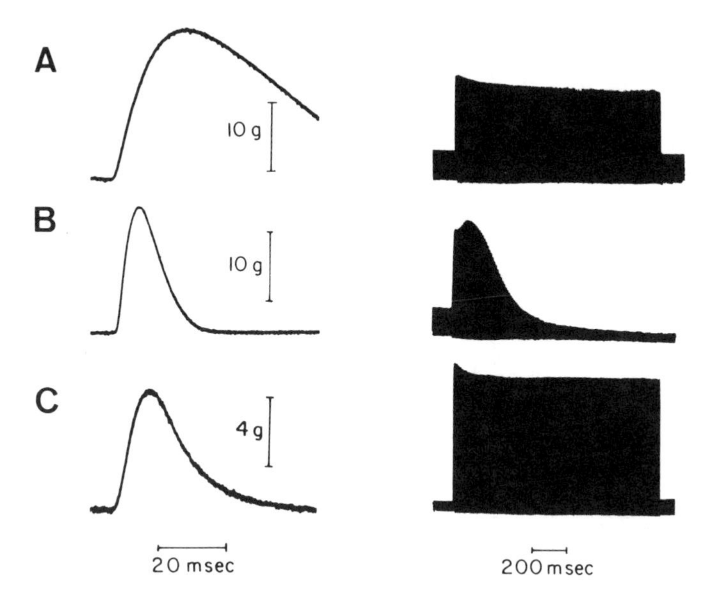

Figure 5 Isometric twitch and fatigue test responses of soleus muscles after about 2 months of denervation and direct electrical stimulation. The muscle in A had been stimulated with 150 pulses at 15 Hz every 15 sec (mean frequency 10 Hz, slow pattern), the muscle in B with 60 pulses at 100 Hz every 1 hr and 40 min (mean frequency 0.01 Hz, fast pattern, low amount), the muscle in C with 60 pulses at 100 Hz every 1.2 sec (mean frequency 50 Hz, fast pattern, high amount). The fatigue test consisted of trains of stimuli at 78 Hz; each train lasted 330 msec and was repeated once every sec for 2 min.

lation, and the fastest (∿12 msec) during intermittent, high frequency stimulation. When the amount of stimulation at a given frequency was reduced, the twitch contraction time was also reduced. For example, at 10 Hz, a 1000-fold reduction in mean stimulus frequency (from 10 Hz to 0.01 Hz) reduced the contraction time from about 45 to 19 msec. However, to make the contraction time as fast as in the edl (∿12 msec), high frequency stimulation was necessary. Thus, by changing both the amount and the frequency of stimulation it was possible to continuously grade the contraction time within a certain range (45 to 12 msec), which I call the adaptive range for this property in the soleus. In the edl, on the other hand, the adaptive range for the twitch contraction time extended from only about 12 msec to less than 25 msec. Neither denervation alone nor tonic, low frequency stimulation of the denervated or innervated rat edl made the contraction time longer than 25 msec (Figure 7; Table 2; Kwong & Vrbová, 1981).

In addition to inducing an edl-like isometric twitch, intermittent, high frequency stimulation altered the myosin ATPase activity of the soleus, so that after alkaline preincubation all the stimulated fibers stained darkly,

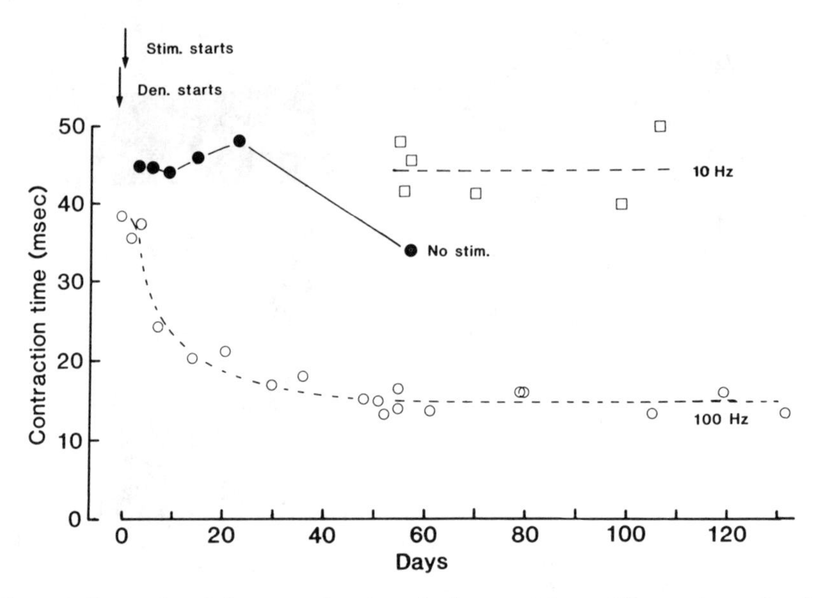

Figure 6 Isometric twitch contraction time of soleus muscles at different times after denervation and onset of electrical stimulation (arrows). (°°°) represents the fast stimulation pattern (60 pulses at 100 Hz every min). □ represents the slow stimulation pattern (continuous 10 Hz). (•••) represents denervated, nonstimulated soleus muscles with sham electrodes implanted. Each (•••) is mean of 2 muscles. Some (°°°) are means of up to eight muscles. The other symbols represent single muscles. From unpublished raw data by Gundersen, Lømo, and Westgaard.

whereas normally most of them (>90%) stain lightly. By these criteria alone, therefore, the soleus might be considered as completely transformed into an edl-like muscle. However, with respect to intrinsic shortening velocity (whole muscle isotonic shortening velocity corrected for differences in fiber length) the soleus became only about half as fast as the normal edl. Furthermore, while gradually acquiring the ability to bind antifast myosin, the soleus fibers continued to bind anti-slow myosin even 4 months after the onset of stimulation (Gorza, Gundersen, Lømo, Schiaffino, & Westgaard, unpublished results). In these respects, therefore, the soleus fibers were incompletely transformed.

Increased amounts of activity have a slowing effect on fast muscles (Eerbeek et al., 1984; Pette et al., 1973; Salmons & Sréter, 1974), while reduced amounts of activity, as obtained by spinal cord section or immobilization, speed up slow muscles (Buller et al., 1960; Davey, Dunlop, Hoh, & Wong, 1981; Fischbach & Robbins, 1969; Gallego, Huizar, Kudo, & Kuno, 1978; Simrad, Spector, & Edgerton, 1982). Therefore, it has been proposed that slow contraction speeds are due to tonic activity per se, while fast speeds may be due to intrinsic muscle properties (Salmons &

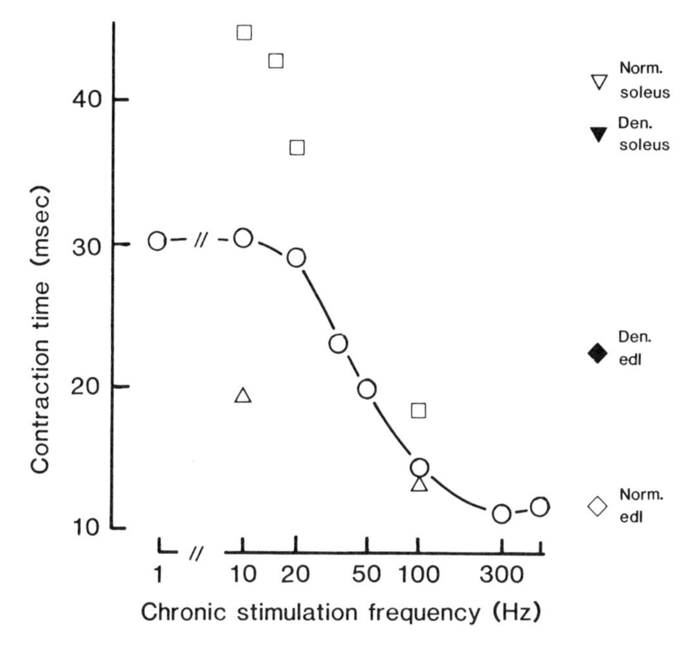

Figure 7 Isometric twitch contraction times measured about 2 months after denervation and stimulation and with the stimulus patterns indicated in Table 1. (°°°) represents muscles stimulated once every min with a train of 60 pulses at the frequencies indicated along the abcissa (mean frequency 1 Hz). □ represents muscles stimulated at 10, 15, 20, and 100 Hz (abcissa), either continuously at 10 Hz or with large numbers of stimulus trains (mean frequencies of 10, 10, 6.7, and 50 Hz respectively). △ represents muscles stimulated once every hour and 40 min with a train of 60 pulses at 10 or 100 Hz (mean frequency 0.01 Hz). Symbols on the right represent normal and denervated control muscles as indicated. Each symbol is the mean of 2-10 muscles. From unpublished raw data by Lømo and Westgaard.

Henriksson, 1981) or some neurotrophic factor (Gallego et al., 1978), tending to make all muscles fast when tonic activity is absent. Accordingly, fast activity patterns have not been considered to play a significant role in determining fast-twitch properties (Jolesz & Sréter, 1981), and, in agreement with this view, the fast speed of cross reinnervated, originally slow muscles has been attributed to the absence of tonic activity rather than to the high frequency activity of fast motoneurones (Salmons & Henriksson, 1981).

Our results suggest a different view. Also we find that the soleus can be made considerably faster merely by reducing the amount of activity, particularly at low stimulation frequency (Figure 7). However, to obtain contraction times as short as those found in normal edl muscles, or in soleus muscles after cross reinnervation, high frequency stimulation is necessary (Figure 7 and Table 2). Furthermore, when high frequency stimulation or innervation by a fast nerve is added to tonic, low frequency

Table 1 Different Stimulus Patterns Used to Stimulate Soleus and edl Muscles Via Implanted Electrodes for Approximately 2 Months, Starting 1 Day After Denervation.

Frequency within stimulus trains Hz	No. of stimulus trains/min	No. of stimuli per train	Train duration sec	No. of stimuli per min	Stimulated time per 24 hours %
1	*Continuous*			60	
10	1	60	6	60	10
20	1	60	3	60	5
35	1	60	1.7	60	2.8
50	1	60	1.2	60	2
100	1	60	0.6	60	1
300	1	60	0.2	60	0.3
500	1	60	0.12	60	0.2
10	*Continuous*			600	100
10	0.01	60	6	0.6	0.1
15	4	150	10	600	67
20	2	200	10	400	33
100	30	60	0.6	1800	50
100	0.01	60	0.6	0.6	0.01

Upper patterns were aimed at varying stimulus frequency, keeping stimulus number constant. Lower patterns (10 and 100 Hz) were aimed at varying stimulus number, keeping stimulus frequency constant.

activity, evoked either by electrical stimulation or naturally by the slow soleus nerve, then the contraction speed increases considerably despite the increased amount of activity (Table 2). Therefore, high frequency activity per se induces fast contractile properties.

By stimulating denervated soleus and edl muscles with appropriate stimulus patterns it is possible to mimic the effects of self- or cross-reinnervation. Thus, the denervated soleus acquires the same slow contraction speed after self-reinnervation (slow nerve) and tonic, low frequency stimulation (slow pattern) and the same fast speed after cross-reinnervation (fast nerve) and intermittent, high frequency stimulation (fast stimulus pattern; Table 2). Comparable results are obtained in the edl (Table 2). These similarities indicate that cross-reinnervation affects contraction speed by evoking different patterns of activity in the muscle. On the other hand, the soleus responds very differently from the edl to reinnervation by the soleus nerve and to tonic, low frequency stimulation; both procedures inducing a contraction time of about 40 msec in the soleus, but less than 25 msec in the edl (Table 2). Such different re-

Table 2 Effects of Different Experimental Procedures on Twitch Contraction Time.

	Experimental Procedure		Contraction time (msec)	
Muscle	Surgical operation	Stimulus pattern	Experimental muscle	Control muscle
Soleus	Reinnervated by edl nerve*		15.6	37.8
Soleus	Transplanted to bed of edl and reinnervated by edl nerve**		13.0	37.0
Soleus	Reinnervated by fibular and soleus nerve (dual innervation)		27.0	41.0
Soleus	Denervated		39.9	41.0
Soleus	Denervated	Fast	12.0	40.4
Soleus	Innervated	Fast	22.9	39.2
Soleus	Denervated	Slow	42.8	41.0
Soleus	Denervated	Fast + Slow	22.3	40.4
Edl	Reinnervated by soleus nerve*		21.3	12.6
Edl	Transplanted to bed of soleus and reinnervated by sol. nerve**		23.6	12.7
Edl	Denervated		22.3	11.9
Edl	Denervated	Slow	21.4	11.9
Edl	Innervated	Slow	22.8	11.9
Edl	Denervated	Fast	12.5	12.9

Each value is mean of 3 to 10 muscles.
*From "The Transformation of Myosin in Cross-Innervated Rat Muscles" by M. Barany and R.I. Close, 1971, *Journal of Physiology*, **213**, p. 461. The twitch speed was measured between 327 and 454 days after operations.
**From "Contractile and Histochemical Properties of Regenerating Cross-Transplanted Fast and Slow Muscles in the Rat" by E. Gutmann and B.M. Carlson, 1975, *Pflügers Archiv*, p. 230. The twitch speed was measured 90 days after operations. The other results are from unpublished work by T. Eken, K. Gundersen, R. Hennig, T. Lømo, and R.H. Westgaard, in which twitch speed was measured between 40 days and half a year after operations. Stimulation started 1 day after denervation and consisted of either intermittent short 100 or 150 Hz stimulus trains (fast pattern) or long 10 or 15 Hz stimulus trains (slow pattern).

sponses to the same input indicate that soleus and edl are intrinsically different.

Reduction in the amount of activity, particularly at low frequency, makes the soleus contract much faster than normal (Figure 7). This appears to explain why the soleus contracts faster after spinal cord section and immobilization, which markedly reduce the amount of activity. The situation is less clear for fast muscles. After similar operations, the isometric twitch contraction time of fast muscle fibers may become shorter (Mayer, Burke, Toop, Hodgson, Kanda, & Walmsley, 1981; Mayer, Burke, Toop, Walmsley, & Hodgson, 1984), longer (Witzmann, Kim, & Fitts, 1982), or be unaffected (Buller et al., 1960; Simrad et al., 1982). Clearly, more information is needed about the firing patterns of fast motoneurones after spinal cord section and immobilization before their effects can be attributed to altered impulse activity.

The role of impulse activity in mediating effects of neural lesions is further illustrated by some recent experiments by R. Hennig (personal communication, 1986). Without affecting the innervation of the soleus, Hennig cut one of the nerves in the leg (the fibular nerve) and observed, as others have (Fex, 1969; Guth & Wells, 1972), that the soleus contracted faster. In addition, he recorded the spontaneous activity of single soleus motor units and found that for several weeks after the nerve cut the soleus motor units generated much less activity. In addition, many of the soleus units generated high frequency double discharges and brief bursts of impulses, which they never do normally (Hennig & Lømo, 1985). Consequently, it is reasonable to attribute the faster contraction speed partly to the reduced amount of activity and partly to the high frequency discharges (see Figure 7).

The adaptive range. This term implies that a contractile property, such as twitch speed, may be continuously adjusted to varying functional demands within certain limits. An example is provided by the effects of increased impulse frequencies on the tension-frequency (t-f) relation of the muscle fibers. As twitch speed increases, the steep part of the tension-frequency curve moves to the right (i.e., towards the imposed frequency), and, as a result, rate modulation of force output becomes more effective around the new frequency (Figure 8). An optimum effect would be expected when the steepest part of the t-f curve moves sufficiently to coincide with the imposed frequency. Usually, however, this does not occur because twitch speed is determined not only by impulse frequency but also by the amount of activity. High amounts of activity have a slowing effect on twitch speed, even at high frequency, (Figure 7; Eerbeek et al., 1984; Hudlicka, Tyler, Srihari, Heilig, & Pette, 1982; Sréter, Pintér, Jolesz, & Mabuchi, 1982), which tends to move the t-f curve in the opposite direction, towards lower frequencies. This effect seems advantageous in postural muscles, which, by becoming slower, may maintain a high tension output at low frequency and at low energy cost (Crow & Kushmeric, 1982). Apparently, this is how soleus motor units normally behave, since they generate 80% or more of maximum tetanic tension at the frequency prevailing during tonic activity (∼20 Hz; Hennig & Lømo, 1985). On the other hand, rate modulation becomes less efficient; but, presumably, this is of lesser importance during postural activity. Thus, by adaptive mechanisms such as these, motor units may adjust their contraction speeds to the combined influences of the amount and the frequency of impulse activity, and strike a functionally meaningful

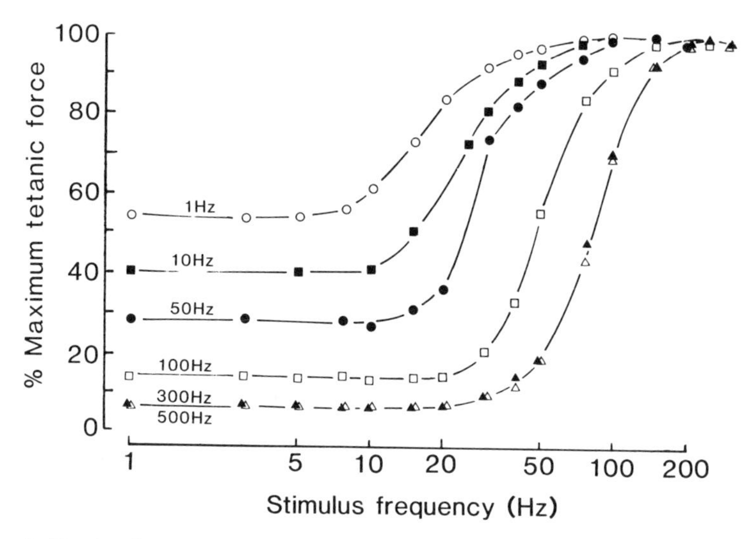

Figure 8 Tension-frequency curves of soleus muscles which had been denervated and stimulated electrically for about 2 months with trains of stimuli at 1, 10, 50, 100, 300, or 500 Hz. Each train, which consisted of 60 pulses, was delivered every 60 sec so that a mean frequency of 1 Hz was always obtained (see also Table 1). Each symbol represents the mean of 2 to 5 muscles. Note that the twitch-tetanus ratio falls and the steep part of the tension frequency curve moves towards the imposed frequencies for each increase in chronic stimulation frequency between 1 and 300 Hz. From unpublished raw data by Lømo and Westgaard.

compromise between the needs for effective rate modulation and force production.

The spectacular improvements in athletic performance obtained in recent years lead naturally to questions about their limitations. The well-defined adaptive ranges for individual contractile properties demonstrated here suggest that clear, perhaps genetically predetermined, limits exist. With respect to twitch speed, however, the adjustments obtained by artificial stimulation are far greater than any adjustments so far obtained by training. Consequently, only a small part of the adaptive range may normally be used at least with respect to twitch speed. Of course, other limitations also exist; for example, at the level of the motoneurone. The extent to which the frequency range of a motoneurone may be altered by training to better exploit the potential for adaptive change in the muscle is quite unclear.

Transformation of fiber types or adaptive change within each fiber type. Exercise, stimulation, or cross reinnervation induce changes in contractile properties that are commonly attributed to partial or complete transformation of fiber types. An alternative view, suggested by the present results, is the following. A muscle fiber is always of the same type. This type is characterized by predetermined adaptive ranges and not by the contraction speed or any other particular contractile property, which may change. Different properties may be independently regulated within different adaptive ranges. Thus, chronic stimulation affects twitch speed earlier than shortening velocity (Gundersen, Lømo, & Westgaard, unpublished raw data), in agreement with reports that stimulation affects the properties of the sarcoplasmic reticulum earlier than the properties of myofibrillar proteins (Pette, 1984). Furthermore, the soleus may become as fast as the edl with respect to twitch speed, but not with respect to intrinsic shortening velocity. Although the adaptive ranges of different fiber types are intrinsically different, they may overlap to a smaller or greater extent. Thus, during fast pattern activity, a soleus type I fiber may begin to stain like an edl type II fiber for myosin ATPase activity and acquire a twitch as fast as in the edl, yet it is not being converted into a type II fiber but merely pushed to the extreme of its own characteristic adaptive range. Similarly, changes induced by training in myosin ATPase staining patterns and energy enzyme activities do not necessarily indicate transformation of fiber types. Type IIA and IIB fibers may either represent different adaptive states of the same fiber type or intrinsically different fiber types. Evidently, a large part of the variability in muscle fiber properties are caused by differences in motor unit activity. If many intrinsically different muscle fibers also exist, this will further increase the variability. For example, type I fibers in the soleus, in the edl, or in other muscles may all be intrinsically different, and the same may be true for type II fibers. The differences may be overt, as demonstrated here for soleus type I fibers and edl type II fibers, or more subtle. The intrinsic differences may arise early in development, and some of them may occur independently of neural inputs (Butler, Cosmos, & Brierley, 1982; Phillips & Bennett, 1984). Evidence that muscle fibers may have different molecular compositions depending on their position along the body axis, comes from reports that muscle fibers are preferentially reinnervated by axons belonging to the same body segments (Wigston & Sanes, 1985).

Muscle fibers are markedly heterogenous and do not readily fit into simple classification systems based on the existence of only a few basic fiber types. Although contraction speed and myosin ATPase activity may be well correlated in some muscles (Kugelberg, 1976; Kugelberg & Thornell, 1983), this is not the case in other muscles, where, for example, a type I fiber may contract faster than a type II fiber (Burke, 1981). Furthermore, no general scheme exists for correlating aerobic oxidative capacity with histochemically assessable myosin ATPase in various mammalian muscles (Reichmann & Pette, 1982). Perhaps the scheme outlined above, which suggests that there are many intrinsically different muscle fibers, each having a set of characteristic adaptive ranges for adjusting their properties to the imposed activity, better accounts for the impressive diversity of muscle fibers.

CONCLUSIONS

Neurons appear to interact on a long-term basis with their target cells via trophic substances moved by anterograde or retrograde transport. In normal muscles such neurotrophic effects appear to be restricted to junctional and perijunctional regions. There is as yet no unequivocal evidence that neurotrophic substances contribute in an essential way to the regulation of extrajunctional membrane properties or contractile properties. On the other hand, motoneurones regulate the properties of the muscle by evoked activity. This regulation depends on both the amount and the frequency of nerve impulses and serves to functionally match the muscle properties to the imposed work. In addition, there is regulation by stretch and substances carried in the blood. The regulation by activity occurs in a continuously graded manner within adaptive ranges that are inherently different in different types of muscle fibers. Thus, the rat edl is fast, partly because the majority of its muscle fibers are inherently of a fast type, and partly because the edl motoneurones typically fire at high frequency. Similarly, the soleus is slow, partly because the majority of its muscle fibers are inherently of a slow type, and partly because the soleus motoneurones typically fire tonically at low frequency. It is proposed that many intrinsically different muscle fibers exist, each having their own predetermined adaptive ranges, and that altered activity does not lead to transformation between fiber types, but to adaptive changes within the limits characteristic of each type.

Acknowledgments

I thank my colleagues Torsten Eken, Kristian Gundersen, Rune Hennig, Kristin Kardel, and Rolf H. Westgaard for collaboration and permission to present unpublished results and Sigrid Schaller for technical assistance. I also thank the Norwegian Research Council for Science and the Humanities, Jahre Foundation and Nansen Foundation for financial support.

REFERENCES

Bray, J.J., Hubbard, J.I, & Mills, R.G. (1979). The trophic influence of tetrodotoxin-inactive nerves on normal and reinnervated rat skeletal muscles. *Journal of Physiology*, **297**, 479-491.

Brown, M.C., Holland, R.L., & Ironton, R. (1978). Degenerating nerve products affect innervated muscle fibres. *Nature*, **275**, 652-654.

Brown, M.C., Hopkins, W.G., & Keynes, R.F. (1982). Comparison of effects of denervation and botulinum toxin on muscle properties in mice. *Journal of Physiology,* **327**, 29-37.

Buller, A.J., Eccles, J.C., & Eccles, R.M. (1960). Interaction between motoneurons and muscles in respect of the characteristic speeds of their responses. *Journal of Physiology,* **150**, 417-439.

Burke, R.E. (1981). Motor units: Anatomy, physiology, and functional organization. In V.B. Brooks (Ed.), *Handbook of physiology: Sec. 1. Vol. 2. Part 1* (pp. 345-422). Bethesda, MD: American Physiological Society.

Butler, J., Cosmos, E., & Brierley, J. (1982). Differentiation of muscle fibre types in aneurogenic brachial muscles of the chick embryo. *Journal of Experimental Zoology,* **224**, 65-80.

Cangiano, A. (1985). Denervation supersensitivity as a model for the neural control of muscle. *Neuroscience,* **14**, 963-971.

Cangiano, A., & Lutzenberger, L. (1977). Partial denervation affects both denervated and innervated fibers in mammalian skeletal muscle. *Science,* **196**, 542-545.

Cangiano, A., & Lutzenberger, L. (1980). Partial denervation in inactive muscle affects innervated and denervated fibres equally. *Nature,* **285**, 233-235.

Cangiano, C., Lutzenberger, L., & Nicotra, L. (1977). Non-equivalence of impulse blockade and denervation in the production of membrane changes in rat skeletal muscle. *Journal of Physiology,* **273**, 691-706.

Cangiano, A., Magherini, P.C., Pasino, E., Pellegrino, M., & Risaliti, R. (1984). Interaction of inactivity and nerve breakdown products in the origin of acute denervation changes in rat skeletal muscle. *Journal of Physiology,* **355**, 345-365.

Close, R. (1969). Dynamic properties of fast and slow skeletal muscles of the rat after nerve cross-union. *Journal of Physiology,* **204**, 331-346.

Close, R.I. (1972). Dynamic properties of mammalian skeletal muscles. *Physiological Reviews,* **52**, 129-197.

Crow, M.T., & Kushmerick, M.J. (1982). The relationship between initial chemical change and recovery chemical input in isolated hindlimb muscles of the mouse. *Journal of General Physiology,* **79**, 147-166.

Davis, H.L., & Kiernan, J.A. (1984). Effect of nerve extract on number of acetylcholine receptors in denervated muscles of rats. *Experimental Neurology,* **83**, 108-117.

Drachman, D.B., Stanley, E.F., Pestronk, A., Griffin, J.W., & Price, D.L. (1982). Neurotrophic regulation of two properties of skeletal muscle by impulse-dependent and spontaneous acetylcholine transmission. *Journal of Neuroscience,* **2**, 232-243.

Eerbeek, O., Kernell, D., & Verhey, B.A. (1984). Effects of fast and slow patterns of tonic long-term stimulation on contractile properties of fast muscles in the cat. *Journal of Physiology,* **352**, 73-90.

Fex, S. (1969). "Trophic" influence of implanted fast nerve on innervated slow muscle. *Physiologica Bohemoslovakia,* **18**, 205-208.

Fischbach, G.D., & Robbins, N. (1969). Changes in contractile properties of disused soleus muscles. *Journal of Physiology,* **201**, 305-320.

Frankeny, J.R., Holy, R.G., & Ashmore, C.R. (1983). Effects of graded durations of stretch on normal and dystrophic skeletal muscle. *Muscle & Nerve,* **4**, 269-277.

Gallego, R., Huizar, P., Kudo, N., & Kuno, M. (1978). Disparity of motoneurone and muscle differentiation following spinal cord transection in the kitten. *Journal of Physiology,* **281**, 253-265.

Grafstein, B., & Edwards, D.L. (1982). Effects of physiological activity in goldfish optic axons on axonal transport of protein and nucleosides. In D.G. Weiss & A. Gorio (Eds.), *Axoplasmic transport in physiology and pathology* (pp. 21-26). Berlin: Springer-Verlag.

Guth, L., Kemerer, V.F., Samaras, T.A., Warnick, J.E., & Albuquerque, E.X. (1981). The roles of disuse and loss of neurotrophic function in denervation atrophy of skeletal muscle. *Experimental Neurology,* **73**, 20-36.

Guth, L. & Wells, J.B. (1972). Physiological and histochemical properties of the soleus muscle after denervation of its antagonists. *Experimental Neurology,* **36**, 463-471.

Gutmann, E., & Carlson, B.M. (1975). Contractile and histochemical properties of regenerating cross-transplanted fast and slow muscles in the rat. *Pflügers Archiv,* **353**, 227-239.

Harris, J.B., & Thesleff, S. (1972). Nerve stump length and membrane changes in denervated skeletal muscle. *Nature New Biology,* **236**, 60.

Hennig, R., & Lømo, T. (1985). Firing patterns of motor units in normal rats. *Nature,* **314**, 164-166.

Hudlická, O., Tyler, K.R., Srihari, T., Heilig, A., & Pette, D. (1982). The effect of different patterns of long-term stimulation on contractile properties and myosin light chains in rabbit muscles. *Pflügers Archiv,* **393**, 164-170.

Jolesz, F., & Sréter, F.A. (1981). Development, innervation, and activity-pattern induced changes in skeletal muscle. *Annual Review of Physiology,* **43**, 531-552.

Jones, R., & Vrbová, G. (1974). Two factors responsible for the development of denervation hypersensitivity. *Journal of Physiology,* **236**, 517-538.

Kugelberg, E. (1976). Adaptive transformation of rat soleus motor units during growth. *Journal of Neurological Sciences,* **27**, 269-289.

Kugelberg, E., & Thornell, L.-E. (1983). Contraction time, histochemical type, and terminal cisternae volume of rat motor units. *Muscle & Nerve,* **6**, 149-153.

Kwong, W.G., & Vrbová, G. (1981). Effects of low-frequency electrical stimulation on fast and slow muscles of the rat. *Pflügers Archiv,* **391**, 200-207.

Luco, J.V., & Eyzaguirre, C. (1955). Fibrillation and hypersensitivity to ACh in denervated muscle: Effect of length of degenerating nerve fibers. *Journal of Neurophysiology,* **18**, 65-73.

Lømo, T., & Gundersen, K. (in press). Neural control of membrane properties of skeletal muscle fibres. In H.L. Fernandez, & J.A. Donoso (Eds.), *Nerve-target cell trophic communication.* Boca Raton, FL: CRC Press.

Lømo, T., & Rosenthal, J. (1972). Control of ACh sensitivity by muscle activity in the rat. *Journal of Physiology,* **221**, 493-513.

Lømo, T., & Westgaard, R.H. (1975). Further studies on the control of ACh sensitivity by muscle activity in the rat. *Journal of Physiology,* **252**, 603-626.

Lømo, T., & Westgaard, R.H. (1976). Control of ACh sensitivity in rat muscle fibres. *Cold Spring Harbor Symposia on Quantitative Biology,* **XL**, 263-274.

Lømo, T., Westgaard, R.H., & Dahl, H.A. (1974). Contractile properties of muscle: Control by pattern of muscle activity in the rat. *Proceedings of the Royal Society of London Series B,* **187**, 99-103.

Matsuda, R., Spector, D., & Strohman, R.C. (1984). There is selective accumulation of a growth factor in chicken skeletal muscle. I. Transferrin accumulation in adult anterior latissimus dorsi. *Developmental Biology,* **103**, 267-275.

Mayer, R.F., Burke, R.E., Toop, J., Hodgson, J.A., Kanda, K., & Walmsley, B. (1981). The effect of long-term immobilization on the motor unit population of the cat medial gastrocnemius muscle. *Neuroscience,* **6**, 725-739.

Mayer, R.F., Burke, R.E., Toop, J., Walmsley, B., & Hodgson, J.A. (1984). The effect of spinal cord transection on motor units in cat medial gastrocnemius muscles. *Muscle & Nerve,* **7**, 23-31.

Max, S.R., & Markelonis, G.J. (1983). Neural control of muscle. *Neurochemistry International,* **5**, 675-683.

Miledi, R., & Slater, C.R. (1969). On the degeneration of rat neuromuscular junctions after nerve sections. *Journal of Physiology,* **207**, 507-528.

Murray, M.A., & Robbins, N. (1982). Cell proliferation in denervated muscle: Time course, distribution and relation to disuse. *Neuroscience,* **7**, 1817-1822.

Pette, D. (1984). Activity-induced fast to slow transitions in mammalian muscle. *Medicine and Science in Sports and Exercise,* **16**, 517-528.

Pette, D., Smith, M.E., Staudte, H.W., & Vrbová, G. (1973). Effects of long-term electrical stimulation on some contractile and metabolic characteristics of fast rabbit muscles. *Pflügers Archiv,* **338**, 257-272.

Phillips, W.D., & Bennett, M.R. (1984). Differentiation of fiber types in wing muscles during embryonic development: Effect of neural tube removal. *Developmental Biology,* **106**, 457-468.

Purves, D. (1976). Long-term regulation in the vertebrate peripheral nervous system. In R. Porter (Ed.), *International review of physiology, neurophysiology II,* **10** (pp. 125-177). Baltimore, MD: University Park Press.

Reichmann, H., & Pette, D. (1982). A comparative microphotometric study of succinate dehydrogenase activity levels in type I, IIA and IIB fibres of mammalian and human muscles. *Histochemistry,* **74**, 27-41.

Salmons, S., & Henriksson, J. (1981). The adaptive response of skeletal muscle to increased use. *Muscle & Nerve,* **4**, 94-105.

Salmons, S., & Vrbová, G. (1969). The influence of activity on some contractile characteristics of mammalian fast and slow muscles. *Journal of Physiology,* **210**, 535-549.

Salmons, S., & Sréter, F.A. (1974). Significance of impulse activity in the transformation of skeletal muscle type. *Nature,* **263**, 30-34.

Simrad, C.P., Spector, S.A., & Edgerton, V.R. (1982). Contractile properties of rat hind limb muscles immobilized at different lengths. *Experimental Neurology,* **77**, 467-482.

Sréter, F.A., Pinter, K., Jolesz, F., & Mabuchi, K. (1982). Fast to slow transformation of fast muscles in response to long-term phasic stimulation. *Experimental Neurology,* **75**, 95-102.

Stewart, D.M. (1972). The role of tension in muscle growth. In R.J. Gross (Ed.), *Regulation of organ and tissue growth* (pp. 77-100). New York: Academic Press.

Thesleff, S., & Sellin, L.C. (1980). Denervation supersensitivity. *Trends in NeuroSciences,* **3**, 122-126.

Wigston, D.J., & Sanes, J.R. (1985). Selective reinnervation of intercostal muscles transported from different segmental levels to a common site. *Journal of Neuroscience,* **5**, 1208-1221.

Witzmann, F.A., Kim, D.H., & Fitts, R.H. (1982). Recovery time course in contractile function of fast and slow skeletal muscle after hind limb immobilization. *Journal of Applied Physiology: Respiration, Environment, & Exercise Physiology,* **52**, 677-682.

Yachnis, A.T., & Mescher, A.L. (1982). Stimulation of DNA synthesis in Balb/c 3T3 cells by peripheral nerve degeneration in vitro. *Experimental Neurology,* **76**, 139-149.

Younkin, S.G., Brett, R.S., Davey, B., & Younkin, L.H. (1978). Substances moved by axonal transport and released by nerve stimulation have an innervation-like effect on the muscle. *Science,* **200**, 1292-1295.

Control of Protein Synthesis in Muscle With Special Reference to Exercise

Frank W. Booth
Paul R. Morrison
The University of Texas Medical School
Houston, Texas, U.S.A.

Muscle can be thought of as a tissue whose phenotypic characteristics are plastic. During the past 2 decades much data has been published to support the concept, which is now well established, that some physiological and biochemical properties of muscle can be altered by a chronic change in the level of its usage (Pette, 1980). It is also clear that the nature of the adaptive response is dependent on the type of exercise employed (Holloszy & Booth, 1976). Various adaptations in the levels of specific proteins in muscle occur depending on the recruitment pattern evoked by the exercise. If the level of a specific protein is altered by the program of physical activity, then either the rate of its synthesis, or the rate of its degradation, or both, can change (Schimke, 1975).

MIXED PROTEIN SYNTHESIS IN SKELETAL MUSCLE DURING EXERCISE

Recent reviews are available concerning the effects of exercise on rates of protein synthesis and degradation and the reader is referred to these for further details (Booth, Nicholson, & Watson, 1982; Booth & Watson, 1985; Pette, 1984). In brief, it appears that rates of protein synthesis decrease during exercise (Booth et al., 1982, 1985). Furthermore, a single study (Bylund-Fellenius et al., 1984) suggests that the rates of protein synthesis in skeletal muscle will not decrease until the intensity of exercise is sufficient to decrease levels of muscle ATP. Evidence was presented that the inhibition of protein synthesis resided at the sites of initiation and elongation of nascent peptide chains (Bylund-Fellenius et al., 1984). These observations need to be replicated for other exercise paradigms. Also, the mechanism by which a decrease in muscle ATP decreases initiation and elongation needs to be delineated.

POSTEXERCISE MIXED PROTEIN SYNTHESIS IN SKELETAL MUSCLE

The consensus of opinion on existing studies is that rates of protein synthesis increase in skeletal muscle in the immediate hours following an exercise bout (Booth et al., 1982, 1985). Numerous suggestions (calcium, prostaglandins, H^+, high-energy phosphate pool, reduction-oxidation ratio and glucose-6-phosphate) have been made for the molecular signal by which exercise could signal an increase in the rate of protein synthesis postexercise (Booth et al., 1985). None of these candidates for the molecular signal has been conclusively proven to be the cause of the postexercise enhancement of muscle protein synthesis. It may turn out that different types of exercise modulate rates of protein synthesis through different signals. The reader is referred to a recent review for further details (Booth et al., 1985).

SITES OF CONTROL FOR GENE EXPRESSION

A productive strategy to identify the mechanisms of exercise modulation of the muscle protein synthetic pathway is to investigate the site in the pathway where synthesis is altered by a change in muscle usage. Figure 1 depicts six possible control sites in gene expression, where gene ex-

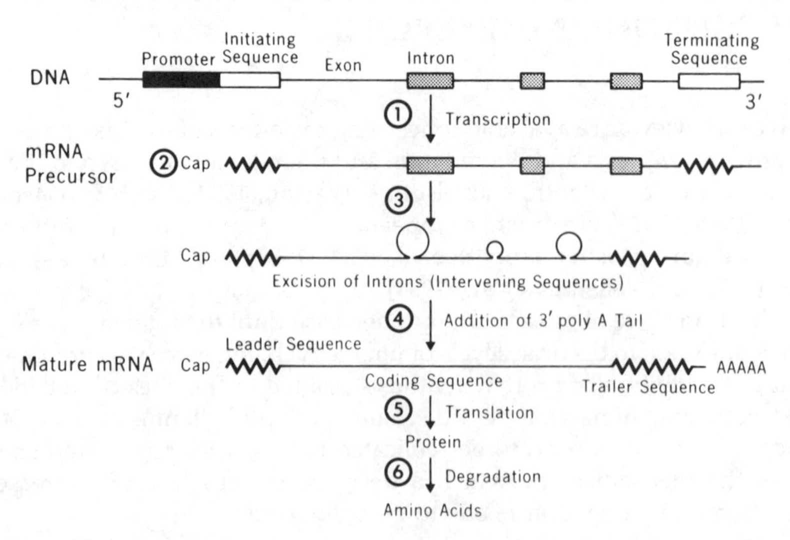

Figure 1 The sequence of gene expression. (See Lewin, 1985, *Gene II*. New York: John Wiley, for explanation).

pression is defined as the phenotype of the muscle. Gene expression can be modulated by (a) the rate of interaction of the RNA polymerases with promotor sites upstream to the gene (transcriptional control), (b) the capping rate of the 5′ end of the mRNA, (c) the splicing rate of the newly transcribed hnRNA, (d) the rate of polyadenylation of the 3′ end of the mRNA, (e) the rate of initiation, elongation or termination of protein synthesis directed by mRNA in the cytoplasm (known as translational control), or (f) alterations in the rates of protein degradation. Items (a) through (d) are pretranslational control. Available evidence suggests that the site of control may vary depending on muscle type and age (Table 1). The information in Table 1 will likely require modification as more data are published.

At present, it is known that pretranslational control is the rate-limiting step for actin protein expression during development (myoblasts through fusion of the myotubes) (Shani et al., 1981), but, translational control appears to be the rate-limiting step for altering the rates of protein synthesis within hours (acute effect) of a change in the contractile activity of adult, fast-twitch muscle. There is virtually no information on control of protein synthesis in contracting slow-twitch muscle. In contrast to those studies that show proportional increases in levels of α actin mRNA and actin synthesis rate in developing skeletal muscle (Shani et al., 1981), in the adult rat gastrocnemius muscle a 66% decrease in the rate of actin synthesis precedes by at least 3 days any change in level of α actin mRNA after the onset of limb immobilization (Watson & Booth, 1984) (Figure 2). This figure suggests that translational control is responsible for the decrease in actin synthesis because the first change in the level of α actin

Table 1 Hypothetical Control Sites for Muscle Protein Synthesis

Control Site	Synthesis	Researchers
Developing skeletal muscle	Transcription mRNA	(Shani et al., 1981)
Adult fast-twitch (many types of stimuli)	Translation (acute) Transcription (chronic)	(Pette, 1984)
Adult fast-twitch (intense mechanical loading)	Transcription rRNA(?)	(Laurent et al., 1978)
Adult heart	Transcription mRNA Transcription rRNA	(Everett et al., 1984) (Siehl et al., 1985)

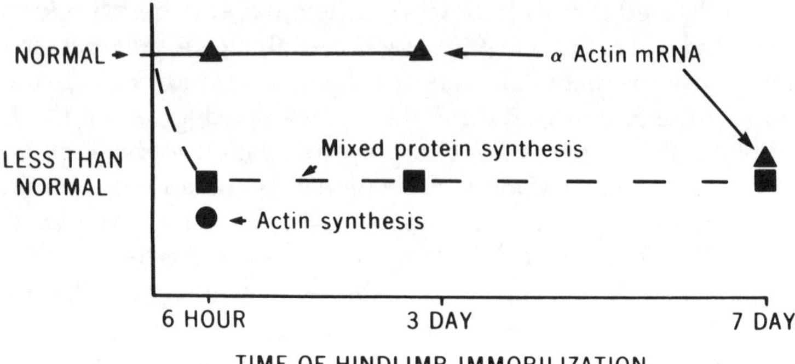

Figure 2 Time course of changes in actin synthesis rate, mixed protein synthesis rate and α actin mRNA level in the gastrocnemius muscle of rat hindlimbs immobilized so that the gastrocnemius is fixed at less than its resting length. Actin synthesis data for 3 and 7 days are not available. From "Protein Synthesis Rate in Atrophied Gastrocnemius Muscle After Limb Immobilization" by K.R. Tucker, M.J. Seider, and F.W. Booth, 1981, *Journal of Applied Physiology*, **51**, p. 73-77. Copyright 1981 by *American Physiological Society*, and "Changes in Actin Synthesis and α Actin mRNA Content in Rat Muscle During Immobilization" by P.A. Watson and F.W. Booth, 1984, *American Journal of Physiology*, **247**, p. C39-C44. Copyright 1984 by *American Physiological Society*. Adapted by permission.

mRNA was observed several days after the early decrease in actin synthesis rate.

Other such examples of translational control in adult fast-twitch muscle also exist. The examples in Table 2 indicate that the addition of either insulin or branched-chain amino acids to the perfusate of the adult rate hemicorpus will alter within the time frame of a few minutes to 3 hours the initiation rate of polypeptides in the perfused skeletal muscle.

The site of the modulation of gene expression in skeletal muscle varies depending on its age (development vs. adult). In developing muscle, pretranslational control exists, but in maturing or adult skeletal muscle, translation is likely to control protein synthesis rates during the first few hours after certain metabolic and contractile events.

It is also likely that repeated daily exposure (chronic effect) to certain metabolic factors eventually evokes changes in the transcription of genetic information into RNA. Table 3 shows that changes in the content of RNA in skeletal muscle are measurable within 1 to 3 days after various hormonal treatments. Pette (1984) has published data showing that total RNA content of chronically stimulated extensor digitorum longus muscles significantly increased at the 4th day of chronic stimulation. Imposition of higher intensity workloads on skeletal muscle, such as hanging a weight

Table 2 The First Observed Effect of Insulin and Branched Chain Amino Acids on Altering the Synthesis Rates of Mixed Proteins in Adult Fast-Twitch Skeletal Muscle is at the Level of Initiation in the Process of Translation. Times Required to Observe These Changes.

Factors		Time
Insulin	Diabetes + insulin (only fast-twitch muscle)	20-30 min (Flaim, Copenhauer, & Jefferson, 1980)
	No insulin in perfusate + insulin	less than 1 hr (Jefferson, Li, & Rannels, 1977)
	Starvation + insulin	1-3 hours (Li, Higgins, & Jefferson, 1979)
Branched chain amino acids		Less than 1 hr. (Li & Jefferson, 1978)

Table 3 Factors Affecting RNA Capacity (Content) in Skeletal Muscle and Times Required for These Changes to Occur

Factors	Time
Diabetes	2 days (Flaim et al., 1980)
Glucocorticoids (fast-twitch only)	3 days (Rannels & Jefferson, 1980)
Thyroxine	1 day (Flaim et al., 1978)
Starvation	1 day (Li et al., 1979)
Weight on a chicken wing	1 day (Laurent et al., 1978)
Eight hours daily electrical stimulation	4 days (Pette, 1984)

on the wing of a chicken resulted in a 27% increase in RNA/protein after the 1st day of holding the weight (Laurent, Sparrow & Millward, 1978). Thus, higher intensities of exercise may also initiate DNA transcription of rRNA to a greater extent than normal, and therefore, mRNA and/or rRNA accumulates more rapidly.

Limitations to Estimate Protein Synthesis in Skeletal Muscle in Vitro

Over many years of reading reviews of grants and manuscripts from other investigators, it is clear that in vitro muscle preparations have many limitations. Alternate models should be used where possible. Briefly, the limitations that may occur with in vitro models are: (a) Rates of protein degradation can exceed synthesis rates by a factor of 4 (Fulks, Li, & Goldberg, 1975; Waterlow, Garlick, & Millward, 1978). However, very small muscles when incubated with insulin have equal rates of protein synthesis and degradation (Stirewalt & Low, 1983); (b) Rates of protein synthesis, in vitro, are sometimes about 70% less than in vivo (Palmer, Reeds, Lobley, & Smith, 1981); (c) Mechanisms controlling rates of protein synthesis in vitro may be different than mechanisms in vivo if basal rates in vitro are supressed; (d) Diffusion limitations may exist in vitro at 37°C if muscles are not stretched or if muscle size exceeds 30 mg (Crettaz, Prentki, Zaninetti, & Jeanrenaud, 1980); (e) The integrity of muscle preparations may not be assessed (Waterlow et al., 1978); (f) Basal levels of contractile activity and tension in vitro can be less than in vivo; (g) Isolated muscles on rare occasions do not reflect responses occurring in the intact animal. For example, Odedra, Bates, and Millward (1983) wrote that there was no direct evidence that they knew of that glucocorticoid treatment actually lowered the rate of protein degradation in vivo whereas in vitro glucocorticoids suppress protein degradation in incubated skeletal muscle. One acceptable in vivo model is the constant infusion of a radiolabelled amino acid into a rat (Waterlow, Garlick, & Millward, 1978). Many reviewers now require that measurements of the specific radioactivity of aminoacyl tRNA be used to estimate more accurately synthesis rates of proteins, rather than assume that plasma and intracellular specific activity are the same as the precursor aminoacyl tRNA specific activity.

Protein Synthesis in the Heart

The control of protein synthesis rate in another muscle type, the heart, may differ from fast-twitch skeletal muscle of adult rats. Everett et al. (1984) found that it took only 4 hours for the content of α myosin heavy chain mRNA in the adult rat heart to increase after a single injection of 3,5,3-triiodothyronine suggesting pretranslational control of myosin synthesis. Furthermore, their data showed that the relative amounts of synthesized α myosin heavy chain and β myosin heavy chain correlated highly with the relative concentration of their respective mRNAs. In a separate study, after four daily injections of thyroxine into rats, heart mixed protein synthesis increased 24% while the ribosomal RNA concentration in the heart was increased 25% (Siehl, Chua, Lautensack-Belser, & Morgan, 1985). No change in the proportion of total RNA in free ribosomal subunits (an index of translation) in the heart was observed. Siehl et al. (1985) interpreted their data to mean that an increase in ribosomal content (pretranslational control), rather than the initiation or elongation of peptide chains (translational control), was the responsible factor causing the thyroxine-induced stimulation of myocardial protein synthesis rate. Supporting these findings was the observation that increases in the synthesis rates of ribosomal proteins occurred at least 16 hours prior to any increase in the synthesis rates of mixed proteins in the heart following a single injection of thyroxine in vivo (Siehl et al., 1985).

The rate-limiting step of protein synthesis in adult muscles apparently varies depending upon muscle fiber type. Translation is often the site in the protein synthetic pathway that acutely controls gene expression in adult fast-twitch skeletal muscle, whereas in the adult heart increased transcription of specific mRNAs and rRNA may be the acute response to thyroxine.

Multigene Families Produce Multiple Protein Isoforms

Another consideration in the control of gene expression is that contractile proteins can exist as multiple isoforms in muscle and are often encoded by multigene families. The significance of this information is that exercise might alter the relative proportions of protein isoforms present in skeletal muscle, which implies a change in gene expression. Actin is an example of one such multigene family. At least six closely related actin proteins are synthesized by six different actin genes in various cell types (Vandekerckhove & Weber, 1979). The six actins are: One α actin, that is specific for skeletal muscle and a second α actin isoform that is expressed in cardiac muscle (Bains, Ponte, Blau, & Kedes, 1984). Two types of actin are associated with smooth muscle, α and γ. The final two types of actin are the β and γ types that are constituents of the cytoskeleton of nonmuscle cells. The differences between the α cardiac and skeletal actin are minor. There are only four amino acid substitutions (1.1%) between the skeletal muscle and cardiac α actins (Vandekerckhove et al., 1979). The cardiac actin gene is expressed as the fetal isoform in skeletal muscle and as a constitutive tissue-specific isoform in the fetal and adult heart (Minty, Alonzo, Caravatti, & Buckingham, 1982). Why expression of the cardiac actin gene is programmed to decrease in skeletal muscle, but not heart muscle, during development is not known. It is also not known, for example, whether the regeneration of muscle fibers (Vihko, Rantamaki, & Salminen, 1978) following an initial bout of eccentric or exhausting exercise by adult rats is associated with the expression of adult genes or by a sequential expression of a multigene family. However, Matsuda, Spector, and Strohman (1983) reported that muscle fibers derived in culture from satellite cells of previously cold-injured fast- and slow-twitch muscle synthesized a predominantly embryonic pattern of myosin heavy chains and tropomyosin.

Multiple protein isoforms of myosin heavy chain exist in muscle (Jolesz & Sréter, 1981). Usually these isoforms have different levels of actin-activated ATPase activities (Jolesz & Sréter, 1981). These different isoforms of myosin heavy chain appear to be produced from at least seven genes on a single chromosome in the rat (Periasamy, Wieczorek, & Nadal-Ginard, 1984). The expression of these isoforms can be altered physiologically. There is a sequential expression of different myosin heavy chain isoforms in skeletal muscle at various stages of development, which are: a fetal isoform, a neonatal or perinatal isoform, and three adult forms (fast type IIA, fast type IIB, and slow) (Periasamy et al., 1984). Hypothyroidism in the rat leads to a progessive disappearance of the predominant α myosin heavy-chain and the appearance of β-myosin heavy-chain in heart myosin (Hoh, McGrath, & Hale, 1978). Injection of thyroxine into hypothyroid rabbits resulted in a rapid accumulation of α myosin heavy chain mRNA and an increased synthesis of α myosin heavy chain protein in the heart (Everett et al., 1984). This is reasonable since thyroid hormones increase cardiac contractility that would require faster myosin ATPase activities (Skelton, Su, & Pool, 1976; Banergee & Morkin, 1977). Hypothyroid rat hearts contain predominantly myosin V_3 (containing two β-myosin heavy chains per molecule) that has a lower ATPase activity than myosin V_1 (containing two α-myosin heavy chains per molecule) (Hoh, McGrath, & Hale, 1978). Thus, various levels of thyroid hormone can alter myosin heavy chain gene expression.

Hoh showed that the pattern of nervous system activity can also alter the expression of genes for the myosin heavy-chain isoforms in skeletal muscle (Hoh, 1975). Twelve to 15 months following cross-innervation of the soleus muscle with the extensor digitorum longus nerve, the soleus showed only the isoform of fast myosin. The normal rat soleus muscle myosin is composed predominantly of the slow myosin heavy-chain. When the extensor digitorum longus muscle was innervated with the nerve normally innervating the soleus muscle, the slow myosin heavy-chain was expressed. Transformation from fast myosin heavy-chains to slow myosin heavy-chains in rat skeletal muscle occurred during the interval of 2 to 7 weeks of chronic stimulation of a fast nerve with the stimulation frequency of a slow nerve (Brown, Salmons, & Whalen, 1983). Six weeks of immobilization of rat hind limbs result in an increase in the fast myosin isoform in the soleus muscle (Unsworth, Witzmann, & Fitts, 1982). This change was associated with an increase in Ca^{++} activated myosin ATPase activity. It remains to be determined by what molecular mechanism a multigene family such as myosin heavy chain is differentially expressed in adult skeletal muscle in response to changes in muscle activity.

Protein Isoforms from Alternative DNA Transcription Sites and Differential RNA Splicing

Whereas isoforms of actin and myosin heavy-chain are known to be transcribed from a multigene family, another form of gene regulation is involved in the expression of myosin light chains 1 and 3 and of troponin T isoforms. Myosin fast-type light chains 1 and 3 are produced from a single gene by a process involving alternative utilization of two RNA transcription sites and differential RNA splicing of the two primary transcripts (Periasamy, Strehler, et al., 1984). The first 141 amino acids from the carboxyl terminus of myosin fast-type light chains 1 and 3 are identical (see Periasamy, Strehler, et al., 1984, for figure illustrating the expression of myosin light chains 1 and 3). A single gene locus encodes both mRNAs for the 141 identical amino acids in myosin fast-type light chains 1 and 3. However, the amino termini of these light chains differ in length and amino acid sequence. Myosin fast-type light chain 1 has 49 amino acids prior to the common 141 amino acids whereas light chain 3 has 8 amino acids. The genomic transcription start sites and 5′ coding sequences for myosin fast-type light chains 1 and 3 are intermixed prior to the genomic sequence encoding the common 141 amino acids at the carboxy terminus of myosin fast-type light chains 1 and 3 (Periasamy, Strehler et al., 1984). The splicing mechanisms for this process are not well understood.

Differential rates of gene expression for myosin fast-type light chains 1 and 3 have been reported in response to alterations in muscle usage. Chronic stimulation of nerves to fast muscles with a frequency pattern resembling that of a slow motorneuron results in a decrease (and sometimes disappearance) of myosin fast-type light chain 3 while no change in the amount of myosin fast-type light chain 1 was observed (Pette, Müller, Leisner, & Vrbová, 1976). In another study, Brown et al. (1983) noted that myosin fast-type light chains 1 and 3 each accounted for about 3% of the total light chains at the 10th week of chronic stimulation of the tibialis anterior muscle of rabbits. The proportionality of these two light chains seemed to vary during their decline in the 10 weeks of stimulation. Baldwin,

Valdez, Herrick, MacIntosh, and Roy (1982) noted that fewer fast-type myosin light chains were observed in the "overloaded" and hypertrophied plantaris muscle 3 to 4 months following surgical removal of the gastrocnemius and soleus muscles. Thirty days after resectioning the ipsilateral gastrocnemius, an apparent increase in the content of LC_{S1} and LC_{S2} occurred in the hypertrophied plantaris muscle of the rat (Noble, Dabrowski, & Ianuzzo, 1983). These results suggest that variations in the level of contractile activity can alter the gene expression of myosin light chains 1 and 3.

Two isoforms of troponin T, α and β, are derived from a single gene in rat fast-twitch muscle (Medford, Nguyen, Destree, Summers, & Nadal-Ginard, 1984). These isoforms are identical from amino acid 70 to the end of the 3′ untranslated region, with the exception of amino acids 229 to 242. This region of the two isoforms is encoded by two distinct and adjacent miniexons in the fast-twitch troponin T gene. Medford et al. (1984) designated this portion of the gene as the "isotype switch region" and suggested that alternative RNA splicing of these two miniexons results in the incorporation of one of these exons into the mature mRNA, specific for one of the troponin T isoforms. The region of troponin T from amino acids 229 to 242 is the domain of the protein that has been shown to interact with tropomyosin and troponin C (Pearlstone & Smillie, 1983). Medford et al. (1984) suggested that altering the peptide structure of this region, that is, switching from one isoform to another, could alter the physiological response of the actomyosin complex to changes in the calcium level of the sarcoplasm. The potential significance of this process is that the percentage of fiber-type distribution can be transformed by muscle activity and it is possible that troponin isoforms will change with exercise.

SUMMARY

Changes in the expression of protein isoforms in skeletal muscle are likely to occur in response to alterations in the levels of chronic contractile activity. The diversity of pretranslational mechanisms (multigene families, alternate RNA splicing and a combination of differential RNA transcription and splicing) for expression of the isoforms of contractile proteins suggests that a control of muscle phenotype may not be the result of a single, unifying mechanism. Finally, acute responses of protein synthesis to various low-intensity stimuli in fast-twitch muscle appear to be under translational control while pretranslational control becomes predominant after chronic changes in muscle usage. A future challenge is to elucidate the transcriptional, pretranslational, and translational signals by which exercise alters the muscle phenotype.

Acknowledgments

Supported by U.S. Public Health Service Grant AM19393 and Research and Career Development Award AM00826. We thank Ms. Dianne Kirven for typing and Drs. Peter A. Watson, David Essig, John Kennedy, and Peter Schantz for reviewing the manuscript.

REFERENCES

Bains, W., Ponte, P., Blau, H., & Kedes, L. (1984). Cardiac actin is the major actin gene product in skeletal muscle cell differentiation in vitro. *Molecular and Cellular Biology*, **4**, 1449-1453.

Baldwin, K.M., Valdez, V., Herrick, R.E., MacIntosh, A.K., & Roy, R.R. (1982). Biochemical properties of overloaded fast-twitch skeletal muscle. *Journal of Applied Physiology*, **52**, 467-472.

Banerjee, S.K. & Morkin, E. (1977). Actin-activated adenosine triphosphatase activity of native and N-ethylmaleimide-modified cardiac myosin from normal and thyrotoxic rabbits. *Circulation Research*, **41**, 630-634.

Booth, F.W., Nicholson, W.F., & Watson, P.A. (1982). Influence of muscle use on protein synthesis and degradation. *Exercise and Sports Sciences Reviews*, **10**, 27-48.

Booth, F.W., & Watson, P.A. (1985). Control of adaptations in protein levels in response to exercise. *Federation Proceedings*, **44**, 2293-2300.

Brown, W.E., Salmons, S., & Whalen, R.G. (1983). The sequential replacement of myosin subunit isoforms during muscle type transformation induced by long-term electrical stimulation. *Journal of Biological Chemistry*, **258**, 14686-14692.

Bylund-Fellenius, A.-C., Ojama, K.M., Flaim, K.E., Li, J.B., Wassner, S.J., & Jefferson, L.S. (1984). Protein synthesis versus energy state in contracting muscles of perfused rat hindlimb. *American Journal of Physiology*, **246**, E297-E305.

Crettaz, M., Prentki, M., Zaninetti, D., & Jeanrenaud, B. (1980). Insulin resistance in soleus muscle from obese Zucker rats. *Biochemical Journal*, **186**, 525-534.

Everett, A.W., Sinha, A.M., Umeda, P.K., Jakovcic, S., Rabinowitz, M., & Zak, R. (1984). Regulation of myosin synthesis by thyroid hormone: Relative change in the α- and β-myosin heavy chain mRNA levels in rabbit heart. *Biochemistry*, **23**, 1596-1599.

Flaim, K.E., Copenhaver, M.E., & Jefferson, L.S. (1980). Effects of diabetes on protein synthesis in fast- and slow-twitch rat skeletal muscle. *American Journal of Physiology*, **239**, E88-E95.

Flaim, K.E., Li, J.B., & Jefferson, L.S. (1978). Effects of thyroxine on protein turnover in rat skeletal muscle. *American Journal of Physiology,* **235**, E231-E236.

Fulks, R.M., Li, J.B., & Goldberg, A.L. (1975). Effects of insulin, glucose and amino acids on protein turnover in rat diaphragm. *Journal of Biological Chemistry,* **250**, 290-298.

Hoh, J.F.Y. (1975). Neural regulation of mammalian fast and slow muscle myosins: An electrophoretic analysis. *Biochemistry,* **14**, 742-747.

Hoh, J.F.Y., McGrath, P.A., & Hale, H.T. (1978). Electrophoretic analysis of multiple forms of rat cardiac myosin: Effects of hypophysectomy and thyroxine replacement. *Journal of Molecular and Cellular Cardiology,* **10**, 1053-1076.

Holloszy, J.O., & Booth, F.W. (1976). Biochemical adaptations to endurance exercise in muscle. *Annual Review of Physiology,* **38**, 273-291.

Jefferson, L.S., Li, J.B., & Rannels, S.R. (1977). Regulation by insulin of amino acid release and protein turnover in the perfused rat hemicorpus. *Journal of Biological Chemistry,* **252**, 1476-1483.

Jolesz, F., & Sréter, F.A. (1981). Development, innervation, and activity pattern-induced changes in skeletal muscle. *Annual Review of Physiology,* **43**, 531-552.

Laurent, G.J., Sparrow, M.P., & Millward, D.J. (1978). Turnover of muscle protein in the fowl. Changes in rates of protein synthesis and breakdown during hypertrophy of the anterior and posterior latissimus dorsi muscles. *Biochemical Journal,* **176**, 407-417.

Li, J.B., & Jefferson, L.S. (1978). Influence of amino acid availability on protein turnover in perfused skeletal muscle. *Biochimica et Biophysica Acta,* **544**, 351-359.

Li, J.B., Higgins, J.E., & Jefferson, L.S. (1979). Changes in protein turnover in skeletal muscle in response to fasting. *American Journal of Physiology,* **236**, E222-E228.

Matsuda, R., Spector, D.H., & Strohman, R.C. (1983). Regenerating adult chicken skeletal muscle and satellite cell cultures express embryonic patterns of myosin and tropomyosin isoforms. *Developmental Biology,* **100**, 478-488.

Medford, R.M., Nguyen, H.T., Destree, A.T., Summers, E., & Nadal-Ginard, B. (1984). A novel mechanism of alternative RNA splicing for the developmentally regulated generation of troponin T isoforms from a single gene. *Cell,* **38**, 409-421.

Minty, A.J., Alonzo, S., Caravatti, M., & Buckingham, M.E. (1982). A fetal skeletal muscle actin mRNA in the mouse and its identity with cardiac actin mRNA. *Cell,* **30**, 185-192.

Noble, E.G., Dabrowski, B.L., & Ianuzzo, C.D. (1983). Myosin transformation in hypertrophied rat muscle. *Pflügers Archiv,* **396**, 260-262.

Odedra, B.R., Bates, P.C., & Millward, D.J. (1983). Time course of the effect of catabolic doses of corticosterone on protein turnover in rat skeletal muscle and liver. *Biochemical Journal,* **214**, 617-627.

Palmer, R.M., Reeds, P.J., Lobley, G.E., & Smith, R.H. (1981). The effect of intermittent changes in tension on protein and collagen synthesis in isolated rabbits muscles. *Biochemical Journal,* **198**, 491-498.

Pearlstone, J.R., & Smillie, L.B. (1983). Effects of troponin-I plus -C on the binding of troponin-I and its fragments to α-tropomyosin. *Journal of Biological Chemistry,* **258**, 2534-2542.

Periasamy, M., Strehler, E.E., Garfinkel, L.I., Gubits, R.M., Ruiz-Opazo, N., & Nadal-Ginard, B. (1984). Fast skeletal muscle myosin light chains 1 and 3 are produced from a single gene by a combined process of differential RNA transcription and splicing. *Journal of Biological Chemistry,* **259**, 13595-13604.

Periasamy, M., Wieczorek, D.F., & Nadal-Ginard, B. (1984). Characterization of a developmentally regulated perinatal myosin heavy-chain gene expressed in skeletal muscle. *Journal of Biological Chemistry,* **259**, 13573-13578.

Pette, D. (1980). *Plasticity of muscle.* Berlin: Walter de Gruyter.

Pette, D. (1984). Activity-induced fast to slow transitions in mammalian muscle. *Medicine and Science in Sports and Exercise,* **16**, 517-528.

Pette, D., Müller, W., Leisner, E., & Vrbová, G. (1976). Time dependent effects on contractile properties, fibre population, myosin light chains and enzymes of energy metabolism in intermittently and continuously stimulated fast-twitch muscles of the rabbit. *Pflügers Archiv,* **364**, 103-112.

Rannels, S.R., & Jefferson, L.S. (1980). Effects of glucocorticoids on muscle protein turnover in perfused rat hemocorpus. *American Journal of Physiology,* **238**, E564-E572.

Schimke, R.T. (1975). Methods for analysis of enzyme synthesis and degradation in animal tissues. *Methods in Enzymology,* **40**, 241-255.

Shani, M., Zevin-Sonkin, D., Saxel, O., Carmon, Y., Katcoff, D., Nudel, U., & Yaffe, D. (1981). The correlation between the synthesis of skeletal muscle actin, myosin heavy chain, and myosin light chain and the accumulation of corresponding mRNA sequences during myogenesis. *Developmental Biology,* **86**, 483-492.

Siehl, D., Chua, B.H.L., Lautensack-Belser, N., & Morgan, H.E. (1985). Faster protein and ribosome synthesis in thyroxine-induced hypertrophy of rat heart. *American Journal of Physiology,* **248**, C309-C319.

Skelton, C.L., Su, J.Y., & Pool, P.E. (1976). Influence of hyperthyroidism on glycerol-extracted cardiac muscle from rabbits. *Cardiovascular Research,* **10**, 380-384.

Stirewalt, W.S. & Low, R.B. (1983). Effects of insulin *in vitro* on protein turnover in rat epitrochlearis muscle. *Biochemical Journal,* **210**, 323-330.

Tucker, K.R., Seider, M.J., & Booth, F.W. (1981). Protein synthesis rate in atrophied gastrocnemius muscle after limb immobilization. *Journal of Applied Physiology,* **51**, 73-77.

Unsworth, B.R., Witzmann, F.A., & Fitts, R.H. (1982). A comparison of rat myosin from fast and slow skeletal muscle and the effect of disuse. *Journal of Biological Chemistry,* **257**, 15129-15136.

Vandekerckhove, J., & Weber, K. (1979). The complete amino acid sequence of actins from bovine aorta, bovine heart, bovine fast skeletal muscle, and rabbit slow skeletal muscle. *Differentiation,* **14**, 123-133.

Vihko, V., Rantamaki, J., & Salminen, A. (1978). Exhaustive physical exercise and acid hydrolase activity in mouse skeletal muscle. *Histochemistry,* **57**, 237-249.

Waterlow, J.C., Garlick, P.J., & Millward, D.J. (1978). *Protein turnover in mammalian tissues and the whole body* (p. 152, 575). Amsterdam: North Holland.

Watson, P.A., & Booth, F.W. (1984). Changes in actin synthesis and α actin mRNA content in rat muscle during immobilization. *American Journal of Physiology,* **247**, C-39-C44.

Adaptations in Skeletal Muscle to Training and Detraining: The Role of Protein Synthesis and Degradation

Michael E. Houston
University of Waterloo
Waterloo, Ontario, Canada

Skeletal muscle has been extensively studied from the perspective of its responses or adaptation to altered use, hormonal environment, neural influence and disease. A number of models have been employed, and some of these are shown in Figure 1. Although muscle adaptation may be studied from a variety of perspectives, it must be emphasized that the phenotype of a muscle cell, including its primary contribution in force development and secondary role as a body protein reserve, is largely determined by the amounts and kinds of protein it synthesizes and contains. Accordingly, the essential feature of muscle adaptation is predicated on the changes in quantitative and/or qualitative aspects of proteins in the muscle cell.

The focus of this review is on the role played by exercise training and detraining in modifying the concentrations of specific muscle proteins in

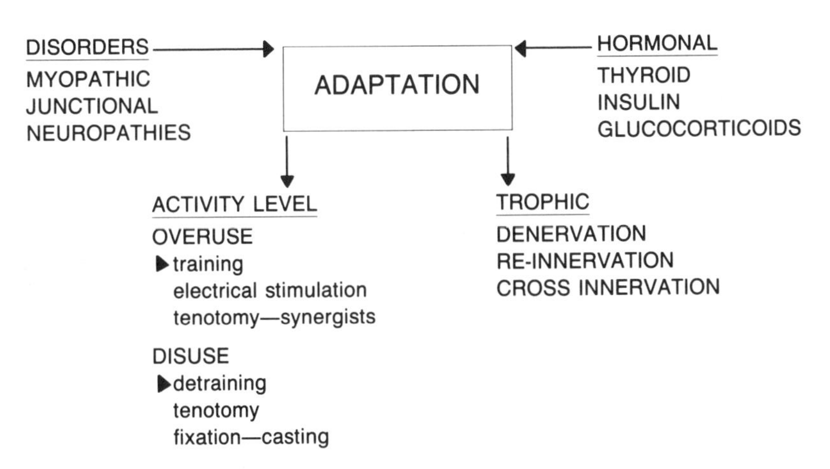

Figure 1 Experimental models used for the study of skeletal muscle adaptation.

man. In this regard, considerable attention will be placed on studies that have examined the effects of acute exercise on whole body and muscle protein metabolism in man. Where evidence from human studies is inconclusive or lacking, results of experiments employing specific animal models will be considered.

PROTEIN ADAPTATIONS TO EXERCISE TRAINING AND DETRAINING

Adaptations in skeletal muscle to exercise training are such that the trained muscle is better able to tolerate work compared to untrained muscle. This is mainly the result of increased concentrations of specific muscle proteins. However, the nature and duration of the exercise stimulus play a critical role in specifying the adaptations in specific muscle proteins. For example, heavy resistance training (weight lifting), anaerobic (sprint) training, and endurance training primarily result in specific increases in myofibrillar proteins, glycolytic enzymes, and enzymes of oxidative metabolism, respectively (as reviewed by Booth & Watson, 1985; Holloszy & Booth, 1976; Howald, 1982; Salmons & Henriksson, 1981).

While the responses of human muscle proteins to training, particularly endurance training, have received considerable attention, detraining, that is, withdrawal of the exercise stimulus, has not been examined as extensively. After relatively short periods of training (ca. 8 weeks) involving cycling (Henriksson & Reitman, 1977; Klausen, Andersen, & Pelle, 1981) or skiing (Schantz, Henriksson, & Jansson, 1983) in which selected muscle oxidative enzyme activities increased by 40 to 90%, detraining periods of an equally short duration largely abolished these increases. Such responses are typical to that shown in Figure 2 for a female subject who trained one leg on a cycle ergometer for 10 weeks, followed by 12 weeks of detraining. In the trained leg, succinate dehydrogenase (SDH) activity was increased by 70%. However, this adaptation was essentially lost after only four weeks of detraining.

For subjects who have performed endurance training for considerably longer periods of time, the reductions in oxidative enzyme activities with detraining are similar in direction, but less in magnitude compared to those observed in subjects who have trained for shorter periods (Chi et al., 1983; Houston, Bentzen, & Larsen, 1979). The results reported by Chi et al. (1983) are particularly revealing in this regard. Whereas most studies have measured enzyme activities in whole homogenates, Chi et al. (1983) assayed enzyme activities in fragments of human type I and II muscle fibers before and up to 12 weeks after detraining. Briefly, their data revealed that the loss in oxidative enzyme activities with detraining was

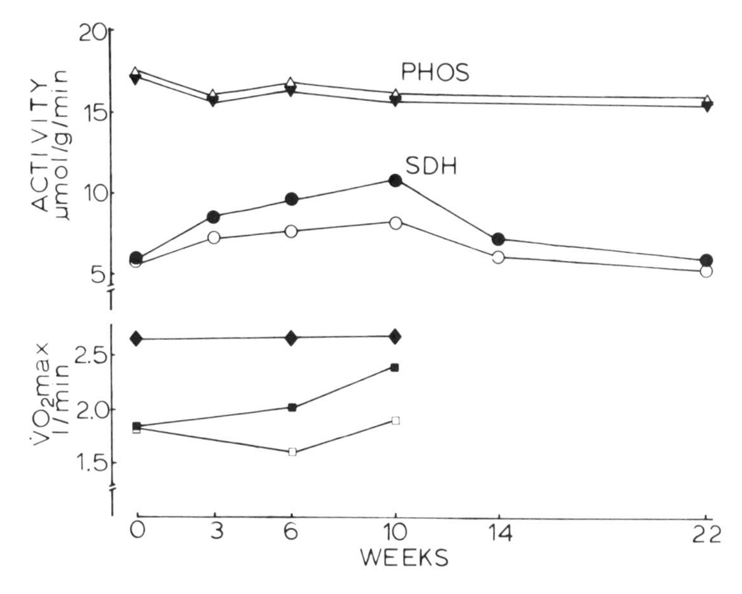

Figure 2 The response of skeletal muscle phosphorylase (PHOS) and succinate dehydrogenase (SDH) activity in the vastus lateralis to 10 weeks of one-leg cycle training and 12 weeks of detraining in a young adult female. $\dot{V}O_2max$ measures during two leg (upper curve) and one leg cycling are also shown. Closed symbols and open symbols refer to data obtained from the trained and untrained leg, respectively.

more significant for type I fibers. In fact, after 12 weeks of detraining mitochondrial enzyme levels in type I fibers decreased almost to the level found in untrained subjects, but those activities in type II fibers were still 50 to 80% higher than levels found in untrained subjects.

Although heavy resistance or weight training is a common recreational activity, and underlies the training for a variety of sporting events, it has been poorly studied from the perspective of its effects on specific muscle protein concentrations. Although the myofibrillar content of hypertrophied muscle must certainly increase (McDonagh & Davies, 1984), stereological analysis of electron microscopic sections from triceps brachii before and after 6 months of weight training revealed that, although muscle fiber areas were enlarged, myofibrillar volume density was not significantly increased, whereas mitochondrial volume density was decreased (MacDougall et al., 1979). These data may be interpreted as showing either an actual loss of mitochondrial protein or a dilution in mitochondrial protein due to an increase in contractile proteins in strength training.

Results from training studies involving brief high intensity isometric or dynamic contractions on the activities of enzymes involved in glycolytic and oxidative pathways are equivocal. Based on assays of enzyme activities in muscle biopsy samples taken before and after training using repeated bouts of 6-s isokinetic contractions, Costill, Coyle, Fink, Lesmes, and Witzmann (1979) noted a significant increase only for phosphofructokinase activity. When the training contractions were 30 s in duration, significant increases were also noted in several oxidative enzymes (Costill et al., 1979). On the other hand, Komi, Viitasalo, Rauramaa, and Vihko (1978) reported significant increases in malate dehydrogenase, succinate dehydrogenase, and hexokinase, while lactate dehydrogenase activity was decreased following isometric strength training. In contrast to the above studies, we found no significant changes in the activities of glycolytic and oxidative enzymes from serial biopsy samples obtained before, during, and after a 10-week strength training program (Houston, Froese, Valeriote, Green, & Ranney, 1983). Despite the fact that fast-twitch muscle fibers were significantly enlarged, the lack of a change in these enzyme activities was apparent whether the activities were expressed per unit weight of muscle (Houston et al., 1983) or per unit of muscle protein (Houston, unpublished raw data).

Detraining following strength training has received little attention in terms of its effects on specific muscle proteins. We have shown that over a period of 12 weeks, detraining had no significant effect on glycolytic or oxidative enzyme activities (Houston et al., 1983). Moreover, although fast-twitch fibers were reduced in area with detraining, the specific activity of myofibrillar adenosine triphosphatase (ATPase) was unchanged (Houston et al., 1983).

PROTEIN METABOLISM DURING EXERCISE AND TRAINING

The foregoing summary reveals that the presence or withdrawal of a unique training stimulus may significantly and selectively modify the levels of specific proteins in skeletal muscles of man. Muscle protein, as with all cellular protein, is constantly undergoing turnover. This involves synthesis of new protein concurrent with degradation of old protein. While a discussion of these specific processes and control mechanisms is beyond the scope of this review, Figure 3 illustrates the important steps involved. The major question to be addressed is whether the training stimulus, or, with detraining, the absence of a training stimulus, modifies the content of specific muscle proteins by altering the rate of synthesis, the rate of degradation, or both rates in skeletal muscles of man. Ideally, answers to this question must arise from studies measuring both muscle protein synthesis and degradation rates during and following exercise training sessions. Unfortunately, it is difficult to measure the rates

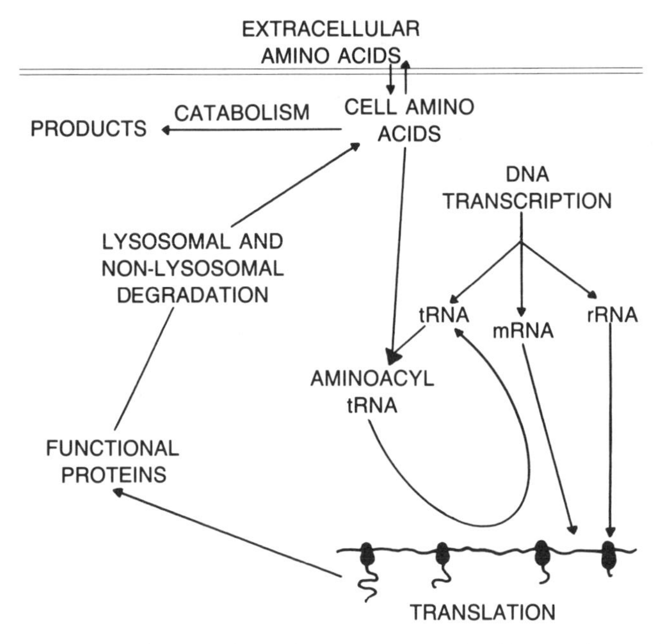

Figure 3 An overview showing the major processes involved in protein metabolism in skeletal muscle.

of these processes in experimental animals and even more difficult in humans, especially during exercise (Lemon, Yarasheski, & Dolny, 1984). However, a variety of techniques have been employed to assess whole body protein metabolism of man in vivo. Moreover, since the protein content of skeletal muscle typically represents more than 60% of all the proteins in the human body (Ballard & Tomas, 1983), it is generally assumed that changes in whole body protein metabolism reflect changes taking place in skeletal muscle protein.

Many of the techniques used to assess protein turnover characteristics in man have been employed in studies of exercise and exercise training (Table 1). All of these techniques have limitations in terms of the reliability of the information provided. Nitrogen balance studies, in which the nitrogen intake is compared to nitrogen losses from all sources, have been reported for human subjects during training (Celejowa & Homa, 1970; Gontzea, Sutzescu, & Dumitrache, 1975). However, the focus of such studies has been directed more to assessing dietary protein and energy relationships since nitrogen balance is sensitive to both considerations (Gontzea et al., 1975). Moreover, data from nitrogen balance studies provide only suggestive information regarding net gain or loss of body protein, and cannot clearly indicate directional changes in protein synthesis and degradation rates. Urinary urea and/or total nitrogen excretion during and following exercise should reflect changes in protein metabolism since urea synthesis is coupled to the catabolism of amino acids. As well, sweat urea measures should also be made since this may represent a significant loss of urea during exercise (Calles-Escandon et al., 1984; Lemon & Mullin, 1980). In general, urea loss from the body is augmented as a result of exercise, but this merely provides indirect evidence for accelerated protein catabolism as has been recently discussed (Lemon et al., 1984). Furthermore, urea production rate during exercise has been shown to be dissociated from leucine oxidation rate (Wolfe et al., 1982).

Several more recent approaches for studying protein metabolism with exercise in man have shown promise. The excretion of 3-methylhistidine has been considered a reliable index of the degradation of the myofibrillar protein actin and myosin because degradation of these proteins is accompanied by the quantitative excretion of 3-methylhistidine in the urine of man (Young & Munro, 1978). Equations have been developed to measure the total rate of muscle protein breakdown or the fractional turnover of muscle protein from urinary measures of 3-methylhistidine or 3-methylhistidine plus creatinine excretion, respectively, provided subjects ingest a meat-free diet (Ballard & Tomas, 1983). Moreover, it has been assumed that this technique should adequately reflect skeletal muscle myofibrillar protein degradation since skeletal muscle in adult males contains approximately 90% of the total body pool of 3-methylhistidine (Table 1; Ballard & Tomas, 1983). Since the measures needed may be obtained noninva-

Table 1 Techniques Utilized for Assessing Protein Turnover Characteristics in Man During Exercise and Exercise Training

Technique	Condition Studied	Selected References
Whole body nitrogen balance	Weight lifting training	Celejowa & Homa, 1970
	Endurance training	Gontzea et al., 1975
Nitrogen excretion + sweat urea	Endurance exercise	Lemon & Mullin, 1980
Excretion of 3-methylhistidine	Endurance exercise	Rennie et al., 1981
Primed, constant infusion of di-[^{15}N] urea	Endurance exercise	Wolfe et al., 1982
Primed, constant infusion of [l-^{13}C] leucine	Endurance exercise	Millward et al., 1982

sively, and since both 3-methylhistidine and creatinine in urine can be measured easily and accurately, this procedure has generated optimism as a means for assessing the effect of exercise on the catabolic rate of skeletal muscle protein.

Results from exercise studies illustrated in Table 2 reveal that, for most exercise tasks studied, 3-methylhistidine excretion was not significantly affected. These results suggest that exercise has little influence on skeletal muscle myofibrillar degradation rates. However, Rennie and Millward (1983) have presented compelling arguments against the use of 3-methylhistidine excretion for assessing skeletal muscle myofibrillar breakdown. These authors pointed out that small, rapidly turned-over pools of protein containing 3-methylhistidine, found, for example, in skin and intestine, contribute substantially to measured 3-methylhistidine in urine. Rennie and Millward (1983) also provided evidence revealing that there is a discrepancy between urinary excretion of 3-methylhistidine and measured rates of skeletal muscle degradation under certain conditions.

A newer technique, which so far has been shown to provide reliable assessments of protein turnover characteristics, involves the use of the

Table 2 Effects of Exercise on 3-Methylhistidine Excretion in Human Subjects

Exercise Conditions	Effect on 3-methylhistidine Excretion	Reference
Running, 100 km race[a]	No significant change	Décombaz et al., 1979
Running, 3.75 hours	Decreased 10 to 20%	Rennie et al., 1981
Running, 16 to 18 km[b]	Increased 80%	Dohm et al., 1982
Weight lifting, 1 hour[a]	Nonsignificant increase	Dohm et al., 1982
Cycling exercise, 1 hour	No significant change	Plante & Houston, 1984a
Intermittent, supramaximal cycling	No significant change	Plante & Houston, 1984b
Cycling exercise, 90 min	Nonsignificant increase	Calles-Escandon et al., 1984
Eccentric cycling, 60 min	No significant change	Plante & Houston, 1984b

[a]Subjects did not consume a meat-free diet.

[b]Only one-half of the subjects consumed a meat-free diet.

stable isotopes ^{15}N and ^{13}C, which can be measured in molecules in plasma, urine and expired air using selected-ion monitoring gas chromatograph-mass spectrometry procedures (Conway, Bier, Motil, Burke, & Young, 1980; Matthews, Motil, Rohrbaugh, Burke, Young, & Bier, 1980; Wolfe et al., 1982). Using a primed, constant infusion of ^{15}N-enriched lysine (Conway et al., 1980) or urea (Wolfe et al., 1982), whole-body net protein degradation can be assessed. More detailed information including leucine oxidation rates and whole body protein synthesis and degradation rates can be obtained using a primed, constant infusion of L-[1-^{13}C] leucine if a bolus of $NaH^{13}CO_3$ is also given to prime the body pool of bicarbonate (Wolfe et al., 1982). The use of [1-^{13}C] leucine is particularly useful if the plasma enrichment of its transamination product (α-ketoisocaproate) is measured because both the whole body protein synthesis and degradation rates are underestimated to the same extent (Wolfe, 1982).

The use of stable isotopes for assessing protein turnover characteristics during exercise in man has received scant attention. It has been shown that leucine oxidation rate is linearly related to exercise intensity (Millward et al., 1982). In fed subjects, whole body protein synthesis rate exceeded degradation, but subsequent prolonged running exercise caused a depression in synthesis rate and an increase in degradation (Rennie et al., 1981). Following the exercise a positive protein balance was established primarily as a result of an increase in protein synthesis. In fasted subjects, two hours of treadmill exercise decreased whole body protein synthesis rate, but this rate was increased following exercise (Millward et al., 1982). However in these fasted subjects, measured whole body degradation rates of protein were similar for the periods before, during, and after exercise. In a related experiment, Millward et al. (1982) reported that glucose ingestion every 15 min depressed protein degradation rates to a similar extent, before, during, and after exercise in fasted subjects. Wolfe et al. (1982) reported that low intensity (30% $\dot{V}O_2max$) exercise carried out for 105 min depressed protein synthesis by 48% and increased catabolism by 21% in subjects in the postabsorptive state using the ^{13}C leucine infusion protocol. The increase in protein catabolism was related to a nearly fourfold increase in leucine oxidation, and it was suggested that a likely source of the degraded protein was skeletal muscle protein (Wolfe et al., 1982).

It is difficult to make clear conclusions as to how acute exercise and training influence protein synthesis and degradation rates in skeletal muscles of man from the information that has been summarized. On the basis of the apparently more reliable primed constant infusion experiments using ^{13}C leucine it would appear that during exercise muscle protein synthesis rate is depressed while the rate of protein degradation is accelerated. Following exercise it seems likely that protein synthesis is augmented, whereas protein degradation rate is maintained or decreased.

Confounding these interpretations is the effect that food intake may play, since the quantity and quality of ingested amino acids as well as carbohydrate can modulate the processes of synthesis and degradation of protein. If such studies are feasible, it would seem that measures of leucine incorporation into protein along with arteriovenous 3-methylhistidine concentration differences during and following exercise could provide more definitive data on rates of protein synthesis and degradation, respectively in exercising and exercised human skeletal muscles.

The use of experimental animal models can often provide valuable answers to problems that are less readily studied in human subjects. This definitely applies to questions concerning the role played by acute exercise and exercise training in modulating protein synthesis and degradation rates in skeletal muscle. Since this topic has been addressed in several recent reviews (Booth & Watson, 1985; Dohm, Kasperek, Tapscott, & Barakat, 1985) only selected studies will be considered.

Cytochrome c turnover has been monitored during training and detraining (Booth & Holloszy, 1977) and following immobilization (Watson, Srivastava, & Booth, 1983). In the former experiment the data strongly suggested that an increase in cytochrome c synthesis rate was responsible for the training-induced increase in cytochrome c concentration in muscle. In the latter experiment, immobilizaton caused a 47% decrease in cytochrome c synthesis rates. These experiments suggest that increases in mitochondrial enzyme levels with training and their decreases with detraining is primarily regulated by altered protein synthesis rates. Using animal hypertrophy models, Laurent and Millward (1980) and Goldspink, Garlick, and McNurlan (1983) demonstrated that while both skeletal muscle protein synthesis and degradation rates were increased, the rapid hypertrophy of these overloaded muscles was due to a greater rate of protein synthesis.

It is tempting to conclude from the evidence reviewed that the adaptations in protein constituents associated with exercise training and detraining are primarily determined by alterations in protein synthesis rates. Additional support for this view comes from two recent reviews (Lebherz, 1984; Rennie, et al., 1983). Lebherz (1984) concluded that regulatory mechanisms acting at the level of protein synthesis, but not degradation, are mainly responsible for specifying the levels of different glycolytic enzyme levels in the various animal muscle fiber types. Furthermore, he proposed that the lower glycolytic enzyme content noted in denervated and dystrophic muscles was due to reductions in synthesis rates rather than to accelerated degradation rates. Finally, Rennie et al. (1983) stated, "there is now strong evidence from studies in animals, normal men and in patients with a variety of diseases to suggest that the muscle mass is regulated primarily by alterations in the protein synthesis rate and that changes in muscle protein degradation are largely secondary and adaptive."

REFERENCES

Ballard, F.J., & Tomas, F.M. (1983). 3-Methylhistidine as a measure of skeletal muscle protein breakdown in human subjects: The case for its continued use. *Clinical Science,* **65**, 209-215.

Booth, F.W., & Holloszy, J.O. (1977). Cytochrome c turnover in rat skeletal muscle. *The Journal of Biological Chemistry,* **252**, 416-419.

Booth, F.W., & Watson, P.A. (1985). Control of adaptations in protein levels in response to exercise. *Federation Proceedings,* **44**, 2293-2300.

Calles-Excandon, J., Cunningham, J.J., Snyder, P., Jacob, R., Huszar, G., Loke, J., & Felig, P. (1984). Influence of exercise on urea, creatinine, and 3-methylhistidine excretion in normal human subjects. *American Journal of Physiology,* **246**, E334-E338.

Celejowa, I., & Homa, M. (1970). Food intake, nitrogen and energy balance in Polish weight lifters during a training camp. *Nutrition and Metabolism,* **12**, 259-274.

Chi, M.M.-Y., Hintz, C.S., Coyle, E.F., Martin III, W.H., Ivy, J.L., Nemeth, P.M., Holloszy, J.O., & Lowry, O.H. (1983). Effects of detraining on enzymes of energy metabolism in individual human muscle fibres. *American Journal of Physiology,* **244**, C276-C287.

Conway, J.M., Bier, D.M., Motil, K.J., Burke, J.F., & Young, V.R. (1980). Whole-body lysine flux in young adult men: Effects of reduced total protein and of lysine intake. *American Journal of Physiology,* **239**, E192-E200.

Costill, D.L., Coyle, E.F., Fink, W.F., Lesmes, G.R., & Witzmann, F.A. (1979). Adaptations in skeletal muscle following strength training. *Journal of Applied Physiology,* **46**, 96-99.

Décombaz, J., Reinhard, P., Anantharaman, K., von Glutz, G., & Poortmans, J.R. (1979). Biochemical changes in a 100 km run: Free amino acids, urea and creatinine. *European Journal of Applied Physiology,* **41**, 61-72.

Dohm, G.L., Kasperek, J., Tapscott, E.B., & Barakat, H.A. (1985). Protein metabolism during endurance exercise. *Federation Proceedings,* **44**, 348-352.

Dohm, G.L., Williams, R.T., Kasperek, G.J., & van Rij, A.M. (1982). Increased excretion of urea and N-methylhistidine by rats and humans after a bout of exercise. *Journal of Applied Physiology,* **52**, 27-33.

Goldspink, D.F., Garlick, P.J., McNurlan, M.A. (1983). Protein turnover measured in vivo and in vitro in muscles undergoing compensatory growth and subsequent denervation atrophy. *Biochemical Journal,* **210**, 84-98.

Gontzea, I., Sutzescu, R., & Dumitrache, S. (1975). The influence of adaptation to physical effort on nitrogen balance in man. *Nutrition Reports International,* **11**, 231-236.

Henriksson, J., & Reitman, J.S. (1977). Time course of changes in human skeletal muscle succinate dehydrogenase and cytochrome oxidase activities and maximal oxygen uptake with physical activity and inactivity. *Acta Physiologica Scandinavica,* **99**, 91-99.

Holloszy, J.O., & Booth, F.W. (1976). Biochemical adaptations to endurance exercise in muscle. *Annual Reviews of Physiology,* **38**, 273-291.

Houston, M.E., Bentzen, H., & Larsen, H. (1979). Interrelationships between skeletal muscle adaptations and performance as studied by detraining and retraining. *Acta Physiologica Scandinavica,* **105**, 163-170.

Houston, M.E., Fruese, E.A., Valeriote, S.P., Green, H.J., & Ranney, D.A. (1983). Muscle performance, morphology and metabolic capacity during strength training and detraining: A one leg model. *European Journal of Applied Physiology,* **51**, 25-35.

Howald, H. (1982). Training-induced morphological and functional changes in skeletal muscle. *International Journal of Sports Medicine,* **3**, 1-12.

Klausen, K., Andersen, L.B., & Pelle, I. (1981). Adaptive changes in work capacity, skeletal muscle capillarization and enzyme levels during training and detraining. *Acta Physiologica Scandinavica,* **113**, 9-16.

Komi, P.V., Viitasalo, J.T., Rauramaa, R., & Vihko, V. (1978). Effect of isometric strength training on mechanical, electrical, and metabolic aspects of muscle function. *European Journal of Applied Physiology,* **40**, 45-55.

Laurent, G.J., & Millward, D.J. (1980). Protein turnover during skeletal muscle hypertrophy. *Federation Proceedings,* **39**, 42-47.

Lebherz, H.G. (1984). Content and synthesis of glycolytic enzymes in normal, denervated, and dystrophic skeletal muscle fibers. *International Journal of Biochemistry,* **16**, 1201-1205.

Lemon, P.W.R., & Mullin, J.P. (1980). Effect of initial glycogen levels on protein catabolism during exercise. *Journal of Applied Physiology,* **48**, 624-629.

Lemon, P.W.R., Yarasheski, K.E., & Dolny, D.G. (1984). The importance of protein for athletes. *Sports Medicine,* **1**, 474-484.

MacDougall, J.D., Sale, D.G., Moroz, J.R., Elder, G.C.B., Sutton, J.R., and Howald, H. (1979). Mitochondrial volume density in human skeletal muscle following heavy resistance training. *Medicine and Science in Sports,* **11**, 164-166.

Matthews, D.E., Motil, K.J., Rohrbaugh, D.K., Burke, J.F., Young, V.R., & Bier, D.M. (1980). Measurement of leucine metabolism in man from a primed, continuous infusion of L-[1-^{13}C] leucine. *American Journal of Physiology,* **238**, E473-E479.

McDonagh, M.J.N, & Davies, C.T.M. (1984). Adaptive response of mammalian skeletal muscle to exercise with high loads. *European Journal of Applied Physiology,* **52**, 139-155.

Millward, D.J., Davies, C.T.M., Halliday, D., Wolman, S.L., Matthews, D., & Rennie, M. (1982). Effects of exercise on protein metabolism in humans as explored with stable isotopes. *Federation Proceedings,* **41**, 2686-2691.

Plante, P.D., & Houston, M.E. (1984b). Effects of concentric and eccentric exercise on protein catabolism in man. *International Journal of Sports Medicine,* **5**, 174-178.

Plante, R.I., & Houston, ME. (1984a). Exercise and protein catabolism in women. *Annals of Nutrition and Metabolism,* **28**, 123-129.

Rennie, M.J., Edwards, R.H.T., Emery, P.W., Halliday, D., Lundholm, K., & Millward, D.J. (1983). Depressed protein synthesis is the dominant characteristic of muscle wasting and cachexia. *Clinical Physiology,* **3**, 387-398.

Rennie, M.J., Edwards, R.H.T., Krywawych, S., Davies, C.T.M., Halliday, D., Waterlow, J.C., & Millward, D.J. (1981). Effect of exercise on protein turnover in man. *Clinical Science,* **61**, 627-639.

Rennie, M.J., & Millward, D.J. (1983). 3-Methylhistidine excretion and the urinary 3-methylhistidine/creatinine ratio are poor indicators of skeletal muscle protein breakdown. *Clinical Science,* **65**, 217-225.

Salmons, S., & Henriksson, J. (1981). The adaptive response of skeletal muscle to increased use. *Muscle & Nerve,* **4**, 94-105.

Schantz, P., Henriksson, J., & Jansson, E. (1983). Adaptation of human skeletal muscle to endurance training of long duration. *Clinical Physiology,* **3**, 141-151.

Watson, P.A., Srivastava, A., & Booth, F.W. (1983). Cytochrome c synthesis rate is decreased in the 6th hour of hindlimb immobilization in the rat. In H.G. Knuttgen, J.A. Vogel, & J. Poortman (Eds.), *Biochemistry of exercise* (pp. 378-384). Champaign, IL: Human Kinetics.

Wolfe, R.R. (1982). Stable isotope approaches for study of energy substrate metabolism. *Federation Proceedings,* **41**, 2692-2697.

Wolfe, R.R., Goodenough, R.D., Wolfe, M.H., Royle, G.T., & Nadel, E.R. (1982). Isotopic analysis of leucine and urea metabolism in exercising human. *Journal of Applied Physiology,* **52**, 458-466.

Young, V.R., & Munro, H.N. (1978). N-methylhistidine (3-methylhistidine) and muscle protein turnover. An overview. *Federation Proceedings,* **37**, 2291-2300.

Part II
Recent Development on Receptors: Importance in Exercise Metabolism

Adrenergic Receptors of Skeletal Muscle

R. Sanders Williams
Duke University
Durham, North Carolina, U.S.A.

Responses of mammalian skeletal muscle to adrenomedullary hormones were initially observed in the 19th century (Oliver & Schaefer, 1985). A considerable array of specific effects of sympathetic stimulation in muscle has subsequently been reported, and in recent years many features of the biochemical mechanisms linking catecholamine exposure to physiological responses have been defined.

This brief review will begin with a summary of current knowledge concerning the biochemical properties of adrenergic receptors of skeletal muscle, will continue with a catalog of major metabolic and physiologic events linked to activation of those receptors, and will conclude with some comments concerning the importance of adrenergic receptor-mediated modulation in the general context of exercise physiology.

BIOCHEMICAL PROPERTIES OF ADRENERGIC RECEPTORS OF SKELETAL MUSCLE

Radioligand binding methods and enzymatic analyses of catecholamine-responsive adenylate cyclase have been employed by several laboratories to study β-adrenergic receptors (βAR) of skeletal muscle, and permit several conclusions to be drawn. Paralleling the conclusions drawn from physiological response studies, radioligand binding indicates that these receptors are of the β_2 subtype, with a greater affinity for epinephrine than for norepinephrine, and for β_2 selective adrenergic antagonists than for β_1 selective agents (Reddy & Engel, 1979).

Skeletal muscle βAR have properties identical to those described for βAR from other tissues (Lefkowitz, Caron, & Stiles, 1984) with no anomalous characteristics as yet described. Binding of agonists to muscle βAR promotes stimulation of adenylate cyclase that is dependent upon an initial interaction between an agonist-receptor complex and the simulatory form of guanine nucleotide regulatory protein and is associated both with a fall in the affinity of the receptor for binding agonist and with hydrolysis of GTP (Smith, 1984; Williams, Caron, & Daniel, 1984). As described in many other tissues (Lefkowitz et al., 1984), the numbers of βAR present in muscle membranes and/or the responsiveness of catecholamine-sensitive adenylate cyclase are subject to regulation by exposure to β adrenergic agonists (Hedberg, Mattsson, Nerme, & Carlsson, 1984; Vallieres, Cote, & Bukowiecki, 1979). In addition, muscle βAR are subject to regulation by thyroid hormone (Sharma & Banerjee, 1978) and by glucocorticoids (Schonberg, Smith, Krichevsky, & Bilezikian, 1981). Furthermore, changes either in βAR number or in receptor-cyclase coupling occur during muscle development (Smith, 1984) and in response to physical conditioning (Dohm, Pennington, & Barakat, 1976; Williams et al., 1984) or denervation (Banerjee, Sharma, & Kung, 1977).

Subcellular fractionation studies indicate that muscle βAR are confined to external membranes, including sarcolemma and transverse tubules, and are distributed in close conjunction with Na^{+} -K^{+} ATPase (Caswell, Baker, Boyd, Potter, & Garcia, 1978; Reddy & Engel, 1979).

From a physiological standpoint, most responses to βAR stimulation are greater in slow-twitch oxidative muscle fibers than in their fast-twitch counterparts (Galbo, 1983), particularly in fast-twitch fibers with high glycolytic and low oxidative capacity. There is general agreement that part of these differences may be explained by fiber type-dependent differences in the properties of muscle βAR (Reddy, Oliver, & Engel, 1979; Williams et al., 1984). In my own laboratory we have observed levels of both βAR number and maximal catecholamine responsive adenylate cyclase activity in homogenates of slow-twitch soleus muscle from the rat to be 2-3 times greater than those present in the mixed fiber type gastrocnemius (Williams et al., 1984). Other laboratories have observed a similar fiber-type dependent difference in catecholamine-sensitivity adenylate cyclase activity in the absence of major differences in βAR binding capacity (Reddy et al., 1979).

This association between βAR characteristics and fiber type seems to be more closely linked to the metabolic than to the twitch properties of muscle fibers, since both βAR binding capacity and adenylate cyclase activity in rat diaphragm, a muscle enriched in fast-twitch oxidative fibers, more closely resemble those found in the soleus than in gastrocnemius (Williams, 1984). A relatively higher number of glucocorticoid receptors in slow-twitch as opposed to fast-twitch fibers (DuBois & Almon, 1984), in conjunction with these data concerning βAR, suggests a generally greater profile of hormonal responsiveness in slow-twitch than in fast-twitch fibers.

Concerning alpha adrenergic receptors, there are numerous reports of physiologic responses produced in muscle, by pharmacologic challenge that is selective for stimulation of alpha receptors, and likewise reports of responses to mixed adrenergic agonists (e.g., epinephrine and norepinephrine) that are inhibited selectively by alpha adrenergic antagonists

(Akaike, 1981; Clark, Patten, Filsell, & Rattigan, 1983; Richter, 1984). However, biochemical characterization of muscle alpha adrenergic receptors of skeletal muscle has lagged considerably behind that of muscle βAR. In preliminary studies from my own laboratory, muscle homogenates contain binding sites for alpha adrenergic ligands that appear to conform to the properties expected of alpha adrenergic receptors, but, in the rat at least, these binding sites are present in concentrations only 5% to 15% of those found for βAR. Although the technical problems inherent in analyzing receptors present at such low concentrations have so far prevented truly quantitative characterization of these binding sites, it appears that they include receptors of both the $alpha_1$ and $alpha_2$ subtype. Since this latter subtype may reflect the presence within the muscle homogenate of prejunctional receptors derived from intramuscular neurons, these data suggest that the concentration of postjunctional muscle $alpha_1$ receptors may be low indeed. Conversely, the possibility remains that muscle alpha receptors are inactivated during the extraction procedures we have utilized to date and that we have underestimated the concentration present in vivo. A cultured cell line having several properties of skeletal muscle cells expresses alpha adrenergic receptors (Amitai, Brown, & Taylor, 1984) in concentrations more closely approximating those of βAR.

Muscle alpha adrenergic receptors are presumably coupled to subsequent biochemical and physiologic responses via activation of phospholipase C, breakdown of phosphoinositides, and resultant changes in icosanoid synthesis, protein kinase C activation, and Ca^{++} flux as described in other tissues (Majerus, Wilson, Connolly, Bross, & Neufeld, 1985). Physiologic responses to alpha adrenergic stimulation in skeletal muscle do appear to be independent of cAMP (Clark et al., 1983) and associated with alterations in Ca^{++} transport (Amitai et al., 1984), but in comparison with other tissues such as brain or smooth muscle, lower activities of protein kinase C are present in skeletal muscle (Kuo, Schatzman, Turner, & Mazzei, 1984). Other details of the immediate biochemical sequelae of alpha adrenergic activation in skeletal muscle remain to be clarified.

As a final comment, it should be recognized that receptor analyses performed in muscle homogenates cannot discriminate between receptors truly derived from muscle fibers, and those derived from other cellular elements such as arterioles, neurons, or fibroblasts. There has been a general consistency between the characteristics of βAR studied in muscle homogenates and the results of similar analyses in cultured muscle cells (Hughes, Boyle, Brown, Taylor, & Ingel, 1982; Manger, Vassent, & Bockaert, 1981; Schonberg et al., 1981), but adequate data from histochemical or single fiber analyses to permit quantitative discrimination between muscle and nonmuscle adrenergic receptors have not yet been reported.

METABOLIC AND PHYSIOLOGIC SEQUELAE OF ADRENERGIC RECEPTOR STIMULATION IN SKELETAL MUSCLE

The major metabolic and physiologic responses that have been reported to follow activation of adrenergic receptors in skeletal muscle are listed in Table 1. Some of these effects remain controversial, in that conflicting results have been reported from different laboratories, or in that direct effects of sympathetic stimulation upon a specific metabolic event have not been fully distinguished from indirect effects resulting from other catecholamine-mediated processes.

The biochemical mechanisms that govern glycogen metabolism in skeletal muscle have been described in elegant detail, facilitating an understanding of the role of adrenergic stimulation upon this response. Beta-adrenergic stimulation promotes the direct phosphorylation of glycogen phosphorylase kinase and of phosphorylase phosphatase inhibitor by cAMP-dependent protein kinase (Randle, 1981). The interactions of these effects of adrenergic stimulation with the effects of neurally stimulated Ca^{++} release, and of the effects of other homones (e.g., insulin) have also been described in some detail (Cohen, 1982; Sheorain, Juhl, Bass, & Soderling, 1984) and have been employed to provide a satisfactory biochemical explanation for many of the physiologic observations that have been made. For example, the differential rates of glycogenolysis observed in slow-twitch and in fast-twitch muscle fibers during adrenergic stimulation at high versus low contraction frequencies can be plausibly attributed to established biochemical mechanisms of regulation of enzymes of glycogen metabolism by allosteric regulators, substrate availability, and hormonal second messengers (Chasiotis, 1983; Galbo, 1983; Richter, 1984).

The biochemical mechanisms that underlie the other responses listed in Table 1 are less well characterized and, as mentioned previously, often controversial. To highlight only one response, adrenergic stimulation produces different effects upon contractile characteristics in slow-twitch versus fast-twitch muscle under physiologic ionic conditions (Bowman & Zaimis, 1958). As a potential mechanism of this difference, it has been observed that cAMP-dependent protein kinase phosphorylates phospholamban in sarcoplasmic reticulum of slow-twitch but not of fast-twitch fibers (Martonosi & Beeler, 1983). This phenomenon illustrates how biochemical differences remote from the adrenergic receptor-adenylate cyclase complex itself may account for fiber-type dependent variations in physiologic responses to adrenergic stimulation.

In addition to the acute or intermediate-term responses to adrenergic stimulation listed in Table 1, the hypothesis has been raised that chronic stimulation of adrenergic receptors may promote long-term adaptations

Table 1 Metabolic and Physiologic Responses to Adrenergic Stimulation of Skeletal Muscle

Metabolic responses	References
Glycogenolysis	Chasiotis, 1983 Cohen, 1982 Galbo, 1983 Kaiser, 1984 Randle, 1981 Richter, 1984
Triglyceride lipolysis	Stankiewicz-Choroszucha & Gorski, 1978
Glycolytic flux (phosphofructo-kinase)	Clark et al., 1983 Hofer & Sørensen-Ziganke, 1979 Mansour, 1972
Glucose transport	Chaisson, Shikama, Chu, & Exton, 1981 Galbo, 1983
Proteolysis and amino acid transport	Ezrailson, Entman, & Garber, 1983
Physiologic responses	
Contractile force	Bowman & Zaimis, 1958 Galbo, 1983 Martonosi & Beeler, 1983 Scharf & Bark, 1984
Twitch duration	Bowman & Zaimis, 1958 Galbo, 1983 Martonosi & Beeler, 1983 Scharf & Bark, 1984
Cation transport	Clausen, 1983 Pfleigler, Szabo, & Kovacs, 1983 Williams, Gerrino, et al., 1985
Calorigenesis	Landsberg & Young, 1978 Newsholme & Crabtree, 1982 Richter, Christensen, Ploug, & Galbo, 1984

of specific enzymes or metabolic pathways of skeletal muscle, resembling, for example, the response to endurance training. Although this hypothesis may well prove to be valid for specific muscle proteins, most of the evidence currently available indicates that long-term effects of catecholamine exposure upon major structural or biochemical characteristics of skeletal muscle are either absent, or minimal when compared with powerful stimuli such as the long-term pattern of contractile activity (Fell, Terblanche, Winder, & Holloszy, 1981; Henriksson, Svedenhag, Richter, Christensen, & Galbo, 1985).

THE PHYSIOLOGICAL IMPORTANCE OF SKELETAL MUSCLE ADRENERGIC RECEPTORS: AN OVERVIEW

Because essentially all of the known effects of adrenergic receptor stimulation can also be induced by other regulators that are independent of receptor mechanisms, it is a difficult task to ascribe a quantitative importance to adrenoceptor-dependent versus adrenoceptor-independent mechanisms that account for a given metabolic or physiologic result. Nonetheless, I will cautiously extend several generalizations.

First, at the grossest level of resolution one can pose several simple questions: Is there any aspect of normal muscle metabolism or function that is absolutely dependent upon adrenergic stimulation? Is there any specific syndrome of muscle dysfunction that can be attributed to a defect in muscle adrenoceptor mechanisms? At the current time both of these questions would be answered negatively. Activation of adrenergic receptors initiates responses in skeletal muscle that amplify or diminish responses to more primary regulatory factors but do not exert the sole or even the dominant control over any vital cellular function.

However, at a finer level of resolution, one can identify conditions where intact adrenergic mechanisms do seem to produce effects that are physiologically advantageous for the muscle. In general, this situation is encountered during prolonged, as opposed to brief, periods of contractile effort, and under conditions in which the ability of nonadrenergic mechanisms to compensate for the removal of sympathetic drive are compromised. For example, glycogen breakdown during brief, intense contractile activity is stimulated to maximal levels in the absence of catecholamine stimulation, but adrenergic input is required to maintain glycogenolysis during sustained contractions. If the availability of exogenous substrate is also reduced, under these conditions the muscle is compelled either to utilize endogenous protein as a fuel source, or to limit contractile performance (Ezrailson, Entman, & Garber, 1983; Galbo, 1983; Scharf & Bark, 1984) if catecholamine-dependent glycogenolysis is inhibited.

The principle that adrenergic mechanisms will assume greater relative importance under conditions where parallel receptor-independent mechanisms governing the same process are compromised can, I think, serve as a guideline for future research in this area. This principle suggests that experimental results derived from studies of healthy animals or humans should not be extrapolated directly to individuals with myopathic states, to individuals with systemic diseases that exert indirect effects on muscle, to individuals receiving drugs with direct or indirect pharmacologic effects on muscle, or to normal individuals subjected to exotic environmental conditions. This principle is illustrated by the examples of malignant hyperthermia (Willner, Cerri, & Wood, 1981), hypokalemic and hyperkalemic periodic paralysis (Wang & Clausen, 1976; Yeung & Tse, 1974) and by diaphragmatic fatigue during hypovolemic shock (Scharf & Bark, 1984), where adrenergic mechanisms may assume greater importance for muscle function than under normal conditions.

REFERENCES

Akaike, N. (1981). Sodium pump in skeletal muscle: Central nervous system-induced suppression by αadrenoceptors. *Science,* **213**, 1252-1254.

Amitai, G., Brown, R.D., & Taylor, P. (1984). The relationship between α_1-adrenergic receptor occupation and the mobilization of intracellular calcium. *Journal of Biological Chemistry,* **259**, 12519-12527.

Banerjee, S.P., Sharma, V.K., & Kung, L.S. (1977). Beta-adrenergic receptors in innervated and denervated skeletal muscle. *Biochimica et Biophysica Acta,* **470**, 123-127.

Bowman, W.C., & Zaimis, E. (1958). The effects of adrenaline, noradrenaline and isoprenaline on skeletal muscle contractions in the cat. *Journal of Physiology,* **144**, 92-107.

Caswell, A.H., Baker, S.P., Boyd, H., Potter, L.T., & Garcia, M. (1978). Beta-adrenergic receptor and adenylate cyclase in transverse tubules of skeletal muscle. *Journal of Biological Chemistry,* **253**, 3049-3054.

Chaisson, J., Shikama, H., Chu, D.T.W., & Exton, J.H. (1981). Inhibitory effect of epinephrine on insulin-stimulated glucose uptake by rat skeletal muscle. *Journal of Clinical Investigation,* **68**, 706-713.

Chasiotis, D. (1983). The regulation of glycogen phosphorylase and glycogen breakdown in human skeletal muscle. *Acta Physiologica Scandinavica,* (Suppl. 518), 1-68.

Clark, M.G., Patten, G.S., Filsell, O.H., & Rattigan, S. (1983). Co-ordinated regulation of muscle glycolysis and hepatic glucose output in exercise by catecholamines acting via α-receptors. *Federation of the European Biochemistry Society Letters,* **158**, 1-6.

Clausen, T. (1983). Adrenergic control of Na^+-K^+-homeostasis. *Acta Medica Scandinavica,* (Suppl. 672), 111-115.

Cohen, P. (1982). The role of protein phosphorylation in neural and hormonal control of cellular activity. *Nature,* **296**, 613-620.

Dohm, G.L., Pennington, S.N., & Barakat, H. (1976). Effects of exercise training on adenyl cyclase and phosphodiesterase in skeletal muscle, heart and liver. *Biochemical Medicine,* **16**, 138-142.

DuBois, D.C., & Almon, R.R. (1984). Glucocorticoid sites in skeletal muscle: Adrenalectomy, maturation, fiber type and sex. *American Journal of Physiology,* **247**, E118-E125.

Ezrailson, E.G., Entman, M.L., & Garber, A.J. (1983). Adrenergic and serotonergic regulation of skeletal muscle metabolism in the rat. 1. The effects of adrenergic and serotonergic antagonists on the regulation of muscle amino acid release, glycogenolysis and cyclic nucleotide levels. *Journal of Biological Chemistry,* **258**, 12494-12498.

Fell, R.D., Terblanche, S.E., Winder, W.W., & Holloszy, J.O. (1981). Adaptive responses of rats to prolonged treatment with epinephrine. *American Journal of Physiology,* **241**, C55-C58.

Galbo, H. (1983). *Hormonal and metabolic adaptation to exercise.* New York: Thieme-Stratton.

Hedberg, A., Mattsson, H., Nerme, V., & Carlsson, E. (1984). Effects of in vivo treatment with isoprenaline or prenalterol on beta-adrenoceptor mechanisms in the heart and soleus muscle of the cat. *Naunyn-Schmiedeberg's Archives of Pharmacology,* **325**, 251-258.

Henriksson, J., Svedenhag, J., Richter, E.A., Christensen, N.J., & Galbo, H. (1985). Skeletal muscle and hormonal adaptation to physical training in the rat: Role of the sympatho-adrenal system. *Acta Physiologica Scandinavica,* **123**, 127-138.

Hofer, H.W., & Sørensen-Ziganke, B. (1979). Phosphorylation of phosphofructokinase from skeletal muscle: Correlations between phosphorylation and muscle function. *Biochemical and Biophysical Research Communications,* **90**, 199-203.

Hughes, R.J., Boyle, M.R., Brown, R.D., Taylor, P., & Ingel, P.A. (1982). Characterisation of co-existing $alpha_1$ and $beta_2$ adrenergic receptors on a cloned muscle cell line, BC3H-1. *Molecular Pharmacology,* **22**, 258-266.

Kaiser, P. (1984). Physical performance and muscle metabolism during β-adrenergic blockade in man. *Acta Physiologica Scandinavica,* (Suppl. 536), 1-53.

Kuo, J.F., Schatzman, R.C., Turner, R.S., & Mazzei, G.J. (1984). Phospholipid-sensitive Ca^{++}-dependent protein kinase: A major protein phosphorylation system. *Molecular and Cellular Endocrinology,* **35**, 65-73.

Landsberg, L., & Young, J.B. (1978). Fasting, feeding and regulation of the sympathetic nervous system. *New England Journal of Medicine,* **298**, 1295-1301.

Lefkowitz, R.J., Caron, M.G., & Stiles, G.L. (1984). Mechanisms of membrane-receptor regulation. *New England Journal of Medicine,* **310**, 1570-1579.

Majerus, P.W., Wilson, D.B., Connolly, T.M., Bross, T.E., & Neufeld, E.J. (1985). Phosphoinositide turnover provides a link in stimulus-response coupling. *Trends in Biochemical Sciences,* **10**, 168-171.

Manger, J.P., Vassent, G., & Bockaert, J. (1981). High and low affinity states of β-adrenergic receptors and their coupling to adenylate cyclase in a muscle cell line. *Federation of the European Biochemistry Society Letters,* **127**, 267-271.

Mansour, T.E. (1972). Phosphofructokinase activity in skeletal muscle extracts following administration of epinephrine. *Journal of Biological Chemistry,* **247**, 6059-6066.

Martonosi, A.N., & Beeler, T.J. (1983). Mechanism of Ca^{++} transport by sarcoplasmic reticulum. In L.D. Peachey (Ed.), *Handbook of physiology: Section 10: Skeletal muscle* (pp. 417-485). Bethesda, MD: American Physiological Society.

Newsholme, E.A., & Crabtree, B. (1982). Reflections on the effect of catecholamines on energy metabolism. In R.A. Riemersma & M.F. Oliver (Eds.), *Catecholamines in the non-ischaemic and ischaemic myocardium* (pp. 61-76). Oxford: Elsevier Biomedical Press.

Oliver, G., & Schafer, E.A. (1895). The physiological effects of extracts of the suprarenal capsules. *Journal of Physiology,* **18**, 230-276.

Pfliegler, G., Szabo, I., & Kovacs, T. (1983). The influence of catecholamines on Na,K transport in slow- and fast-twitch muscles of the rat. *Pflügers Archiv,* **398**, 236-240.

Randle, P.J. (1981). Phosphorylation-dephosphorylation cycles and the regulation of fuel selection in mammals. *Current Topics in Cellular Regulation,* **18**, 107-129.

Reddy, N.B., & Engel, W.K. (1979). *In vitro* characterization of skeletal muscle β-adrenergic receptors coupled to adenylate cyclase. *Biochemica et Biophysica Acta,* **585**, 343-359.

Reddy, N.B., Oliver, K.L., & Engel, W.K. (1979). Differences in catecholamine-sensitive adenylate cyclase and β-adrenergic receptor binding between fast-twitch and slow-twitch skeletal muscle membranes. *Life Sciences,* **24**, 1765-1772.

Richter, E.A. (1984). Influence of the sympatho-adrenal system on some metabolic and hormonal responses to exercise in the rat. *Acta Physiologica Scandinavica,* (Suppl. 528), 1-42.

Richter, E.A., Christensen, N.J., Ploug, T., & Galbo, H. (1984). Endurance training augments the stimulatory effect of epinephrine on oxygen consumption in perfused skeletal muscle. *Acta Physiologica Scandinavica,* **120**, 613-615.

Scharf, S.M., & Bark, H. (1984). Function of canine diaphragm with hypovolemic shock and β-adrenergic blockade. *Journal of Applied Physiology,* **56**, 648-655.

Schonberg, M., Smith, T.J., Krichevsky, A., & Bilezikian, J.P. (1981). Glucocorticoids enhance glucose uptake and affect differentiation and β-adrenergic responsiveness in muscle cell cultures. *Cellular Differentiation,* **10**, 101-107.

Sharma, V.K., & Banerjee, S.P. (1978). Beta-adrenergic receptors in rat skeletal muscle: Effects of thyroidectomy. *Biochimica et Biophysica Acta,* **539**, 538-542.

Sheorain, V.S., Juhl, H., Bass, M., & Soderling, T.R. (1984). Effects of epinephrine, diabetes and insulin on rabbit skeletal muscle glycogen synthase. *Journal of Biological Chemistry,* **259**, 7024-7030.

Smith, P.B. (1984). Developmental alterations in guanine nucleotide regulation of the β-adrenergic receptor-adenylate cyclase system of skeletal muscle. *Journal of Biological Chemistry,* **259**, 7294-7299.

Stankiewicz-Choroszucha, B., & Gorski, J. (1978). Effect of beta-adrenergic blockade on intramuscular triglyceride mobilization during exercise. *Experientia,* **34**, 357-358.

Vallieres, J., Cote, C., & Bukowiecki, L. (1979). Regulation of β-adrenergic receptors in rat skeletal muscles by catecholamines *in vivo. General Pharmacology,* **10**, 63-67.

Wang, P., & Clausen, T. (1976). Treatment of attacks in hyperkalemic familial periodic paralysis by inhalation of salbutamol. *Lancet,* **1**, 221-223.

Williams, M.E., Gerrino, E.V., Rosa, R.M., Landsberg, L., Young, J.B., Silva, P., & Epstein, F.H. (1985). Catecholamine modulation of rapid potassium shifts during exercise. *New England Journal of Medicine,* **312**, 823-827.

Williams, R.S. (1984). Beta-adrenergic receptor properties in rat diaphragm: Further evidence of a correlation between oxidative capacity and receptor density in skeletal muscle. *Clinical Research,* **32**, 217A.

Williams, R.S., Caron, M.G., & Daniel, K. (1984). Skeletal muscle β-adrenergic receptors: variations due to fiber type and training. *American Journal of Physiology,* **246**, E160-E167.

Willner, J.H., Cerri, C.G., & Wood, D.S. (1981). High skeletal muscle adenylate cyclase in malignant hyperthermia. *Journal of Clinical Investigation,* **68**, 1119-1124.

Yeung, R.T.T., & Tse, T.F. (1974). Thyrotoxic periodic paralysis: Effect of propanolol. *American Journal of Medicine,* **57**, 584-590.

Effects of Acute Exercise and Physical Training on Insulin Receptors and Insulin Action

Oluf Pedersen
Jens Bak
University Clinic of Internal Medicine
Aarhus, Denmark

During acute exercise, glucose uptake by the working muscle is increased several fold above the basal level in the presence of a fall in the plasma insulin concentration (Vranic & Berger, 1979). Moreover, physical training results in an improved glucose tolerance (Le Blanc, Nadeau, Boulay, & Rousseau-Migneron, 1979) and an increased insulin sensitivity of peripheral tissue (Wallberg-Henriksson et al., 1982). Hence, these findings suggest that both acute and chronic exercise causes an increase in the sensitivity of muscle tissue to insulin-stimulated carbohydrate metabolism.

This brief review will deal with our present knowledge on the interaction between insulin and its receptor and the effects of acute exercise and chronic training on insulin receptors and insulin action.

SOME BIOCHEMICAL CHARACTERISTICS OF INSULIN RECEPTORS

The insulin receptor is a glycoprotein that is localized in the plasma membrane and composed minimally of four subunits: two alpha subunits with a molecular weight of 135.000 and two beta subunits with a molecular weight of 95.000 (Pilch & Czech, 1980). The two different subunits of the receptor are considered to have different functions. The alpha subunit is able to bind insulin, whereas the beta subunit may be important for the signal transmission from the receptor to the other components of the cell (Kasuga, Karlsson, & Kahn, 1982). The initial interaction of insulin and its receptor in the cell surface membrane is followed by internalization of the insulin receptor complex by endocytosis (Gorden, Carpentier, Freychet, & Orci, 1980). Insulin is for the greatest part degraded, whereas the receptors may escape degradation and recycle to the plasma membrane.

Binding sites for insulin have also been identified on intracellular organelles including the nuclear membrane (Goldfine, Smith, Wong, & Jones, 1977). The physiological significance of these binding sites is uncertain but it has been postulated that the long-acting effects on insulin, for example, on protein synthesis, may be mediated through nuclear receptors.

REGULATION OF INSULIN RECEPTORS

The action of insulin at the receptor level is subject to regulation by numerous intra- and extracellular factors including ATP, pH, different ions, hormones, metabolites, drugs, diet, and physical activity (for review see Pedersen, 1984). One major factor in insulin receptor regulation appears to be insulin itself, which may induce a down regulation of insulin receptors by internalization of the insulin-receptor complexes (Marshall & Olefsky, 1981).

SIGNAL TRANSMISSION FROM THE RECEPTOR TO INSULIN-DEPENDENT SUBSTRATE CARRIERS AND ENZYMES

The communication of signals from the insulin-receptor complex to membrane and intracellular events is not clarified. It has been argued that internalized insulin or degradation products of insulin may be mediator of the signal (Goldfine et al., 1977). Another possible transmitter of the insulin signal is the beta subunit of the receptor. The beta subunit is a tyrosin-specific kinase. Insulin stimulates the kinase activity of the receptor that in turn phosphorylates itself (Kasuga et al., 1982). This phosphorylation may trigger other enzyme phosphorylations resulting in final biological effects of insulin. It has also been shown that the formation of the insulin-receptor complex leads to activation of a protease that liberates a small peptide that may serve as a second messenger for the activation of pyruvate dehydrogenase and glycogen synthetase (Jarret & Seals, 1979; Larner et al., 1979). However, despite the number of potential second messengers, no chemical compound has yet been shown to mediate all the known membrane and intracellular effects of insulin.

TISSUE-SPECIFIC CHANGES OF INSULIN RECEPTORS

A major question in receptor studies is whether changes of insulin binding in one type of cell reflect those in other insulin binding targets. However, due to functional differences of various insulin binding tissues, and due to differences in exposition and sensitivity to receptor regulatory factors, insulin receptors exhibit a differentiated tissue-specific rather than a uniform, overall behavior (Pedersen, 1984). Thus, it is important to emphasize that generalization of insulin receptor data from one cell type to other target cells for insulin is not appropriate.

It is also characteristic that the receptor affinity for insulin varies greatly depending on species and tissue. As an example, it may be mentioned that the receptor affinity of intact rat soleus muscle (Le Marchand-Brustel, Jeanrenaud, & Freychet, 1978) is 50 times lower than in human adipocytes (Pedersen, 1984) and 10 times lower than in rat adipocytes (Gammeltoft & Gliemann, 1973).

ROLE OF THE INSULIN RECEPTOR AS DETERMINANT FOR THE CELLULAR INSULIN SENSITIVITY

The relationship between insulin receptors and insulin action is also complex due to the "spare receptor" phenomenon (Kono & Barham, 1971). This concept is based on the observation that a maximal insulin effect is achieved at an insulin concentration where only about 20% of the total receptor amount is occupied. Thus, the functional consequence of a decreased insulin binding will be a decreased insulin sensitivity of the target tissue; that is, higher insulin concentrations are required to elicit the same biological response. A decrease in insulin binding up to 80% maximal binding will not cause a decrease in maximal insulin effect since the decrease of binding does not exceed the proportion of spare receptors. Since changes of insulin receptor binding usually are in the range of 20% to 50% of normal binding, the consequence of the receptor change is a shift of the insulin dose-response curve with no alterations of the maximal insulin response. In some studies (Le Marchand-Brustel et al., 1978) a straightforward relationship is found between changes of insulin binding and insulin sensitivity. However, in several clinical studies (for review see Pedersen, 1984) divergent alterations of insulin binding and insulin sensitivity are shown. These findings suggest the existence of intervening variables that may diminish or amplify the signals from the insulin receptor interaction. Hence, we may conclude that the insulin receptor is the first and a necessary step in the cellular insulin action. The insulin receptor binding is changed under a variety of conditions. However, the final biological response to insulin of a given metabolic pathway is unpredictable from changes in insulin binding.

THE INSULIN RECEPTOR RESPONSE TO PHYSICAL TRAINING

Physically trained people have an increased insulin binding to circulating monocytes (Heath et al., 1983; Koivisto et al., 1979; Le Blanc et al., 1979) when compared with sedentary control subjects. Studies in rodents have also shown that physical training is associated with an increased insulin binding to plasma membranes from slow-twitch soleus and fast-twitch extensor digitorum longus (EDL) muscles but an unaltered insulin binding to hepatic plasma membranes (Tan, Bonen, & Clune, 1985). Adipocytes of exercise-trained rats show a higher insulin binding capacity (Craig, Hammons, Garthwaite, Jarret, & Holloszy, 1981).

Taken together the available literature suggest that the increase in insulin sensitivity of peripheral tissue with training (Berger et al., 1979; Mondon, Dolkas, & Reaven, 1980) in part may be mediated through an enhanced insulin receptor binding. The molecular mediators in receptor upregulation are unknown, but the reduced fasting plasma insulin levels of trained individuals may contribute to the higher insulin receptor level through the negative feedback control between hormone and receptor.

THE EFFECTS OF ACUTE SUBMAXIMAL EXERCISE ON INSULIN RECEPTORS AND INSULIN ACTION

Acute submaximal exercise has been shown to increase the insulin binding to circulating blood cells (monocytes or erythrocytes) from sedentary normals (Koivisto et al., 1979), from obese subjects (Koivisto, Soman, & Felig, 1980) and from insulin-dependent diabetics (Pedersen, Beck-Nielsen, & Heding, 1980). In contrast, insulin receptors on monocytes from athletes drop during submaximal exercise (Koivisto et al., 1979).

Based on blood cell receptor changes to exercise, it may be concluded that the receptor response to exercise depends on the level of physical fitness, and it has been speculated that the exercise-induced fall in insulin binding in highly trained people might afford a decline of insulin-mediated glucose uptake, thus enhancing free fatty acid uptake by trained muscles during exercise (Koivisto et al., 1979).

However, as emphasized earlier in this review, receptor findings on blood cells cannot be extrapolated to metabolically relevant tissue as skeletal muscles. A recent study of the isolated, perfused rat hindlimb (Richter, Garetto, Goodman, & Ruderman, 1982) has demonstrated that acute submaximal exercise results in significant leftward shifts of the insulin-dose response curves for glucose uptake and glycogen synthesis. In parallel with this study, Bonen, Tan, and Watson-Wright (1984) have studied the effects of mild acute exercise on glucose uptake in soleus and EDL muscles from rats. In both slow-twitch and fast-twitch muscles, insulin-stimulated glucose uptake was enhanced postexercise, whereas insulin binding to the two different types of skeletal muscles remained unchanged. Hence, the latter study indicates that the exercise-induced rise of cellular insulin sensitivity may occur in the absence of changes of insulin receptor binding. The findings in rodents have recently been corroborated in human studies where submaximal exercise for 1 hr caused no alterations in insulin binding to plasma membranes from musculus vastus lateralis (Bonen, Tan, Hood, & Clune, 1985).

EFFECTS OF EXHAUSTIVE EXERCISE

Exhaustive exercise in rodents brings about a significant fall of insulin binding to fast-twitch muscles and an unchanged insulin binding to slow-twitch muscles. In both muscle preparations, insulin-stimulated glucose utilization was enhanced (Bonen et al., 1985). The same investigators found that maximal work loads in humans caused a 40% decrease of insulin binding to musculus vastus lateralis.

It thus appears that maximal acute exercise has muscle fiber-specific effects on insulin receptor binding. However, the major finding is that the enhanced insulin-mediated glucose utilization postexercise is not related to an increased insulin receptor activity of working muscles. The receptor regulatory factors during acute exercise are unknown.

CONCLUSIONS

Physically trained individuals have increased insulin sensitivity to carbohydrate metabolism of peripheral tissue. Studies in rodents suggest that the concomitant higher level of insulin receptor binding to muscle and adipose tissue may contribute to the improved insulin action after physical training.

Acute, submaximal exercise in rodents is associated with an increased insulin stimulated glucose utilization of skeletal muscle despite no change of insulin binding to muscles. Exhaustive exercise may even cause a fall in insulin receptor activity on skeletal muscle membranes. Thus, it may be concluded that the enhancing effect of acute exercise on insulin-stimulated glucose metabolism of skeletal muscles occurs at postbinding steps.

REFERENCES

Berger, M., Kemmer, F.W., Becker, K., Herberg, L., Schwenen, M., Gjinavci, A., & Berchtold, P. (1979). Effect of physical training on glucose tolerance and on glucose metabolism of skeletal muscle in anaesthetized normal rats. *Diabetologia,* **16**, 179-184.

Bonen, A., Tan, M.H., Hood, D.A., & Clune, P. (1985). Effects of exercise, substrates and hormones on insulin binding in rodent and human muscle. *Clinical Physiology,* **5** (Suppl. 4), (Abstract No. 28).

Bonen, A., Tan, M.H., & Watson-Wright, W.M. (1984). Effects of exercise on insulin binding and glucose metabolism in muscle. *Canadian Journal of Physical Pharmacology,* **62**, 1500-1504.

Craig, B.W., Hammons, G.T., Garthwaite, S.M., Jarret, L., & Holloszy, J.O. (1981). Adaptations of fat cells to exercise: Response to glucose uptake and oxidation to insulin. *Journal of Applied Physiology: Respiration and Environmental Exercise Physiology,* **51**, 1500-1506.

Gammeltoft, S., & Gliemann, J. (1973). Binding and degradation of ^{125}I-labelled insulin by isolated rat fat cells. *Biochimica et Biophysica Acta,* **320**, 16-32.

Goldfine, I.D., Smith, G.J., Wong, K.Y., & Jones, A.L. (1977). Cellular uptake and nuclear binding of insulin in human cultured lymphocytes: Evidence for potential intracellular site of insulin action. *Proceedings of the National Academy of Sciences of the United States of America,* **74**, 1368-1372.

Gorden, P., Carpentier, J.L., Freychet, P., & Orci, L. (1980). Internalization of polypeptide hormones: Mechanism, intracellular localization and significance. *Diabetologia,* **18**, 263-274.

Heath, G.W., Gavin III, J.R., Hinderliter, J.M., Hagberg, J.M., Bloomfield, S.A., & Holloszy, J.O. (1983). Effects of exercise and lack of exercise on glucose tolerance and insulin sensitivity. *Journal of Applied Physiology: Respiration, Environment, Exercise Physiology,* **55**, 512-517.

Jarret, L., & Seals, J.R. (1979). Pyruvate dehydrogenase activation in adipocyte mitochondria by an insulin-generated mediator from muscle. *Science,* **206**, 1407-1408.

Kasuga, M., Karlsson, F.A., & Kahn, C.R. (1982). Insulin stimulates the phosphorylation of the 95.000 dalton subunit of its own receptor. *Science,* **215**, 185-187.

Koivisto, V., Soman, V., & Felig, P. (1979). Effects of acute exercise on on insulin binding to monocytes in trained athletes: Changes in the resting state and after exercise. *Journal of Clinical Investigation,* **64**, 1011-1015.

Koivisto, V., Soman, V., & Felig, P. (1980). Effects of acute exercise on insulin binding to monocytes in obesity. *Metabolism,* **39**, 168-172.

Kono, T., & Barham, F.W. (1971). The relationship between the insulin binding capacity of fat cells and the cellular response to insulin. Studies with intact and trypsin-treated fat cells. *Journal of Biological Chemistry,* **246**, 6210-6216.

Larner, J., Galasko, G., Cheng, K., De Paoli-Roach, A.A., Huang, L., Daggy, P., & Kellog, J. (1979). Generation by insulin of a chemical mediator that controls protein phosphorylation and dephosphorylation. *Science,* **206**, 1408-1410.

Le Blanc, J., Nadeau, A., Boulay, M., & Rosseau-Migneron, S. (1979). Effects of physical training and adiposity on glucose metabolism and ^{125}I-insulin binding. *Journal of Applied Physiology: Respiration, Environment, Exercise Physiology,* **46**, 235-239.

Le Marchand-Brustel, Y., Jeanrenaud, B., & Freychet, P. (1978). Insulin binding and effects in isolated solens muscle of lean and obese mice. *American Journal of Physiology: Endocrinological, Metabolic and Gastro-intestinal Physiology,* **3**, E 348-358.

Marshall, S., & Olefsky, J. (1981). Characterization of insulin-induced receptor loss and evidence for internalization of the insulin receptor. *Diabetes,* **30**, 746-753.

Mondon, C.E., Dolkas, C.B., & Reaven, V.M. (1980). Site of enhanced insulin sensitivity in exercise-trained rats at rest. *American Journal of Physiology,* **239**, E 169-177.

Pedersen, O. (1984). Studies of insulin receptor binding and insulin action in humans. *Danish Medical Bulletin,* **31**, 1-32.

Pedersen, O., Beck-Nielsen, H., & Heding, L. (1980). Increased insulin receptors after exercise in patients with insulin-dependent diabetes mellitus. *New England Journal of Medicine,* **302**, 886-892.

Pilch, P.F., & Czech, M.P. (1980). The subunit structure of the high affinity insulin receptor: Evidence for a disulfide-linked receptor complex in fat cell and liver plasma membrane. *Journal of Biological Chemistry,* **225**, 1722-1728.

Richter, E.A., Garetto, L.P., Goodman, M.N., & Ruderman, N.B. (1982). Muscle glucose metabolism following exercise in the rat. *Journal of Clinical Investigation,* **69**, 785-793.

Tan, M.H., Bonen, A., & Clune, P.A. (1985). Physical training enhances insulin binding in skeletal muscles but not in liver. *Clinical Physiology,* **5** (Suppl. 4) (Abstract No. 31).

Vranic, M., & Berger, M. (1979). Exercise and diabetes mellitus. *Diabetes,* **28**, 147-163.

Wallberg-Henriksson, H., Gunnarsson, R., Henriksson, J., De Fronzo, R., Felig, P., Östman, J., & Wahren, J. (1982). Increased peripheral insulin sensitivity and muscle mitochondrial enzymes but unchanged blood glucose control in type I diabetics after physical training. *Diabetes,* **31**, 1044-1050.

Steroid Hormone Receptors in Skeletal Muscle

Marek Snochowski
Ewa Wolinska-Witort
Wieslaw A.M. Perkowski
Polish Academy of Sciences
Jablonna-near-Warsaw, Poland

A good muscle performance during exercise depends upon a complex system of interactions between nutritional, metabolic, and hormonal factors (Buskirk, 1981; Saltin, Henriksson, Nygaard, Andersson, & Jansson, 1977). Intensive training may influence the concentration of hormones in blood (Frey, 1982; Galbo, 1981; Galbo, 1983) and in certain situations may affect hormonal balance resulting in, for example, gonadal dysfunction (Baker, 1981; Frisch et al., 1981). The immediate effects of exercise on hormones in blood differ with the type of training (Hale, Kosasa, Krieger, & Pepper, 1983) and give different response in men and women (Weiss, Cureton, & Thompson, 1983). On the other hand, treatment with hormones can directly influence skeletal muscle by increasing or decreasing anabolic or catabolic processes dependent on the type of hormone used (Buttery & Vernon, 1983; Holloszy & Booth, 1976; Kurowski, Chatterton, & Hickson, 1984; McGrath & Goldspink, 1982; Shoji & Pennington, 1977b).

The effects of steroid hormone administration in clinical practice is relatively well recognized (Frohman, Feling, Broadus, & Baxter, 1981) and the same holds for veterinarian experience with domestic animals (Buttery & Vernon, 1983; Lu & Rendel, 1975).

Androgens are considered to be anabolic, stimulating nitrogen retention (Kochakian, 1976) by increasing RNA synthesis (Rogozkin, 1979a; Rogozkin, 1979b) and amino acid incorporation into proteins (Brauer & Florini, 1965; Powers & Florini, 1975). The effect of treatment was shown to produce increased muscle weight, cross sectional area, tension-generating capacity, and mean fiber diameter (Salmons, 1983). In humans, androgens are recommended only for therapy of hypogonadal men (Wilson & Griffin, 1980), but unfortunately they are also used (misused) by athletes in order to stimulate muscle mass and strength, irrespective of side effects and causing serious health problems (Lamb, 1984; Ryan, 1981).

Glucocorticoids have their main catabolic effect on protein metabolism (Baxter, 1976) by inhibiting amino acid incorporation into proteins

(McGrath & Goldspink, 1982; Shoji & Pennington, 1977b) and by increasing the activity of proteolytic enzymes (Mayer, Shafir, Kaiser, Milholland, & Rosen, 1976). The muscle weakness or atrophy produced by glucocorticoid treatment is not due to decreased sarcolemmal membrane potential and excitability of muscle fibers (Ruff, Stuhmer, & Almers, 1982).

A direct effect of estrogens on skeletal muscle has been much less investigated. In farm animal breeding, they are successfully used as promotors of food utilization in ruminants which, as a final effect, give increased carcass weight (Heitzman, 1979; Jasiorowski, 1981; Roche & Quirke, in press). In humans and rats, estrogens have more catabolic effects (Buttery & Vernon, 1983).

STEROID CONVERSION IN SKELETAL MUSCLE

Intracellular conversion of hormones coming from blood to particular tissues, creates the possibility of mediating its own activity. The skeletal muscle seems to possess such an ability, at least as far as androgens are concerned. Based on direct or indirect observations there are four active enzymes reported.

1. 3-alpha(3-beta)-steroid oxidoreductase (E.C.1.1.1.50) is probably the most active steroid converting enzyme in the muscle, converting 5-alpha-dihydrotestosterone to 3-alpha(3-beta),17-beta-androstane-diols within wide concentration range 10E-9 to 10E-6 mol/dm^3 even at low temperature (Dionne, Dube, & Tremblay, 1977; Snochowski, Dahlberg, & Gustafsson, 1980). Because 3-alpha(3-beta),17-beta-androstane-diols are unable to bind the androgen receptor (Krieg, Smith, & Bartsh, 1978; Snochowski et al., 1980), such conversion means the elimination of active androgen from the receptor-mediated regulatory system (Graf, Reichel, Engelhardt, & Karl, 1981; Krieg et al., 1978).
2. Aromatization of testosterone and androst-4-en-3,17-dione by enzyme complex (possibly by 19-hydroxylase/oxidase-lyase), has been described by Longcope, Pratt, Schneider, and Fineberg (1978). Its activity was greater in men than in women, and according to the authors the muscle may be responsible for 25% to 30% of the peripheral estrogens production from androgens.
3. 17-beta-steroid oxidoreductase (E.C.1.1.1.63) is also active in the human muscle with potential of 10% to 15% of extragonadal conversion of androst-4-en-3,17-dione to testosterone (Longcope, Pratt, Schneider, & Fineberg, 1976).

4. 5-alpha steroid reductase (3-oxo-5-alpha-steroid:NADP-4-ene-reductase; E.C.1.3.1.22) has low activity in muscle (11 fCat/g of prot.) and has no, or no significant, regulatory activity (Stenstad & Eik-Nes, 1981).

No clear data are published on estrogen and glucocorticoid conversion in skeletal muscle.

STEROIDS IN BLOOD

Steroids are secreted by endocrine glands into the bloodstream and are transported to target cells, mostly reversibly bound with plasma proteins such as sex-hormone-binding globulin, corticosteroid-binding globulin, and albumin (Giorgi, 1980; Siiteri et al., 1982). The distribution of particular steroids and different ligands is dependent on concentrations, binding affinities, and quantities of all circulating steroids (Dunn, Nisula, & Rodbard, 1981). Changes of steroid concentration or introduction of drugs may result in the decrease or increase of biologically active forms of other steroids and their availability for target cells (Pugeat, Dunn, & Nisula, 1981).

STEROIDS IN TARGET CELLS

The basic feature of target cells is the presence of a specific receptor able to receive hormonal information and elicit the appropriate changes in cells activity. The steroid receptors, their structure, and their function have been extensively studied during the last 15 years, but mainly in mononuclear cell tissues. Grody, Schrader, and O'Malley (1982) compared and summarized reported findings and concluded that there are great similarities between the receptors for estrogens, progestagens, glucocorticoids, androgens, 1,25-dihydroxy-vitamin D and insect moltiny hormone-ecdysone. The authors presented the following generally accepted common features of steroid hormone action in the cell:

1. Formation of steroid-receptor complex
2. *Activation* to the DNA-binding or nuclear-binding form
3. *Translocation* into nuclear compartment
4. Binding to *acceptor* sites located near DNA sequences, whose transcription is to be induced by possible unwinding of DNA, allowing the entry of RNA-polimerase into double helix

5. Loss of bound ligand
6. Migration of aporeceptor to cytoplasma.

Each steroid receptor possesses its own specific hormone-binding domain, DNA-binding domain, and immunoreactive domain (Grody et al., 1982; Gustafsson et al., 1983).

DNA-regarding techniques, properties of different receptors, their specific functions and gene expression abilities, are published in an excellent book edited by Eriksson and Gustafsson (1983).

STEROID RECEPTORS IN SKELETAL MUSCLE

Steroid receptors are present in most mammalian tissues with great qualitative similarities but in different quantities (Ballard, Baxter, Higgins, Rousseau, & Tomkins, 1974; Liao, Chang, & Saltzman, 1983; Rousseau, 1984).

The presence and particular characteristics of the androgen receptor in skeletal muscle have been presented by several authors (Dahlberg, Snochowski, & Gustafsson, 1981; Dube, Lesage, & Tremblay, 1976; Krieg, 1976; Michel & Baulieu, 1974, 1980; Saartok, 1984; Snochowski et al., 1980; Snochowski, Lundstroem, Dahlberg, Peterson, & Edquist, 1981; Snochowski, Saartok, Dahlberg, Eriksson, & Gustafsson, 1981). Its dissociation constant is less than 10E-9 mol/dm^3, and its maximum number of binding sites varies with sex, age, and type of muscle (Gustafsson et al., 1984).

The glucocorticoid receptor has a dissociation constant above 10E-9 mol/dm^3 and a binding capacity 10 to 20 times greater than the androgen receptor, and it varies with the type of muscle but less with age and sex (Ballard et al., 1974; Dahlberg et al., 1981; DuBois & Almon, 1984a; DuBois & Almon, 1984b; Mayer et al., 1976; Saartok, 1984; Shoji & Pennington, 1977a; Snochowski et al., 1980; Snochowski, Lundstroem, et al., 1981; Snochowski, Saartok, et al., 1981).

The receptor for estrogens in skeletal muscle has also been identified but much less investigated (Dahlberg, 1982; Dionne, Lesage, Dube, & Tremblay, 1979; Dube et al., 1976; Meyer & Rapp, 1985; Saartok, 1984). The binding affinity and capacity is similar to that of the androgen receptor and varies with the type of muscle, sex, and age (Saartok, 1984).

The presence of progestagen or mineralocorticoid receptors in skeletal muscle has not been reported.

MOLECULAR ACTION OF STEROID RECEPTORS IN SKELETAL MUSCLE

In all the studies on steroid receptors in muscle cited above, the authors assumed the validity of the general model of mechanism of receptor action described for mononuclear cells. For these cells Cheek, Holt, Hill, and Talbert (1971) formulated the basic concept of the DNA unit, which permits such simplification. On the other hand, still open is the question of how similar is the response to steroids in fiber satellite cells, which seem to be exclusively responsible for the increased number of fiber nuclei during postnatal growth (Moss & Leblond, 1970). Moreover, the metabolic role of muscle as a nitrogen depot dependent on age, sex, and exercise (Cahill, 1971), as well as basic muscle function of contracting and creating movement (Bloch & Iberall, 1982), requires detailed verification of existing data before interpreting steroid receptor activity in this tissue.

The general model for steroid receptor action in skeletal muscle presented in Figure 1 seems to be valid for the androgen glucocorticoid as well as for the estrogen receptor.

1. The Steroid (S) coming from the blood capillary system enters fibers, and we raise the question of whether the hormone is able to fuse along the fibers or is strictly localized in the DNA unit compartment. The same is valid for the distribution of the steroid receptor. At this stage,

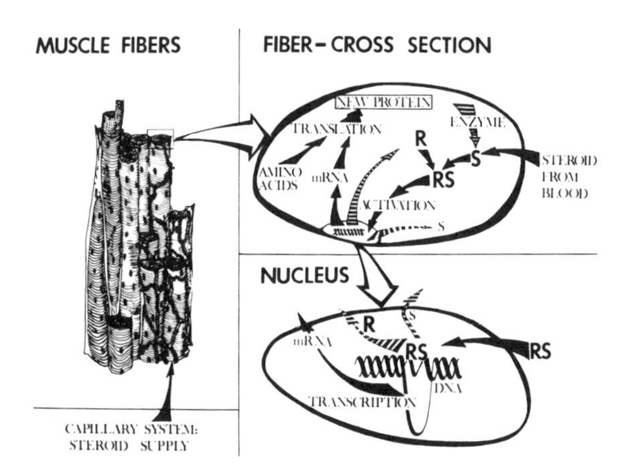

Figure 1 Model for steroid hormone action in skeletal muscle.

enzymatic conversion of steroid hormones can take place, changing its regulatory potential (see Figure 1).

2. The specific receptor (R) present in cytoplasm binds the steroid, and the receptor-steroid complex (RS) is activated. This process is generally associated with the change of sedimentation coefficient from 8 to 9S to 4 to 5S and can be performed in vitro by high ionic strength, higher temperature or UV-irradiation (Haase, Ofenloch, & Eisele, 1983).
3. The activated receptor-steroid complex is then translocated into the nuclear compartment (Bicikova, Hampl, & Starka, 1977; Krieg, Smith, & Elvers, 1980; Stepanov & Fel'dkoren, 1984).
4. Inside the nucleus, the steroid-receptor complex is bound to a specific DNA-acceptor site, where it initiates the transcription process resulting in new mRNA formation, from which, after translation on ribosomes, new steroid-induced protein is synthesized (Grody et al., 1982; Gustafsson et al., 1984).

During the interaction with DNA, the receptor loses its steroid and moves back to the cytosolic compartment. The released steroid is probably eliminated from the fibers. There are no reports available on intranuclear receptor action in skeletal muscle, apart from in vitro experiments, in which retention of androgen, estrogen and glucocorticoid receptors on DNA-cellulose or DNA-agarose was shown (Dahlberg, 1982; Snochowski et al., 1980).

The described mode of action of steroid receptors in skeletal muscle is compatible with the generally accepted model.

RECEPTOR QUANTITATION

In all reported studies of radioligand techniques, radioactive synthetic steroids, which do not interact with blood plasma-binding globulins and are resistant to enzymatic conversion, are used as markers (Bonne & Raynaud, 1975; Raynaud & Ojasoo, 1983).

For the routine assay procedure of one receptor measurement (except the one point assay), 1 to 4 g of tissue samples are needed. The cytosol obtained from 100,000*g centrifugation of tissue homogenate is incubated in portions with different amounts of radioligand at low temperature for the time needed to reach an equilibrium (12 to 20 hr), and then a receptor-bound fraction is separated, usually by a charcoal method, and radioactivity is counted. The results obtained in this way can be used for the calculation of the apparent binding affinity and apparent binding capacity of receptor, allowing statistical evaluation (Dahlberg et al., 1982; Snochowski et al., 1980). In some reported studies, one point assay and the gel filtration step were used with an attempt to increase activity of the assay (DuBois & Almon, 1984a).

The reliability of the steroid receptor assay is difficult to assess due to a lack of standard receptor preparations and unified criteria for common use as an internal quality control procedure (Jordan et al., 1983).

For an appropriate determination of cytosolic receptors, the hormone should be measured, which could represent the property of the tissue for steroid hormone regulation. Negative findings, that is, no cytosolic receptor binding, can be interpreted in two ways: (a) lack of detectable amounts of cytosolic receptor in the tissue; or (b) all receptors are saturated with the steroid and already translocated into nuclei. Quantitation of the nuclear receptor is very difficult due to the technical problems of isolating nuclei from skeletal muscle homogenates (Kuehl, 1977).

INTERPRETATIONS OF STEROID RECEPTOR DATA

The evaluation of receptor activity within physiological limits is rather difficult. It is not known how the receptor really acts; that is, whether it follows steichiometrical relations or behaves more catalically. In the first case, the receptor quantities expressed in units of concentration will give expected information, but if the latter is valid, then the relation to the cellular unit will be more appropriate. The answer to this question can be given after exploring experimental data.

The Steroid Receptor in Human Skeletal Muscle

Androgen and glucocorticoid receptors were identified and quantified in human striated muscle, but insufficient human material did not allow researchers to draw conclusions concerning age, sex, and type of muscle (Snochowski, Saartok, et al., 1981).

The only published study of muscle receptors is related to quantitative comparison of both sides of erector spinae muscle in scoliotic patients (Saartok, Dahlberg, Bylund, Eriksson, & Gustafsson, 1984). The authors evaluated androgen and glucocorticoid receptor binding capacities expressed per tissue wet weight, cytosolic proteins and DNA, and found that the only significant difference was in the glucocorticoid receptor presented as the concentration per gram of tissue wet weight that was higher on the convex side. They concluded, irrespective of the fact that receptor data were estimated in different ways, that interpretation, that is, prediction, of the biological response to steroid hormones in scoliotic back muscles, remains to be verified in vivo.

The Androgen Receptor in Experimental Animals

In Tables 1 to 4, mean values of androgen receptor taken from different experiments with animals are presented.

In Table 1, data taken from Saartok (1984) comparing rabbit m. gastrocnemius/plantaris (fast twitch) with m. soleus (slow twitch) are shown. A significant difference was obtained in receptor amount in relation to cytosolic proteins and to the whole muscle content. In this case the difference in receptor quantity in the whole muscle is obviously due to muscle mass as well as to cytosolic protein concentration in the muscle. The author concluded that androgen responsiveness can be similar in both types of muscles, which is not the case for glucocorticoid and estrogen receptors.

The effect of muscle atrophy in rabbit m. gastrocnemius induced by tenotomy or denervation is presented in Table 2.

A significant increase in androgen receptors was found in relation to tissue weight and to cytosolic proteins. The authors suggested that this might be due to a concentration effect caused by a general loss of proteins.

The effect of diet on androgen receptor in m. gluteus medius of young rats is presented in Table 3.

Rats kept on 6% of protein supply (basic requirement) differ significantly from the other group (60% of protein in the diet) in terms of androgen receptors expressed per DNA content as well as per whole muscle mass. These differences in receptor quantity seem to be the true indicator of differentiation between muscle cells, the growth of which is dependent upon protein supply limited by diet.

Table 1 Muscle atrophy; male rabbit m. gastrocnemius 3 weeks after denervation or tenotomy (operated) and contralateral muscle

Muscle	Muscle weight (in g)	Androgen receptor binding (Bmax)			
		fmol/g tissue	fmol/mg protein	fmol/mg DNA	fmol/ muscle
Control	12.3	63	1.05	151	783
Operated	7.7	109	2.19	127	890
Difference (%)	-38.	89	115.	12 (n.s.)	15 (n.s.)

n.s. = not significant ($p > 0.05$).

Table 2 Muscle type comparison; rabbit male m. gastrocnemius/plantaris (fast twitch) and m. soleus (slow twitch)

Muscle	Muscle weight (in g)	Androgen receptor binding (Bmax)			
		fmol/g tissue	fmol/mg protein	fmol/mg DNA	fmol/ muscle
Slow twitch	0.89	197	5.18	197	154
Fast twitch	5.20	162	2.76	256	803
Difference (%)	484.	-18 (n.s.)	-46.	30 (n.s.)	421

n.s. = not significant ($p > 0.05$).
Note: From *Changes in Androgen, Estrogen, and Glucocorticoid Receptors, Cytosolic Protein and Tissue DNA in Rabbit Gastrocnemius Muscle Following Tenatomy or Denervation* by T. Saartok, T. Haeggmark, E. Dahlberg, M. Snochowski, E. Eriksson, and J.-A. Gustafson. Manuscript submitted for publication.

Table 3 Influence of diet on male rat m. gluteus medius; 21-day-old rats fed ad libitum for 9 days isocaloric diet containing 6% (basal metabolic requirement) or 60% of protein.

Protein in diet (%)	Muscle weight (in g)	Androgen receptor binding (Bmax)			
		fmol/g tissue	fmol/mg protein	fmol/mg DNA	fmol/ muscle
6	0.116	73	1.97	25.2	8.47
60	0.228	82	1.91	39.0	18.69
Difference (%)	97.	12 (n.s.)	3.00 (n.s.)	55.0	121.

n.s. = not significant ($p > 0.05$).
Note: From *Androgen, Glucocorticoid and Estrogen Receptors in M. Gluteus Medius of Male and Female Rats Fed with Different Protein Levels in Diet* by M. Snochowski, E. Wolinska, W. Perkowski, D. Lis, B. Pastuszewska, and K. Kubuj. Unpublished manuscript.

Androgen receptor data in m. gluteus medius during compensatory growth which was induced by dietary manipulation, are presented in Table 4.

Table 4 Compensatory growth; male rats fed with isocaloric diet containing 6% of protein (L) for 1 week following 2 weeks feeding with 60% of protein (H). Control group was kept on high protein diet only

Diet	m. gluteus medius (in g)	Androgen receptor binding (Bmax)			
		fmol/g tissue	fmol/mg protein	fmol/mg DNA	fmol/ muscle
H	0.669	114	1.41	95	73
L-H	0.755	84	1.80	49	63
Difference (%)	17.	-26 (n.s.)	28. (n.s.)	-48	-14 (n.s.)

n.s. = not significant ($p > 0.05$).
Note: From *Androgen, Glucocorticoid and Estrogen Receptors in M. Gluteus Medius of Male and Female Rats Fed with Different Protein Levels in Diet* by M. Snochowski, E. Wolinska, W. Perkowski, D. Lis, B. Pastuszewska, and K. Kubuj. Unpublished manuscript.

In this case, the only significant difference was in data expressed per DNA content, which were lower in the case of compensatory growth. This effect may well be brought about by the amount of receptor or it may be due to its intracellular translocation. From all presented examples it is clear that quantitation of steroid receptors leads to different conclusions depending on their expression.

In conclusion, the skeletal muscle contains specific steroid receptors for androgens, glucocorticoids and estrogens, the mode of action for which is in agreement with the generally accepted model for classical target tissues. Quantitative data, apart from the problems related to specific fiber structure, show that the amount of each receptor varies with the type of muscle, sex, age, and nutritional conditions as well as with its physical activity.

FUTURE CONSIDERATIONS

Progress in the understanding of steroid receptor action in skeletal muscle is expected to stem from work at the level of gene expression, which can help in the identification and characterization of proteins specifically induced by a steroid receptor-mediated mechanism in muscle fibers as well as in satellite cells. This may enable the setting up of an analytical system designed to study the effects of steroid hormone action. On the other hand, very promising studies on visual demonstration of receptors in different tissues by protein labelling or ligand labelling methods (Gustafsson et al., 1983; Martin & Sheridan, 1982) gives possibilities for application in muscle fiber studies.

Acknowledgments

Drs. T. Saartok, E. Dahlberg, and Prof. J.-A. Gustafsson are greatly acknowledged for the valuable discussions in which they were involved during collaboration in the past.

REFERENCES

Baker, E.R. (1981). Menstrual dysfunction and hormonal status in athletic women: A review. *Fertility and Sterility,* **36**, 691-696.

Ballard, P.L., Baxter, J.D., Higgins, S.J., Rousseau, G.G., & Tomkins, G.M. (1974). General presence of glucocorticoid receptors in mammalian tissues. *Endocrinology,* **94**, 998-1002.

Baxter, J.D. (1976). Glucocorticoid hormone action. *Pharmacology & Therapeutics,* **B2**, 605-569.

Bicikova, M., Hampl, R., & Starka, L. (1977). The requirement of cytosolic receptor for entry of testosterone into nuclei of rat muscle. *Endocrinologia Experimentalis,* **11**, 271-275.

Bloch, E.H., & Iberall, A.S. (1982). Toward a concept of the functional unit of mammalian skeletal muscle. *The American Journal of Physiology,* **242**, R411-R420.

Bonne, C., & Raynaud, J.P. (1975). Methyltrienolone, a specific ligand for cellular androgen receptors. *Steroids,* **26**, 227-232.

Brauer, C.B., & Florini, J.R. (1965). Amino acid incorporation into protein by cell free system from rat skeletal muscle IV. Effects of animal age, androgens and catabolic agents on activity of skeletal muscle ribosomes. *Biochemistry,* **4**, 1544-1550.

Buskirk, E.R. (1981). Some nutritional considerations in the conditioning of athletes. *Annual Review of Nutrition,* **1**, 319-350.

Buttery, P.J., & Vernon, B.G. (1983). Protein metabolism in animals treated with anabolic agents. *Veterinary Research Communications,* **7**, 11-17.

Cahill, G.F. Jr. (1971). Metabolic role of muscle. In B. Pernow & B. Saltin (Eds.), *Muscle metabolism during exercise* (pp. 103-109). New York: Plenum Press.

Cheek, D.B., Holt, A.B., Hill, D.E., & Talbert, J.L. (1971). Skeletal muscle cell mass and growth: The concept of the deoxyribonucleic acid unit. *Pediatric Research,* **5**, 312-328.

Dahlberg, E. (1982). Characterization of the cytosolic estrogen receptor in rat skeletal muscle. *Biochimica et Biophysica Acta,* **717**, 65-75.

Dahlberg, E., Snochowski, M., & Gustafsson, J.-A. (1981). Regulation of the androgen and glucocorticoid receptors in rat and mouse skeletal muscle cytosol. *Endocrinology,* **108**, 1431-1440.

Dionne, F.T., Dube, J.Y., & Tremblay, R.R. (1977). Apparent saturability of a 4S dihydrotestosterone-binding protein in rat muscle cystosol: Role of 3-alpha-hydroxysteroid dehydrogenase and albumin. *Canadian Journal of Biochemistry,* **55**, 995-1000.

Dionne, F.T., Lesage, R.L., Dube, J.Y., & Tremblay, R.R. (1979). Estrogen binding proteins in rat skeletal and perineal muscles: In vitro and in vivo studies. *Journal of Steroid Biochemistry,* **11**, 1073-1080.

Dube, J.Y., Lesage, R.L., & Tremblay, R.R. (1976). Androgen and estrogen binding in rat skeletal and perineal muscles. *Canadian Journal of Biochemistry,* **54**, 50-55.

DuBois, D.C., & Almon, R.R. (1984a). Glucocorticoid sites in skeletal muscle: Adrenalectomy, maturation, fiber type, and sex. *The American Journal of Physiology,* **247**, E118-E125.

DuBois, D.C., & Almon, R.R. (1984b). Perineal muscles: Possible androgen regulation of glucocorticoid receptor sites in the rat. *Journal of Endocrinology,* **102**, 225-229.

Dunn, J.F., Nisula, B.C., & Rodbard, D. (1981). Transport of steroid hormones: Binding of 21 endogenous steroids to both testosterone-binding globulin and corticosteroid-binding globulin in human plasma. *Journal of Clinical Endocrinology and Metabolism,* **53**, 58-68.

Eriksson, H., & Gustafsson, J.-A. (Eds.), (1983). *Steroid hormone receptors: Structure and function.* Nobel Symposium No. 57. Amsterdam/New York/Oxford: Elsevier Science.

Frey, H. (1982). The endocrine response to physical activity. *The Scandinavian Journal of Social Medicine,* (Suppl. 29), 71-75.

Frisch, R.E., Gotz-Welbergen, A.V., McArthur, J.W., Albright, T., Witschi, J., Bullen, B., Birnholz, J., Reed, R., & Hermann, H. (1981). Delayed menarche and amenorrhea of college athletes in relation to age of onset of training. *Journal of the American Medical Association,* **246**, 1559-1563.

Frohman, R.A., Feling, P., Broadus, A.E., & Baxter, J.D. (1981). The clinical manifestation of endocrine disease. In P. Feling, J.D. Baxter, A.E. Broadus, & L.A. Frohman (Eds.), *Endocrinology and metabolism.* (pp. 3-14). New York: McGraw-Hill Book Co.

Galbo, H. (1981). Endocrinology and metabolism in exercise. *International Journal of Sports Medicine,* **2**, 203-211.

Galbo, H. (1983). *Hormonal and metabolic adaptation to exercise* (pp. 1-124). Stuttgart: Thieme Verlag.

Giorgi, E.P. (1980). The transport of steroid hormones into animal cells. *International Review of Cytology*, **65**, 49-115.

Graf, D., Reichel, G., Engelhardt, D., & Karl, H.J. (1981). Metabolism of androgens in human skeletal, heart and smooth muscle tissue. *Acta Endocrinologica*, **96** (Suppl. 240), 103-104.

Grody, W.W., Schrader, W.T., & O'Malley, B.W. (1982). Activation, transformation, and subunit structure of steroid hormone receptors. *Endocrine Reviews*, **3**, 141-163.

Gustafsson, J.-A., Okret, S., Wikstroem, A.C., Andersson, B., Radojcic, M., Wrange, O., Sachs, W., Doupe, A.J., Patterson, P.H., Cordell, B., & Fuxe, K. (1983). On the use of poly- and monoclonal antibodies in studies on the structure and function of the glucocorticoid receptor. In H. Eriksson & J.-A. Gustafsson (Eds.), *Steroid hormone receptors: Structure and function*. (pp. 355-388). Amsterdam: Elsevier Science.

Gustafsson, J.-A., Saartok, T., Dahlberg, E., Snochowski, M., Haeggmark, T., & Eriksson, E. (1984). Studies of steriod receptors in human and rabbit skeletal muscle—clues to the understanding of the mechanism of action of anabolic steroids. *Progress in Clinical & Biological Research*, **142**, 261-290.

Haase, A., Ofenloch, B., & Eisele, K. (1983). Correlation of the 4-5 S form and the 8 S form of the cytosolic androgen receptor in murine skeletal muscle. *Biochemistry International*, **7**, 541-548.

Hale, R.W., Kosasa, T., Krieger, J., & Pepper, S. (1983). A marathon: The immediate effect on female runners luteinizing hormone, follicle-stimulating hormone, prolactin, testosterone, and cortisol levels. *The American Journal of Obstetrics and Gynecology*, **146**, 550-554.

Heitzman, R.J. (1979). The efficiency and mechanism of action of anabolic agents as growth promotors in farm animals. *Journal of Steroid Biochemistry*, **11**, 927-930.

Holloszy, J.O., & Booth, F.W. (1976). Biochemical adaptations to endurance exercise in muscle. *Annual Review of Physiology*, **38**, 273-291.

Jasiorowski, H. (Ed.). (1981). *Steroids in animal production. International Symposium*. (pp. 1-261). Warsaw: Warsaw Agricultural University.

Jordan, V.C., Zava, D.T., Eppenburger, U., Kiser, A., Sebek, S., Dowdle, E., Krozowski, Z., Bennett, R.C., Funder, J., Holdaway, I.M., & Wittliff, J.L. (1983). Reliability of steroid hormone receptor assays: An international study. *European Journal of Cancer and Clinical Oncology*, **19**, 357-363.

Kochakian, C.D. (1976). *Anabolic-androgenic steroids*. Berlin/Heidelberg/New York: Springer Verlag.

Krieg, M. (1976). Characterization of the androgen receptor in the skeletal muscle of the rat. *Steroids*, **28**, 261-274.

Krieg, M., Smith, K., & Bartsh, W. (1978). Demonstration of specific androgen receptor in rat heart muscle: Relationship between binding, metabolism, and tissue levels of androgens. *Endocrinology,* **103**, 1686-1694.

Krieg, M., Smith, K., & Elvers, B. (1980). Androgen receptor translocation from cytosol of rat heart muscle, bulbocavernosus/levator ani muscle and prostate into heart muscle nuclei. *Journal of Steroid Biochemistry,* **13**, 577-587.

Kuehl, L. (1977). Isolation of skeletal muscle nuclei. *Methods in Cellular Biology,* **15**, 79-88.

Kurowski, T.T., Chatterton, R.T., Jr., & Hickson, R.C. (1984). Countereffects of compensatory overload and glucocorticoids in skeletal muscle: Androgen and glucocorticoid cytosol receptor binding. *Journal of Steroid Biochemistry,* **21**, 137-145.

Lamb, D.R. (1984). Anabolic steroids in athletics: How well do they work and how dangerous are they? *The American Journal of Sports Medicine,* **12**, 31-37.

Liao, S., Chang, C., & Saltzman, A.G. (1983). Androgen receptor interaction—An overview. In H. Eriksson & J.-A. Gustafsson (Eds.), *Steroid hormone receptors: Structure and function.* (pp. 407-418). Amsterdam: Elsevier Science.

Longcope, C., Pratt, J.H., Schneider, S.H., & Fineberg, S.E. (1976). The in vivo metabolism of androgens by muscle and adipose tissue of normal men. *Steroids,* **28**, 521-533.

Longcope, C., Pratt, J.H., Schneider, S.H., & Fineberg, S.E. (1978). Aromatisation of androgens by muscle and adipose tissue in vivo. *Journal of Clinical Endocrinology and Metabolism,* **46**, 146-152.

Lu, F.C., & Rendel, J. (1975). *Anabolic agents in animal production.* Stuttgart: Thieme Verlag.

Martin, P.M., & Sheridan, P.J. (1982). Towards a new model for the mechanism of action of steroids. *Journal of Steroid Biochemistry,* **16**, 215-229.

Mayer, M., Shafir, E., Kaiser, N., Milholland, R.J., & Rosen, F. (1976). Interaction of glucocorticoid hormones with rat skeletal muscle: Catabolic effects and hormone binding. *Metabolism,* **25**, 157-167.

McGrath, J.A., & Goldspink, D.F. (1982). Glucocorticoid action on protein synthesis and protein breakdown in isolated skeletal muscles. *Biochemical Journal,* **206**, 641-645.

Meyer, H.H.D., & Rapp, M. (1985). Estrogen receptor in bovine skeletal muscle. *Journal of Animal Science,* **60**, 294-300.

Michel, G., & Baulieu, E.-E. (1974). Récepteur cytosoluble des androgènes dans un muscle strié squelettique. *Competes Rendus des Séances de l'Académie des Sciences,* **279**, 421-424.

Michel, G., & Baulieu, E.-E. (1980). Androgen receptor in rat skeletal muscle: Characterization and physiological variations. *Endocrinology,* **107**, 2088-2098.

Moss, F.P., & Leblond, C.P. (1970). Nature of dividing nuclei in skeletal muscle of growing rats. *Zeitschrift für Zellforschung und Biologie,* **44**, 459-462.

Powers, M.L., & Florini, J.R. (1975). A direct effect of testosterone on muscle cells in tissue culture. *Endocrinology,* **97**, 1043-1047.

Pugeat, M.M., Dunn, J.F., & Nisula, B.C. (1981). Transport of steroid hormones: Interaction of 70 drugs with testosterone-binding globulin in human plasma. *Journal of Endocrinology and Metabolism,* **53**, 69-75.

Raynaud, J.-P., & Ojasoo, T. (1983). The relevance of structure-affinity relationships in the study of steroid hormone action. In H. Eriksson & J.-A. Gustafsson (Eds.), *Steroid hormone receptors: Structure and function* (pp. 141-170). Amsterdam: Elsevier Science.

Roche, J.F., & Quirke, J.F. (in press). The effects of steroid hormones and xenobiotics on growth of farm animals. In P.J. Buttery, N.B. Haynes, & D.B. Lindsay (Eds.), *Control of manipulation of animal growth.* London: Butterworths.

Rogozkin, V.A. (1979a). Anabolic steroid metabolism in skeletal muscle. *Journal of Steroid Biochemistry,* **11**, 923-936.

Rogozkin, V.A. (1979b). Metabolic effects of anabolic steroid on skeletal muscle. *Journal of Steroid Biochemistry,* **11**, 160-163.

Rousseau, G.G. (1984). Structure and regulation of the glucocorticoid hormone receptor. *Molecular and Cellular Endocrinology,* **38**, 1-11.

Ruff, R.L., Stuhmer, W., & Almers, W. (1982). Effects of glucocorticoid treatment on the excitability of rat skeletal muscle. *Pflügers Archiv,* **395**, 132-137.

Ryan, A.J. (1981). Anabolic steroids are fool's gold. *Federation Proceedings,* **40**, 2682-2688.

Saartok, T. (1984). Steroid receptors in two types of rabbit skeletal muscle. *International Journal of Sports Medicine,* **5**, 130-136.

Saartok, T., Dahlberg, E., Bylund, P., Eriksson, E., & Gustafsson, J.-A. (1984). Steroid hormone receptors protein and DNA in erector spinae muscle from scoliotic patients. *Clinical Orthopaedics and Related Research,* **183**, 197-207.

Salmons, S. (1983). Myotrophic effects of anabolic steroids. *Veterinary Research Communications,* **7**, 19-26.

Saltin, B., Henriksson, J., Nygaard, E., Andersson, P., & Jansson, E. (1977). Fiber types and metabolic potentials of skeletal muscles in sedentary man and endurance runners. *Annals of New York Academy of Sciences,* **301**, 3-29.

Shoji, S., & Pennington, R.J.T. (1977a). Binding of dexamethasone and cortisol to cytosol receptors in rat extensor digitorum longus and soleus muscles. *Experimental Neurology,* **57**, 342-348.

Shoji, S., & Pennington, R.J.T. (1977b). The effects of cortisone on protein breakdown and synthesis in rat skeletal muscle. *Molecular and Cellular Endocrinology,* **6**, 159-169.

Siiteri, P.K., Murai, J.T., Hammond, G.L., Nisker, J.A., Raymoure, W.J., & Kuhn, R.W. (1982). The serum transport of steroid hormones. *Recent Progress in Hormone Research,* **38**, 457-510.

Snochowski, M., Dahlberg, E., & Gustafsson, J.-A. (1980). Characterization and quantification of the androgen and glucocorticoid receptors in cytosol from rat skeletal muscle. *European Journal of Biochemistry,* **111**, 603-616.

Snochowski, M., Lundstroem, K., Dahlberg, E., Peterson, H., & Edquist, L.-E. (1981). Androgen and glucocorticoid receptors in porcine skeletal muscle cytosol. *Journal of Animal Science,* **53**, 80-90.

Snochowski, M., Saartok, T., Dahlberg, E., Eriksson, E., & Gustafsson, J.-A. (1981). Androgen and glucocorticoid receptors in human skeletal muscle cytosol. *Journal of Steroid Biochemistry,* **14**, 765-771.

Stenstad, P., & Eik-Nes, K.B. (1981). Androgen metabolism in rat skeletal muscle in vitro. *Biochimica et Biophysica Acta,* **663**, 169-176.

Stepanov, M.G., Fel'dkoren, B.I. (1984). Androgen binding by skeletal muscle nuclei, *Bulletin of Experimental Biology and Medicine,* **37**, 606-608.

Weiss, L.W., Cureton, K.J., & Thompson, F.N. (1983). Comparison of serum testosterone and androstenedione responses to weight lifting in men and women. *European Journal of Applied Physiology,* **50**, 413-419.

Wilson, J.D., & Griffin, J.E. (1980). The use and misuse of androgens. *Metabolism,* **29**, 1278-1295.

The Somatogenic Receptor in Rat Liver: Properties, Subcellular Distribution, and Sex Difference

Göran Andersson
Bolette Husman
Gunnar Norstedt
Jan-Åke Gustafsson
Karolinska Institute
Huddinge, Sweden

The lactogenic or Prl receptor in rat liver membranes is regulated by the hypothalamo-pituitary axis (see Gustafsson, Mode, Norstedt, Eneroth, & Hökfelt, 1983). The considerably higher receptor level in female than in male rat liver (Kelly, Posner, Tsushima, & Friesen, 1974) may be due to sex differences in the growth hormone (GH) secretory pattern (Edén, 1979; Norstedt, Mode, Eneroth, & Gustafsson, 1981). The female GH pattern is characterized by irregular oscillations with low peaks and absence of deep troughs. This pattern can be simulated by infusing rat or human GH to normal male or hypophysectomized male or female rats using osmotic minipumps and results in induction of lactogenic receptors to the female level (Norstedt, 1982). As a logical continuation of our previous studies on the hormonal control of lactogenic receptors and steroid hormone metabolism in rat liver, we have begun to focus our attention on somatogenic or GH receptors in the same tissue. As a marker for somatogenic receptors in rat liver [^{125}I]-iodo-bGH was used. It was demonstrated that a low density membrane fraction containing elements of the Golgi complex and possibly endocytic vesicles is much enriched in somatogenic receptors when compared to a total membrane fraction. Using 3 M $MgCl_2$, endogenous ligand could be removed and subsequently the total level of somatogenic receptors was measured. Finally, the hepatic somatogenic receptors are found at a higher concentration in pregnant rats when compared to female and male rats. This indicates that endocrine factors influence somatogenic receptor levels.

METHODS

Subcellular Fractionation

The total particulate fraction, microsomes, Golgi I and Golgi II were isolated by a sequential procedure (Andersson, Torndal, & Eriksson, 1978). Lyosome-enriched fractions were isolated by the method of Wattiaux, Wattiaux-De Coninck, Ronveux-Dupal, and Dubois (1978), using Metrizamide gradients for the separation of lysosomes from a light mitochondrial-lysosomal fraction. Fractions were defined by marker enzyme analysis and by electron microscopy, as previously described (Norstedt, Andersson, & Gustafsson, 1984). L1 and L2 fractions, according to Wattiaux et al. (1978), were pooled for GH receptor analysis. After density gradient centrifugations, all subcellular fractions were concentrated by centrifugation at 105,000 × g for 90 min. The pellets were resuspended in phosphate buffer (50 mM, pH 7.4).

Radioiodination of bGH

[^{125}I]-iodo-bGH was prepared by the ''iodogen'' method of Fraker and Speck, Jr. (1978). All radioiodinations of bGH were performed at 4 °C. A specific activity of 20 to 40μCi/μg bGH was repeatedly obtained using this iodination method.

Binding Assays

Estimation of total binding of bGH was performed in triplicate assays using 1.5 ml Eppendorf vials (Eppendorf, Hamburg, West Germany). Approximately 30,000 cpm [^{125}I]-idio-bGH (corresponding to 0.7 ng hormone), dissolved in 0.1 ml phosphate buffer (50 mM, pH 7.4) containing 0.1% (w/v) BSA, was incubated with 0.5 ml microsomal, Golgi or lysosomal fractions. Nonspecific binding was determined from triplicate incubations to which 1 μg bGH was added. Golgi (50 μg/incubation) and microsomes (300 μg/incubation) were incubated at room temperature for 16 hr and 20 hr, respectively (standard incubation). Lysosomes (50 μg protein) were incubated at 4 °C for 66 hr. The incubation volume was 0.7 ml. Incubations were terminated by centrifugation at 8,800 × g (Centrifuge 5413, Eppendorf, West Germany) for 7 min. The tip of the tube containing the pellet was removed and counted in a γ-scintillation counter.

The number of binding sites and the dissociation constant (K_d) were measured according to Scatchard (1949) using a fixed amount of tracer and increasing concentrations of unlabelled bGH. Removal of endogenous ligand from the receptor was performed by exposing the membranes to $MgCl_2$; a similar method has been described by Kelly, Leblanc, and Djiane (1979) for the analysis of total Prl receptors. Membranes sufficient for seven incubations were centrifuged at 3,200 × g for 30 min. The pellets were resuspended in 0.5 ml of 3 M $MgCl_2$. After vortexing for 1.5 min, 4 ml phosphate buffer (50 mM, pH 7.4) containing 0.1% (w/v) BSA was added and the suspension was recentrifuged at 3,200 × g for 15 min. In parallel vials, membranes were exposed to distilled water instead of 3 M $MgCl_2$, but were otherwise treated identically to $MgCl_2$ exposed membranes. The pellet was resuspended in 3.5 ml assay buffer and incubations were performed as described above.

The results of $MgCl_2$ treatments are expressed as percentage specific binding/50 μg protein. The protein value is related to the amount before $MgCl_2$ treatment.

RESULTS AND DISCUSSION

Characterization of [^{125}I]-iodo-bGH Binding in the Liver

Binding of [^{125}I]-iodo-bGH to microsomes and Golgi/endosomes was time and temperature dependent. At 22° C, a steady state was observed after 16 to 20 hr. Prolongation of the incubation time (~ 30 hr) resulted in a decline in [^{125}I]-iodo-bGH binding to both microsomal and Golgi fractions (data not shown).

Specific binding of [^{125}I]-iodo-bGH was almost linearly dependent upon protein concentration up to 1000 and 60 μg protein/incubation for microsomal and Golgi/endosomal membranes, respectively (data not shown).

The specificity of [^{125}I]-iodo-bGH binding to pooled Golgi I and Golgi II membrane fractions from male, female and pregnant female livers is shown in Figure 1. Bovine GH, rGH and hGH displaced [^{125}I]-iodo-bGH in a similar manner, while rPrl was a considerably less efficient competitor. These results indicate that [^{125}I]-iodo-bGH preferentially binds to a somatogenic receptor in rat liver.

Subcellular Distribution of Somatogenic Receptors

Since lactogenic receptors in rat liver have been shown to be highly concentrated in low density membrane fractions, mainly consisting of Golgi

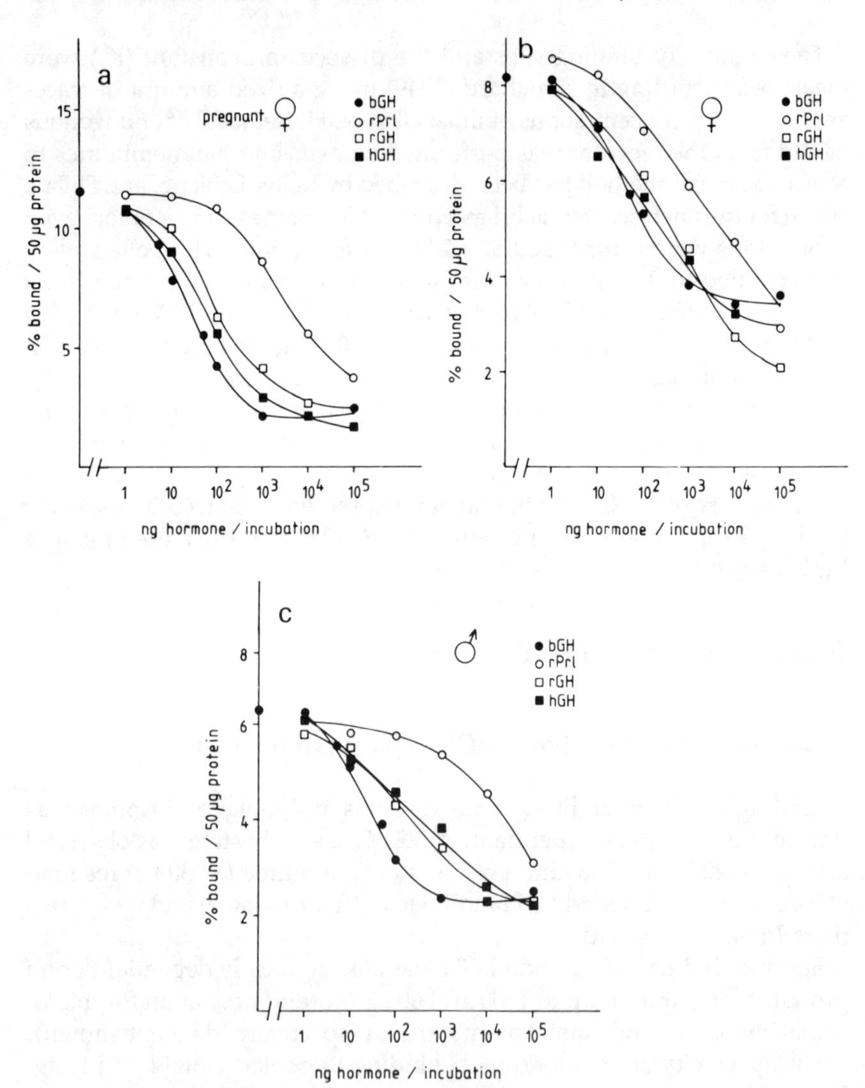

Figure 1 Displacement of bound [^{125}I]-iodo-bGH from pooled Golgi I and II fractions. Membranes were prepared from (a) 3 pooled pregnant female livers, (b) 5 pooled female livers, and (c) 4 pooled male livers. The binding of [^{125}I]-iodo-bGH was determined as described in Material and Methods, with 50 μg protein in each incubate. Incubation time was 16 hr at room temperature. The abscissa shows the amount of unlabelled hormones added to each incubation. The ordinate shows the percent of the total radioactivity bound to the membranes. Each point is the mean of triplicate determinations. The experiment is representative of three experiments.

complex membranes and possibly endocytic vesicles (Norstedt et al., 1984; Posner, Josefsberg, & Bergeron, 1979), it was of interest to investigate whether the same was true for somatogenic receptors. Experiments concerning the subcellular distribution of somatogenic receptors in female liver (Table 2) demonstrated that the level of specific binding sites for [^{125}I]-iodo-bGH in the two Golgi fractions (Golgi I, mainly secretory vesicles; Golgi II, mainly Golgi cisternae) was 20- to 25-fold higher than in a total particulate fraction (TPF). The residual microsomes I and II devoid of Golgi-derived and endosomal components and mainly consisting of endoplasmic reticulum were concentrated 1.4- to 2.2-fold with regard to somatogenic receptors. The intermediate fraction was approximately 10-fold

Table 1 Subcellular distribution of somatogenic receptors in rat liver membrane fractions isolated from female rats

Fraction	% SB/50 μg protein	mg protein/g liver	% SB/g liver	yield (%)	relative SB
Total particulate fraction	0.24 ± 0.08	121 ± 10	578	100	1
Residual microsomes I	0.52 ± 0.13	14.0 ± 1.8	146	25.2	2.2
Intermediate I	2.49 ± 0.25	0.54 ± 0.1	26.9	4.6	10.4
Golgi I	5.62 ± 0.45	0.25 ± 0.05	28.1	4.8	23.4
Residual microsomes II	0.33 ± 0.08	10.0 ± 2.0	66.0	11.4	1.4
Intermediate II	2.10 ± 0.18	0.47 ± 0.15	19.8	3.4	8.8
Golgi II	4.81 ± 0.51	0.54 ± 0.1	45.1	7.8	20.0
Lyosomes	0.82 ± 0.18	0.60 ± 0.2	9.8	1.7	3.4

Analysis of [^{125}I]-iodo-bGH binding to subcellular fractions prepared and characterized from 2 pooled female rat livers as described in Materials and Methods. Each value represents the mean ± SD of three different membrane preparations assayed in triplicate. SB = specific binding.

enriched, showing about 50% of the specific binding present in Golgi I and II fractions (Table 1).

The level of somatogenic receptors in the pooled (L1 and L2) lysosomal fraction showed 3- to 4-fold enrichment compared to TPF, that is, 14% to 17% of the SB in the Golgi I and II fractions.

Somatogenic Receptors in Male and Female Rat Livers

We could not demonstrate any marked sex-difference in somatogenic receptor levels in male and female Golgi fractions, not even after treatment of Golgi fractions with 3 M $MgCl_2$ (Table 2). However, during pregnancy, somatogenic receptors were more than 5-fold elevated in the Golgi fractions, both in untreated and $MgCl_2$-washed membranes (Table 2). The higher level of GH binding in pregnant females could be attributed to a larger number of binding sites in pregnant female Golgi fractions compared to nonpregnant females (Table 2).

When displacement curves were constructed according to the method of Scatchard (1949), linear plots were obtained that also indicated a high affinity ($0.25\text{-}0.45 \times 10^{-9}$M) and low capacity binding of bGH. The numbers of binding sites were 110 and 120 fmol/mg protein in male and female Golgi fractions, respectively (Table 2). An interesting observation

Table 2 Binding of [^{125}I]-iodo-bGH to Golgi fractions prepared from livers of female, male and pregnant female rats

Animals	Liver fraction	% SB/50 μg protein		K_d (10^{-9} M)	N(fmol/mg protein
		$-MgCl_2$	$+MgCl_2$		
Female	Golgi I and II	3.00 ± 0.62	6.1 ± 1.47	0.24 ± 0.03	121 ± 12
Male	Golgi I and II	2.2 ± 0.55	6.7 ± 1.60	0.27 ± 0.09	111 ± 37
Female Pregnant	Golgi I and II	7.7 ± 1.21	14.2 ± 3.88	0.44 ± 0.13	622 ± 193

Golgi I and II fractions were prepared as described under Methods. The specific binding (SB) of [^{125}I]-iodo-bGH was analyzed using standard incubation conditions. Values of SB are expressed as the mean ± SD of 3 to 5 individually prepared and analyzed animals. Golgi membranes (not exposed to $MgCl_2$) were pooled from the respective groups and the estimated number of binding states (N) and the apparent dissociation constant (K_d) were determined according to the method of Scatchard.

regarding the ligand specifity of the somatogenic receptor was noted in the male rat, where considerably higher amounts of rGH and hGH were required to give 50% inhibition of [^{125}I]bGH binding compared to those in female rats, including those in late pregnancy.

Acknowledgments

This work was supported by Grants 13X-2819 and 12X-7141 from the Swedish Medical Research Council.

REFERENCES

Andersson, G.N., Torndal, U.-B., & Eriksson, L.C. (1978). Sequential preparation of rat liver microsomal and Golgi membranes. *Biochimica and Biophysica Acta,* **512**, 539-549.

Edén, S. (1979). Age- and sex-related differences in episodic growth hormone secretion in the rat. *Endocrinology,* **105**, 555-560.

Fraker, P.J., & Speck, J.C., Jr. (1978). Protein and cell membrane iodinations with a sparingly soluble chloroamide 1,3,4,6-tetrachloro-3α,6α-diphenyl-glycoluril. *Biochemistry and Biophysics Research Communications,* **80**, 849-857.

Gustafsson, J.-Å., Mode, A., Norstedt, G., Eneroth, P., & Hökfelt, T. (1983). Central control of prolactin and estrogen receptors in rat liver-expression of a novel endocrine system, the hypothalamo-pituitary-liver axis. *Annual Review of Pharmacology and Toxicology,* **23**, 259-278.

Kelly, P., Leblanc, G., & Djiane, J. (1979). Estimation of total prolactin binding sites after *in vitro* desaturation. *Endocrinology,* **104**, 1631-1638.

Kelly, P., Posner, B., Tsushima, T., & Friesen, H. (1974). Studies of insulin, growth hormone, and prolactin binding: Ontogenesis, effects of sex and pregnancy. *Endocrinology,* **95**, 532-539.

Norstedt, G. (1982). A comparison between the effects of growth hormone on prolactin receptors and estrogen receptors in rat liver. *Endocrinology,* **110**, 2107-2112.

Norstedt, G., Andersson, G.N., & Gustafsson, J.-Å. (1984). Growth hormone induction of lactogenic receptors at intracellular sites. *Endocrinology,* **115**, 672-680.

Norstedt, G., Mode, A., Eneroth, P., & Gustafsson, J.-Å. (1981). Induction of prolactin receptors in rat liver after the administration of growth hormone. *Endocrinology,* **108**, 1855-1861.

Posner, B.I., Josefsberg, F., & Bergeron, J.J.M. (1979). Intracellular polypeptide hormone receptors: Characterization and induction of lactogen receptors in the Golgi apparatus of rat liver. *Journal of Biological Chemistry,* **254**, 12494-12499.

Scatchard, G. (1949). The interaction of proteins for small molecules and ions. *Annals of the New York Academy of Science,* **51**, 660-672.

Wattiaux, R., Wattiaux-De Coninck, S., Ronveux-Dupal, M.F., & Dubois, F. (1978). Isolation of rat liver lysosomes by isopycnic centrifugation in a Metrizamide gradient. *Journal of Cell Biology,* **78**, 349-368.

Discussion from the Session

Recent Development on Receptors: Importance in Exercise Metabolism

Michael G. Clark
University of Tasmania
Tasmania, Australia

The speakers were Sandy Williams from Durham, North Carolina, U.S.A. (adrenergic receptors), Olaf Pedersen from Aarhus, Denmark (insulin receptors),Marek Snochowski from Warsaw, Poland (steroid receptors) and Göran Andersson from Stockholm, Sweden (prolactin receptors).

ADRENERGIC RECEPTORS OF SKELETAL MUSCLE

Sandy Williams' paper, which highlighted the changes in adrenergic receptors in various tissues and particularly muscle as a result of short bouts of exercise and exercise training, prompted four questions. The first focused on the issue of data interpretation and referred to a recent publication from Williams and his colleagues (Williams, Schiable, Bishop, & Morey, 1984). In that work it was reported that the dissociation constant for the α_1 antagonist, prazosin, was approximately 70 pM whereas that for the β antagonist, dihydroalprenolol was approximately 1000 pM. Even though the population densities for the two types of adrenergic receptors differed only marginally, could the lower affinity constant for the α_1 antagonist imply that this receptor population played a predominant role in cell metabolism, particularly at low concentrations of epinephrine? Williams replied that in his view it was important to distinguish dissociation constants for agonists from dissociation constants for antagonists. Changes in antagonist affinities that are reported would probably be part of the experimental noise. There appeared to be no systems in which antagonist affinities could be linked to physiological responses. On the other hand, differences in, or indeed changes in, agonist affinities would be physiologically relevant. A change in agonist affinities could occur independent of receptor number and would affect response data.

The second question probed the possibility that the reported endurance training-induced changes in adrenergic binding might be an artifact and rather reflect changes in membrane vesicular orientation and recovery. Williams agreed that this was a problem inherent in studies using broken cell preparations. However, the problem is diminished if similar results can be produced by different modes of preparing the membranes and if different denominators such as DNA, protein, and wet weight are used. One of the problems of receptor quantitation has been the lack of a gold standard in terms of relating binding capacity. Methods have been developed to look at in vivo characterization of receptors. For example, autoradiographic methods allowed an alternative approach to quantitating receptors without having to go to broken cell preparations. But these methods also had their drawbacks. However, the problem of orientation was probably not pertinent to the findings discussed in the present paper, since the binding was done in hypertonic buffer. Recovery labels including sarcolemma markers can be used to ascertain if the recovery is constant from one tissue preparation to another. The question of measuring purification is difficult. Purification cannot be measured at the first step and it is difficult to definitively relate the properties of the membrane preparation to the intact tissue. One cannot assume that the receptor population measured in the membrane preparation faithfully reflects the physiologically relevant population. For example, binding sites that are uncoupled can exist in the cell surface and binding sites exist in internal sites that are unavailable for binding in the intact cell, but each of the populations may become available for binding the ligand once the cell is ruptured. Clearly all of these considerations complicate conclusions drawn from binding studies on isolated membrane preparations.

The third question directed to Williams related to catecholamine metabolism and queried whether anything was known about the affinity of catecholamine conjugates (e.g., sulpho-norepinephrine) for the adrenergic receptors, particularly since a significant proportion of the circulating catecholamines would become conjugated. A specific answer could not be given but in general, fairly minor modifications of the catecholamine molecules clearly affected their binding properties.

The fourth question was concerned with discriminating between receptors involved in nerve synapse function and those available for circulating catecholamines. Williams responded by referring to vascular smooth muscle, where a functional distinction can be made between receptors that respond to nerve stimulation preferentially, and receptors that respond to humorally circulating catecholamines. In a variety of vascular beds, the receptor that responds to locally released norepinephrine, which is called subsynaptic, of subjunctional location, is of the α_1 subtype. The receptors that are distinct from the synapse and respond primarily to the circulating catecholamines appear in large measure to be of the α_2 subtype. This type of distinction is most clearly shown in vascular smooth muscle but may well exist in other tissues.

EFFECTS OF ACUTE EXERCISE AND PHYSICAL TRAINING ON INSULIN RECEPTORS AND INSULIN ACTION

Olaf Pedersen's talk examined changes in insulin receptors after exercise and reported on observed alterations in insulin binding to muscle, adipocytes, erythrocytes and monocytes. In general it was felt that the change in receptor binding did not necessarily reflect a change in sensitivity in metabolic terms. It was therefore questioned whether the insulin receptor system was a useful indicator of exercise-induced changes in glucose tolerance. However, one member of the audience pointed out that there were conditions where an alteration in insulin receptor number in muscle was accompanied by a parallel change in biological effect of insulin (e.g., starvation). Williams reiterated the point made previously that the reservations concerning the extrapolation of binding data from the membrane preparation in vitro to the organism in vivo would equally apply to insulin as for adrenergic receptors.

Pedersen's reported findings for diabetics prompted the question as to whether any changes in glucose clearance or glucose transport had occurred in spite of unaltered or decreased binding. Pedersen's answer focused on findings from adipocytes where glucose transport, glucose metabolism and the lipid effect of insulin had been assessed. There was absolutely no change in either binding or in insulin action in these cells. Pedersen stressed that the major effects of exercise on insulin action in muscle cells are, in effect, on postbinding mechanisms. There appeared to be no studies as yet that have elucidated these mechanisms but it is clear that there is an effect of exercise on glucose transport. This effect may be due to an increase in the number of glucose carriers or their affinity for glucose. There may also be an effect of exercise on the subunit of the insulin receptor that affects autophosphorylation. The possibility of a circulating mediator to account for the increased postbinding activity after exercise should be explored. Pedersen referred to Bonen's poster (Bonen, Tan, Hood, & Clune, 1985) where it was suggested that it might be due to changes in the free fatty acid content in serum or intermediates within the cell. It was then pointed out that Cushman's group (Hissin, Karnieli, Simpson, Salans, & Cushman, 1982) had shown that fat-feeding of rats reduced the total number of glucose transporters in fat cells. It was therefore possible that exercise, which increased fat metabolism, may induce the synthesis of glucose transporters and thereby improve insulin responsiveness.

A final comment from a member of the audience indicated that exercise also increased insulin sensitivity for the control of aminoisobutyrate uptake. The change in control of aminoisobutyrate uptake exactly paralleled the change in control of glucose transport. Thus, whatever explanation was invoked in terms of a postreceptor event will have to explain the transport of aminoisobutyrate as well as the transport of glucose.

STEROID HORMONE RECEPTORS IN SKELETAL MUSCLE

Marek Snochowski's paper on steroid receptors prompted two questions. The first challenged the view that anabolic steroids directly controlled protein turnover in muscle. A recent study by Ballard (1985) in which growth factors, steroids, and so forth were tested for their effects on protein synthesis and protein degradation in cultured muscle cells indicated that androgens were without effect. Thus the possibility emerges that anabolic steroids control muscle protein turnover indirectly by their effects on insulin and insulin-like growth factors (Ballard, 1985). Snochowski replied that this was a question that should be solved on a methodological basis. The mammary tissue culture was cited as an example. When oestrogens are present in the medium the cells can be cultured until casein is produced. In the absence of oestrogens cells can only be cultured if the cells were taken in vivo at a particular time after high levels of oestrogens were present in the bloodstream. Therefore conclusions regarding the response of cultured cells to steroid hormones require that the test system is rigorously standardized.

The second questioner asked Snochowski to comment on the apparent association between glucocorticoid receptor concentration and the degree of muscle atrophy. Again it was felt that the problem related to how the data were treated. If the binding data were expressed relative to protein content, then a change would only be valid when there is no change in muscle cell protein concentration. However, if the protein concentration is affected, then such expression is not valid and the binding data should be expressed in terms of DNA content. So atrophy, which results from the degradation of huge amounts of protein, but does not involve receptor proteins, gives the impression that the glucocorticoid receptors have increased. Obviously this is not true. Nevertheless such tissues may be expected to be more sensitive to glucocorticoids.

THE SOMATOGENIC RECEPTOR IN RAT LIVER: PROPERTIES, SUBCELLULAR DISTRIBUTION, AND SEX DIFFERENCES

Göran Andersson's paper focused attention on prolactin receptors in liver. His findings raised questions about the physiological role, if any, that prolactin receptors may have in the control of hepatic function. Indeed it appeared that no metabolic effects were elicited by infusion of the liver with prolactin although cleavage of the hormone does take place. Andersson pointed out that it was still a matter of discussion whether the hormone that is secreted from the pituitary is the ultimate hormone or if it is modified in some peripheral tissue.

GENERAL DISCUSSION

The first question concerned growth hormone and whether there was any growth hormone receptors on muscle. This appeared to be important since some body builders used growth hormone injections. Was there any reason to believe that they would benefit from that? Andersson replied that the masculinizing effect of growth hormone was only achieved by intermittent injections possibly affecting sex steroid metabolism in liver. However, investigations using intermittent injections indicated that growth hormone did not affect hepatic prolactin receptors in either female or male rats. Snochowski indicated that data from farm animals suggested that growth hormone injections provided benefit only when either the hormone was lacking or when nutrients were limiting. Discussion then focused on IGF_1. It was pointed out that this growth factor is the mediator of skeletal and cartilage growth and that IGF_1 regulates protein accretion in cultured muscle cell lines. However, if rats are injected with radio-labelled bovine growth hormone, the bulk of the radioactivity accumulates in muscle tissue. Growth hormone also has acute effects on amino acid and glucose transport in muscle but the discussants were unaware of information on growth hormone receptors in muscle.

Another questioner sought information on the apparent parallel changes in both catecholamine concentration and catecholamine receptors during exercise. Which of the two changes was considered the most important? In response Williams cited the heart as an example. During an acute bout of exercise catecholamine levels are markedly elevated with contributions from both circulating catecholamines and the release of norepinephrine within the heart. Recent data indicate that as a result of the marked change in concentration, the catecholamine sensitivity of the dog heart, following an hour of acute exercise, is reduced about 3-fold. This is measured as net sensitivity to the chronotropic effects of isoproterenol. Thus, 1 hr of exercise at about 70% of $\dot{V}O_2max$ reduces the response and sensitivity to a subsequent dose of isoproterenol by a factor of about 3-1/2 even though the test dose of isoproterenol is given 10 min following exercise when the heart rate has returned to the resting level. Whether this is due to receptor desensitization or whether it is a postreceptor effect is uncertain, but the effect is relatively short-lived and the catecholamine sensitivity returns to normal within 3 hr. Williams went on to point out that the phenomena of agonist-induced desensitization also probably occurs during exercise. The desensitization may be due to down-regulation of the receptor number but there may be other mechanisms as well. Thus, as tissues are exposed to high levels of catecholamines, their sensitivity is reduced and this may be pertinent to phenomena that take place in the immediate postexercise period. However, this change is probably short-lived and could be expected to revert to normal fairly soon in the postexercise period. The effects of chronic exercise are very tissue specific. Thus when responsiveness is studied 24 or 48 hr after the last bout of acute exercise, different effects are found in the different tissues (e.g., adipocytes, skeletal muscle, heart, etc.). It therefore seems reasonable to comment that changes in monocytes or lymphocytes may be of interest as phenomena in receptor regulation but that they may not necessarily have a physiologic meaning.

ADDITIONAL ISSUES

Michael Clark then directed attention to two issues that had not been addressed. First, the α_2 adrenergic receptors on endocrine pancreas had not been considered. Was it likely that this population of receptors was altered in exercise or exercise training? Secondly, despite clear physiological data indicating the presence of an α-adrenergic mechanism for the control of glucose and oxygen uptake in skeletal muscle, there was no evidence for α adrenergic receptors.

Pancreatic Receptors

Williams admitted that for completeness' sake the pancreatic α_2 receptors should have been considered. Clearly these receptors participate in the reduction of insulin release during exercise. In response to the second question it was not clear why α-adrenergic receptors (particularly α_1) could not be found in skeletal muscle membrane preparations. Williams pointed out that a similar situation appears to exist for the α-receptor of the heart, particularly when considering species differences. Alpha-adrenergic responses, both inotropic and metabolic, have been observed in most, but not all, mammalian species. However there is a marked difference in the concentration of α-receptors. For example, comparing the rat and dog heart, which both respond to the positive inotropic effects of α-agonists, α-receptors are readily demonstrated in the rat but cannot be found in the dog. Perhaps it is possible for the physiologic responses to be induced by a concentration of α-receptors that are as yet below the detection limit of our current methods. Alternatively the α-receptors may be very labile and inactivated during membrane preparation.

Another question concerned the role of α_2-receptors in adipose tissue. Have these been studied and were they involved in fat metabolism during exercise? This question took on added significance because of attempts to design an antiobesity drug based on phenoxybenzamine and aimed at blocking out α_2 inhibitory action at adenyl cyclase and thereby enhancing β adrenergic-mediated lipolysis (Comai & Sullivan, 1982). It was agreed that this was an area for further research even though phenoxybenzamine did not appear to be successful at reducing adiposity when compared with the β-agonist LY79771 (Shaw, Schmiegel, et al., 1981).

Adrenergic Receptors in Skeletal Muscle

The question of α_1 adrenergic receptors in skeletal muscle was not completely resolved and discussion focused once again on this issue. It was argued that if insulin binding is studied by using radioactive insulin, why couldn't a search for catecholamine receptors usefully employ radioactive epinephrine or norepinephrine—particularly since it is possible that a subtype may be present on skeletal muscle that is neither α_1 nor α_2. Williams responded by making the point that agonists have much lower affinity, and it thus becomes more difficult to identify the sites against the noise of the nonspecific binding. The affinity of epinephrine for adrenergic receptors is often micromolar whereas the affinity for antagonists is usually a nanomolar or even picomolar. This is so even though dose-response curves indicate half-maximal responses to epinephrine in the nanomolar range. Thus if a nanomolar concentration of radioactively labelled epinephrine is used for binding studies the high affinity sites will be occupied, but the bulk of the binding will be converted to the low affinity form. Williams said that despite the use of the high-affinity, high-specific activity-iodinated α antagonists his group could not reproducibly characterize α receptors on skeletal muscle.

Insulin Sensitivity and Exercise

The final question was concerned with distinguishing the effects of a single bout of exercise versus physical training on insulin sensitivity. Were in fact the effects the same? Pedersen pointed out that if one measures insulin sensitivity after a bout of exercise in highly trained and untrained people the effects do not differ, particularly if measured in vivo. But the effects of the same bout of exercise on insulin receptor binding do differ for the two groups.

REFERENCES

Ballard, F.J. (1985). Protein turnover in muscle: An overview. *Proceedings of the Australian Biochemical Society,* **17** (Abstract S57).

Bonen, A., Tan, M.H., Hood, D.A., & Clune, P. (1985). Effects of exercise, substrates and hormones on insulin binding in rodent and human muscle. *Clinical Physiology,* **5** (Suppl. 4) (Abstract 28).

Comai, K., & Sullivan, A.C. (1982). Effect of phenoxybenzamine on development of adipose tissue in lean and obese Zucker rats. *American Journal of Physiology,* **243**, E398-E406.

Hissin, P.J., Karnieli, E., Simpson, I.A., Salans, L.B., & Cushman, S.W. (1982). A possible mechanism of insulin resistance in the rat adipose cell with high-fat/low-carbohydrate feeding. Depletion of intracellular glucose transport systems. *Diabetes,* **31**, 589-592.

Shaw, W.N., Schmiegel, K.K., Yen, T.T., Toomey, R.E., Meyers, D.B., & Mills, J. (1981). LY79771: A novel compound for weight control. *Life Sciences,* **29**, 2091-2101.

Williams, R.S., Schaible, T.F., Bishop, T., & Morey, M. (1984). Effects of endurance training on cholinergic and adrenergic receptors of rat heart. *Journal of Molecular and Cellular Cardiology,* **16**, 395-403.

Part III

Regulation of Metabolism During Exercise

SECTION A
NUCLEOTIDES

Purine Nucleotide Cycle Function in Contracting Muscle

Ronald L. Terjung
Gary A. Dudley
Ronald A. Meyer
David A. Hood
Jan Gorski
Upstate Medical Center
State University of New York
Syracuse, New York, U.S.A.

The hydrolysis of ATP is abruptly increased in muscle with the initiation of contraction. The exact rate of ATP hydrolysis is determined by the intensity of the contraction conditions. Although each of the three general skeletal muscle fiber types can be characterized by fairly distinct physiological and biochemical features (Saltin & Gollnick, 1983), all muscle fibers have the same requirement of meeting this energy demand during contractions, if contractile function is to be maintained. Rephosphorylation of ADP occurs by the action of creatine phosphokinase, by substrate level phosphorylations, and by the electron transport complex within the mitochondria. The inherent biochemical capacities of each different fiber type influences, in part, the relative contributions of each rephosphorylation process for a given contraction condition. This ATP hydrolysis/ADP rephosphorylation cycling process defines a major aspect of adenine nucleotide metabolism in contracting muscle. However, the adenine nucleotides are involved in a variety of other reactions that can play an important role during muscle contraction. For example, hydrolysis of AMP to its nucleoside, adenosine, by the action of 5′-nucleotidase, appears to exert an important role in active hyperemia in the heart (Berne & Rubio, 1979) and possibly skeletal muscle (Sparks & Fuchs, 1983). This role is extracellular and can lead to an efflux, albeit quantitatively small, of muscle adenine nucleotides. Another set of reactions involving the adenine nucleotides, known as the purine nucleotide cycle (Lowenstein, 1972), is internal to the cell. Adenine nucleotide entry into the purine nucleotide cycle occurs by the action of AMP deaminase. This reaction deaminates AMP to IMP and ammonia (Figure 1).

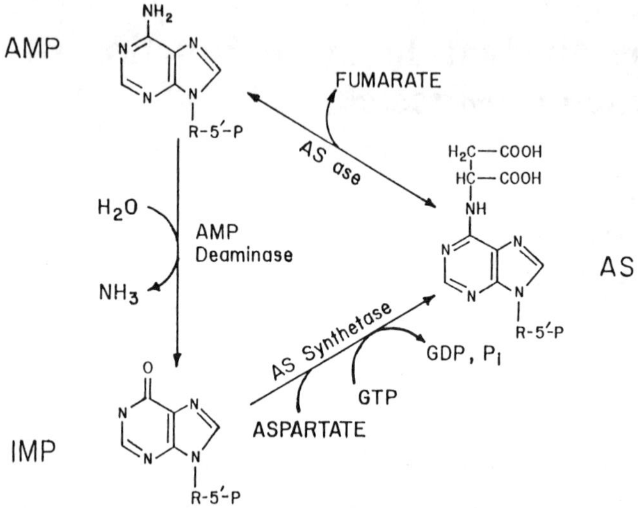

Figure 1 Reactions of the purine nucleotide cycle. Abbreviations: Adenylosuccinate Synthetase (AS synthetase), Adenylosuccinate Lyase (ASase), Adenylosuccinate (AS).

Reamination of IMP occurs by the reactions catalyzed by adenylosuccinate synthetase and adenylosuccinate lyase, respectively (Lowenstein, 1972). The activity of the cycle is expected to be low in resting muscle, since the activity of AMP deaminase is effectively inhibited by orthophosphate at physiological levels (1.0 mM), and the concentration of "free" AMP is well below (approximately 1000-fold) the apparent K_m of approximately 1.0 mM (Wheeler & Lowenstein, 1979). Further, the enzyme is activated by an environment not typical of resting muscle. This includes an elevation in ADP concentration and an acidic pH (Wheeler & Lowenstein, 1979). The reamination of IMP, driven by GTP, requires the amine donated by aspartate (Figure 1) and occurs when the IMP concentration is elevated (Goodman & Lowenstein, 1977; Manfredi & Holmes, 1984). When there is one full turn of the purine nucleotide cycle, the net reaction results in the hydrolysis of GTP and the deamination of aspartate to fumarate and ammonia (Figure 1).

THE CYCLE'S ROLE IN CONTRACTING MUSCLE

The purine nucleotide cycle may have several physiological functions in contracting muscle (Lowenstein, 1972; Aragon, Tornheim, Goodman, & Lowenstein, 1981) including the following:

- Maintenance of a high ATP/ADP ratio by regulating the relative AMP, ADP and ATP levels through the removal of AMP to IMP.
- Regulation of phosphofructokinase activity by elevations in ammonia content.
- Regulation of phosphorylase b activity by accumulation of IMP.
- Replenishment of citric acid cycle intermediates by the production of fumarate.
- Deamination of amino acids for oxidative metabolism.

We will consider the evidence in support of each of these possible functions in contracting muscle.

AMP Deamination to IMP and Ammonia

The recognition that ammonia is produced in contracting muscle, by the deamination of AMP (Parnas, 1929a,b), was made over 50 years ago. This appears to be a general response in animals with skeletal muscle containing a high potential for AMP deaminase activity (Driedzic & Hochachka, 1976; Goodman & Lowenstein, 1977; Meyer & Terjung, 1979; Rubio, Berne, & Dobson, 1973; Sabina et al., 1984; Sahlin, Palmskog, & Hultman, 1978; Snow, Harris, & Gash, 1985; Sutton, Toews, Ward, & Fox, 1980). Activation of AMP deaminase can be extensive and lead to a large decrease in adenine nucleotide content (approximately 50%) and a stoichiometric increase in IMP content (Meyer & Terjung, 1979). This occurs only during intense contraction conditions where the energy demands are excessive. Large increases in IMP and ammonia content do not occur during more mild contraction conditions (Meyer & Terjung, 1980). The decrease in total adenine nucleotide content is found primarily as a decline in ATP concentration, since the myokinase reaction maintains relatively constant ratios between the available ATP, ADP and AMP concentrations (approximately 60,000 : 250 : 1, expected for resting muscle; Lawson & Veech, 1979). The ammonia content of contracting muscle increases stoichiometrically during the initial stages of AMP deamination. However, as time progresses the 1:1 stoichiometry is not maintained, since ammonia is readily lost from the muscle (Meyer, Dudley, & Terjung, 1980; Meyer & Terjung, 1979). In contrast, nearly all of the 70- to 90-fold increase in IMP content remains within the muscle (Meyer & Terjung, 1980). This large increase in IMP content (e.g., 3 to 4 μmole/g) represents a fairly innocuous metabolic fate of ATP hydrolysis products. The 50% decline in ATP content would have created an inordinate increase in the free ADP and free AMP content of the muscle, if AMP deaminase activity had not reduced the total adenine nucleotide pool. Thus, the proposed function of the purine nucleotide cycle of protecting against an inordinate fall in the ATP/ADP ratio (Lowenstein, 1972), primarily by limiting the elevation in ADP concentration, seems to be established. This function is solely due to the action of the first enzyme of the cycle, AMP deaminase, does not require the actions of the reamination enzymes, and occurs when the metabolic stress induced by contractions is excessive. Although the functional significance of this process has not been established, it may be presumed to retard failure of the contractile process, since loss of tension is correlated with elevations in free ADP content (Dawson, Gadian, & Wilkie, 1980). This hypothesis is consistent with the exercise intolerance found in patients who do not produce IMP and ammonia during exercise because of an enzyme deficiency in muscle AMP deaminase (Sabina et al., 1984).

Fiber type response. Although the deamination of AMP appears to be greatest in "white" muscle and least in "red" (pigeon breast) muscle (Gerez & Kirsten, 1965), characterization of a muscle's potential for IMP and ammonia production cannot be made simply on the basis of general muscle appearance (e.g., redness due to mitochondrial content). For example, during intense contraction conditions both fast-twitch red and fast-twitch white muscle fiber types of the rat deplete their ATP content (approximately 50%) and produce IMP and ammonia to a similar extent (Meyer & Terjung, 1979). There is at least a 4- to 5-fold difference in the mitochondrial content (Baldwin, Klinkerfuss, Terjung, Mole, & Holloszy, 1972) and blood flow capacity (Laughlin & Armstrong, 1985; Mackie & Terjung, 1983) between these two fiber types. Thus, the existence of an inherently high capacity for aerobic metabolism is little assurance that AMP deaminase will not be activated, if the exercise conditions are sufficiently severe. In contrast, slow-twitch red fibers of the rat do not deplete their ATP content (Meyer & Terjung, 1979; Hintz et al., 1982), nor develop a significant increase in IMP or ammonia during intense stimulation conditions, even though contraction failure, evident by loss of tension development, can be essentially complete (Meyer & Terjung, 1979). Thus, there appears to be a fundamental difference between fast-twitch and slow-twitch muscle in the management of their adenine nucleotide content during intense stimulation conditions. The fast-twitch muscle ATP depletion, caused by activation of AMP deaminase, occurs coincident with loss of contractile function. In slow-twitch muscle, loss of contractile function occurs while ATP content is well maintained and AMP deaminase is not appreciably activated. Although this contrasting response could be due to inherent differences in enzyme capacity (Winder, Terjung, Baldwin, & Holloszy, 1974) and/or isozyme patterns (Raggi, Bergamini, & Ronca, 1975; Van Waarde, & Kesbeke, 1981), it is most likely due to the presence or absence of important modifying conditions within the cell that are known to alter AMP deaminase activity. For example, the rate of AMP deamination should be extremely sensitive to increases in the concentrations of free AMP (its substrate) and free ADP, both of which are expected to increase with muscle contractions (Dudley & Terjung, 1985b; Goodman & Lowenstein, 1977). Further, it appears that an extreme cellular acidosis can enhance AMP deaminase activity during intense contractions (Dudley & Terjung, 1985b). This latter condition probably separates fast-twitch and slow-twitch muscle in the above mentioned results (Meyer & Terjung, 1979).

The production of ammonia by fast-twitch muscle probably accounts for the elevated blood concentration of ammonia during intense exercise (Dudley, Staron, Murray, Hagerman, & Luginbuhl, 1983; Wilkerson, Batterton, & Horvath, 1977). It is also probable that the difference in response between fast-twitch and slow-twitch muscle is a general response also found in humans. Dudley et al. (1983) found a much greater increase in blood ammonia content during intense exercise in individuals with a high fraction of fast-twitch fibers (approximately 75%) in their leg muscles as compared to individuals with a low fraction (approximately 25%) exercising at the same supramaximal intensity.

Influence of oxidative capacity. It is apparent that, even in muscles which are capable of a high rate of AMP deamination (e.g., fast-twitch white and fast-twitch red fibers), very different responses in ammonia and IMP production can occur. During moderately intense twitch contraction conditions of 5 Hz, rat fast-twitch white muscle fibers become extremely acidotic, deplete their phosphocreatine content, decrease their adenine nucleotide pool by 50% and produce a stoichiometric increase in ammonia and IMP content (Dudley & Terjung, 1985a,b). In contrast, the high-oxidative fast-twitch red fiber section of the same contracting muscle exhibits a moderate increase in lactate, a partial decrease in phosphocreatine and a well-maintained ATP content (Dudley & Terjung, 1985a). This contrasting response during stimulation was entirely due to differences in aerobic metabolism. Ligation of the blood supply to the fast-twitch red muscle just prior to stimulation resulted in a similar metabolite response and depletion of adenine nucleotide contents as found in the fast-twitch white muscle (Dudley & Terjung, 1985a). Further, enhancing the functional aerobic capacity of the fast-twitch muscle by prior endurance-type training, reduced the depletion in ATP content and production of ammonia and IMP (Dudley & Terjung, 1985a). These results indicate that the inherent oxidative capacity of the muscle fiber influences the extent to which AMP deamination occurs. When the rate of ADP rephosphorylation is inadequate relative to the rate of ATP hydrolysis, cellular conditions develop that lead to activation of AMP deaminase and thereby adenine nucleotide depletion. These are the same conditions (e.g., acidosis, increase in free ADP concentration) that correlate with a failure of contractile function (Dawson et al., 1980; Hermansen, 1981). On the other hand, in muscle fibers with a relatively high aerobic capacity, the same high rate of ATP hydrolysis is better matched by a high rate of ADP rephosphorylation, such that an excellent energy balance is achieved without development of conditions which activate AMP deaminase. Thus, depletion of adenine nucleotides occurs in contracting muscle when the rate of ATP hydrolysis is excessive, relative to the ability of the cell for ADP rephosphorylation. Intense supramaximal or ischemic contraction conditions lead to a similar response in all fast-twitch fibers. In contrast, moderately intense stimulation can lead to a heterogeneous response, where depletion of adenine nucleotides occurs primarily in the low oxidative fast-twitch white fibers.

Regulation of Phosphofructokinase Activity by Ammonium Ion

Ammonium ion is one of many factors that activate phosphofructokinase (Abrahams & Younathan, 1971), a regulatory enzyme of glycolysis. The apparent dissociation constant of 0.33 mM is within the physiological range for ammonia in resting skeletal muscle (Goodman & Lowenstein, 1977; Meyer & Terjung, 1979). An increase in ammonium ion concentration to 2.0 mM increases the apparent affinity for the inhibitory effects of citrate and high ATP concentration (Abrahams & Younathan, 1971). These changes should stimulate the carbon flux through glycolysis and could contribute to the high rate of glycolysis typical of contracting muscle, especially during severe contraction conditions. A careful comparison of the time course of ammonia production and lactate production in contracting muscle, however, suggests that the potential contribution of ammonium ion may be minor. During stimulation conditions, known to cause a high rate of ammonia production in rat fast-twitch muscle, there is an abrupt increase in lactate accumulation to approximately 20 to 25 μmole/g wet weight, well before tissue ammonia content increases significantly (Meyer & Terjung, 1979; Dudley & Terjung, 1985a). Ammonia accumulation then proceeds at a high rate, coincident with the continued high rate of lactate production to approximately 45 to 50 μmole/g wet weight (Dudley & Terjung, 1985a). However, it is clear that the high rate of glycolysis was well underway before the ammonium ion increase could have had a major impact. Indeed, it is probable that the acidosis associated with the rapid accumulation of lactic acid within the cell is a contributing factor activating AMP deaminase and, thereby, leads to the rapid production of ammonia (Dudley & Terjung, 1985b). The observed high rate of phosphofructokinase activity during contraction was probably achieved by the influence of other more sensitive positive modulators of the enzyme including increases in free AMP, free ADP, fructose-6-diphosphate and orthophosphate concentrations (Hochachka & Somero, 1973). This suggests that ammonium ion probably exerts a minor influence in stimulating phosphofructokinase activity during muscle contractions. It is also probable that the buffering impact of ammonia production is relatively small (Dudley & Terjung, 1985b; Hultman & Sahlin, 1980) because of the delay in ammonia production and its relatively meager accumulation relative to lactic acid.

Regulation of Phosphorylase b Activity by IMP

Inosine monophosphate can affect glycogen breakdown by stimulating the activity of phosphorylase b. This response probably accounts for the high rate of glycolysis found in contracting muscle of mice unable to produce phosphorylase a (phosphorylase b kinase deficiency) (Rahim, Perrett, Lutaya, & Griffiths, 1980). Since the relatively high K_m of 5.0 mM (Aragon, Tornheim, & Lowenstein, 1980) is well above the typical IMP concentration in muscle and since conversion of phosphorylase b to phosphorylase a occurs abruptly at the onset of contractions, the physiological role of IMP in glycogen breakdown in normal muscle may not be obvious. The activity of phosphorylase a in muscle, however, rapidly declines soon after the initiation of contractions (Aragon, Tornheim, & Lowenstein, 1980; Conlee, McLane, Rennie, Winder, & Holloszy, 1979), and the IMP concentration can increase to approximately 5.0 mM during severe stimulation conditions (Dudley & Terjung, 1985a; Meyer & Terjung, 1979). Whether this increase in IMP concentration is effective in stimulating glycogen breakdown depends on the time course of events within the contracting muscle. The initial high rate of glycogenolysis and lactate production observed in contracting muscle is most likely due to the activity of phosphorylase a, since the onset of IMP production, if it occurs, is somewhat delayed (Aragon, Tornheim, & Lowenstein, 1980; Meyer & Terjung, 1979; Dudley & Terjung, 1985a). Nonetheless, the increase in IMP concentration may coincide with the return of phosphorylase a to the phosphorylase b form. Thus, it is possible that the elevation in IMP could be important in maintaining a relatively high rate of glycogenolysis. It is apparent, however, that this hypothesized role for IMP occurs at a time when a major portion of the stored glycogen (e.g., up to one-half) already has been hydrolyzed to support glycolysis (Aragon, Tornheim, & Lowenstein, 1980; Dudley & Terjung, 1985a). Further, during intense contraction conditions in which large increases in IMP occur, there is a coincident loss of contractile function (Meyer & Terjung, 1979). This probably places the role of IMP as having a sustaining influence on the rate of glycogenolysis during conditions when muscle failure is occurring. Whether this is important to the cellular function remains to be determined experimentally. Further, the potential regulation of lower rates of glycogenolysis by relatively small increases in IMP concentration, that may occur during more moderate contraction conditions, remains to be established.

Replenishment of Citric Acid Cycle Intermediates

It is apparent from Figure 1 that one complete sequence of AMP deamination and IMP reamination by the purine nucleotide cycle leads to the deamination of aspartate and the production of fumarate. A significant production of fumarate could occur without a large decrease in adenine nucleotide content, if the rate of AMP deamination is matched simultaneously by an equivalent rate of IMP reamination. Provision of fumarate by the operation of the purine nucleotide cycle has been shown to enhance mitochondrial respiration (Scislowski, Aleksandrowicz, & Swierczynski, 1982). Thus, production of fumarate during muscle contractions could help support oxidative metabolism by increasing the pool of citric acid cycle intermediates (Aragon, Tornheim, Goodman, & Lowenstein, 1981). This may be most important in the initial stages of muscle contraction during the transition from a low resting rate of respiration to a high rate of mitochondrial function.

Changes in tissue content. Assessment of the operation of the purine nucleotide cycle in contracting muscle is not a simple task. Measurements of tissue content changes of both the substrate (aspartate) and products (fumarate and ammonia) do not necessarily represent the rate of purine nucleotide cycling, since these metabolites are involved in other cellular reactions or can be lost from the muscle. Further, measurement of tissue IMP content is not necessarily instructive, since its accumulation is a function of its production rate relative to its removal rate. As we have seen, the production of IMP is due to activation of AMP deaminase and not the steps involved in aspartate deamination (Figure 1). However, if the reamination of IMP can be inhibited, then any excess accumulation of IMP content within the muscle should represent the turnover of the purine nucleotide cycle and, thus, the extent of fumarate production. This approach was used by Meyer and Terjung (1980) during muscle stimulation in situ and during treadmill running in vivo. Blocking IMP reamination, by the adenylosuccinate synthetase inhibitor hadacidin, had no effect during 30 min of relatively mild contraction conditions (1 Hz twitch) that would increase oxygen consumption approximately 6- to 7-fold. However, during more intense stimulation conditions of 3 Hz twitch contractions, there was an excess accumulation of IMP in the muscle (Meyer & Terjung, 1980). Further, at a fairly intense contraction sequence of 5 Hz there was an even greater accumulation of IMP. These data provided convincing evidence that both IMP formation and IMP reamination occurred during the 30 min period. Thus, the reactions of the purine nucleotide cycle operated to deaminate aspartate to fumarate.

It is evident from the data of this study (Meyer & Terjung, 1980), however, that IMP accumulation occurred only as the frequency of contractions became more severe. Further, a comparison of the responses between the two fast-twitch fiber types indicated that they did not respond similarly. IMP content was not significantly increased in the fast-twitch red muscle after 30 min of contractions at any of the stimulation frequencies. Apparently, the metabolic stress caused by these stimulation conditions was relatively moderate for this fiber type, since there was no significant AMP deamination evident. In contrast, a large IMP accumulation was found in the low-oxidative fast-twitch white fiber section at both 3 and 5 Hz. This seemed anomalous, since one would expect the operation of the purine nucleotide cycle, to produce fumarate for mitochondrial respiration, to be most apparent in the high-mitochondrial red fibers. Further, evaluation of the response in the fast-twitch white muscle during the 30 min contraction period demonstrated that accumulation of IMP was not progressive over time. Rather, during 5 Hz stimulation all of the IMP was produced initially, within the first 5 min of contractions. During the subsequent 25 min of stimulation, recovery of the adenine nucleotide pool proceeded by the reamination of IMP. Thus, the processes of AMP deamination and IMP reamination did not occur simultaneously. This would be important if the adenine nucleotide depletion is to be minimal and if aspartate is to be continuously converted to fumarate (Figure 1). Similar evidence was found with rats running on a treadmill. During prolonged moderate exercise conditions, IMP accumulation was not found (Meyer & Terjung, 1980). However, when the required running speed became exceptionally fast, IMP accumulation occurred rapidly coincident with failure to maintain the exercise pace (Meyer, Dudley, & Terjung, 1980). Therefore, doubts arise as to the concurrent operation of both legs of the purine nucleotide cycle in producing fumarate during prolonged steady-state muscle contraction conditions.

Aragon, Tornheim, and Lowenstein (1980) also evaluated the potential that operation of the purine nucleotide cycle may contribute to the increase in citric acid cycle intermediates. They stimulated the mixed-fibered hindlimb muscles of the rat in situ at 5 Hz twitch contractions. An expansion of the citric acid cycle intermediates, primarily by an increase in malate content, occurred at a rate of 138 nmole/min/g dry weight during the first 10 min of contractions. When the reamination of IMP was blocked by hadacidin, the accumulation of IMP was accelerated by a rate of 100 nmole/min/g dry weight. Further, an inhibition of fumarate production was suggested by a smaller increase in malate content. Thus, approximately 75% of the expansion in citric acid cycle intermediates was attributed to the operation of the purine nucleotide cycle (Aragon, Tornheim, & Lowenstein,

1980). Unfortunately, the interpretation of their data is complicated by the use of mixed-fibered muscle samples. The muscles, quick-frozen in their experiment, are primarily composed of fast-twitch white and fast-twitch red fibers (Armstrong & Phelps, 1984). As mentioned above, these two fiber types exhibit a keen difference in IMP accumulation during 5 Hz twitch stimulation conditions (Meyer & Terjung, 1980). The fast-twitch white fibers produce relatively large amounts of IMP, while the fast-twitch red fibers do not (Meyer & Terjung, 1980; Dudley & Terjung, 1985a). This heterogeneous fiber type response would not be detected in a sample of mixed-fiber muscle. As a result, their measurements represent a mass-averaged ''mixture'' of metabolite contents. Thus, the results of Aragon, Tornheim, and Lowenstein (1980) cannot be interpreted to show that operation of the purine nucleotide cycle serves to increase citric acid cycle intermediates in contracting muscle.

An evaluation of the above mentioned evidence, especially in the context of the control of AMP deamination, suggests the following interpretation. During mild to moderate contraction conditions, deamination of AMP to IMP does not proceed at a high rate. Consequently, the reamination process leading to the production of fumarate does not proceed at a high rate. It is possible, however, that a low rate of operation of the purine nucleotide cycle could occur during mild to moderate contraction conditions. Although this potential for a low rate of purine nucleotide cycling has not been established experimentally, a value exceeding approximately 30 nmole/min/g dry weight would probably have been detected in the experiments of Meyer and Terjung (1980). Thus, the rate of expansion of the citric acid cycle intermediates by fumarate production is probably relatively small, equivalent to approximately 2% of the total pool size of intermediates in resting muscle. Nonetheless, this could be significant and could contribute to the function of the citric acid cycle in contracting muscle. Whether a low operation rate of the purine nucleotide cycle serves to provide fumarate during steady-state muscle contractions remains to be established experimentally.

Exercise tolerance. Disruption of the purine nucleotide cycle could have adverse effects on muscle function. This was not evident, however, during muscle stimulation in situ or during treadmill running in vivo (Meyer & Terjung, 1980). In both of these cases, however, the exercise conditions were not excessively demanding and did not produce undue fatigue. In contrast, when the severity of muscle usage is excessive, accelerated failure of muscle performance has been reported. This was found during intense muscle stimulation conditions that produced essentially complete contraction failure (i.e., tension output $< 10\%$ of initial) within one minute (Swain, Hines, Sabina, Harbury, & Holmes, 1984). A similar exercise intolerance is apparent in patients with AMP deaminase deficiency (Sabina et al., 1984). Although the work capacity of these patients is rather low, the degree of exercise intolerance is generally variable. A low level of exercise can be performed, but exercise intolerance becomes apparent as the intensity is increased (Fishbein, Armbrustmacher, & Griffin, 1978; Sabina et al., 1984; Shumate et al., 1979). An explanation for this exercise intolerance can be offered. The inability of these patients to deaminate AMP and reduce the adenine nucleotide pool during contractions may lead to an inordinate increase in ADP concentration. An increase in ADP concentration in muscle has been correlated with a loss of muscle tension (Dawson et al., 1980). An inordinate elevation in ADP concentration would not be expected during low level exercise. Rather, it should be most apparent as the metabolic stress becomes excessive when the work rate is increased.

Deamination of Amino Acids by the Purine Nucleotide Cycle

Again, reference to Figure 1 illustrates that one complete sequence of AMP deamination and IMP reamination by the purine nucleotide cycle leads to the deamination of aspartate to fumarate and ammonia. This process could lead to the deamination of other amino acids within the muscle, since aspartate can be formed by a transamination reaction with the amine originating from other amino acids. If the rate of utilization of the aspartate amine via the purine nucleotide cycle were matched by an equivalent rate of aspartate production via transamination, then the net result would be the deamination of amino acids other than aspartate. While this could potentially lead to a carbon source (keto acids) that could be oxidized as energy substrates during exercise, it would require a steady rate of purine nucleotide cycling. As discussed above, it is unlikely that this occurs at an appreciable rate during sustained steady state submaximal exercise. Further, this potential process of amino acid deamination would simply serve to produce ammonia instead of alanine, an amino acid known to carry amine nitrogen from working muscle (Felig & Wahren, 1971). Nonetheless, the significance of the potential for amino acid deamination, via the purine nucleotide cycle during exercise, has not been experimentally evaluated. However, as discussed below, amine nitrogen originating from amino acids other than aspartate is important following intense contraction conditions when extensive ATP depletion occurs.

Recovery of the adenine nucleotide content, requiring the reamination of IMP with the amine donated from aspartate (Newton & Perry, 1960), occurs following stimulation conditions where ATP depletion has been extensive (Meyer & Terjung, 1979). Interestingly, the quantity of amine necessary for full recovery of the adenine nucleotide pool can be approximately 10 times the content of aspartate in the muscle. Thus, another source of amine must be available within the cell for transamination to aspartate, and the subsequent reamination of IMP to proceed. Branched chain amino acid (BCAA) metabolism is a probable candidate, since (a) muscle has a high capacity for BCAA transaminase activity (Shinnick & Harper, 1977) and (b) the BCAA are readily oxidized in muscle (Buse, Biggers, Drier, & Buse, 1973; Odessey & Goldberg, 1972). It is, therefore, possible that the uptake of leucine by muscle could represent an important amine source for the return of ATP levels.

Recent evidence, obtained by perfusing muscle with ^{15}N-leucine during only the recovery period following intense stimulation conditions, indicates that a significant fraction ($14 \pm 3\%$) of the 6-amino nitrogen of resynthesized ATP originated from extracellular leucine (Gorski, Hood, Brown, & Terjung, 1985). Further, when perfusion of ^{15}N-leucine was begun 30 min prior to stimulation, to permit better equilibration with the intracellular leucine pool, the contribution of ^{15}N-amine from leucine to ATP was increased to approximately 25% of the total IMP reaminated. Although a high perfusion concentration of 1.0 mM leucine was used in these experiments, estimates of the rate of leucine uptake by skeletal muscle at a normal plasma concentration (Goldberg & Odessey, 1972) indicates that the enrichment of adenine nucleotides by the amine of leucine could also be significant in vivo. Thus, branched-chain amino acid uptake by muscle may play a potentially important role in adenine nucleotide metabolism following intense muscle contractions.

SUMMARY

Although the functions of the purine nucleotide cycle in contracting muscle have not been fully established, considerable information is known. It is likely that the deamination of AMP and subsequent decrease in adenine nucleotide content that occurs during intense contraction conditions, serves to maintain the ATP/ADP ratio within the cell. The cellular conditions necessary to activate AMP deaminase develop rapidly during excessive metabolic stress in fast-twitch muscle, but not in slow-twitch muscle. Further, these cellular conditions in fast-twitch muscle are influenced by the inherent metabolic capacity of the fiber type. This can establish a heterogeneous response in adenine nucleotide metabolism between fast-twitch white and fast-twitch red fibers during moderately intense muscle contractions. It is unlikely that IMP and ammonia accumulation within the cell are important modulators of glycolysis. Rather, the extensive acidosis, associated with lactate accumulation, is probably an important contributor to IMP and ammonia formation. Thus, the potential buffering effect of ammonia is relatively minor. Complete operation of the purine nucleotide cycle, with concurrent rates of AMP deamination and IMP reamination, could be important in producing fumarate, a citric acid cycle intermediate, and deaminating amino acids other than aspartate. At the present time, however, there is insufficient evidence in support of this operation of the purine nucleotide cycle during steady-state exercise. However, nonaspartate amine derived via transamination (e.g., from leucine) could be an important nitrogen source for the reamination of IMP during recovery of the adenine nucleotide pool following intense contraction conditions. While much has yet to be learned about the significance of the purine nucleotide cycle operation, it is apparent that these reactions are important to adenine nucleotide metabolism and normal muscle function.

Acknowledgments

The work from the authors' laboratory was supported by NIH Grant AM 21617, NIH Research Career Development Award AM 00681 (to R.L.T.) and the Francis Hendricks Endowment for Medical Research.

REFERENCES

Abrahams, S.L., & Younathan, E.S. (1971). Modulation of the kinetic properties of phosphofructokinase by ammonium ions. *Journal of Biological Chemistry*, **246**, 2464-2467.

Aragon, J.J., Tornheim, K., Goodman, M.N., & Lowenstein, J.M. (1981). Replenishment of citric acid cycle intermediates by the purine nucleotide cycle in rat skeletal muscle. *Current Topics In Cellular Regulation*, **18**, 131-149.

Aragon, J.J., Tornheim, K., & Lowenstein, J.M. (1980). On a possible role of IMP in the regulation of phosphorylase activity in skeletal muscle. *Federation of the European Biochemistry Society Letters*, **117** (Suppl.), K56-K64.

Armstrong, R.B., & Phelps, R.O. (1984). Muscle fiber type composition of the rat hindlimb. *American Journal of Anatomy*, **171**, 259-272.

Baldwin, K.M., Klinkerfuss, G.H., Terjung, R.L., Mole, P.A., & Holloszy, J.O. (1972). Respiratory capacity of white, red and intermediate muscle: Adaptive response to exercise. *American Journal of Physiology*, **222**, 373-378.

Berne, R.M., & Rubio, R. (1979). Coronary circulation. In R.M. Berne (Ed.), *Handbook of physiology: Sec. 2* (pp. 873-952). Washington: American Physiological Society.

Buse, M.G., Biggers, J.F., Drier, C., & Buse, J.F. (1973). The effect of epinephrine, glucagon, and the nutritional state of the oxidation of branched chain amino acids and pyruvate by isolated hearts and diaphragms of the rat. *Journal of Biological Chemistry,* **248**, 697-706.

Conlee, R.K., McLane, J.A., Rennie, M.J., Winder, W.W., & Holloszy, J.O. (1979). Reversal of phosphorylase activation in muscle despite continued contractile activity. *American Journal of Physiology,* **237**, R291-R296.

Dawson, M.J., Gadian, D.G., & Wilkie, D.R. (1980). Mechanical relaxation rate and metabolism studied in fatiguing muscle by phosphorus nuclear magnetic resonance. *Journal of Physiology* (London), **299**, 465-484.

Driedzic, W.R., & Hochachka, P.W. (1976). Control of energy metabolism in fish white muscle. *American Journal of Physiology,* **230**, 579-582.

Dudley, G.A., Staron, R.S., Murray, T.F., Hagerman, R.C., & Luginbuhl, A. (1983). Muscle fiber composition and blood ammonia levels after intense exercise in humans. *Journal of Applied Physiology,* **54**, 582-586.

Dudley, G.A., & Terjung, R.L. (1985a). Influence of aerobic metabolism on IMP accumulation in fast-twitch muscle. *American Journal of Physiology,* **248**, C37-C42.

Dudley, G.A., & Terjung, R.L. (1985b). Influence of acidosis on AMP deaminase activity in contracting fast-twitch muscle. *American Journal of Physiology,* **248**, C43-C50.

Felig, P., & Wahren, J. (1971). Amino acid metabolism in exercising man. *Journal of Clinical Investigation,* **50**, 2703-2714.

Fishbein, W.N., Armbrustmacher, V.W., & Griffin, J.L. (1978). Myoadenylate deaminase deficiency: A new disease of muscle. *Science,* **341**, 534-542.

Gerez, C., & Kirsten, R. (1965). Untersuchungen über Ammoniakbildung bei der Muskelarbeit. *Biochemical Zeitschrift,* **341**, 534-542.

Goldberg, A.L., & Odessey, R. (1972). Oxidation of amino acids by diaphragms from fed and fasted rats. *American Journal of Physiology,* **223**, 1384-1391.

Goodman, M.N., & Lowenstein, J.M. (1977). The purine nucleotide cycle. Studies of ammonia production by skeletal muscle in situ and in perfused preparations. *Journal of Biological Chemistry,* **252**, 5054-5060.

Gorski, J., Hood, D.A., Brown, O.M., & Terjung, R.L. (1985). Incorporation of ^{15}N-leucine amine into ATP of fast-twitch muscle following stimulation. *Biochemical and Biophysical Research Communications,* **128**, 1254-1260.

Hermansen, L. (1981). Effect of metabolic changes on force generation in skeletal muscle during maximal exercise. In R. Porter & J. Whelan (Eds.), *Human muscle fatigue: Physiological mechanisms.* (pp. 75-88). London: Pitman.

Hintz, C.S., Chi, M.M.Y., Fell, R.D., Ivy, J.L., Kaiser, K.K., Lowry, O.H. (1982). Metabolite changes in individual rat muscle fibers during stimulation. *American Journal of Physiology,* **242**, C218-C228.

Hochachka, P.W., & Somero, G.N. (1973). *Strategies of biochemica adaptation* (pp. 36-38). Philadelphia: W.B. Saunders.

Hultman, E., & Sahlin, K. (1980). Acid-base balance during exercise. *Exercise and Sport Sciences Reviews,* **8**, 41-128.

Laughlin, M.H., & Armstrong, R.B. (1985). Muscle blood flow during locomotory exercise. *Exercise and Sport Sciences Reviews,* **13**, 95-136.

Lawson, J.W., & Veech, R.L. (1979). Effects of pH and free Mg^{2+} on the Keq of the creatine kinase reaction and other phosphate hydrolyses and phosphate transfer reactions. *Journal of Biological Chemistry,* **254**, 6528-6537.

Lowenstein, J.M. (1972). Ammonia production in muscle and other tissue: The purine nucleotide cycle. *Physiological Reviews,* **52**, 382-414.

Mackie, B.G., & Terjung, R.L. (1983). Blood flow to the different skeletal muscle fiber types during contraction. *American Journal of Physiology,* **245**, H265-H275.

Manfredi, J.P., & Holmes, E.W. (1984). Control of the purine nucleotide cycle in extracts of rat skeletal muscle: Effects of energy state and concentrations of cycle intermediates. *Archives of Biochemistry and Biophysics,* **233**, 515-529.

Meyer, R.A., Dudley, G.A., & Terjung, R.L. (1980). Ammonia and IMP in different skeletal muscle fibers after exercise in rats. *Journal of Applied Physiology,* **49**, 1037-1041.

Meyer, R.A., & Terjung, R.A. (1979). Differences in ammonia and adenylate metabolism in contracting fast and slow muscle. *American Journal of Physiology,* **237**, C111-C118.

Meyer, R.A., & Terjung, R.L. (1980). AMP deamination and IMP reamination in working skeletal muscle. *American Journal of Physiology,* **239**, C32-C38.

Newton, A.A., & Perry, S.V. (1960). The incorporation of ^{15}N into adenine nucleotides and their formation from inosine monophosphate by skeletal-muscle preparations. *Biochemical Journal,* **74**, 127-136.

Odessey, R., & Goldberg, A.L. (1972). Oxidation of leucine by rat skeletal muscle. *American Journal of Physiology,* **223**, 1376-1383.

Parnas, J.K. (1929a). Ammonia formation in muscle and its source. *Journal of Physiology,* **90**, 467.

Parnas, J.K. (1929b). Uber die Ammoniakbildung im Muskel und ihren Zusammenhang mit Funktion und Zustandsanderung. 6. Der Zusammenhang der Ammoniakbildung und der Umwandlung des Adeninnucleotids zu Inosinsaure. *Biochemical Zeitschrift,* **206**, 16-38.

Raggi, A., Bergamini, C., & Ronca, G. (1975). Isozymes of AMP deaminase in red and white skeletal muscles. *Federation of the European Biochemistry Society Letters*, **58**, 19-23.

Rahim, Z.H.A., Perrett, D., Lutaya, G., & Griffiths, J.R. (1980). Metabolic adaptation in phosphorylase kinase deficiency. Changes in metabolite concentrations during tetanic stimulation of mouse leg muscles. *Biochemical Journal*, **186**, 331-341.

Rubio, R., Berne, R.M., & Dobson, J.G. (1973). Sites of adenosine production in cardiac and skeletal muscle. *American Journal of Physiology*, **225**, 938-953.

Sabina, R.L., Swain, J.L., Olanow, C.W., Bradley, W.G., Fishbein, W.N., DiMauro, S., & Holmes, E.W. (1984). Myoadenylate deaminase deficiency. Functional and metabolic abnormalities associated with disruption of the purine nucleotide cycle. *Journal of Clinical Investigation*, **73**, 720-730.

Sahlin, K., Palmskog, G., & Hultman, E. (1978). Adenine nucleotide and IMP contents of the quadriceps muscle in man after exercise. *Pflügers Archiv*, **374**, 193-198.

Saltin, B., & Gollnick, P.D. (1983). Skeletal muscle adaptability: Significance for metabolism and performance. In L.D. Peachy, R.H. Adrian, & S.R. Geiger (Eds.), *Handbook of physiology: Sec. 10: Skeletal muscle* (pp. 555-631). Washington: American Physiological Society.

Scislowski, P.W.D., Aleksandrowicz, Z., & Swierczynski, J. (1982). Purine nucleotide cycle as a possible anapleurotic process in rat skeletal muscle. *Experientia*, **38**, 1035-1037.

Shinnick, F.L., & Harper, A.E. (1977). Branched-chain amino acid oxidation by isolated rat tissue preparations. *Biochimica et Biophysica Acta*, **437**, 477-486.

Shumate, J.B., Katnick, R., Ruiz, M., Kaiser, K., Frieden, C., Brooke, M.H., & Carroll, J.E. (1979). Myoadenylate deaminase deficiency. *Muscle and Nerve*, **2**, 213-216.

Snow, D.H., Harris, R.C., & Gash, S.D. (1985). Metabolic response of equine muscle to intermittent maximal exercise. *Journal of Applied Physiology*, **58**, 1689-1697.

Sparks, H.V., & Fuchs, B.D. (1983). Adenosine as a mediator of sustained exercise hypermia. In K.T. Borer, D.W. Edington, & T.P. White (Eds.), *Frontiers of Exercise Biology* (pp. 119-127). Champaign, IL: Human Kinetics.

Sutton, J.R., Toews, C.J., Ward, G.R., & Fox, I.H. (1980). Purine metabolism during strenuous muscular exercise in man. *Metabolism*, **29**, 254-260.

Swain, J.L., Hines, J.J., Sabina, R.L., Harbury, O.L., & Holmes, E.W. (1984). Disruption of the purine nucleotide cycle by inhibition of adenylosuccinate lyase produces skeletal muscle dysfuction. *Journal of Clinical Investigation*, **74**, 1422-1427.

Van Waarde, A., & Kesbeke, F. (1981). Regulatory properties of AMP-deaminase from lateral red muscle and dorsal white muscle of goldfish, casassius auratus. *Comparative Biochemistry and Physiology*, **69B**, 413-423.

Wheeler, T.J., & Lowenstein, J.M. (1979). Adenylate deaminase from rat muscle. Regulation by purine nucleotides and orthophosphate in the presence of 150 mM KCl. *Journal of Biological Chemistry*, **254**, 8894-8999.

Wilkerson, J.E., Batterton, D.L., & Horvath, S.M. (1977). Exercise-induced changes in blood ammonia levels in humans. *European Journal of Applied Physiology and Occupational Physiology*, **37**, 255-263.

Winder, W.W., Terjung, R.L., Baldwin, K.M., & Holloszy, J.O. (1974). Effect of exercise on AMP deaminase and adenylosuccinase in rat skeletal muscle. *American Journal of Physiology*, **227**, 1411-1414.

SECTION B
GLUCOSE METABOLISM

Regulation of Carbohydrate Metabolism in Exercise

Erik A. Richter
Bente Sonne
Thorkil Ploug
Michael Kjær
Kari Mikines
Henrik Galbo
University of Copenhagen
Copenhagen, Denmark

This review will discuss some aspects of carbohydrate metabolism in exercise. Emphasis will be put on some new and partly controversial findings. The topic is divided into three main parts: regulation of hepatic glucose production, regulation of muscle glycogenolysis, and regulation of muscle glucose uptake.

REGULATION OF HEPATIC GLUCOSE PRODUCTION IN EXERCISE

The traditional view on regulation of hepatic glucose production in exercise is that hepatic glucose production is increased via feedback mechanisms that operate to prevent a decrease in plasma glucose concentration that would otherwise occur as a result of increased glucose uptake in the working muscles (Felig & Wahren, 1979; Newsholme, 1979; Zinman, Vranic, Albisser, Leibel, & Marliss, 1979). However, results published by Sonne and Galbo (1985a) indicate that in the rat, the exercise-induced increase in hepatic glucose production initially exceeds the increase in peripheral glucose utilization with the result that plasma glucose concentrations increase (Figure 1). The increase in hepatic glucose production is dependent upon the intensity of exercise (Figure 1), and furthermore, at identical running speeds the increase is larger in rats with a high liver glycogen concentration than in rats with a low liver glycogen concentration (Sonne & Galbo, 1985b). These findings do not suggest feedback regulation of hepatic glucose production at the onset of exercise, but they do

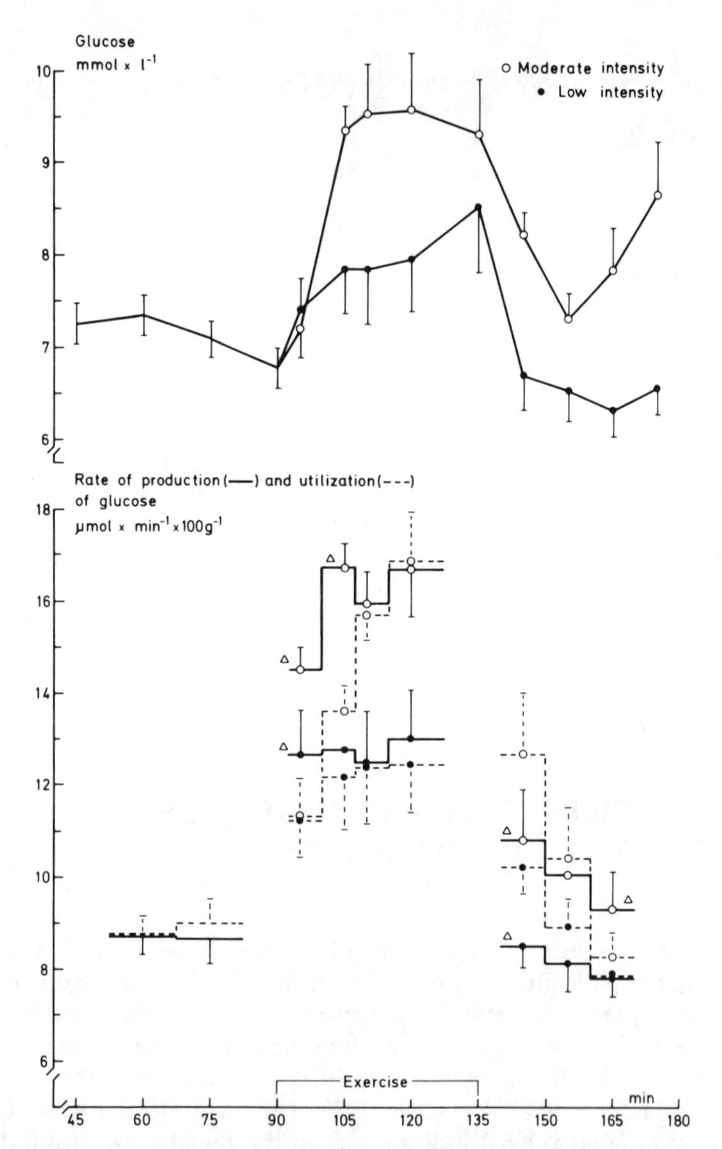

Figure 1 Concentration and turnover of glucose in plasma (mean ± SE) at rest (n=16), during and after running on the level at either low intensity (LIE, 14 m • min^{-1}, n=8) or moderate intensity (MIE, 21 m • min^{-1}, n=8). Glucose: All °-values from 105-145 and 165-175 min different ($p < 0.05$) from the basal level. All •-values from 95-135 min different ($p <$ 0.05) from the basal level. From 105-175 min all °-values different from corresponding •-values except at 135 min. Glucose production (R_a) and utilization (R_d): All exercise values different ($p < 0.05$) from the basal level. All postexercise values different ($p < 0.05$) from corresponding values at end of exercise. R_a at MIE different ($p < 0.05$) from R_a at LIE from 105-145 min. R_d at MIE different ($p < 0.05$) from R_d at LIE from 110-145 min. Δ R_a different ($p < 0.05$) from R_d. Adapted from "Carbohydrate Metabolism During and After Exercise in Rats. Studies with Radioglucose" by B. Sonne and H. Galbo, 1985, *Journal of Applied Physiology*, **59**, 1627-1639. Adapted by permission.

suggest the existence of ''feedforward'' regulation. According to this view, the increase in hepatic glucose production at the onset of exercise is a primary event related to activity in the motor neurons of the cerebral cortex. The view holds that at the onset of exercise, receptors in the working muscles and/or irradiation from motor neurons in the brain elicit workload dependent signals to areas in the central nervous system that influence hepatic glucose production (Galbo, 1983). The results by Sonne and Galbo (1985a, 1985b), however, do not exclude the operation of feedback mechanisms; for example, it could be that the plasma glucose setpoint at the onset of exercise was reset to a higher level and that feedback mechanisms operate to reach the new higher level. There is little doubt that feedback mechanisms do operate during the later stages of prolonged exercise.

The above mentioned findings were obtained in rats, but also in postabsorptive man it has recently been shown that during graded exercise from 60% to 110% of maximum oxygen consumption, hepatic glucose production does increase more rapidly than peripheral glucose utilization, with the result that plasma glucose concentration increases (Kjær, Farrel, Christensen, & Galbo, 1985). The mismatch between hepatic glucose production and peripheral glucose utilization was most pronounced during the heavy exercise and the increase in hepatic glucose production and plasma glucose concentration was larger in a group of endurance-trained athletes than in a group of nontrained controls (Kjær et al., 1985). Since endurance-trained athletes might be expected to have a higher liver glycogen concentration than untrained subjects (Galbo, Richter, Holst, & Christensen, 1977), such a difference might explain the larger increase in hepatic glucose production in the trained group compared to the untrained group. Endurance-trained athletes, however, also had a larger increase in plasma concentrations of epinephrine during heavy exercise than untrained subjects (Kjær et al., 1985). This finding is in itself surprising, since the traditional view on sympathoadrenal activity and endurance training is that endurance training results in a reduced plasma concentration of epinephrine during exercise (Winder, Hagberg, Hickson, Ehsani, & McLane, 1978). However, this concept apparently only holds true when trained and untrained subjects exercise at the same absolute workload. The findings by Kjær et al. (1985) that during maximum and ''supramaximum'' exercise of identical duration and relative intensity plasma epinephrine concentrations are higher in athletes than in untrained individuals indicate that long-term endurance training may lead to an increased maximum capacity to secrete epinephrine. In accordance with this hypothesis, during similar insulin-induced hypoglycemia higher plasma concentrations of epinephrine were found in endurance-trained athletes than in untrained controls (Kjær et al., 1984).

The higher plasma concentration of epinephrine in trained compared to untrained subjects at heavy workloads, combined with the trained subjects' higher rate of hepatic glucose production during exercise, suggests but does not prove that epinephrine enhances hepatic glucose production in exercise. This interpretation is in keeping with previous findings in the rat: During the early part of a bout of prolonged swimming, hepatic glycogen breakdown was diminished in rats that had their adrenal medulla destroyed 3 weeks before swimming (Richter, Galbo, & Christensen, 1981; Richter, Galbo, Sonne, Holst, & Christensen, 1980). To further investigate the role of the sympathoadrenal system in the regulation of hepatic glucose production in exercise, glucose turnover was studied in rats at rest and during 35 min of treadmill running at 21m/min (eliciting approximately 70% of maximum oxygen uptake). Three groups of rats were used: controls, rats that had the autonomic innervation of the liver selectively removed by surgery 1 week in advance, and rats that had their adrenal medullas destroyed 3 weeks before the exercise test. It was found (Figure 2) that adrenodemedullation diminished the exercise-induced increase in hepatic glucose production and hepatic glycogen breakdown, whereas sympathectomy of the liver did not influence these variables (Sonne, Mikines, Richter, Christensen, & Galbo, 1985). These findings indicate that in the rat, hepatic glucose production and glycogen breakdown at least during the early phases of exercise are increased by adrenomedullary hormones, presumably epinephrine, since the concentration of norepin-

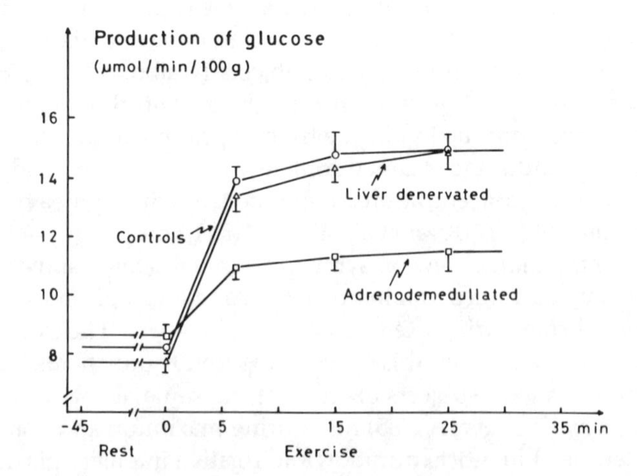

Figure 2 Rates of glucose production at rest and during running at 21 m/min on the level. Rats were either sham-operated controls (n = 11), liver denervated (n = 9), or adrenodemedullated (n = 8). Values are means ± SE. All exercise values are different ($p < 0.01$) from the basal levels. All values during running in adrenodemedullated rats are different ($p < 0.05$) from values in other groups. Modified from "Role of Liver Nerves and Adrenal Medulla in Glucose Turnover in Running Rats" by B. Sonne, K.J. Mikines, E.A. Richter, N.J. Christiansen, and H. Galbo, 1985, *Journal of Applied Physiology*, **59**, 1640-1646. Adapted by permission.

ephrine was only slightly affected by adrenodemedullation (Sonne et al., 1985). In contrast to these findings, older studies by Gollnick, Soule, Taylor, Williams, and Ianuzzo (1970) on endurance-trained rats and recent studies by Carlson et al. (1985) suggest that adrenomedullary hormones are not essential for increasing hepatic glycogenolysis during exercise. Winder, Terry, and Mitchell (1985) recently found that in fasted rats epinephrine is essential for the exercise-induced increase in muscle glycogenolysis and with it release of lactate, and they hypothesized that hepatic gluconeogenesis was stimulated by the epinephrine-induced increase in availability of lactate.

Thus, the role of epinephrine in increasing hepatic glucose production during exercise is not quite clear and differences between species also make for some confusion of the area. Since plasma concentrations of epinephrine in man do not increase much at exercise intensities below 60% to 70% of maximum oxygen uptake except during prolonged exercise, it is probably reasonable to assume that in man epinephrine plays a role for increasing hepatic glucose production mainly at high intensities of exercise or late during prolonged exercise. In contrast, in the rat, plasma epinephrine has been shown to be increased already after 2-1/2 min of running at 70% of maximum oxygen consumption even though the rats were thoroughly accustomed to treadmill running (Sonne et al., 1985). Therefore, in the rat, epinephrine probably plays a more important role than in the human being for increasing hepatic glucose production at the onset of exercise.

As mentioned above, the role of the sympathetic nerves to the liver for increasing hepatic glucose production in exercise seems at least in the rat not to be significant (Sonne et al., 1985), even though it has been found that the concentration of norepinephrine in the liver decreases with exercise (Sonne et al., 1985; Winder, Beattie, Piquette, & Holman, 1983). Such a decrease would suggest that exercise activates the sympathetic nerves of the liver. The lack of a role for the sympathetic nerves in increasing hepatic glucose production during exercise in the rat does not exclude that these nerves do in fact play a role for increasing hepatic glucose production in exercising man. This is so, since the rat has a rather scanty supply of sympathetic nerves to the liver compared to many other species including man (Moghimzadeh, Nobin, & Rosengren, 1983).

Other hormones have been implicated in the regulation of hepatic glucose production during exercise. One of them is glucagon. There is little doubt that in the dog glucagon plays a role for increasing hepatic glucose production during exercise (Wasserman, Lickley, & Vranic, 1984). In the rat glucagon also seems to play a role in enhancing hepatic glucose output in exercise. We have shown that in swimming rats treated with glucagon antibodies, hepatic glycogen breakdown during swimming was significantly reduced compared to rats treated with control gamma globulins (Richter, Galbo, Holst, & Sonne, 1981). In man the role of glucagon for the exercise-induced increase in hepatic glucose production has been studied by Bjorkman, Felig, Hagenfeldt, and Wahren (1981). In this study, plasma glucagon concentrations were decreased below resting levels by an infusion of somatostatin. Nevertheless, the exercise-induced increase in hepatic glucose production (estimated using hepatic venous catherization) was unaffected, indicating that even basal concentrations of glucagon are not necessary for the normal increase in hepatic glucose production during exercise in man. Thus, in man there is no convincing evidence indicating a role for glucagon during exercise. This interpretation is in accordance with the fact that in man plasma concentrations of glucagon only increase late during prolonged exercise at a time when plasma glucose concentrations begin to decrease (Galbo, 1983). It should, however, be mentioned that lack of change in the peripheral plasma concentration of glucagon does not exclude that small changes in portal venous plasma concentration do take place. Whether this is the case remains to be clarified.

Insulin is a powerful inhibitor of hepatic glucose production at rest (Rizza, Mandarino, & Gerich, 1981). It is therefore reasonable to expect that the decrease in plasma insulin concentration seen in exercise above 50% of maximum oxygen uptake (Galbo, 1983) plays a role for the increase in hepatic glucose production during exercise. Whereas the normal decrease in plasma insulin concentration during exercise does not seem to be indispensable for the increase in hepatic glucose production during exercise (Zinman et al., 1979), there is good evidence that the decrease in plasma insulin concentration during exercise has a physiological role in the enhancement of glucose output from the liver. This has been nicely demonstrated in a study by Issekutz (1980) in which mannoheptulose was infused into running dogs. Mannoheptulose has the effect that the plasma insulin concentration is decreased even below the ordinary low levels found during exercise. Furthermore, mannoheptulose does not by itself affect hepatic glucose production. Infusion of mannoheptulose sharply increased hepatic glucose production during steady state exercise, demonstrating that a decrease in plasma insulin concentration during exercise immediately increases hepatic glucose production (Issekutz, 1980).

Thus, in summary, according to recent findings hepatic glucose production in exercise is regulated as follows: The increase in hepatic glucose production at the onset of exercise is probably a primary event depending upon the intensity of exercise as well as on the hepatic glycogen concentration. Hepatic glucose production is increased during exercise due to increases in plasma epinephrine and glucagon concentrations, and due to a decrease in plasma insulin concentration. The role of the sympathetic innervation of the liver seems to be unimportant, at least in the rat. The relative importance of the various neuroendocrine changes in exercise, however, depends upon species and exercise intensity.

REGULATION OF MUSCLE GLYCOGEN BREAKDOWN DURING EXERCISE

It has been known for many years that muscle contractions, even in isolated muscle, will increase glycogen breakdown. The mechanisms responsible for this appear to be several. During muscle contractions, Ca^{++} is liberated from the sarcoplasmic reticulum, and it is believed that this Ca^{++} by increasing the activity of phosphorylase *b* kinase will elicit an increase in the activity of phosphorylase *a* due to conversion of phosphorylase *b* to *a*. This increase in phosphorylase *a* activity is, however, quite short-lived and phosphorylase *a* activity will decrease to resting or even lower levels in spite of continued contractions and presumably Ca^{++} release (Richter, 1984).

The concentration of AMP and IMP may increase in contracting muscle and mainly so in fast-twitch muscle (Meyer & Terjung, 1979). Since AMP may increase the activity of phosphorylase *a* and IMP may increase that of phosphorylase *b*, these increases in the concentration of AMP and IMP may be of importance for increasing glycogenolysis during muscle contractions.

Other factors may be responsible for the contraction-induced increase in glycogenolysis in skeletal muscle. It has recently been suggested (Chasiotis, 1983) that the contraction-induced increase in the concentration of inorganic phosphate (Pi) plays an important role. Pi is one of the substrates for phosphorylase, the other substrate being glycogen. In resting fast-twitch muscle the concentration of Pi is, according to estimates by Nuclear Magnetic Resonance, lower than previously thought and well below the calculated Km of phosphorylase for Pi (Chasiotis, 1983). This view holds that an increase in the concentration of Pi will by itself increase the rate of glycogen breakdown in muscle. This interpretation is probably mainly valid in fast-twitch muscle since only in this fiber type do contractions bring about a large increase in Pi, and since in slow-twitch fibers the resting concentration of Pi seems to be quite high (approximately 10 mM) (Meyer, Brown, & Cushmerick, 1985). The Km of phosphorylase for Pi has been calculated to be 26 mM for phosphorylase ($a + b$) and 7 mM for phosphorylase *a* (Chasiotis, 1983). If the value for Pi in slow-twitch muscle (10mM) is correct, the concentration of Pi in resting slow-twitch muscle is above the Km for phosphorylase *a* and not very much lower than the Km for phosphorylase ($a + b$) and therefore the rate of glycogen breakdown in this fiber type cannot only be controlled by just varying the concentration of Pi. This is in accordance with the finding that during prolonged electrical stimulation of isolated muscle, glycogen breakdown is short-lived whereas Pi levels presumably remain elevated (Richter, Ruderman, Gavras, Belur, & Galbo, 1982). However, as discussed below and in Richter and Galbo (1985), for enzymes, Km-estimates obtained in test-tube experiments may be far from the actual Km of the enzyme in vivo, and therefore caution should be exercised when discussing substrate-enzyme interactions in vivo.

The rate of glycogen breakdown in contracting muscle has, in parallel to findings in the liver, been shown to be under external regulation. It has been found that epinephrine secreted from the adrenal medulla has an enhancing effect on muscle glycogen breakdown during exercise in the rat (Carlson et al., 1985; Richter, 1984; Winder et al., 1985). An enhancing effect of epinephrine on muscle glycogen breakdown during exercise has also been found in man (Jansson, Hjemdahl, & Kaijser, 1984) and dog (Issekutz, 1985). Experiments in which beta-adrenergic receptors were blocked by propranolol during exercise have given conflicting results as to the effect on muscle glycogen breakdown. In some studies beta-adrenergic blockade was found to reduce exercise-induced muscle glycogenolysis in man (Chasiotis, 1983; Galbo, Holst, Christensen, & Hilsted, 1976), dog (Issekutz, 1978) and rat (Gorski & Pietrzyk, 1982), whereas in other studies it has been found to increase glycogenolysis in dog (Nazar, Brezezinska, & Kowalski, 1972) and rat (Juhlin-Dannfelt, Terblanche, Fell, Young, & Holloszy, 1982). The diverging results obtained in these studies are not easily explained, but it should be borne in mind that beta-adrenergic blockade has profound inhibitory effects on lipolysis, in turn possibly increasing glycogenolysis in working muscle.

That epinephrine has a direct enhancing effect on glycogenolysis in contracting muscle has been confirmed in isolated, perfused muscle: During intense contractile activity, glycogen breakdown was increased by epinephrine in slow-twitch muscle but not in fast-twitch muscle (Richter et al., 1982). The mechanism behind the effect on slow-twitch muscle seemed to be related to the ability of epinephrine to cause a sustained increase in the activity of phosphorylase *a* (Figure 3). In fast-twitch muscle epinephrine increased glycogen breakdown during less intense contractile activity (Richter et al., 1982). There seems to be no effect of the sympathetic nervous innervation of the muscles on glycogen breakdown during exercise (Richter, Galbo, & Christensen, 1981).

Insulin is a powerful stimulator of muscle glycogen synthesis (Richter, Garetto, Goodman, & Ruderman, 1984) and therefore one might expect that a decrease in plasma insulin concentration during exercise facilitates muscle glycogenolysis. In fact, in perfused rat muscle it was found that a high insulin concentration did decrease the breakdown of glycogen during muscle contractions (Berger, Hagg, Goodman, & Ruderman, 1976). However, it has not been directly studied whether the decrease in plasma insulin concentration that may occur during exercise actually plays a physiological role for increasing muscle glycogen breakdown during exercise.

As in liver, the concentration of glycogen in the muscle seems to influence the rate of glycogen breakdown during muscle contractions. We have

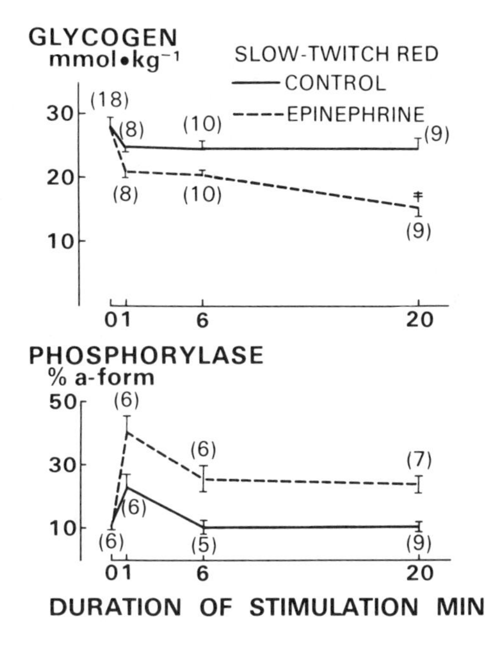

Figure 3 Glycogen concentrations and phosphorylase *a* activity (expressed as percent of total activity) in slow-twitch red fibers (soleus muscle) of perfused hindquarters at rest and after contractions for various periods. Contractions were induced by stimulation of the sciatic nerve at a frequency of 180 double pulses /min. Flow was 25 ml/min. Values are means ± SE with numbers of determinations in parentheses. Epinephrine, when added, was at a concentration of 2.4×10^{-8} M. ‡ $p < 0.02$ compared to value at 6 min. Adapted from "Muscle Glycogenolysis During Exercise: Dual Control by Epinephrine and Contractions" by E.A. Richter, N.B. Ruderman, H. Gavras, E.R. Belur, and H. Galbo, 1982, *American Journal of Physiology,* **242**, p. E25-E32. Adapted by permission.

recently shown that in perfused, electrically stimulated muscle the rate of glycogen breakdown is higher in muscles from rats that were glycogen supercompensated than in control rats (Richter & Galbo, 1985). Furthermore, the rate of lactate release was increased from glycogen supercompensated muscle (Richter & Galbo, 1985). This was so even though oxygen uptake and tension development were similar in supercompensated and control rats. Furthermore, since supramaximum electrical stimulation of the sciatic nerve was used, no difference in recruitment of muscle fibers between supercompensated and control rats existed during stimulation. Thus, our findings more clearly demonstrate that glycogen breakdown in contracting muscles depends upon the pre-exercise glycogen concentration than do earlier in vivo studies (Gollnick, Pernow, Essen, Jansson, & Saltin, 1981), in which differences in muscle fiber recruitment patterns might exist between working legs with high and low muscle glycogen levels. These findings also indicate that lactate production during muscle contractions is not only controlled by oxygen availability but also simply by the rate of glycogen breakdown. This is in accordance with findings by Connet, Gayeski, and Honig (1984) and by Gollnick et al. (1981).

The finding of glycogen concentrations influencing rate of glycogen breakdown during muscle contractions is in contrast to the test-tube findings of phosphorylase having a very low Km for glycogen around 1-2 mM (glucose units) (Newsholme, 1979). According to this finding the phosphorylase enzyme should at almost all times be saturated with glycogen and since phosphorylase is considered the rate-limiting enzyme for glycogen breakdown, the rate of breakdown should not be influenced by the glycogen concentration. However, it should be appreciated that in the muscle glycogen is not found in a homogeneous solution, but rather is found as particles distributed unevenly within the cell. Under these circumstances test tube results may have little meaning and the actual Km of phosphorylase for glycogen may in vivo actually be much higher if in fact one at all can talk about saturation kinetics for phosphorylase in the muscle cell in vivo.

Glycogen breakdown in working muscle may be inhibited by high plasma concentrations of free fatty acids and ketone bodies. However, the evidence for this belief is at present controversial (Rennie & Holloszy, 1977; Richter et al., 1982; Ruderman, Goodman, Connover, & Berger, 1979) and will not be discussed further in this review.

In summary, glycogen breakdown in working skeletal muscle is increased by contractions per se, possibly via a transient increase in the activity of phosphorylase *a* and at least in fast-twitch muscle also by an increase in the concentration of Pi. In fast-twitch muscle an increase in the concentration of AMP and IMP may increase the activity of phosphorylase. As in liver, the rate of glycogen breakdown in contracting muscle is directly dependent upon the glycogen concentration and is also subject to external regulation: Glycogen breakdown is increased by epinephrine and possibly inhibited by insulin. The sympathetic nervous innervation of the muscles does not seem to influence the rate of glycogen breakdown during exercise.

REGULATION OF MUSCLE GLUCOSE UPTAKE DURING EXERCISE

It has been known for many years that contractions elicit an increase in glucose uptake by muscle. It has also been the prevailing opinion for the last 10 years that muscle contractions will only elicit an increase in glucose uptake when in the presence of an ill-defined, so-called "permissive" concentration of insulin (Berger et al., 1975; Vranic & Berger, 1979).

However, we have recently obtained data that indicate that this concept is probably not true: In perfused hindquarters of rats in severe diabetic ketoacidosis that furthermore had been preperfused for 1 hr in the presence of insulin antiserum, electrically induced muscle contractions elicited an increase in glucose uptake (Table 1) (Ploug, Galbo, & Richter, 1984). As only about one third of the perfused muscle mass actually contracts during electrical stimulation, it can be calculated that glucose uptake was increased by a factor 5 by contractions. Furthermore, it was ruled out that the antiserum in some way was responsible for the increase in glucose uptake during contractions, since similar findings were obtained in the absence of antiserum (Table 1). Similar findings have recently been published by Wallberg-Henriksson and Holloszy (1984). We also found that the increase in glucose uptake was associated with increased glucose transport as measured by the uptake of the non-metabolizable glucose analog 3-0-methylglucose (Ploug et al., 1984). Thus, it would appear that contractions indeed can increase transport and uptake of glucose in muscle even in the absence of insulin.

Table 1 Glucose uptake in perfused rat hindquarter

Group	Rest 0 to 30 min	Contractions 30 to 60 min
Diabetic + antiserum	2.1 ± 0.5	5.1 ± 0.5[a]
Diabetic No antiserum	2.2 ± 0.4	5.5 ± 0.4[a]
Normal + antiserum	4.3 ± 0.5[b]	8.5 ± 0.7[ac]

Glucose uptake μmol/g perfused muscle/hr

Note. Hindquarters from diabetic rats were washed out with 25 ml of perfusate and preperfused for 30 min with or without insulin antiserum in the perfusate. Hindquarters from overnight fasted normal rats were also washed out with 25 ml of perfusate and preperfused for 1 hr with a medium containing insulin antiserum. Glucose uptake at rest was measured over the 30 min following preperfusion (0 to 30 min) at a flow of 12.5 ml/min. Then flow was increased to 25 ml/min and electrical stimulation of both hindlegs via the sciatic nerves was carried out for 30 min, over which glucose uptake was measured (30 to 60 min). Values are means ± SE of 6 hindquarters: a) $p < 0.005$ compared to values at rest; b) $p < 0.01$ compared to values in diabetic rats; c) $p < 0.005$ compared to values in diabetic rats. Modified from "Increased Muscle Glucose Uptake During Contractions: No Need for Insulin" by T. Ploug, H. Galbo, and E.A. Richter, 1984, *American Journal of Physiology*, **247**, p. E726-E731. Adapted by permission.

The finding that insulin is not required for muscle contractions to elicit an increase in transport and uptake of glucose does not mean that insulin does not influence glucose transport and uptake in muscle during and after exercise. In fact, it has recently been shown that in red skeletal muscle, contractions and insulin have additive effects on glucose transport (Ploug, Galbo, & Richter, 1985). In fast-twitch white skeletal muscle the effect of maximal effective insulin concentrations on glucose transport could be increased by contractions whereas the effect of maximally effective contractions could not be increased by insulin (Ploug et al., 1985).

The knowledge about which mechanisms actually bring about an increase in glucose transport and uptake during exercise is almost nonexisting. The increase in cytosolic calcium that takes place during muscle contractions has been proposed to initiate events in the muscle that eventually lead to increased permeability of the muscle membrane to glucose (Clausen, 1980; Holloszy & Narahara, 1967). A Ca^{++} mediated mechanism would be compatible with the fact that after exercise, reversal of contraction-induced increased permeability of muscle to glucose is monoexponential (Ploug et al., 1985). However, we have also recently observed that in the contracting soleus muscle of the rat a dissociation between contractile activity and presumably calcium release on the one hand and increased glucose transport on the other hand can be found (Ploug et al., 1984). This suggests that release of calcium may not always be enough to elicit increased muscle membrane transport of glucose, in agreement with findings in muscle cell cultures (Klip, Ramial, & Mack, 1985).

In summary, the regulation of muscle glucose uptake during exercise is not well understood. It does, however, seem clear that muscle can increase the transport and uptake of glucose during contractions in the absence of insulin. On the other hand, both insulin and contractions increase muscle glucose transport; in red muscle the effect of insulin and contractions is additive. The mechanism by which contractions increase muscle glucose transport is basically unknown. A role for Ca^{++} has been proposed.

Acknowledgments

The authors' studies on which this review is based were supported by grants from The Danish Medical Research Council, P. Carl Petersens Fund, Novo's Fund, The Danish Medical Association, The Danish Sports Research Council, The Danish Diabetes Foundation, Ib Henriksens Foundation, Nordisk Insulin Foundation, The Carlsberg Foundation, and The Danish Heart Foundation.

REFERENCES

Berger, M., Hagg, S., Goodman, M.G., & Ruderman, N.B. (1976). Glucose metabolism in perfused skeletal muscle. Effects of starvation, diabetes, fatty acids, acetoacetate, insulin and exercise on glucose uptake and disposition. *Biochemical Journal*, **158**, 191-202.

Berger, M., Hagg, S., & Ruderman, N.B. (1975). Glucose metabolism in perfused skeletal muscle. Interaction of insulin and exercise on glucose uptake. *Biochemical Journal*, **146**, 231-238.

Bjorkman, O., Felig, P., Hagenfeldt, L., & Wahren, J. (1981). Influence of hypoglucagonemia on splanchnic glucose output during leg exercise in man. *Clinical Physiology*, **1**, 43-57.

Carlson, K.I., Marker, J.C., Arnall, D.A., Terry, M.L., Yang, H.T., Lindsay, L.G., Bracken, M.E., & Winder, W.W. (1985). Epinephrine is unessential for stimulation of liver glycogenolysis during exercise. *American Journal of Physiology*, **58**, 544-548.

Chasiotis, D. (1983). The regulation of glycogen phosphorylase and glycogen breakdown in human skeletal muscle. *Acta Physiologica Scandinavica* (Suppl. 518), 1-68.

Clausen, T. (1980). The role of calcium in the activation of the glucose transport system. *Cell Calcium*, **1**, 311-325.

Connet, R.J., Gayeski, T.E.J., & Honig, C.R. (1984). Lactate accumulation in fully aerobic, working dog gracilis muscle. *American Journal of Physiology*, **246**, H120-H128.

Felig, P., & Wahren, J. (1979). Role of insulin and glucagon in the regulation of hepatic glucose production during exercise. *Diabetes*, **28** (Suppl. 1), 71-75.

Galbo, H. (1983). *Hormonal and metabolic adaptation to exercise.* Stuttgart, New York: Georg Thieme Verlag.

Galbo, H., Holst, J.J., Christensen, N.J., & Hilsted, J. (1976). Glucagon and plasma catecholamines during beta-receptor blockade in exercising man. *Journal of Applied Physiology*, **40**, 855-863.

Galbo, H., Richter, E.A., Holst, J.J., & Christensen, N.J. (1977). Diminished hormonal response to exercise in trained rats. *Journal of Applied Physiology: Respiratory, Environmental, Exercise Physiology*, **43**, 953-958.

Gollnick, P.D., Pernow, B., Essen, B., Jansson, E., & Saltin, B. (1981). Availability of glycogen and plasma FFA for substrate utilization in leg muscle of man during exercise. *Clinical Physiology*, **1**, 27-42.

Gollnick, P.D., Soule, R.G., Taylor, A.W., Williams, C., & Ianuzzo, C.D. (1970). Exercise-induced glycogenolysis and lipolysis in the rat: Hormonal influence. *American Journal of Physiology*, **219**, 729-733.

Gorski, J., & Pietrzyk, K. (1982). The effect of beta-adrenergic receptor blockade on intramuscular glycogen mobilization during exercise in the rat. *European Journal of Applied Physiology,* **48**, 201-205.

Holloszy, J.O., & Narahara, H.T. (1967). Enhanced permeability to sugar associated with muscle contraction. *Journal of General Physiology,* **50**, 551-562.

Issekutz, B. (1978). Role of beta-adrenergic receptors in mobilization of energy sources in exercising dogs. *Journal of Applied Physiology: Respiratory, Environmental, Exercise Physiology,* **44**, 869-876.

Issekutz, B. (1980). The role of hypoinsulinemia in exercise metabolism. *Diabetes,* **29**, 629-635.

Issekutz, B. (1985). Effect of epinephrine on carbohydrate metabolism in exercising dogs. *Metabolism,* **34**, 457-464.

Jansson, E., Hjemdahl, P., & Kaijser, L. (1984). Effects of adrenaline on leg muscle metabolism during exercise in man. *Acta Physiologica Scandinavica,* **120**, 49A.

Juhlin-Dannfelt, A.C., Terblanche, S.E., Fell., R.D., Young, J.C., & Holloszy, J.O. (1982). Effects of β-adrenergic receptor blockade on glycogenolysis during exercise. *Journal of Applied Physiology: Respiratory, Environmental, Exercise Physiology,* **53**, 549-554.

Kjær, M., Farrel, P., Christensen, N.J., & Galbo, H. (1985). Responsiveness of adrenal medullary secretion to exercise in trained and untrained humans. *Clinical Physiology,* **5** (Suppl. 4), 54.

Kjær, M., Mikines, K.J., Christensen, N.J., Tronier, B., Vinten, J., Sonne, B., Richter, E.A., & Galbo, H. (1984). Glucose turnover and hormonal changes during insulin-induced hypoglycemia in trained humans. *Journal of Applied Physiology: Respiratory, Environmental, Exercise Physiology,* **57**, 21-27.

Klip, A., Ramial, T., & Mack, E. (1985). Effect of K^+-depolarisation and insulin on hexose transport. *Clinical Physiology,* **5** (Suppl. 4), 65.

Meyer, R.A., Brown, T.R., & Cushmerick, M.J. (1985). Phosphorus nuclear magnetic resonance of fast- and slow-twitch muscle. *American Journal of Physiology,* **248**, C279-C287.

Meyer, R.A., & Terjung, R.L. (1979). Differences in ammonia and adenylate metabolism in contracting fast and slow muscle. *American Journal of Physiology,* **237**, C111-C118.

Moghimzadeh, E., Nobin, A., & Rosengren, E. (1983). Fluorescence microscopical and chemical characterization of the adrenergic innervation in mammalian liver tissue. *Cell Tissue Research,* **230**, 605-613.

Nazar, K., Brezezinska, Z., & Kowalski, W. (1972). Mechanism of impaired capacity for prolonged muscular work following beta-adrenergic blockade in dogs. *Pflügers Archiv,* **336**, 72-78.

Newsholme, E.A. (1979). The control of fuel utilization by muscle during exercise and starvation. *Diabetes,* **28** (Suppl. 1), 1-7.

Ploug, T., Galbo, H., & Richter, E.A. (1984). Increased muscle glucose uptake during contractions: No need for insulin. *American Journal of Physiology*, **247**, E726-E731.

Ploug, T., Galbo, H., & Richter, E.A. (1985). Contraction induced glucose transport in rat skeletal muscle: Additive effect of insulin and monoexponential, glycogen independent reversal in slow and fast twitch red muscle. *Clinical Physiology*, **5** (Suppl. 4), 68.

Rennie, M.J., & Holloszy, J.O. (1977). Inhibition of glucose uptake and glycogenolysis by availability of oleate in well-oxygenated perfused skeletal muscle. *Biochemical Journal*, **168**, 161-170.

Richter, E.A. (1984). Influence of the sympatho-adrenal system on some metabolic and hormonal responses to exercise in the rat. With special reference to the effect on glycogenolysis in skeletal muscle. *Acta Physiologica Scandinavica* (Suppl. 528), 1-42.

Richter, E.A., Galbo, H. (1985). Rate of glycogen breakdown and lactate release in contracting, isolated skeletal muscle is dependent upon glycogen concentration. *Clinical Physiology*, **5** (Suppl. 4), 82.

Richter, E.A., Galbo, H., & Christensen, N.J. (1981). Control of exercise-induced muscular glycogenolysis by adrenal medullary hormones in rats. *Journal of Applied Physiology: Respiratory, Environmental, Exercise Physiology*, **50**, 21-26.

Richter, E.A., Galbo, H., Holst, J.J., & Sonne, B. (1981). Significance of glucagon for insulin secretion and hepatic glycogenolysis during exercise in rats. *Hormone and Metabolic Research*, **13**, 323-326.

Richter, E.A., Galbo, H., Sonne, B., Holst, J.J., & Christensen, N.J. (1980). Adrenal medullary control of muscular and hepatic glycogenolysis and of pancreatic hormonal secretion in exercising rats. *Acta Physiologica Scandinavica*, **108**, 235-242.

Richter, E.A., Garetto, L.P., Goodman, M.G., & Ruderman, N.B. (1984). Enhanced muscle glucose metabolism after exercise: Modulation by local factors. *American Journal of Physiology*, **246**, E476-E482.

Richter, E.A., Ruderman, N.B., Gavras, H., Belur, E.R., & Galbo, H. (1982). Muscle glycogenolysis during exercise: Dual control by epinephrine and contractions. *American Journal of Physiology*, **242**, E25-E32.

Rizza, R.A., Mandarino, L.J., & Gerich, J.E. (1981). Dose-response characteristics for effects of insulin on production and utilization of glucose in man. *American Journal of Physiology*, **240**, E630-E639.

Ruderman, N.B., Goodman, M.N., Connover, C.A., & Berger, M. (1979). Substrate utilization in perfused skeletal muscle. *Diabetes*, 28 (Suppl. 1), 13-17.

Sonne, B., & Galbo, H. (1985a). Carbohydrate metabolism during and after exercise in rats. Studies with radioglucose. *Journal of Applied Physiology*, **59**, 1627-1639.

Sonne, B., & Galbo, H. (1985b). Regulation of hepatic glucose production in exercise. An alternative view. *Clinical Physiology,* **5** (Suppl. 4), 57.

Sonne, B., Mikines, K.J., Richter, E.A., Christensen, N.J., & Galbo, H. (1985). Role of liver nerves and adrenal medulla in glucose turnover in running rats. *Journal of Applied Physiology,* **59**, 1640-1646.

Vranic, M., & Berger, M. (1979). Exercise and diabetes mellitus. *Diabetes,* **28**, 147-163.

Wallberg-Henriksson, H., & Holloszy, J.O. (1984). Contractile activity increases glucose uptake by muscle in severely diabetic rats. *Journal of Applied Physiology: Respiratory, Environmental, Exercise Physiology,* **57**, 1045-1049.

Wasserman, D.H., Lickley, H.L., & Vranic, M. (1984). Interactions between glucagon and other counterregulatory hormones during normoglycemic and hypoglycemic exercise in dogs. *Journal of Clinical Investigation,* **74**, 1404-1413.

Winder, W.W., Beattie, M.A., Piquette, C., & Holman, R.T. (1983). Decrease in liver norepinephrine in response to exercise and hypoglycemia. *American Journal of Physiology,* **244**, R845-R849.

Winder, W.W., Hagberg, J.M., Hickson, R.C., Ehsani, A.A., & McLane, J.A. (1978). Time course of sympathoadrenal adaptation to endurance training in man. *Journal of Applied Physiology,* **45**, 370-374.

Winder, W.W., Terry, M.L., & Mitchell, V.M. (1985). Role of plasma epinephrine in fasted exercising rats. *American Journal of Physiology,* **248**, R302-R307.

Zinman, B., Vranic, M., Albisser, A.M., Leibel, B.S., & Marliss, E.B. (1979). The role of insulin in the metabolic response to exercise in diabetic man. *Diabetes,* **28** (Suppl. 1), 76-81.

Interaction Between Insulin, Glucagon, and Catecholamines in the Regulation of Glucose Production and Uptake During Exercise: Physiology and Diabetes

David H. Wasserman
Mladen Vranic
University of Toronto
Toronto, Ontario, Canada

Total glucose uptake increases approximately 3-fold during exercise and yet in normal subjects the blood glucose concentration generally remains constant. The reason for this is that the increase in hepatic glucose production is dynamically and quantitatively equal in magnitude to the increased glucose utilization that occurs during muscular work. The apparent coupling of glucose production to its accelerated rate of uptake in contracting muscle is largely, but not exclusively, mediated by the endocrine system. The critical role of the endocrine system in control of glucose fluxes during exercise is clearly evidenced by the problems associated with exercise in diabetics, in whom insulin release is diminished and insulin counterregulatory hormone release is exaggerated. The aim of this review is to describe work from our laboratory illustrating how glucagon and insulin act on the liver in concert with the catecholamines and insulin in the periphery to control glucose fluxes during exercise in health and with diabetes.

CONTROL OF HEPATIC GLUCOSE PRODUCTION: THE VITAL ROLE OF GLUCAGON-INSULIN INTERACTION

Suppressing glucagon below basal with somatostatin during steady and nonsteady state treadmill exercise in dogs causes a reduction in hepatic glucose production, a consequent fall in plasma glucose of 25 mg$\cdot$ dl^{-1}, and an attenuation in glucose uptake (Issekutz & Vranic, 1980; Wasserman, Lickley, & Vranic, 1984). When glucagon is replaced during

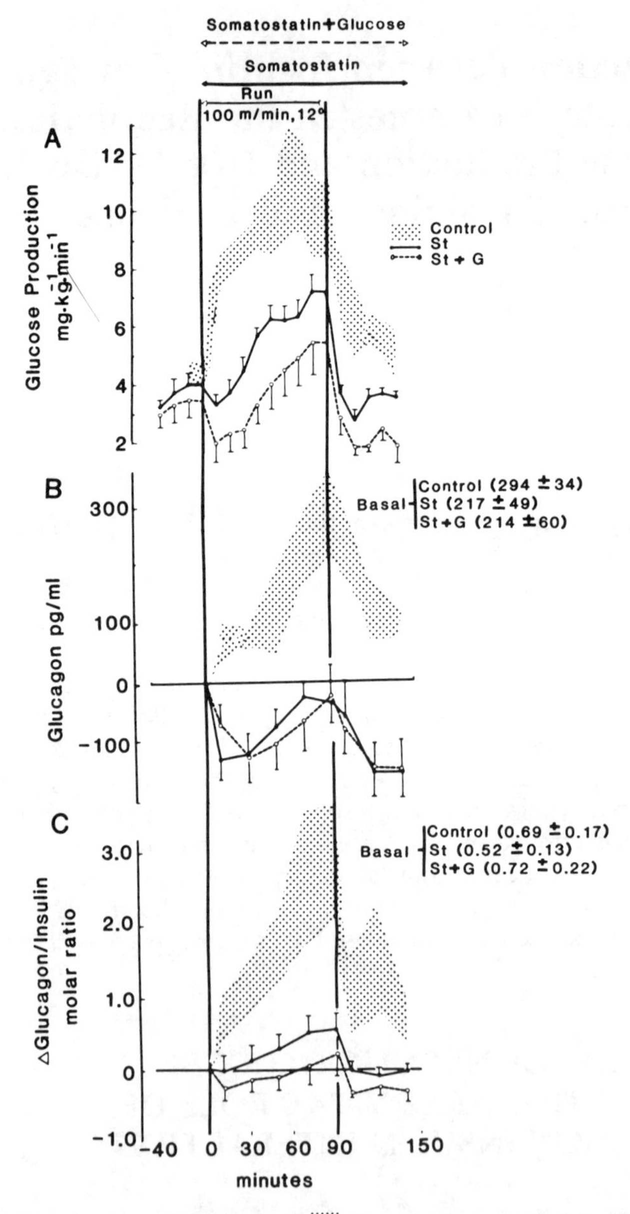

Figure 1 Effect of exercise alone (control, ⁙), exercise + somatostatin (St, •---•), or exercise + somatostatin + glucose (St + G, o---o) on (A) the rate of hepatic glucose production, (B) changes in plasma glucagon, and (C) changes in the glucagon/insulin molar ratio. Glucagon and the glucagon/insulin molar ratio are shown as deviations (Δ) from basal values. Exercise and somatostatin and glucose infusions were begun at t=0. The stippled area represents mean ± SE for exercise alone. Vertical bars represent the SE. N=5 for all protocols. Modified from "Interactions between glucagon and other counterregulatory hormones during normoglycemic and hypoglycemic exercise" by D.H. Wasserman, H.L.A. Lickley, and H. Vranic, 1984, *Journal of Clinical Investigation*, **74**, p. 1404-1413. Adapted by permission.

somatostatin infusion to exercise levels, normal glucose concentrations and kinetics are restored. Figure 1 illustrates the time course of hepatic glucose production, glucagon, and the glucagon/insulin molar ratio during exercise alone or during somatostatin infusion with and without glucose replacement. It could be calculated that during exercise under conditions of mild hypoglycemia, glucagon is responsible for 3.9 mg • kg^{-1} • min^{-1} or 39% of the glucose released from the liver (Wasserman et al., 1984). With the addition of euglycemic glucose replacement during somatostatin infusion, we were able to isolate the effects of counterregulatory mechanisms that may act during moderate hypoglycemia (Wasserman et al., 1984). Under these circumstances glucagon suppression resulted in a 5.7 mg • kg^{-1} • min^{-1} or 61% reduction in endogenous glucose production. Thus, it was concluded from these studies that glucagon is the primary controller of hepatic glucose production during exercise. Furthermore, by subtracting the extent of attenuation of glucose production during hypoglycemic glucagon suppression from that seen during euglycemic glucagon suppression, it can be seen that counterregulatory mechanisms acting during moderately hypoglycemic exercise may account for 1.8 mg • kg^{-1} • min^{-1} of glucose released from the liver.

Alloxan-diabetic dogs in poor metabolic control have elevated glucagon levels at rest and a greatly exaggerated glucagon response to exercise compared to normal dogs (Wasserman et al., 1984), and yet glucagon suppression with somatostatin results in a reduction in hepatic glucose production that is slightly less than that seen in normal dogs. It was determined that glucagon controls at least 52% (4.4 mg • kg^{-1} • min^{-1}) of the glucose released from the liver (Wasserman et al., 1984). Comparison of work from resting, normal (Cherrington, Liljenquist, Shulman, Williams, & Lacy, 1979) and alloxan-diabetic (Lickley, Kemmer, Doi, & Vranic, 1983) dogs during somatostatin-induced glucagon suppression with the effects of glucagon suppression in exercising dogs (Figure 2) indicates that during exercise, glucagon controls over twice as much of the glucose released from the liver than at rest. Interestingly, glucagon controls about the same percentage of hepatic glucose production during rest and exercise in normal dogs, but less during rest (33%) than with exercise (52%) in the alloxan-diabetic dogs. This is consistent with a decreased sensitivity of liver to glucagon in diabetes (Lickley et al., 1983), and may reflect a greater importance of beta-adrenergic mechanisms in control of basal hepatic glucose production in diabetes (Sherwin, Shamoon, Hendler, Sacca, Eigler, & Walesky, 1980).

In both normal and alloxan-diabetic dogs, the strongest correlate to hepatic glucose production was not glucagon alone, but the glucagon/insulin ratio. This indicates that in addition to glucagon, the fall in insulin is also important in the regulation of glucose production during exercise. Figure 3 illustrates the relationship between hepatic glucose production and the glucagon/insulin ratio in normal dogs. A very close temporal

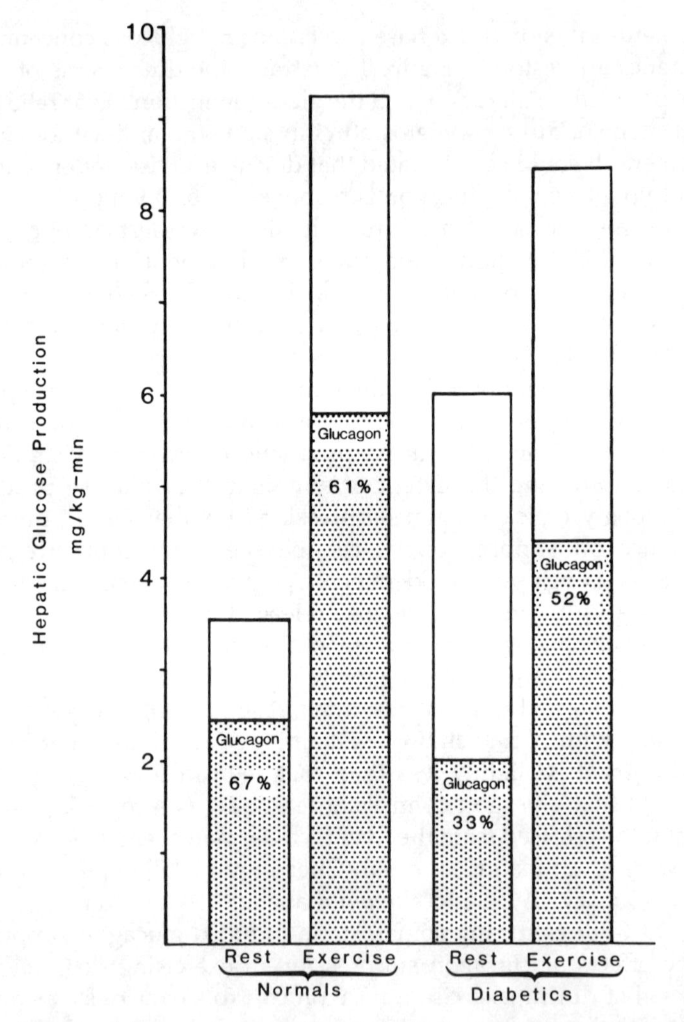

Figure 2 The role of glucagon in regulation of hepatic glucose production during rest and exercise in normal and alloxan-diabetic dogs. The shaded area represents the portion of the hepatic glucose production controlled by glucagon. Resting values for normal dogs were modified from "Importance of Hypoglycemia-Induced Glucose Production During Isolated Glucagon Deficiency" by A.D. Cherrington, J.E. Liljenquist, G.I. Schulman, P.E. Williams, and W.W. Lacy, 1979, *American Journal of Physiology*, **236**, p. E263-E271. Adapted by permission. Resting values for alloxan-diabetic dogs were modified from "Glucagon Suppression Improves Glucoregulation in Moderate but not Chronic Severe Diabetes" by H.L.A. Lickley, F.W. Kemmer, K. Doi, and M. Vranic, 1983, *American Journal of Physiology*, **241**, p. E424-E429. Adapted by permission. Exercise values for normal and alloxan-diabetic dogs were modified from "Interactions Between Glucagon and Other Counterregulatory Hormones During Normoglycemic and Hypoglycemic Exercise" by D.H. Wasserman, H.L.A. Lickley, and M. Vranic, 1984, *Journal of Clinical Investigation*, **74**, p. 1404-1413. Adapted by permission. And "Important role of glucagon during exercise in diabetic dogs" by D.H. Wasserman, H.L.A. Lickley, and M. Vranic, in press, *Journal of Applied Physiology*. Adapted by permission.

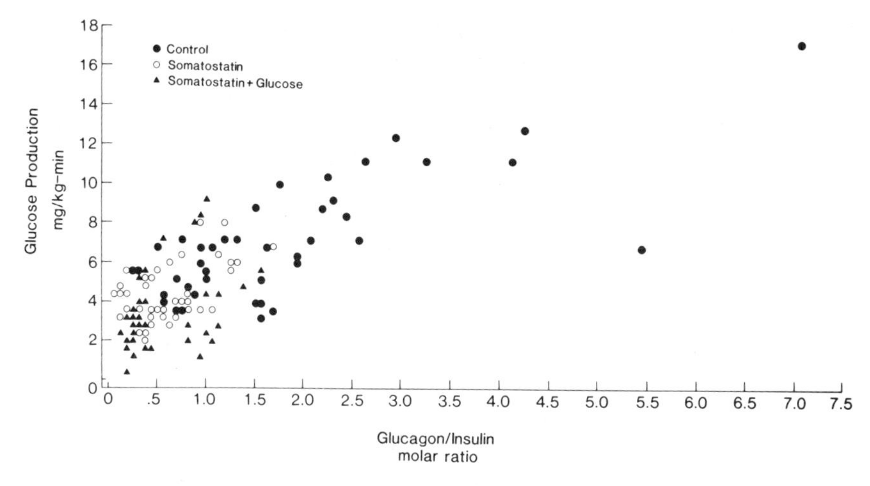

Figure 3 The relationship between hepatic glucose production and the glucagon/insulin molar ratio. Plotted are values pooled from exercise alone (control, n = 20), exercise + somatostatin (n = 20), exercise + somatostatin + glucagon (n = 20). Correlation coefficient for pooled data equals 0.86. Modified from Wasserman et al. (1984).

relationship between the glucagon/insulin molar ratio and hepatic glucose production can also be seen in Figure 1 by comparing panels A and C. Evidence for the importance of insulin levels in control of hepatic glucose production during exercise has also been seen in depancreatized dogs (Kawamori & Vranic, 1977) and in diabetic humans (Zinman et al., 1977) when it was demonstrated that glucose production did not increase substantially when insulin absorption from subcutaneous depots increased during exercise. Moreover, it has been shown in running dogs that when insulin is suppressed with mannoheptulose an additional 2 μU/ml below the normal exercise response, hepatic glucose production increased by nearly 3-fold (Issekutz, 1980).

Although the glucagon/insulin ratio was the strongest correlate to hepatic glucose production in normal and diabetic dogs, the correlation coefficient was 2-fold higher in the normals (r = 0.86) than in the diabetics (r = 0.43). There are several possible reasons for the apparent uncoupling of the pancreatic hormones from changes in glucose production. First, alloxan-diabetic dogs are characterized by large increases in the catecholamines in response to exercise, which may provide an alternate stimulus to the liver (Gray, Lickley, & Vranic, 1980; Perez, Kemmer, Lickley, & Vranic, 1981). However, we have not observed a strong correlation between the catecholamines and glucose production in either normal (Wasserman et al., 1984) or diabetic dogs (Wasserman, Lickley, & Vranic, 1985b). Secondly, the elevated plasma glucose levels may tend to diminish the hepatic effects of the pancreatic hormones (Bergman, 1977). Finally, in the diabetic dogs there may be down-regulation of hepatic glucagon receptors (Bhatena, Voyles, Smith, & Recant, 1978) and other factors contributing to a decreased efficiency of glucagon at the liver (Dighe, Rojas, Birnbaumer, & Garber, 1984; Lickley et al., 1983). In a sense the decreased correlation between glucose production and the glucagon/insulin ratio may be advantageous to the diabetic dogs. The diabetic dogs achieved a glucagon/insulin ratio of 8.5, which is far in excess of that observed in normal dogs. It can be extrapolated from Figure 3 that if the same relationship between the glucagon/insulin ratio and hepatic glucose production did exist in diabetics as in normal dogs, a glucagon/insulin ratio of 8.5 would correspond to a hepatic glucose output of 17 mg • kg • min. Releasing glucose at this rate would quickly deplete hepatic glycogen stores and greatly alter substrate balance.

The uncoupling of the increment in hepatic glucose production from the change in the glucagon/insulin ratio in the diabetic dogs can be further seen at the onset of exercise (Figure 4). In normal dogs, a difference in the change of glucagon/insulin of 1 unit results in a 6.5 mg • kg^{-1} • min^{-1} reduction in glucose production, but in alloxan-diabetic dogs a change in glucagon/insulin of 1.7 resulted in a difference of only 4.0 mg • kg^{-1} • min^{-1}. Thus, at the onset of exercise, a given increment in the ratio of glucagon/insulin causes a 270% greater increment in glucose production in normal dogs than in diabetic dogs.

Since glucagon controls at least 50% to 60% of the glucose released from the liver during exercise in both health and diabetes, it can be concluded that regulation of as much as 50% of the hepatic glucose production is unaccounted for. Since glucagon was suppressed only 50% to 70% below normal exercise levels by somatostatin, it is conceivable that unsuppressed glucagon may control at least part of the remaining glucose production. Nevertheless, it is also likely that other neural and hormonal factors could play a role in the accelerated hepatic glucose production seen during exercise.

Considering the potent stimulatory effect of epinephrine infusion on the dynamics of hepatic glucose output in resting diabetic dogs (Perez et al., 1981), we chose to examine the effects of diminishing catecholamine action by administration of beta-adrenergic blockade during exercise. Earlier studies in normal dogs indicated that beta-adrenergic mechanisms of the catecholamines were not important in control of hepatic glucose production during exercise (Issekutz, 1978). To see if beta-adrenergic mechanisms may be more pronounced in poorly controlled diabetes, characterized by an exaggerated catecholamine response to exercise, we studied alloxan-diabetic dogs during exercise with beta-blockade (Wasserman, Lickley, & Vranic, 1985c). Our results indicate that, as in normal dogs, beta-blockade does not affect hepatic glucose production in diabetic dogs either at the onset of exercise (Figure 4) or at 90 min of

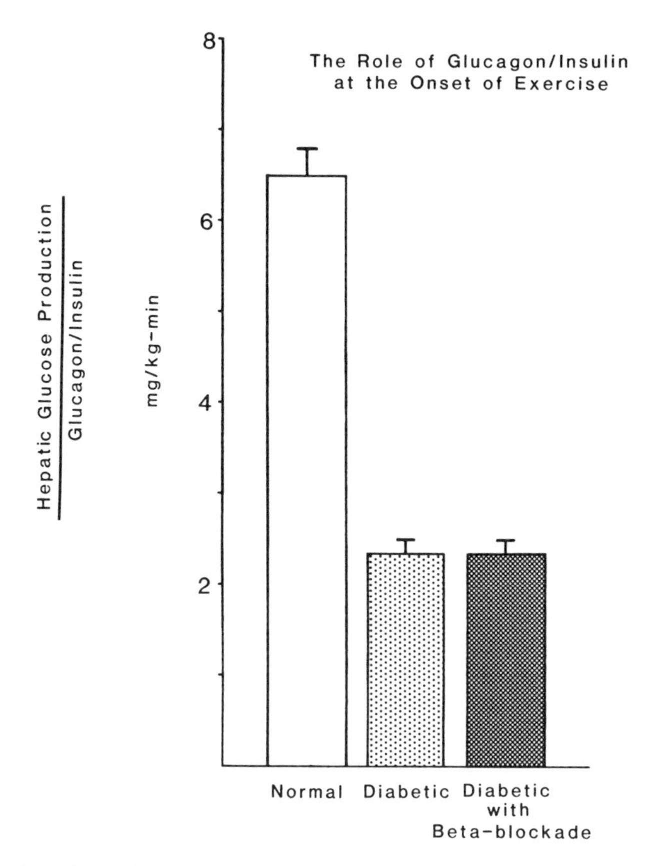

Figure 4 The relationship of the glucagon/insulin molar ratio to hepatic glucose production at the onset of exercise (initial 10 minutes of exercise) in normal and alloxan-diabetic dogs, and the effect of beta-blockade on this relationship in diabetes. Values were calculated by taking the difference of the control responses of the glucagon/insulin ratio and hepatic glucose production at 10 minutes of exercise from the corresponding sample when glucagon was suppressed with somatostatin (in the presence or in the absence of beta-blockade.

exercise (Figure 5). Even in the absence of basal glucagon levels, beta-adrenergic mechanisms do not show any additional compensatory stimulation of glucose production. This was evidenced by similar levels of glucose production, whether somatostatin was infused alone or together with a beta-blocker (Figure 5).

Thus, glucagon, or more specifically the glucagon/insulin ratio, is the most important controller of hepatic glucose production in normal and diabetic dogs. Although the catecholamines do not appear to affect hepatic glucose output via beta-adrenergic mechanisms during exercise, one cannot rule out some role for alpha-adrenergic mechanisms.

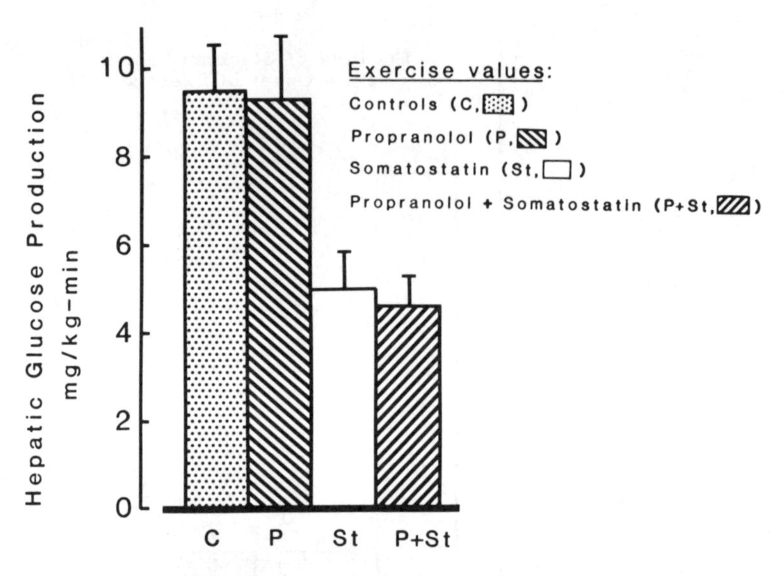

Figure 5 Effect of exercise alone (C, ▒), exercise + propranolol (P, ▧), exercise + somatostatin (St, □), and exercise + somatostatin + propranolol (P + St, ▨) in alloxan-diabetic dogs on hepatic glucose production after 90 minutes, of exercise. Values are mean ± SE at 90 minutes. n = 6 for C, P, and St; n = 5 for P + St. Modified from "The Role of Beta-adrenergic Mechanisms During Exercise in Poorly-controlled Diabetes" by D.H. Wasserman, H.L.A. Lickley, and M. Vranic, 1985c, *Journal of Applied Physiology*, **59**, 1282-1289. Adapted by permission.

CONTROL OF GLUCOSE UPTAKE: INTERACTION BETWEEN INSULIN AND THE CATECHOLAMINES

In earlier work from our laboratory in depancreatized dogs, we showed that a small amount of insulin was needed for the increased glucose metabolic clearance seen during exercise (Vranic, Kawamori, Pek, Kovacevic, & Wrenshall, 1976). However, comparisons of exercising normal and alloxan-diabetic dogs indicate that insulin levels are not the only factor determining the increment in glucose clearance during exercise. Alloxan-diabetic dogs have insulin levels that are reduced by about 70% relative to normal controls. Whereas in normal dogs insulin levels decrease during exercise, in alloxan-diabetic dogs the already low insulin levels are constant during rest and exercise (Wasserman et al., 1984). This fall in insulin in normal dogs, coupled with the nonchanging but already diminished insulin values in the diabetics, creates similar insulin levels during exer-

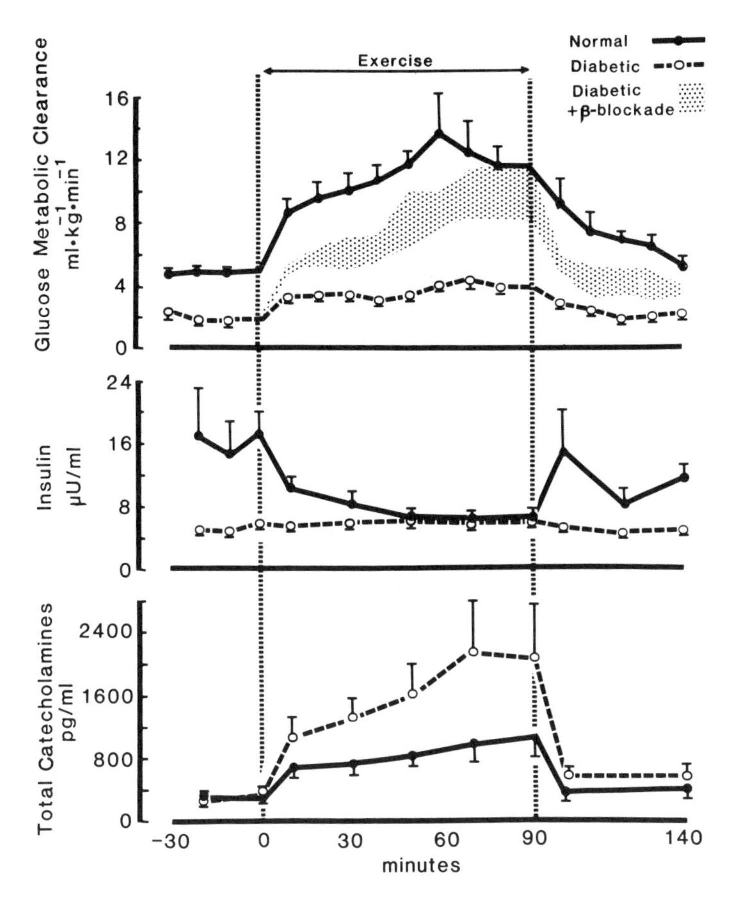

Figure 6 Effect of exercise alone on the rate of glucose metabolic clearance, plasma insulin concentrations, and total plasma catecholamine concentration in normal (n = 5, •---•) and alloxan-diabetic (n = 6, o---o) dogs. Stippled area represents the effect of beta-blockade on glucose clearance in diabetic dogs.

cise in both groups (Figure 6). However, the exercise-induced increment in glucose clearance in the diabetic dogs is only about 25% to 30% of that seen in normal dogs and plasma free fatty acid (FFA) and lactate levels are exaggerated. The catecholamines are known to antagonize peripheral insulin action and since they are excessively elevated during exercise in diabetes, it was hypothesized that effects of the catecholamines may diminish the increment in glucose clearance with exercise via excessive mobilization of extrahepatic substrate (muscle and adipose tissue, esterified fat, and muscle glycogen). Beta-adrenergic blockade-increased glucose clearance to a level of 9.4 ml • kg^{-1} • min^{-1} after 90 min of exercise, compared to a level of 10.1 ml • kg^{-1} • min^{-1} observed in normal dogs. Thus, when the beta-adrenergic effects of the catecholamines were blocked in diabetes, glucose clearance was restored to 93% of the normal response. Using concentrations of plasma lactate and FFA as indices of glycogenolysis and lipolysis (Issekutz, 1978), respectively, beta-blockade appears to have diminished these processes substantially as lactate and FFA levels were reduced to levels similar to those seen in normal dogs. Hence, beta-blockade may increase glucose uptake by decreasing the mobilization of extrahepatic substrates, but also a direct antagonistic effect of beta-receptors on insulin-stimulated glucose transport cannot be ruled out.

Further evidence for the role of catecholamines in control of glucose uptake was seen during hypoglycemic exercise in normal dogs (Wasserman et al., 1984). Moderate hypoglycemia was shown to elicit an exaggerated increase in epinephrine in exercising dogs, which corresponded to elevated plasma FFA and lactate levels, as well as a 2.0 ml/kg-min attenuation in glucose clearance (Figure 7). Thus, epinephrine, at least in part, prevented a more severe fall in plasma glucose by stimulating extrahepatic substrate mobilization.

Considering the antagonistic effect of the catecholamines on glucose uptake, it was particularly interesting that despite 4-fold greater norepinephrine levels and almost 7-fold greater epinephrine levels, anemia caused nearly a 4-fold greater increase in glucose clearance than in normal controls after 90 min of exercise (Wasserman, Lickley, & Vranic, 1985a). Since carbohydrates are the obligate substrate for anaerobic metabolism, tissue hypoxia caused by a 25% reduction in hematocrit would require a greater intracellular glucose flux than nonhypoxic exercise. This is consistent with other work showing that the metabolic demand of working muscle is a powerful determinant of glucose uptake (Wahren, Felig, Ahlborg, & Jorfeldt, 1971; Walker, Idstrom, Schersten, & Bylund-Fellenius, 1982). This increased metabolic demand by far outweighed the peripheral counterregulatory effects of the catecholamines. Therefore, when examining aspects of glucose metabolism, the metabolic state of the tissue must be considered as well as the glucoregulatory hormone levels. Figure 7 summarizes the effect of exercise on glucose metabolic clearance in the experiments described above.

SUMMARY

Glucose production during exercise is largely controlled by the interaction of glucagon and insulin at the liver, such that an increase in the glucagon/insulin ratio results in an increase in glucose release from the liver. On the other hand, glucose uptake is controlled by the action of

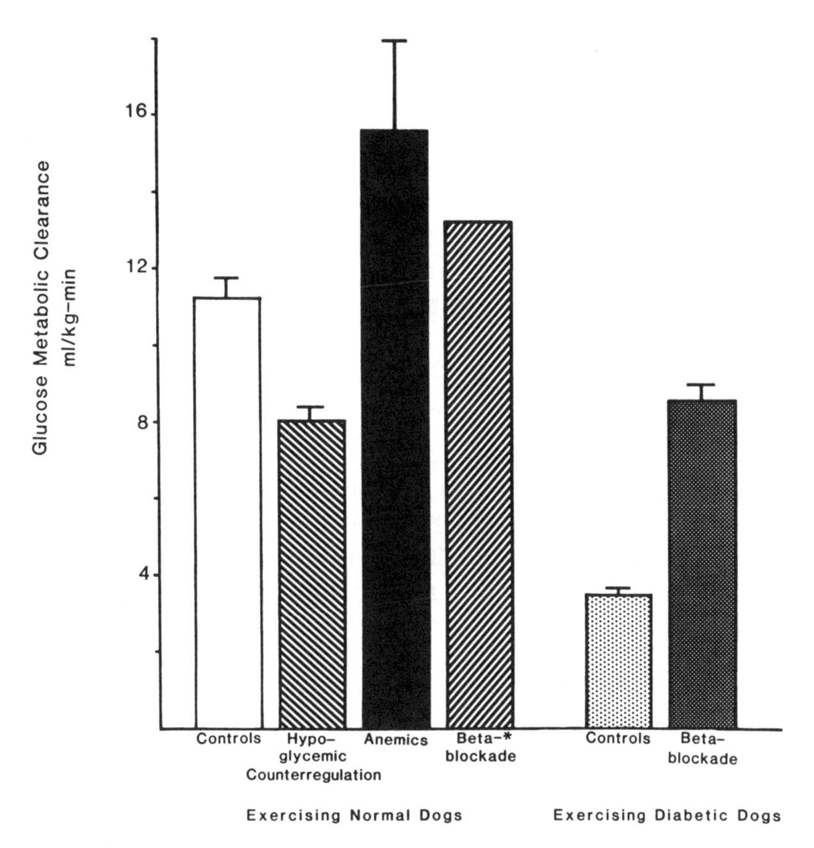

Figure 7 Effect of exercise on glucose metabolic clearance and the modifying effects of exaggerated hypoglycemic counterregulation, anemia, diabetes, and beta-blockade in both diabetics and normals. *Data on beta-blockade in normal dogs were modified from "Role of Beta-adrenergic Receptors in Mobilization of Energy Sources in Exercising Dogs" by B. Issekutz, 1978, *Journal of Applied Physiology*, **44**, p. 869-876. Adapted by permission.

the catecholamines and insulin. An increase in catecholamines and a decrease in insulin will result in an increase in the mobilization of fat and muscle glycogen, which effectively decreases the reliance of muscle on blood-born glucose. It is interesting that although a mild reduction in hematocrit causes a large increase in catecholamine release during exercise, glucose uptake is still excessive as the resulting tissue hypoxia is able to effectively counterbalance the effects of the catecholamines. Therefore, in addition to hormonal mechanisms, oxygen availability and metabolic demand must also be considered important in control of glucose fluxes during exercise.

Acknowledgments

We are indebted to D. Bilinski, L. Cook, and N. Kovacevic for their excellent technical assistance. This work was supported by the Medical Research Council of Canada, and the Canadian Diabetes Association, and an Edward Christie Stevens Fellowship of the University of Toronto to DHW. We thank E. Lien of Wyeth Laboratoris for the generous gift of somatostatin. We also thank Novo and Connaught-Novo for supporting M. Vranic's travel expenses to the symposium.

REFERENCES

Bergman, R.N. (1977). Integrated control of hepatic glucose metabolism. *Federation Proceedings,* **36**, 265-270.

Bhatena, S.J., Voyles, N.R., Smith, S., & Recant, L. (1978). Decreased glucagon receptors in diabetic rat hepatocrytes. Evidence for regulation of glucagon receptors by hyperglucagonemia. *Journal of Clinical Investigation,* **61**, 1488-1497.

Cherrington, A.D., Liljenquist, J.E., Schulman, G.I., Williams, P.E., & Lacy, W.W. (1979). Importance of hypoglycemia-induced glucose production during isolated glucagon deficiency. *American Journal of Physiology,* **236**, E263-E271.

Dighe, R.R., Rojas, F.J., Birnbaumer, L., & Garber, A.J. (1984). The impact of stimulable adenylyl cyclase in rat liver. The impact of streptozotocin-induced diabetes mellitus. *Journal of Clinical Investigation,* **73**, 1013-1023.

Gray, D.E., Lickley, H.L.A., & Vranic, M. (1980). Physiological effects of epinephrine on glucose turnover and plasma free fatty acid concentration mediated independently of glucagon. *Diabetes,* **29**, 600-609.

Issekutz, B. (1978). Role of beta-adrenergic receptors in mobilization of energy sources in exercising dogs. *Journal of Applied Physiology,* **44**, 869-876.

Issekutz, B. (1980). The role of hypoinsulinemia in exercise metabolism. *Diabetes,* **29**, 629-635.

Issekutz, B., & Vranic, M. (1980). Significance of glucagon in the control of glucose production during exercise in dogs. *American Journal of Physiology,* **238**, E13-E20.

Kawamori, R., & Vranic, M. (1977). Mechanism of exercise-induced hypoglycemia in depancreatized dogs maintained on long-acting insulin. *Journal of Clinical Investigation,* **59**, 331-337.

Lickley, H.L.A., Kemmer, F.W., Doi, K., & Vranic, M. (1983). Glucagon suppression improves glucoregulation in moderate but not chronic severe diabetes. *American Journal of Physiology,* **245**, E424-E429.

Perez, G., Kemmer, F.W., Lickley, H.L.A., & Vranic, M. (1981). Importance of glucagon in mediating epinephrine-induced hyperglycemia in alloxan-diabetic dogs. *American Journal of Physiology,* **241**, E328-E335.

Sherwin, R.S., Shamoon, H., Hendler, R., Sacca, L., Eigler, N., & Walesky, M. (1980). Epinephrine and the regulation of glucose metabolism: Effect of diabetes and hormonal interactions. *Metabolism,* **29**, 1146-1154.

Vranic, M., Kawamori, R., Pek, S, Kovacevic, N., & Wrenshall, G.A. (1976). The essentiality of insulin and the role of glucagon in regulating glucose utilization and production during strenuous exercise in dogs. *Journal of Clinical Investigation,* **57**, 245-255.

Wahren, J., Felig, P., Ahlborg, G., & Jorfeldt, L. (1971). Glucose metabolism during leg exercise in man. *Journal of Clinical Investigation,* **50**, 2715-2725.

Walker, P.M., Idstrom, J.P., Schersten, T., & Bylund-Fellenius, A.-C. (1982). Glucose uptake in relation to metabolic state in perfused rat hindlimb at rest and during exercise. *European Journal of Applied Physiology,* **48**, 163-176.

Wasserman, D.H., Lickley, H.L.A., & Vranic, M. (1984). Interactions between glucagon and other counterregulatory hormones during normoglycemic and hypoglycemic exercise. *Journal of Clinical Investigation,* **74**, 1404-1413.

Wasserman, D.H., Lickley, H.L.A., & Vranic, M. (1985a). Effect of hematocrit reduction on hormonal and metabolic responses to exercise. *Journal of Applied Physiology,* **58**, 1257-1262.

Wasserman, D.H., Lickley, H.L.A., & Vranic, M. (1985b). Important role of glucagon during exercise in diabetic dogs. *Journal of Applied Physiology.*

Wasserman, D.H., Lickley, H.L.A., & Vranic, M. (1985c). The role of beta-adrenergic mechanisms during exercise in poorly-controlled diabetes. *Journal of Applied Physiology.*

Zinman, B., Murray, F.T., Vranic, M., Albisser, A.M., Leibel, B.S., McClean, P.A., & Marliss, E.B. (1977). Glucoregulation during moderate exercise in insulin-treated diabetics. *Journal of Clinical Endocrinology and Metabolism,* **45**, 641-652.

SECTION C
TRAINING RESPONSE

Utilization of Fat as Substrate During Exercise: Effect of Training

John O. Holloszy
Gail P. Dalsky
P.M. Nemeth
B.F. Hurley
W.H. Martin III
James M. Hagberg
Washington University
St. Louis, Missouri, U.S.A.

One of the major metabolic consequences of the adaptations to endurance exercise training is an increased reliance on fat oxidation as an energy source during prolonged submaximal exercise. Studies in which the respiratory exchange ratio (R) was used to evaluate the relative contributions of fat and carbohydrate to oxidative metabolism have shown that a larger proportion of the energy requirement for submaximal exercise is provided by oxidation of fatty acids in the trained than in the untrained state (Henriksson, 1977; Hermansen, Hultman, & Saltin, 1967). This finding led to an investigation of the effects of endurance exercise training on the capacity of skeletal muscle to oxidize fatty acids.

OXIDATION OF FATTY ACIDS

Studies on rats trained by means of a prolonged and strenuous program of treadmill running showed that endurance exercise can induce a large increase in the capacity of skeletal muscle to oxidize fatty acids (Baldwin et al., 1972; Molé, Oscai, & Holloszy, 1971). This increase in ability of muscle to oxidize fat is made possible by an increase in the mitochondrial content of the trained skeletal muscles (Holloszy, 1967; Holloszy & Booth, 1976). Subsequent studies in which marker enzymes of the fatty acid oxidation pathway were measured on muscle biopsy samples have shown that endurance training also induces large increases in the capacity to oxidize fatty acids in humans (Chi et al., 1983; Costill, Fink, Getchell, Ivy, & Witzman, 1979; Jansson & Kaijser, 1977).

The increase in muscle mitochondria induced by endurance training results in comparable increases in the capacities to oxidize fatty acids and carbohydrate, that is, pyruvate (Holloszy & Booth, 1976). This raises the question: Why is proportionally more fat and less carbohydrate oxidized in the trained than in the untrained state? The answer to this question relates, at least in part, to the functioning of the "glucose-fatty acid cycle" first described by Randle, Garland, Hales, and Newsholme (1963) in heart muscle. They found that glucose uptake, glycolysis, glycogenolysis and pyruvate oxidation are partially inhibited in the myocardium by oxidation of fatty acids. An important factor in this inhibition is the accumulation of citrate, which inhibits phosphofructokinase activity, resulting in glucose-6-phosphate accumulation and inhibition of hexokinase. However, a number of investigators were unable to demonstrate an inhibitory effect of fatty acids on glucose metabolism in skeletal muscle, leading some to conclude that the glucose-fatty acid cycle functions only in heart muscle (cf. Rennie, Winder, & Holloszy, 1976).

Arguing against this conclusion was the evidence that the progressive rise in plasma free fatty acid (FFA) concentration during prolonged exercise is associated with a decrease in R. The decline in R, which indicates a change in the carbon source for oxidative metabolism from carbohydrate to fat, is evident long before glycogen stores are depleted (cf. Rennie et al., 1976). This observation, which suggested that the increase in plasma FFA during exercise results in increased oxidation of FFA with inhibition of carbohydrate utilization, led to a reinvestigation of whether or not glucose-fatty acid cycle activity is present in skeletal muscle.

One experimental approach used was to elevate plasma FFA by feeding a fat meal followed 3 hours later by injection of heparin. Raising the concentration of plasma FFA by this procedure was found to result in a slowing of the rate of muscle glycogen depletion in rats during standardized bouts of treadmill running (Rennie et al., 1976). This finding was soon confirmed in humans (Costill et al., 1977). Studies on rats also showed that raising plasma FFA slows liver glycogen depletion (Hickson, Rennie, Conlee, Winder, & Holloszy, 1977; Rennie et al., 1976), and markedly improves endurance as reflected in run time to exhaustion (Hickson et al., 1977). The increase in endurance appeared to be due to the muscle and liver glycogen sparing effects of increased FFA utilization (Hickson et al., 1977).

The finding that raising plasma FFA slows hepatic glycogen depletion during exercise suggested that the rate of glucose uptake by muscle was decreased. A partial inhibition of glucose uptake by FFA oxidation was confirmed in studies using a well-oxygenated, perfused rat hindquarter preparation (Rennie & Holloszy, 1977). Glucose uptake and lactate production by well-oxygenated rat hindlimb muscles were inhibited approximately 30%, both at rest and during muscle contraction when a high concentration of oleate was included in the perfusion medium (Rennie & Holloszy, 1977). Addition of oleate to the perfusion medium also protected against glycogen depletion in the fast-twitch and slow-twitch red types of muscle during sciatic nerve stimulation (Rennie & Holloszy, 1977). The concentrations of citrate and glucose-6-PO_4 were both increased in red muscle perfused with oleate (Rennie & Holloszy, 1977). These and other studies show that, as in heart muscle, oxidation of FFA inhibits glucose uptake and glycolysis, and has a glycogen sparing effect in skeletal muscle.

FFA CONCENTRATION AND RATE OF OXIDATION

There appears to be a linear relationship between the concentration of plasma FFA and their rate of oxidation (Hagenfeldt, 1975). Thus, one mechanism for increasing the rate of FFA oxidation is to increase the concentration of FFA to which the muscles are exposed, as was done in the studies reviewed above (Hagenfeldt, 1975; Hickson et al., 1977; Randle et al., 1963; Rennie & Holloszy, 1977; Rennie et al., 1976). However, measurements on the same individuals before and after adaptation to a strenuous program of endurance training indicate that plasma FFA concentration is usually lower in the trained than in the untrained state during exercise of the same absolute intensity (Winder, Hickson, Hagberg, Ehsani, & McLane, 1979).

The lower plasma FFA concentration in the trained state could result from either increased utilization or decreased production. It appears from available evidence that a slower rate of FFA release from adipose tissue is responsible. Blood glycerol concentration usually reflects changes in the rate of lipolysis in adipose tissue (Hetenyi, Perez, & Vranic, 1983). In this context, the finding that blood glycerol concentration during exercise of the same intensity is also lower in the trained than in the untrained state (Winder et al., 1979), favors the interpretation that the rate of lipolysis in adipose tissue is decreased. This interpretation is supported by the preliminary results of a study currently in progress in which we are measuring the rates of [1-^{13}C] palmitate turnover in the same individuals performing the same prolonged exercise test before and after an intense program of endurance training.

It appears from our preliminary results that the rates of plasma FFA appearance and disappearance are approximately 40% lower following the training program, and that the rate of plasma palmitate oxidation after training is approximately 35% lower than in the untrained state (Dalsky et al., 1984). This slower rate of palmitate oxidation after training is apparently due to the lower plasma palmitate concentration, since the metabolic clearance rate was not significantly different. In these studies, in which we are making the assumption that total plasma FFA behaves similarly to palmitate with respect to turnover and oxidation, there was a good correlation between plasma palmitate concentration and palmitate oxidation both before and after training. R was lower during exercise in the trained state, despite the evidence for a slower rate of plasma FFA oxidation (Dalsky et al., 1984).

Endurance training of the type used in our studies results in a marked blunting of the plasma catecholamine response to submaximal exercise (Winder et al., 1979). The finding of a lower plasma FFA concentration, with a concomitant decrease in the rate of plasma FFA oxidation, is therefore not surprising, as the decrease in sympathoadrenal activity could account for a decreased stimulation of lipolysis in adipose tissue. The resulting reduction in plasma FFA concentration could, in turn, explain the slower rate of plasma FFA oxidation, as there is usually a linear relationship between plasma FFA concentration and oxidation (Hagenfeldt, 1975).

FAT OXIDATION AND EXERCISE

The evidence that the rate of fat oxidation is higher in the trained than in the untrained state during submaximal exercise despite a lower rate of plasma FFA oxidation indicates that training must result in increased utilization of fatty acids derived from a source other than plasma. Muscle triglyceride concentration can decrease sufficiently during prolonged exercise to provide a large portion of the fat that is oxidized (Essen, 1977). We, therefore, investigated the possibility that endurance exercise training might result in increased muscle triglyceride utilization during prolonged exercise (Hurley et al., 1985).

Nine men performed a prolonged bout of exercise of the same intensity before and after adapting to a 12-week-long program of running and cycling that resulted in a 26% increase in $\dot{V}O_2$max before training. Plasma FFA and glycerol concentrations and R during the prolonged exercise were lower in the trained than in the untrained state. The proportion of the caloric expenditure derived from fat calculated from the R increased from 35% before training to 57% after training. Muscle glycogen utilization was 42% lower, while the decrease in muscle triglyceride concentration was roughly twice as great in the trained state. The decrease in muscle triglyceride concentration was sufficiently larger in the trained than in the untrained state to account for the greater amount of fat oxidized (estimated from R and $\dot{V}O_2$) in the trained state.

The increased utilization of fat as a source of energy has the obvious benefit of delaying the depletion of muscle and hepatic glycogen stores during prolonged strenuous exercise. However, it is not clear at present whether increased utilization of muscle triglyceride, in preference to plasma FFA has any physiological advantages, or is just a compensatory mechanism made necessary by decreased β-adrenergic stimulation of lipolysis in adipose tissue in the trained state.

The mechanisms responsible for the greater oxidation of fatty acids in the trained than in the untrained state during submaximal exercise have not yet been completely elucidated. It seems well documented that one important factor that determines the rate of fatty acid oxidation is FFA concentration (Hagenfeldt, 1975). There appears to be a linear relationship between plasma FFA concentration and the rate of removal and oxidation of plasma FFA. Thus, one way of increasing FFA oxidation is to increase plasma FFA concentration. It seems clear that this mechanism can not account for the higher rate of fat oxidation in the trained state, because plasma FFA concentration is lower, not higher, in the trained than in the untrained state during exercise of the same absolute submaximal intensity (Winder et al., 1979). However, the rate at which muscle oxidizes fatty acids is not determined directly by plasma FFA concentration, but by (a) the concentration of fatty acids in the cytoplasm to which the mitochondria are exposed, (b) the mitochondrial content of the muscle, and (c) likely also by the availability of competing substrate (cf. Holloszy & Coyle, 1984). Plasma FFA concentration is only one of the factors determining cytoplasmic fatty acid concentration, which could also be influenced by the rate of intramuscular triglyceride lipolysis. There is currently no information available regarding the concentrations of fatty acids in trained and untrained muscles. Thus, the possibility exists that the intracellular fatty acid concentration may be higher in trained than in untrained muscle during submaximal exercise, which could play a role in accounting for the higher rate of fat oxidation.

Endurance exercise training results in an increase in muscle mitochondria (Holloszy, 1967; Holloszy & Booth, 1976), which is associated with an increase in the capacity of muscle to oxidize fatty acids (Molé et al., 1971). If the intracellular concentration of fatty acids during exercise is similar in the trained and untrained states, the adaptive increase in mitochondria, and particularly of the mitochondrial enzymes of the pathway for fatty acid oxidation, may be entirely responsible for the greater oxidation of fat in the trained state (Holloszy & Booth, 1976; Holloszy & Coyle, 1984; Molé et al., 1971). While the overall rate of substrate oxidation in muscle is determined by the rate of ATP hydrolysis, which is a function of work rate, the relative rates of carbohydrate and of fat oxidation are determined by (a) availability of FFA and pyruvate, (b) the activities of the rate-limiting enzymes in the pathways for generating acetyl-CoA from carbohydrate and fatty acids, and (c) by a number of regulatory mechanisms.

Of the regulatory mechanisms, perhaps the most important are (a) less activation of glycolysis at the same work rate in trained than in untrained muscles (Holloszy & Coyle, 1984), and (b) slowing of glucose uptake and glycolysis by the inhibitory effects of fat oxidation (Hickson et al., 1977; Rennie et al., 1976; Rennie & Holloszy, 1977).

CONCLUSIONS

In summary, it seems well established that the increased oxidation of fat in the trained state plays a major role in bringing about the slower utilization of carbohydrate during submaximal exercise. The results of a recent study provide evidence that the greater utilization of fat in the trained than in the untrained state during submaximal exercise of the same absolute intensity is fueled by increased lipolysis of muscle triglycerides. The mechanism responsible for the greater oxidation of fat in the trained state have not yet been fully elucidated; however, it is probable that the increase in muscle mitochondria induced by exercise training plays a major role.

REFERENCES

Baldwin, K.M., Klinkerfuss, G.H., Terjung, R.L., Molé, P.A., & Holloszy, J.O. (1972). Respiratory capacity of white, red and intermediate muscle: adaptive response to exercise. *American Journal of Physiology*, **222**, 373-378.

Chi, M.M.-Y., Hintz, C.S., Coyle, E.F., Martin III, W.H., Ivy, J.L., Nemeth, P.M., Holloszy, J.O., & Lowry, O.H. (1983). Effects of detraining on enzymes of energy metabolism in individual human muscle fibers. *American Journal of Physiology*, **244**, C276-C287.

Costill, D.L., Coyle, E., Dalsky, G., Evans, W., Fink, W., & Hoopes, D. (1977). Effects of elevated plasma FFA and insulin on muscle glycogen usage during exercise. *Journal of Applied Physiology*, **43**, 695-699.

Costill, D.L., Fink, W.J., Getchell, L.H., Ivy, J.L., & Witzman, F.A. (1979). Lipid metabolism in skeletal muscle of endurance-trained males and females. *Journal of Applied Physiology*, **47**, 787-791.

Dalsky, G., Martin, W., Hurley, B., Matthews, D., Bier, D., Hagberg, J., & Holloszy, J.O. (1984). Oxidation of plasma FFA during endurance exercise. *Medicine and Science in Sports and Exercise,* **16**, 202.

Essen, B. (1977). Intramuscular substrate utilization during prolonged exercise. *Annals of the New York Academy of Sciences,* **301**, 30-44.

Hagenfeldt, L. (1975). Turnover of individual free fatty acids in man. *Federation Proceedings,* **34**, 2236-2240.

Henriksson, J. (1977). Training induced adaptations of skeletal muscle and metabolism during submaximal exercise. *Journal of Physiology,* **270**, 661-675.

Hermansen, L.E., Hultman, E., & Saltin, B. (1967). Muscle glycogen during prolonged severe exercise. *Acta Physiologica Scandinavica,* **71**, 129-139.

Hetenyi Jr., G., Perez, G., & Vranic, M. (1983). Turnover and precurser-product relationships of non lipid metabolites. *Physiological Reviews,* **63**, 606-667.

Hickson, R.C., Rennie, M.J., Conlee, R.K., Winder, W.W., & Holloszy, J.O. (1977). Effects of increased plasma fatty acids on glycogen utilization and endurance. *Journal of Applied Physiology,* **43**, 829-833.

Holloszy, J.O. (1967). Biochemical adaptations in muscle. Effects of exercise on mitochondrial oxygen uptake and respiratory enzyme activity in skeletal muscle. *Journal of Biological Chemistry,* **242**, 2278-2282.

Holloszy, J.O., & Booth, F.W., (1976). Biochemical adaptations to endurance exercise in muscle. *Annual Review of Physiology,* **38**, 273-291.

Holloszy, J.O, & Coyle, E.F. (1984). Adaptations of skeletal muscle to endurance exercise and their metabolic consequences. *Journal of Applied Physiology,* **56**, 831-838.

Hurley, B.F., Nemeth, P.M., Martin III, W.H., Dalsky, G.P., Hagberg, J.M., & Holloszy, J.O. (1985). The effects of endurance exercise training on intramuscular substrate use during prolonged submaximal exercise. *Medicine and Science in Sports and Exercise,* **17**, 259.

Jansson, E., & Kaijser, L. (1977). Muscle adaptation to extreme endurance in man. *Acta Physiologica Scandinavica,* **100**, 315-324.

Molé, P.A., Oscai, L.B., & Holloszy, J.O. (1971). Adaptation of muscle to exercise. Increase in levels of palmityl CoA in synthetase, carnitine palmityltransferase, and palmityl CoA dehydrogenase and in the capacity to oxidize fatty acids. *Journal of Clinical Investigation,* **50**, 2323-2330.

Randle, P.J., Garland, P.B., Hales, C.N., & Newsholme, E.A. (1963). The glucose-fatty-acid cycle. Its role in insulin sensitivity and the metabolic disturbances of diabetes mellitus. *Lancet,* **i**, 785-789.

Rennie, M.J., & Holloszy, J.O. (1977). Inhibition of glucose uptake and glycogenolysis by availability of oleate in well-oxygenated perfused skeletal muscle. *Biochemical Journal,* **168**, 161-170.

Rennie, M.J., Winder, W.W., & Holloszy, J.O. (1976). A sparing effect of increased plasma fatty acids on muscle and liver glycogen content in the exercising rat. *Biochemical Journal*, **156**, 647-655.

Winder, W.W., Hickson, R.C., Hagberg, J.M., Ehsani, A.A., & McLane, J.A. (1979). Training-induced changes in hormonal and metabolic responses to submaximal exercise. *Journal of Applied Physiology*, **46**, 766-771.

Enzymatic Adaptation and its Significance for Metabolic Response to Exercise

Philip D. Gollnick
David R. Hodgson
Washington State University
Pullman, Washington, U.S.A.

Skeletal muscles are biological machines capable of converting chemical energy to mechanical energy during the performance of work. The transducers for this energy transformation are the actin and myosin filaments that interact during shortening of the sarcomeres. In the process of their interaction, energy stored in ATP is consumed. Several biochemical pathways exist in muscle to produce ATP via the oxidation of energy compounds that are either stored in or delivered to the muscles. To what extent each pathway is used, and how important each is in the overall ATP production, depends on factors such as the nature and duration of the activity, the state of physical training, and the availability of substrates as influenced by diet and the extent of the exercise.

ADAPTATIONS THAT OCCUR WITH EXERCISE

An important characteristic of the muscular system is the diversity of its response to the commands of the central nervous system when required to perform differing tasks. What patterns of contractile activity a muscle is required to execute and with what frequency greatly influences the character of that muscle. This adaptation to the demands placed upon it takes the form of a ''remodeling'' and is normally initiated either before or immediately after birth, when muscles are first used extensively. The remodeling can occur either within the fibers themselves or in the support tissues such as the capillaries.

With heavy resistance exercise the adaptive response is an increase in the size of the muscle, produced by hypertrophy of the fibers (Goldspink, 1983; Gollnick, Timson, Moore, & Riedy, 1981; MacDougall, Sale, Alway, & Sutton, 1984; Tesch, Thorsson, & Kaiser, 1984). The advantage of this hypertrophic response is to increase the cross-sectional area of the muscle, which increases its capacity to generate force. An associated negative effect a is often a lower oxidative potential per unit of muscle, produced by a ''growth dilution'' in the concentration of mitochondria (Gollnick,

Armstrong, Saubert, Piehl, & Saltin, 1972). There can also be a lowering of the capillary-to-fiber area, which will reduce the capacity to supply fuel (including oxygen) to the fibers (Tesch et al., 1984). The end result of these changes is an enhanced ability of the muscle to generate tension at the expense of endurance.

Equally impressive, though less visible externally, are the adaptations that occur in skeletal muscle with endurance training. These are exemplified by an increased ability to perform prolonged exercise and are characterized by greater concentrations of mitochondria (either more or larger mitochondria or expansion of a mitochondrial reticulum, if they in fact exist as such), glycogen, and perhaps triglycerides in the muscle fibers (Saltin & Gollnick, 1983). Endurance training also results in an increased number of capillaries per fiber. Endurance training also produces an increase in the total body maximal oxygen uptake ($\dot{V}O_2max$) (Blomqvist, 1983; Rowell, 1974). However, when viewed from the perspective of its relative importance, the increase in oxidative potential of the skeletal muscle appears to be less important to the increase in total body $\dot{V}O_2max$ than to the ability to continue exercise (Davies, Packer, & Brooks, 1981, 1982). This conclusion is based upon the observation that after endurance training the capacities of the citric acid cycle, electron transport chain, and beta oxidation pathway increase more than does total body $\dot{V}O_2max$. There is also a closer matching of the $\dot{V}O_2max$ with the capacity of the circulatory system to deliver oxygen to the muscle than with that of the oxidative capacity of the skeletal muscles (Rowell, 1974).

The ability of endurance-trained individuals to exercise for longer periods of time than sedentary or sprint-trained individuals, and to do so at higher percentages of their $\dot{V}O_2max$, lies in the ability of trained muscles to oxidize a higher percentage of fat (Christensen, 1932; Karlsson, Nordesjö, & Saltin, 1974) and to maintain lower concentrations of lactate in blood and muscle (Bang, 1936; Gollnick & Saltin, 1982; Karlsson et al., 1974). This results in a slower rate of glycogen depletion, and because the exhaustion of the muscle glycogen stores is closely correlated with the onset of exhaustion, enables the muscular work to continue for extended periods of time.

THE TRAINING EFFECT ON METABOLIC REGULATION

The question addressed in this paper is: How do the changes in the concentration of mitochondrial enzymes that occur with training result in an enhanced combustion of fat and a sparing of glycogen? This problem must be approached from the basis of known principles for metabolic regulation and how such regulation could be influenced by changes occurring in muscle in response to endurance training. Basic to this discussion is an understanding that although there is an increase in the $\dot{V}O_2max$ after endurance training, very little exercise is done at $\dot{V}O_2max$ and the more impressive difference between the trained and nontrained individual is the ability of the trained individual to sustain submaximal exercise. Crucial to this discussion of the role of the adaptations occurring in response to endurance training is the question of whether the capacities of the cardiovascular system and of the oxidative pathways of the sedentary person are adequate to support all the metabolic demands of submaximal exercise. Several pieces of evidence suggest that they are adequate. One is the observation that whole body $\dot{V}O_2$ for an exercise of set power production, where no refinement of motion occurs with training, is essentially unchanged by training. Also, under these conditions cardiac output is the same before and after training as is blood flow through the muscle, even though there is an increase in capillary density in the muscle with endurance training (Blomqvist, 1983; Freedman, Snider, Brostoff, Kimelblot, & Katz, 1955; Rowell, 1974).

Studies in which subjects trained only one leg and then performed two-leg exercise also demonstrate that for submaximal exercise neither the capacity of the circulatory system to deliver oxygen nor the capacity of the metabolic pathways for oxygen use within muscle is limiting (Henriksson, 1977; Saltin et al., 1978). In these experiments, the $\dot{V}O_2$s and the muscle blood flows of the two legs were remarkably similar, whereas the metabolic responses were markedly different, as reflected by the source of fuel metabolized (RQ) and the dynamics of lactate flux, as determined from blood and muscle lactate concentrations and as calculated from the A-V differences. From the determinations of the blood gases, it was clear that the trained leg used more fat and less glycogen than did the nontrained leg. There were also differences in the dynamics of lactate, with a net influx into the trained leg and there was a net efflux from the nontrained leg. Moreover, the concentration of lactate in the muscle was lower in the trained than in the nontrained leg. These findings are similar to those in which comparisons were made between whole body metabolism and that of working muscles, both before and after training (Bang, 1936; Christensen, 1932; Hermansen, Hultman, & Saltin, 1967; Karlsson et al., 1974). In addition, the onset of lactate accumulation in muscle and blood occurs at a higher absolute and relative oxygen consumption in the trained as compared to the nontrained state. (Bang, 1936; Hermansen & Saltin, 1969).

REGULATION OF MITOCHONDRIAL RESPIRATION AND GLYCOLYSIS

The results from studies examining total body and individual muscle metabolism before and after training allow the conclusion to be drawn that the elevation in oxidative potential of muscle in response to endurance training is more related to the ability of the muscle to regulate the relative use of fat and carbohydrate than to an increase in the $\dot{V}O_2max$. How then can a change in enzyme concentrations lead to a shift in metabolic control and affect the choice of fuel used by working muscle? Any scheme that attempts to explain how endurance training, and the increase in the mitochondrial protein concentration in muscle accompanying training, alters metabolic control so that there is an augmented fat oxidation and a diminished carbohydrate and lactate production, must explain how these events occur. We believe this question must be approached by examining the factors known to be key regulators of mitochondrial respiration and glycolysis, and how differences in the total concentration of mitochondrial protein can influence this regulation.

Theories of Regulation

As a background for this discussion, a short description of some of the theories of regulation is presented. It is brief as this topic has recently been reviewed (Jacobus, 1985; Mela-Riker & Bukoski, 1985; Tager et al., 1983). At least 5 regulatory factors have been suggested as controlling mitochondrial respiration. These are: (a) oxygen availability, (b) the cytosolic phosphate potential, defined as the ratio of the free concentrations of ATP/ ADP × *Pi*, (c) the ratio of ATP to ADP, either in the cytosol or mitochondria, (d) the concentration of inorganic phosphate in the cytosol, and (e) the capacity of the adenine nucleotide translocase system.

Of these, oxygen availability is an unlikely candidate as a regulator of mitochondrial respiration since its Michaelis constant (Km) is in the range of 0.03 to 0.24 uM. This suggests that mitochondrial respiration is not regulated by the oxygen concentration existing in vivo under normal physiological conditions. This is not to intimate that conditions do not exist where the absence of oxygen will influence metabolism. In the absence of oxygen there is an obligatory degradation of glycogen to lactate to replace ATP as it is consumed. Some skeletal muscle is well equipped for such metabolism. However, lactate production is not always synonymous with the existence of an anaerobic state in muscle (Connett, Yagyeski, & Honig, 1984; Jöbsis & Stainsby, 1968; Kobayashi & Neely, 1979). The catabolism of glycogen and glucose always proceeds through the Embden-Myerhof pathway with the production of pyruvate. The amount of pyruvate produced is crucial in determining the extent to which it is transported into the mitochondria or is reduced to lactate via lactic dehydrogenase. The fact that small amounts of lactate are normally found in muscle, even in highly aerobic muscle with a high resting blood flow, demonstrates that some lactate may be produced even under aerobic conditions. When glycogenolysis is activated during muscular contraction, pyruvate production may exceed the amount needed to provide acetyl units to the mitochondria. An excess pyruvate concentration will promote lactate formation even when the oxygen concentration is adequate to support mitochondrial respiration at a rate sufficient to meet all ATP requirements. This lactate production is simply a ''spill over'' of an excessive pyruvate production by a mass action effect of lactic dehydrogenase.

It is also unlikely that the concentration of *Pi* is a regulator of mitochondrial respiration. Its concentration increases during exercise into the millimolar range, which is far above its Km for transport into mitochondria.

Estimates of the changes in free ADP suggest that it may increase into the micromolar range, which is near its Km for stimulating mitochondrial respiration and for transport into the mitochondria by the adenine nucleotide translocase system. On this basis it seems either ADP itself, or its relationship with other factors, perhaps as the ATP/ADP ratio or phosphate potential, is the prime regulator of mitochondrial respiration. In addition to being an activator of mitochondrial respiration, changes in the cytosolic ATP/ADP ratio may also influence the regulation of glycolysis. With a decrease in this ratio the normal inhibition of phosphofructokinase is relieved to allow for an increased flux through the Embden-Myerhof pathway. AMP, produced via the myokinase reaction where 2 ADPs are converted to 1 ATP and 1 AMP, is also a powerful activator of phosphorylase and of phosphofructokinase.

The capacity of the adenine nucleotide translocase system has been suggested (Tager et al., 1983) as being the key regulator of mitochondrial respiratory rate. However, in tissues with high concentrations of mitochondrial protein, such as the heart, this has been disputed.

During exercise the major source of ADP is the breakdown of ATP during the interaction of the actin and myosin filaments. This will change the ATP/ADP ratio in the cytosol. The question considered here is: How does a change in the concentration of mitochondrial protein alter metabolic control? The model proposed is based on the assumption that mitochondrial respiration is controlled by changes in ADP concentration. Since ADP within the mitochondria appears to be required as a phosphate acceptor and in its absence respiration is essentially zero, the problem is to transport either the ADP that is produced by the contraction, or some equivalent of ADP (creatine), to the mitochondria. This may occur by simple diffusion of the ADP from its site of production at the myofibrils to the mitochondria or via a transport system. It has been suggested that a phosphorylcreatine shuttle is involved in this process (Bessman & Geiger, 1981; Jacobus, 1985; Wallimann, Scholsser, & Eppenberger, 1984). This system is envisaged as having the cytosolic creatine phosphate (CP) rapidly rephosphorylating ADP to ATP, catalyzed by the enzyme creatine kinase, which exists bound to the M-band of the myosin filaments (Wallimann et al., 1984). The creatine formed in this process is shuttled to the mitochondria for rephosphorylation by ATP on the outer surface of the inner mitochondrial membrane by the mitochondrially-bound creatine kinase. This is in essence a transfer of ADP from the cytosol to the immediate area of the adenine nucleotide translocase of the inner mitochondrial membrane. In this system, there is a rapid buffering of the ATP at the site of its degradation. The existence of a creatine shuttle system is an attractive hypothesis for steady state conditions, such as those existing in the heart, where there would be little change in CP during normal activity. It does not encompass the role of CP in buffering the decline in ATP in skeletal muscle as would occur during heavy exercise, where there are declines in CP. Of importance to this point is the general observation that an inverse relationship exists between aerobic potential (mitochondrial protein concentration) and the creatine phosphate concentration in skeletal muscle. Thus, in this tissue the CP may truly represent a high energy phosphate reserve rather than being merely an ATP shuttle.

Effect of Mitochondrial Protein Concentration on ADP Transport

The speed with which the ADP, or its equivalent in the form of creatine, is transported into the mitochondria will be directly related to the concentration of mitochondrial protein. This conclusion is based on the fact that by having a greater concentration of mitochondrial protein, whether as a result of an increase in their number, size, or overall volume (should mitochondria exist as a reticulum), there will be a greater surface area, that is, more translocase, sites for interaction with the cytosolic ADP and for the transport of other metabolites (fatty acids, pyruvate, etc.) into the mitochondria. The net effect of this will be to facilitate a rapid translocation of ADP into the mitochondria thereby promoting a rapid onset of oxygen uptake and maintaining a low ADP concentration in the cytosol. This will result in a smaller displacement of the ATP/ADP ratio, or the ATP/ADP × *Pi* ratio, from the rest value. Since one of the prime regulators of glycolysis is the ATP/ADP ratio, this will be effective in retarding glycogen degradation. As less pyruvate is produced, there is a smaller possibility of it being reduced to lactate via a mass action (spill over) effect. With a lower pyruvate production and therefore lower local concentration, acetyl units derived from the beta oxidation of fatty acids will be able to compete more favorably with those generated from the pyruvate dehydrogenase complex. The increases in total surface area of the mitochondria will also support a more rapid uptake of fatty acids and pyruvate by mitochondria. The elevated activity of enzymes for fatty acid degradation, such as 3-hydroxacyl-CoA dehydrogenase, will also favor an increased contribution of fat to the total metabolism. The net effect of the increase in mitochondria will be to improve the responsiveness of the system at the onset of contractile activity, enhance fat use, and suppress glycogen use. These responses are precisely those occurring for muscle and for the body as a whole in response to endurance training.

Response of Mitochondrial Respiration to ADP Translocation

The fact that the steady state $\dot{V}O_2$ for a standard power production is the same for nontrained and trained individuals, demonstrates that mitochondria of the active muscles of these individuals are able to support the same metabolic rate and ATP-ADP flux under both conditions. This demonstrates that mitochondrial protein concentration is not limiting to the steady state oxygen uptake at submaximal efforts. In the proposed model, the increases in mitochondrial respiration are believed to occur in response to translocation of ADP into the mitochondria. When there is an accumulation of ADP at the inner mitochondrial membrane (produced by its diffusion from the myofilaments or the creatine shuttle) so that there is a steady state ADP/ATP exchange equivalent to that occurring at the myofilament level, the oxygen uptake will be equal to that needed to support ATP production. Based on simple Henri-Michaelis-Menten kinetics (Gollnick & Saltin, 1982), when few mitochondria are available, a higher concentration of cytosolic ADP will result for a given energy demand above a certain baseline. When mitochondrial adenine nucleotide translocase is increased, via increased mitochondrial number and/or increased reticulum size, more ADP can be exchanged for ATP, thus keeping the cytosolic ADP concentration minimized. The accumulation of ADP in the cytosol will promote a continuation of glycogenolysis at a level where pyruvate production exceeds the need of the citric acid cycle for acetyl units and lactate production will occur under completely aerobic conditions. Thus an elevation in mitochondrial concentration has two effects: (a) to speed the responsiveness of the system, and (b) to maintain a low cytosolic ADP concentration.

STUDIES ON TISSUE RESPIRATION

Support for the contention that increases in mitochondrial protein concentration of muscle will promote a rapid rise in respiration during exercise is demonstrated by experiments in which the number of twitches needed to produce a half-maximal rise in the oxygen uptake of heart and skeletal muscle were examined (Chance & Connelley, 1957; Ramírez, 1959). In these studies more than twice the number of twitches were required in the skeletal muscle as compared to heart muscle to produce a half-maximal rise in tissue respiration. For man, it has also been observed that there is a more rapid rise in total body $\dot{V}O_2$ at the onset of exercise when trained and nontrained individuals are compared (Whipp & Wasserman, 1972), or when subjects are assessed before and after training (Hagberg, Hickson, Ashani, & Holloszy, 1980). These data from isolated preparations and from man support the concept that an elevation in mitochondrial protein concentration is important in increasing the sensitivity of the respiratory process in skeletal muscle at the onset of exercise. This increased sensitivity, with its ability to regulate the cytosolic ADP concentration, is probably responsible for the shift toward a greater utilization of fat during prolonged exercise after endurance training. Further evidence supporting the hypothesis that one of the major roles of the increase in mitochondrial protein is to produce a cellular environment that can more efficiently handle the ADP as it is produced, is the finding of Karlsson, Nordesjö, Jorfeldt, and Saltin (1972) that the decline in phosphagen content (ATP and CP) during exercise was greater at the same absolute power production before as compared to after training in man. More recently, Dudley and Terjung (1985) have reported that with electrical stimulation there was a smaller accumulation of IMP and loss of ATP, and lower concentrations of lactate and ammonia in highly oxidative muscle fibers as compared to the low oxidative fibers. With endurance training there was a shift of the normal response, with the normally low oxidative fibers becoming more like the highly oxidative fibers. This is further evidence that the increase in total mitochondrial protein of muscle with endurance training results in a more effective control of metabolism to avoid an accumulation of ADP in the cytosol.

REFERENCES

Bang, O. (1936). The lactate content of the blood during and after muscular exercise in man. *Skandinavisches Archives für Physiology,* **74**, 51-82.

Bessman, S.P., & Geiger, P.J. (1981). Transport of energy in muscle: The phosphorylcreatine shuttle. *Science,* **211**, 448-452.

Blomqvist, C.G. (1983). Cardiovascular adaptations to physical training. *Annual Review of Physiology,* **45**, 169-189.

Chance, B., & Connelly, C.M. (1957). A method for the estimation of the increase in concentration of adenosine diphosphate in muscle sarcosomes following a contraction. *Nature,* **179**, 1235-1237.

Christensen, E.H. (1932). Beitrage zur physiologie schwerer korperlicher Arbeit. *Arbeitsphysiologie,* **5**, 463-478.

Connett, R.J., Yagyeski, T.E.J., & Honig, C.R. (1984). Lactate accumulation in fully aerobic, working, dog gracilis muscle. *American Journal of Physiology,* **246**, H120-H128.

Davies, K.J.A., Packer, L., & Brooks, G.A. (1981). Biochemical adaptations of mitochondria, muscle, and whole-animal respiration to endurance training. *Archives of Biochemistry and Biophysics,* **209**, 538-553.

Davies, K.J.A., Packer, L., & Brooks, G.A. (1982). Exercise bioenergetics following sprint training. *Archives of Biochemistry and Biophysics,* **215**, 260-265.

Dudley, G.A., & Terjung, R.L. (1985). Influence of aerobic metabolism on IMP accumulation in fast-twitch muscle. *American Journal of Physiology,* **248**, C37-C42.

Freedman, M.E., Snider, G.L., Brostoff, P., Kimelblot, S., & Katz, L.N. (1955). Effects of training on response of cardiac output to muscular exercise in athletes. *Journal of Applied Physiology,* **8**, 37-47.

Gollnick, P.D., Armstrong, R.B., Saubert IV, C.W., Piehl, K., & Saltin, B. (1972). Enzyme activity and fiber composition in skeletal muscle of nontrained and trained men. *Journal of Applied Physiology,* **33**, 312-319.

Gollnick, P.D., & Saltin, B. (1982). Significance of skeletal muscle oxidative enzyme enhancement with endurance exercise. *Clinical Physiology,* **2**, 1-12.

Gollnick, P.D., Timson, B.F., Moore, R.L., & Riedy, M. (1981). Muscular enlargement and number of fibers in skeletal muscles of rats. *Journal of Applied Physiology,* **50**, 936-943.

Goldspink, G. (1983). Alterations in myofibril size and structure during growth, exercise, and changes in environmental temperature. In L.D. Peachy, R.H. Adrian, & S.R. Geiger (Eds.) *Handbook of physiology: Skeletal muscle.* (pp. 539-554), Baltimore, MD: Williams and Wilkins.

Hagberg, J.M., Hickson, R.C., Ashani, A.A., & Holloszy, J.O. (1980). Faster adjustment to and recovery from submaximal exercise in the trained state. *Journal of Applied Physiology,* **48**, 218-224.

Henriksson, J. (1977). Training induced adaptations of skeletal muscle and metabolism during submaximal exercise. *Journal of Physiology,* **270**, 661-675.

Hermansen, L., Hultman, E., & Saltin, B. (1967). Muscle glycogen during prolonged severe exercise. *Acta Physiologica Scandinavica,* **71**, 129-139.

Hermansen, L., & Saltin, B. (1969). Blood lactate concentration during exercise at acute exposure to altitude. In R. Maragaria (Ed.), *Exercise at altitude* (pp. 48-53). Amsterdam: Excerpta Medical Foundation.

Jacobus, W.E. (1985). Respiratory control and the integration of heart high-energy phosphate metabolism by mitochondrial creatine kinase. *Annual Review of Physiology,* **47**, 707-725.

Jöbsis, F.F., & Stainsby, W.N. (1968). Oxidation of NADH during contractions of circulated mammalian skeletal muscle. *Respiration Physiology,* **4**, 292-300.

Karlsson, J., Nordesjö, L.-O., & Saltin, B. (1974). Muscle glycogen utilization during exercise after physical training. *Acta Physiologica Scandinavica,* **90**, 210-217.

Karlsson, J., Nordesjö, L.-O., Jorfeldt, J., & Saltin, B. (1972). Muscle lactate, ATP, and CP levels during exercise after physical training in man. *Journal of Applied Physiology,* **33**, 199-203.

Kobayashi, K., and Neely, J.R. (1979). Control of maximal rates of glycolysis in rat cardiac muscle. *Circulation Research,* **44**, 166-175.

MacDougall, J.D., Sale, D.G., Alway, S.E., & Sutton, J.R. (1984). Muscle fiber number in biceps brachii in bodybuilders and control subjects. *Journal of Applied Physiology,* **57**, 1399-1403.

Mela-Riker, L.M., & Bukoski, R.D. (1985). Regulation of mitochondrial activity in cardiac cells. *Annual Review of Physiology,* **47**, 645-663.

Ramírez, J. (1959). Oxidation-reduction changes of cytochromes following stimulation of amphibian cardiac muscle. *Journal of Physiology,* **147**, 14-32.

Rowell, L.B. (1974). Human cardiovascular adjustments to exercise and thermal stress. *Physiological Reviews,* **54**, 75-159.

Saltin, B., Nazar, K., Costill, D.L., Stein, E., Jansson, E., Essén, B., & Gollnick, P.D. (1978). The nature of the training response: Peripheral and central adaptations to one-legged exercise. *Acta Physiologica Scandinavica,* **96**, 289-305.

Saltin, B., & Gollnick, P.D. (1983). Skeletal muscle adaptability: Significance for metabolism and performance. In L.D. Peachy, R.H. Adrian, & S.R. Geiger (Eds.), *Handbook of Physiology: Skeletal Muscle* (pp. 555-631). Baltimore: Williams and Wilkins.

Tager, J.M., Wanders, R.J.A., Groen, A.K., Kunz, W., Bohnensack, R., Kuester, U., Letko, G., Boehme, G., Duszynski, J., & Wojtczak, L. (1983). Control of respiration. *Federation of the European Biochemistry Society Letters,* **151**, 1-9.

Tesch, P.A., Thorsson, A., & Kaiser, P. (1984). Muscle capillary supply and fiber type characteristics in weight and power lifters. *Journal of Applied Physiology,* **56**, 35-38.

Walliman, T., Scholsser, T., & Eppenberger, H.M. (1984). Function of the M-line creatine kinase as intramyofibrillar ATP regenerator at the receiving end of the phosphorylcreatine shuttle in muscle. *Journal of Biological Chemistry,* **259**, 5238-5246.

Whipp, B.J., & Wasserman, K. (1972). Oxygen uptake kinetics for various intensities of constant-load work. *Journal of Applied Physiology,* **33**, 351-356.

SECTION D

VARIOUS FACTORS INFLUENCING THE METABOLISM DURING EXERCISE

Hepatic Metabolism During Hyperthermia and Hypoxemia

Loring B. Rowell
University of Washington
Seattle, Washington, U.S.A.

Several studies from the 1960s pointed to an important role of the liver in humans as a source of glucose during exercise. Some of these studies were reviewed in 1971 (Pernow & Saltin, 1971).

My comments are directed to the metabolic function of the liver in humans who are undergoing both the stress of exercise and an additional stress that has the potential of compromising further the function of the liver. There are two examples. One deals with the effects of sustained splanchnic vasoconstriction that can lead to hepatic ischemia. This occurs during severe exercise in warm environments. The second example deals with the effects of hypoxemia, which can lead to hepatic hypoxia. This could occur in mountaineers who climb at high altitudes. In the first case, the problems stem from reduced perfusion. In the second case, they stem from low arterial O_2 tension and content. In both cases hepatic venous O_2 tension reaches very low values.

PROLONGED HEAVY EXERCISE AND HYPERTHERMIA

During exercise, splanchnic blood flow (SBF) maintains a close inverse relationship to both heart rate and plasma norepinephrine (NE) concentration. Plasma NE concentration is an index of overall sympathetic nervous activity and reflects the increased vasoconstrictor outflow to splanchnic (and other) organs under a variety of stresses (Rowell, 1984).

Hyperthermia during exercise raises heart rate and both NE concentration and splanchnic vascular resistance in close parallel. The higher the heart rate the lower the SBF so that when heart rate approaches maximal values (and core temperature approaches 40 °C) SBF is reduced by as much as 70% (i.e., down to 450 to 500 ml min^{-1}) (Rowell, Brengelmann, Blackmon, Twiss, & Kusumi, 1968). Despite the low hepatic perfusion, O_2 consumption ($\dot{V}O_2$) of the region was maintained by almost complete extraction of O_2; hepatic venous O_2 content fell to 0.5 ml 100 ml^{-1}. In fact, splanchnic $\dot{V}O_2$ actually rose in proportion to the rise in hepatic venous temperature. Because of its low blood flow, the liver-stored heat and hepatic temperature approached 42 °C. Hepatic outpouring of glucose reached 1,200 mg min^{-1} as hepatic venous PO_2 reached its nadir. Low hepatic PO_2 and high circulating epinephrine (not measured but undoubtedly increased) will trigger glycogenolysis. The efficiency of lactate extraction by the liver was abnormally low and in two individuals with the lowest SBF, net release was observed. Taken together, these results suggest that ischemia, if not actually present, was imminent. The severe and well-known gastrointenstinal symptoms of long distance runners who compete on warm days undoubtedly stem from a relative hypoperfusion of splanchnic organs (see Milvy, 1977).

EXERCISE AND HYPOXEMIA

Exercise at simulated high altitude (5,800 m) raises heart rate and plasma NE concentration in close parallel just as at sea level, but in contrast to other stresses, SBF does not fall in inverse proportion to these changes (Rowell, Blackmon, Kenny, & Escourrou, 1984). The increase in sympathetic nervous activity is not directed to splanchnic organs but elsewhere. When subjects performed mild exercise for 72 min during which they breathed 11% O_2 for 20 min (PaO_2 = 32.2 Torr, O_2 content = 12 ml 100 ml^{-1}), splanchnic $\dot{V}O_2$ was maintained constant by 95% extraction of O_2. Hepatic venous O_2 content fell to 1.7 ml 100 ml^{-1} and its PO_2 averaged 7.5 Torr. SBF averaged 1.14 during normoxia and 1.35 1 min^{-1} during hypoxemia. No trend for decreased hepatic removal of lactate was observed. Hepatic glucose production exceeded by 2-fold the normal rates measured during exercise in normoxic conditions (see Pernow & Saltin, 1971). Again, low PO_2 and a high circulating epinephrine concentration (it rose from 0.2 to 0.72 ng ml^{-1}) were probably contributory. Both rate and efficiency of hepatic removal of NE and epinephrine increased during hypoxemia. Extraction of indocyanine green dye was the only measured function of the liver that was compromised by reduced hepatic PO_2.

Thus, in two severe stresses the metabolic function of the liver is preserved, in one case with extreme reduction in its flow, and the other case with extreme reduction in O_2 delivery—but with maintained or increased flow. A crucial adjustment is the ability of the liver to extract nearly all available O_2 from its blood supply. Damage to gastrointestinal organs follows when this adjustment is overwhelmed; for example, in patients with low cardiac output and in hyperthermic distance runners.

REFERENCES

Milvy, P. (Ed.) (1977). *The marathon: Physiological, medical, epidemiological, and psychological studies.* New York: New York Academy of Sciences.

Pernow, B., & Saltin, B. (Eds.) (1971). *Muscle metabolism during exercise.* New York, London: Plenum Press.

Rowell, L.B. (1984). Reflex control of regional circulations in humans. *Journal of the Autonomic Nervous System,* **11**, 101-114.

Rowell, L.B., Blackmon, J.R., Kenny, M.A., & Escourrou, P. (1984). Splanchnic vasomotor and metabolic adjustments to hypoxia and exercise in humans. *American Journal of Physiology, 247 (Heart and Circulatory Physiology,* **16**), H251-H258.

Rowell, L.B., Brengelmann, G.L., Blackmon, J.R., Twiss, R.D., Kusumi, F. (1968). Splanchnic blood flow and metabolism in heat-stressed man. *Journal of Applied Physiology,* **24**, 475-484.

Body Temperature as a Factor Modifying Exercise Metabolism

Stanislaw Kozlowski
Medical Research Center
Polish Academy of Sciences
Warsaw, Poland

During physical exercise body temperature may increase markedly sometimes reaching values above 40 °C. This is accompanied by even greater (by approximately 1 °C) elevations in muscle temperature (T_m). Thus, the temperature of human skeletal muscles varies from 25 to 33 °C at rest to above 41 °C during work. The magnitude of the enhancement in T_m depends mainly on exercise intensity and duration, external thermal conditions, muscle blood flow, and effectiveness of thermoregulation. Both the changes in body temperature per se, and the consequences of thermoregulatory responses (e.g., redistribution of blood, dehydration, etc.) influence muscle function and metabolism. The optimum levels of muscle temperature for various kinds of exercise are different. Thus, in some instances an elevation of muscle temperature can improve performance, whereas in others it can impair it.

EFFECTS OF TEMPERATURE ON DYNAMIC EXERCISE

During an intensive dynamic exercise an increased muscle temperature is considered beneficial mostly due to the enhanced muscle contractility. An ability to develop tension is less dependent on muscle temperature, although the fast contracting muscles in the rat were shown to decrease the twitch tension and to increase the tetanus tension with the temperature increasing from 20 to 35 °C. In human muscles examined in vivo, tension was reported to decrease, increase slightly, or to remain unchanged with the temperature increasing above 30 °C (for review see Bennet, 1984; Faulkner, 1980).

MUSCLE TEMPERATURE AND ENDURANCE EXERCISE

The optimum temperature range for endurance during the sustained or repeated isometric muscle contractions was found to be approximately 28 to 32 °C, the level being below the range usually found during this type of activity under normal conditions.

As it was demonstrated by Edwards et al. (1972), a decrease in endurance with an increased muscle temperature can be attributed to the adverse metabolic changes, namely to an inadequate ATP resynthesis because of the more rapid depletion of creatine phosphate and a decrease in the rate of glycolysis. The latter effect is a consequence of an inhibition of phosphofructokinase activity (PFK) by accumulation of hydrogen ions, which is caused by earlier acceleration of glycolysis at higher muscle temperatures.

Static Exercise and Temperature

The most rapid increase in T_m (up to 1 °C per min) occurs during the isometric static exercise because of an arrest in the muscle blood flow inhibiting heat elimination. However, such exercises are short-term so the absolute T_m levels attained are not as high as those reached during heavy prolonged dynamic efforts (Saltin, Gagge, & Stolwijk, 1968).

Aerobic Exercise and Temperature

The optimum level of body temperature for endurance during aerobic dynamic work with large muscle groups has not been precisely defined. As demonstrated by Schmidt and Brück (1981), and Hessemer, Langusch, Brück, Bödeker, and Breidenbach (1984), lowering of body temperature by a precooling maneuver improves endurance performance. Moreover, cooling of the body during such types of exercise was found to prolong working ability markedly. This was accompanied by a reduced cardiovascular strain, and lowering of blood lactate (LA) concentration (MacDougall, Reddan, Layton, & Dempsey, 1974). Both these findings and less rapid muscle glycogen depletion at lower body temperatures (Fink, Costill, & Van Handel, 1975) suggest that an increase in T_m may influence metabolic processes in working muscles during aerobic exercise.

INCREASED TEMPERATURES AND MUSCLE METABOLISM

To obtain more information on thermal dependence of metabolic processes in muscles during prolonged exercise, experiments were performed in this laboratory on dogs exercising until exhaustion (approximately 60 to 90 min) either under normal control conditions or with external cooling. The latter was done by fixing ice bags to the dogs' trunks as described elsewhere (Kruk, Kaciuba-Uściłko, Nazar, Greenleaf, & Kozlowski, 1985). Cooling resulted in prolongation of time of exercise until exhaustion by approximately 50%. The exercise-induced increases in rectal temperature (T_{re}) and T_m were significantly attenuated in cooled animals, which was accompanied by a reduced heart rate (HR), and respiratory frequency (R_f) as well as by less rapid increases in blood LA, plasma free fatty acid (FFA), glycerol and noradrenaline concentrations in comparison with control experiments without cooling (Table 1a + b).

Table 1a Rectal (T_{re}) and muscle (T_m) temperatures (°C), heart rate (HR, beats/min), and respiratory frequency (R_f, breaths/min) in dogs exercising at 20 ± 1 °C with and without trunk cooling (means ± SE, N = 21)[a]

Variables	Exercise without cooling		Exercise with cooling		
	before	end	before	end	E_c[b]
T_{re}	39.3 ± 0.1	41.8 ± 0.2	38.9 ± 0.1	40.7 ± 0.2	40.4 ± 0.2
T_m	39.3 ± 0.2	42.8 ± 0.3	39.3 ± 0.2	41.6 ± 0.2	41.3 ± 0.2
HR	113 ± 8	261 ± 15	116 ± 12	229 ± 18	220 ± 10
R_f	57 ± 18	289 ± 10	43 ± 5	273 ± 20	267 ± 20

[a]Compiled from "Hypothalamic, Rectal, and Muscle Temperatures in Exercising Dogs: Effect of Cooling" by B. Kruk, H. Kaciuba-Uściłko, K. Nazar, J.E. Greenleaf, and S. Kozlowski, 1985, *Journal of Applied Physiology*, **58**, pp. 1444-1448. And "Exercise Hyperthermia as a Factor Limiting Physical Performance: Temperature Effect on Muscle Metabolism in Dogs" by S. Kozlowski, Z. Brzezińska, B. Kruk, H. Kaciuba-Uściłko, J.E. Greenleaf, and K. Nazar, 1985, *Journal of Applied Physiology*, **59**, 766-773.
[b]Time corresponding to the end of the control run

Table 1b Blood concentrations of lactate (LA), glucose (BG), free fatty acids (FFA), glycerol (mmol/l), and noradrenaline (NA, nmol/l) in dogs exercising at ambient temperature 20 ± 1 °C with and without trunk cooling (means ± SE, n = 7)[a]

Variables	Exercise without cooling		Exercise with cooling		
	before	end	before	end	E_c[b]
LA	1.5 ± 0.18	4.3 ± 0.2	1.3 ± 0.1	3.8 ± 0.2	2.7 ± 0.2
BG	3.7 ± 3.0	2.9 ± 4.0	3.9 ± 2.2	2.9 ± 3.0	3.2 ± 3.0
FFA	0.58 ± 0.03	1.00 ± 0.06	0.61 ± 0.03	0.96 ± 0.1	0.85 ± 0.02
Glycerol	0.20 ± 0.03	0.45 ± 0.04	0.25 ± 0.02	0.40 ± 0.06	0.30 ± 0.03
NA	4.2 ± 0.5	8.2 ± 1.0	3.8 ± 0.3	7.8 ± 0.7	5.0 ± 0.7

[a]Compiled from "Exercise Hyperthermia as a Factor Limiting Physical Performance: Temperature Effect on Muscle Metabolism in Dogs" by S. Kozlowski, Z. Brzezińska, B. Kruk, H. Kaciuba-Uściłko, J.E. Greenleaf, and K. Nazar, 1985, *Journal of Applied Physiology*, **59**, 766-773.
[b]Time corresponding to the end of the control run

As it is shown in Table 2, cooling prevented a decrease in muscle ATP content and resulted in a significantly smaller increase in ADP and much lower elevation in the muscle AMP contents. The calculated ATP/ADP concentration ratio as well as the "energy charge" were maintained higher in cooled than in control animals. Muscle creatine phosphate (CP) and glycogen were decreasing less rapidly. Glycolytic intermediates, above the PFK step, decreased in both experimental situations attaining only slightly lower values in uncooled dogs. The values of LA and pyruvate (PA) were much lower as compared to control conditions. When the muscle to blood LA ratio was calculated it appeared that the ratio was significantly lower in cooled than in control dogs (4.1 vs. 6.5, respectively). A significant correlation ($R = 0.55$, $p < 0.001$) was found between the muscle LA content and T_m.

The obtained data show that hyperthermia induced by exercise, which can be sustained for at least 1 hr, promotes a shift of the equilibrium between high energy phosphate breakdown and resynthesis towards lower values of ATP and CP concentrations. These findings correspond to the results reported by Brooks, Hittelman, Faulkner, and Beyer (1971), demonstrating that an increase in temperature decreases the phosphorylative efficiency of isolated skeletal muscle mitochondria, with a concomittant enhancement in the activity of the mitochondrial oligomycin-sensitive ATP-ase activity.

Table 2 Muscle contents (mmol/kg d.w.) of adenine nucleotides, creatine phosphate, glycogen, pyruvate and lactate during exhaustive exercise performed at ambient temp 20° ± 1 °C by the same dogs with and without trunk cooling (x ± SE; n = 11)[a]

Variables	Exercise without cooling		Exercise with cooling		
	before	end	before	end	E_c[b]
ATP	23.5 ± 0.9	18.6 ± 2.1	23.1 ± 0.8	22.7 ± 1.5	22.9 ± 1.3
ADP	2.45 ± 0.13	3.23 ± 0.24	2.51 ± 0.13	3.06 ± 0.15	2.99 ± 0.15
AMP	0.18 ± 0.02	0.40 ± 0.09	0.15 ± 0.01	0.20 ± 0.01	0.18 ± 0.01
CP	85.8 ± 4.4	49.9 ± 4.8	82.4 ± 2.7	67.9 ± 5.1	68.5 ± 5.6
Glycogen	397.2 ±41.3	161.5 ±27.9	349.7 ±34.8	183.9 ±31.5	231.0 ±28.8
Pyruvate	1.22 ± 0.17	3.87 ± 0.71	1.20 ± 0.10	2.05 ± 0.17	1.85 ± 0.17
Lactate	6.5 ± 0.6	82.5 ± 8.0	5.8 ± 0.5	46.3 ± 3.8	42.5 ± 3.4

[a]Compiled from "Exercise Hyperthermia as a Factor Limiting Physical Performance: Temperature Effect on Muscle Metabolism in Dogs" by S. Kozlowski, Z. Brzezińska, B. Kruk, H. Kaciuba-Uściłko, J.E. Greenleaf, and K. Nazar, 1985, *Journal of Applied Physiology*, **59**, 766-773.
[b]Time corresponding to the end of the control run

The enhanced muscle glycogen depletion at higher muscle temperatures, accompanied by the considerably higher LA content in working muscles indicates an increased rate of glycolysis, which seems to be caused by PFK activation. The latter suggestion has been supported by the fact that the contents of glycolytic intermediates above the PFK step were not altered. Contrary to expectations the enhanced glycogen utilization occurred in hyperthermic animals in spite of the elevated plasma FFA level. However, an influx of FFA to working muscles could have been compromised under these conditions because of the reduced muscle blood flow (Bell, Hales, King, & Fawcett, 1983; Nielsen, Savard, Laszczyńska, Saltin, & Bonde-Petersen, 1985). The higher plasma FFA and glycerol concentrations were most likely due to the greater sympathetic activation in uncooled than in cooled dogs.

The high muscle LA content resulting presumably in high hydrogen ion content, seems to be one of the most important factors contributing to development of fatigue when muscle temperature approaches relatively high values. In dogs, which eliminate heat mainly by panting, respiratory alkalosis may contribute to the greater accumulation of LA in muscles (Hirche, Hombach, Langohr, Wacker, & Busse, 1975). It was demon-

Table 3 Rectal (T_{re}) and muscle (T_m) temperatures (°C), and muscle contents (mmol/kg d.w.) of adenine nucleotides, creatine phosphate (CP), glycogen, and lactate in dogs injected intravenously with pyrogen (means ± SE, n = 5)

Variables	Before pyrogen	End of shivering	Stable fever
T_{re}	39.4 ± 0.3	40.4 ± 0.4	40.9 ± 0.3
T_m	39.6 ± 0.1	41.1 ± 0.2	41.0 ± 0.5
ATP	22.2 ± 2.0	16.0 ± 0.8	21.2 ± 2.0
ADP	2.85 ± 0.20	5.60 ± 0.60	4.20 ± 0.80
AMP	0.12 ± 0.01	0.32 ± 0.02	0.22 ± 0.04
CP	73.3 ± 3.5	60.0 ± 5.0	75.0 ± 2.0
Glycogen	351.0 ± 30.0	220.0 ± 25.0	340.0 ± 30.0
Lactate	10.0 ± 2.0	18.0 ± 3.5	15.0 ± 2.0

Unpublished data collected from preliminary experiments carried out by S. Koszlowski, K. Nazar, Z. Brzezińska, & S. Kruk, 1985.

strated recently in dogs treated with bacterial pyrogen that marked changes in muscle metabolite contents, similar to those found during intensive exercise, occur in fever but only during shivering. They become less pronounced when shivering disappears, although body temperatures (T_{re} and T_m) are still elevated (Table 3). These findings indicate that increased body temperature per se does not affect to any greater extent energy metabolism in inactive muscles.

CONCLUSIONS

The data presented above show that the exercise-induced hyperthermia contributes to the limitation of performance time at submaximal work rate by influencing muscle energy metabolism. The equilibrium between high-energy phosphate breakdown and resynthesis is shifted to the lower values of ATP and CP, and glycolysis is accelerated. It is not clear, however, to what extent these changes are attributed to a direct effect of increased temperature on metabolic processes or to an influence on the circulatory system (e.g., reduced muscle blood flow) with secondary effects on muscle function. Greater activation of the sympathetic nervous system at higher body temperatures should be also considered as one of the factors modifying exercise metabolism.

REFERENCES

Bell, A.W., Hales, J.R.S., King, R.B., & Fawcett, A.A. (1983). Influence of heat stress on exercise-induced changes in regional blood flow in sheep. *Journal of Applied Physiology: Respiratory, Environmental, Exercise Physiology,* **55**, 1916-1923.

Bennet, A.F. (1984). Thermal dependence of muscle function. *American Journal of Physiology: Regulatory Integrative Comparative Physiology,* **16**, 247, R217-R229.

Brooks, G.A., Hittelman, K.J., Faulkner, J.A., & Beyer, R.E. (1971). Temperature, skeletal muscle mitochondrial function and oxygen debt. *American Journal of Physiology,* **220**, 1053-1059.

Edwards, R.H.T., Harris, R.C., Hultman, E., Kaijser, L., Koh, D., & Nordesjö, L.-O. (1972). Effect of temperature on muscle energy metabolism and endurance during successive isometric contractions sustained to fatigue of the quadriceps muscle in man. *Journal of Physiology* (London), **220**, 335-353.

Faulkner, J.A. (1980). Heat and contractile properties of skeletal muscle. In S.M. Horvath & M.K. Yousef (Eds.), *Environmental physiology, aging, heat and altitude* (pp. 191-203).

Fink, W.J., Costill, D.L., & Van Handel, P.J. (1975). Leg muscle metabolism during exercise in the heat and cold. *European Journal of Applied Physiology,* **34**, 183-190.

Hessemer, V., Langusch, D., Brück, K., Bödeker, R.H., & Breidenbach, T. (1984). Effect of slightly lowered body temperatures on endurance performance in humans. *Journal of Applied Physiology: Respiratory, Environmental, Exercise Physiology,* **57**, 1731-1737.

Hirche, H.J., Hombach, V., Langohr, H.D., Wacker, V., & Busse, J. (1975). Lactic acid permeation rate in working gastocnemii of dogs during metabolic alkalosis and acidosis. *Pflügers Archiv,* **356**, 209-222.

Kozlowski, S., Brzezińska, Z., Kruk, B., Kaciuba-Uścilko, H., Greenleaf, J.E., & Nazar, K. (1985). Exercise hyperthermia as a factor limiting physical performance: Temperature effect on muscle metabolism in dogs. *Journal of Applied Physiology,* **59**, 766-773.

Kruk, B., Kaciuba-Uścilko, H., Nazar, K., Greenleaf, J.E., & Kozlowski, S. (1985). Hypothalamic, rectal, and muscle temperatures in exercising dogs: Effect of cooling. *Journal of Applied Physiology,* **58**, 1444-1448.

MacDougall, J.D., Reddan, W.G., Layton, C.R., & Dempsey, J.A. (1974). Effects of metabolic hyperthermia on performance during heavy prolonged exercise. *Journal of Applied Physiology,* **36**, 538-544.

Nielsen, B., Savard, G., Laszczyńska, J., Saltin, B., & Bonde-Petersen, F. (1985). Heat stress and muscle blood flow during exercise in man. *Clinical Physiology,* **5**(Suppl. 4). *(Abstracts of the 6th International Symposium on Biochemistry of Exercise,* **135***)*

Saltin, B., Gagge, A.P., & Stolwijk, J.A. (1968). Muscle temperature during submaximal exercise in man. *Journal of Applied Physiology,* **25**, 679-688.

Schmidt, V., & Brück, K. (1981). Effect of precooling maneuver on body temperature and exercise performance. *Journal of Applied Physiology: Respiratory, Environmental, Exercise Physiology,* **50**, 772-778.

Coupling of Muscle Energy Metabolism With Cardiovascular Response to Exercise in Man

Steven F. Lewis
University of Texas Health Science Center
Dallas, Texas, U.S.A.

There are data to suggest an intimate relation between the metabolic state of contracting skeletal muscle and cardiovascular regulation during exercise but few direct links have been established. Systemically, a close coupling between circulatory and metabolic adaptations is illustrated by an increase in cardiac output of approximately 5 L for each liter of increase in total body oxygen uptake (Lewis et al., 1983). Locally there is a corresponding increase in leg blood flow of approximately 5 L per liter of increase in leg oxygen uptake (Andersen & Saltin, 1985). With a normal hemoglobin concentration and oxygen affinity, approximately 200 ml of oxygen are transported per liter of arterial blood. Increases in cardiac output and local blood flow of approximately 5 L are therefore required to make 1 L of oxygen available to working muscle. Thus, there normally is a tight 1:1 relation between the utilization and transport of oxygen on both the systemic and local levels. The mechanisms involved are poorly understood.

The nature of the system coupling the cardiovascular and metabolic responses to exercise can be explored by posing the following questions:

- What is the mode of feedback by which metabolic events in skeletal muscle are likely to signal increased systemic and local blood flow in exercise?
- What human models are useful for studying these phenomena?
- What is the identity of the critical local metabolic state?

HOW DO METABOLIC EVENTS IN SKELETAL MUSCLE AFFECT CARDIOVASCULAR REGULATION IN EXERCISE?

Increases in heart rate, cardiac output, and blood pressure during exercise are elicited primarily by activation of the medullary cardiovascular centers by impulses originating in: (a) the motor cortex and other higher brain centers, that is, central command, and (b) thin myelinated and unmyelinated skeletal muscle sensory nerves (Groups III and IV) activated by metabolic stimuli (Mitchell & Schmidt, 1983; Shepherd, Blomqvist, Lind, Mitchell, & Saltin, 1981). The relative significance of these central and peripheral control mechanisms in exercising man have been the subject of much debate. Interventions that eliminate either central command (Hultman & Sjöholm, 1982) or input from the muscle afferents (Rowell, Freund, & Hobbs, 1981) do not appreciably alter the normal hemodynamic response to exercise. These control systems are therefore redundant and both are likely to be important under normal conditions. The role of central command in cardiovascular regulation has been reviewed recently (McCloskey, 1981) and is beyond the scope of the present paper.

During exercise there is an α-adrenergic vasoconstriction mediated through afferent pathways likely to involve both central command and excitation of the skeletal muscle afferents. Vasoconstriction persists in inactive tissues, but in working skeletal muscle, is opposed by local vasodilatation, which directs to the muscle much of the increase in cardiac output. In explaining the local vasodilatation, primary emphasis has been given to metabolites, which are released by contracting skeletal muscle and act directly on vascular smooth muscle or at the neuroeffector junctions for sympathetic nerve endings in the blood vessel walls (Shepherd, 1983). Muscle hyperemia also may be influenced by neural, humoral and myogenic factors (Shepherd, 1983). It has recently been postulated that excitation of the metabolically responsive muscle afferents contributes to a selective vasodilatation in exercising muscle (Andersen & Saltin, 1985). Studies employing antidromic stimulation of dorsal roots in cats (Hilton & Marshall, 1980) suggest that muscle vasodilatation could occur via an axon reflex involving the smaller myelinated and unmyelinated afferents.

MODELS FOR STUDYING THE RELATION BETWEEN MUSCLE ENERGY METABOLISM AND CARDIOVASCULAR RESPONSE TO EXERCISE

Local ischemia created by the occlusion of arterial flow to contracting muscle has been valuable in implicating a role for the metabolically sensitive muscle afferents in the cardiovascular response to exercise in man (Alam & Smirk, 1937; Asmussen & Nielsen, 1943; Rowell et al., 1981). The muscle ischemia model does not, however, permit investigation of blood flow to exercising muscle and tends to restrict conclusions regarding the precise nature of the critical local metabolic state. Other limitations of this model have recently been discussed (Lewis, Haller, & Blomqvist, 1984).

A growing body of data suggests that important information about cardiovascular regulation during exercise can be derived from studies of patients with genetic errors in skeletal muscle metabolism. In patients with phosphorylase deficiency (McArdle's disease), carnitine deficiency, ragged-red fiber myopathy, and defective electron transport, there is a hyperkinetic circulatory response to exercise representing an uncoupling of the normal 1:1 relation between systemic oxygen transport and utilization. In these patients cardiac output is normal at rest but increases by more than 10 L per liter of oxygen uptake in contrast with the normal cardiac output increase of 5 L per liter of oxygen uptake (Figure 1). Hemoglobin levels are normal in all cases. The normal increase in cardiac output in relation to oxygen uptake in patients with muscle pain or muscular dystrophy (Haller, Lewis, Cook, & Blomqvist, 1983) suggests that the hyperkinetic circulatory response is not a nonspecific abnormality due to pain, weakness or atrophy. The normal cardiac output response in carnitine palmityl transferase deficiency (Haller et al., 1983) and AMP deaminase deficiency supports the hypothesis that only certain specific metabolic defects result in atypical regulation of cardiac output.

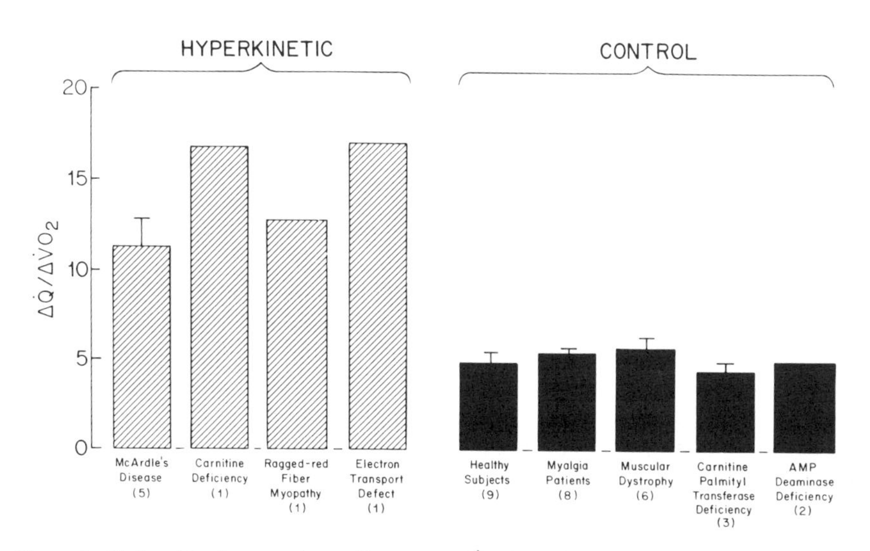

Figure 1 Ratio of the increase in cardiac output ($\dot{Q}$; 1/min) from rest to exercise in relation to that of oxygen uptake ($\dot{V}O_2$; 1/min) from rest to exercise in patients with hyperkinetic circulation ($\Delta\dot{Q}/\Delta\dot{V}O_2 > 10$) and control subjects and patients with normal circulation ($\Delta\dot{Q}/\Delta\dot{V}O_2 \simeq 5$). Data were obtained from Haller et al., (1983), Haller, Lewis & Estabrook, Nunnally, and Foster, (1985), Lewis et al., (1984), and unpublished results (Lewis & Haller) and are shown as means ± SE. Numbers in parentheses denote n.

An important feature of the muscle disease model is that, in some cases, the cardiovascular responses to exercise can be modified by providing substrates that bypass the metabolic defect. Normalization of cardiac output and arteriovenous oxygen difference during exercise was observed after chronic administration of a diet supplemented with medium chain triglycerides in a patient with carnitine deficiency and an abnormal accumulation of lipid in muscle (Haller, Cook, Lewis, & Blomqvist, 1979; Lewis, Haller, & Blomqvist, 1984). In McArdle's disease, heart rate and cardiac output were lower during bicycle exercise at a given oxygen uptake after interventions that elevated plasma glucose or free fatty acid concentration (Lewis, Haller, Cook, & Blomqvist, 1984). Lowering of plasma free fatty acid concentration after administration of nicotinic acid had opposite hemodynamic effects. Data from ^{31}P NMR experiments (Lewis, Haller, Cook, & Nunnally, 1985) demonstrate that during exercise in McArdle's disease glucose infusion results in an improved energy supply in working muscle as reflected in a smaller decline in phosphocreatine and a reduced elevation in inorganic phosphate.

In muscle disease patients with hyperkinetic cardiac output responses, there is an atypically steep decline in total peripheral resistance in relation to oxygen uptake (Linderholm, Muller, Ringqvist, & Sornas, 1969; Lewis & Haller, in press). There is evidence that the excessive cardiac output is directed to working muscle (Barcroft et al., 1966; Linderholm et al., 1969; McArdle, 1951) probably as a consequence of an abnormally large local metabolic vasodilatation.

THE NATURE OF THE CRITICAL LOCAL METABOLIC STATE

Exposure of the muscle afferents of animals to a variety of known or potential excitatory substances has thus far failed to identify a metabolic candidate or metabolic state that fulfills all criteria to qualify as a single mediator (Mitchell & Schmidt, 1983). There also are no data from animal experiments that permit a complete explanation of the exercise hyperemia on the basis of a single local vasodilator metabolite (Shepherd, 1983). Table 1 summarizes the extent to which a number of metabolic candidates are generally held to be involved in local muscle vasodilatation and/or excitation of the groups III and IV muscle afferents. One reason for the failure to detect the "perfect" active substance is that a metabolite that is unknown or has not conventionally been considered a local vasodilatator or an activator of muscle afferents might be involved. An alternative, and perhaps more likely explanation, is that a complex metabolic state consisting of a variety of factors may be critical. Redundancy, that is, the

Table 1 Circulatory Effects of Locally Active Muscle Metabolites[a]

Metabolite/ Metabolic State	Muscle Afferents	Local Vasodilator
Acetate	?[b]	+[c]
Adenosine	?	++
Bradykinin	+++	+
Hydrogen ions	+	+
Inorganic Phosphate	+	++
Lactate	+	+
Osmolarity	+	+
↑pCO_2	+	+
↓pO_2	+	+
Potassium	+++	++
Prostaglandins	+	++

[a]Compiled from a number of sources in the literature; [b]? = effect unknown; [c]Number of plus symbols corresponds approximately to the degree of positive effect

fact that two or more metabolites may be sufficient but each not necessary for excitation of the muscle afferents or local vasodilatation, also may be an important feature of the control system.

The local metabolic state has been studied in some detail in patients with McArdle's disease. In contrast to normal subjects, venous blood draining the exercising limbs of McArdle patients shows no changes in lactate, pH, or pCO_2 and an increased oxygen saturation in relation to resting levels (Barcroft et al., 1966; Pernow, Havel, & Jennings, 1967) thus supporting a nonobligatory role for several metabolic candidates in mediating excessive systemic and local blood flow. Greater than normal levels of potassium have been reported in the working muscle venous effluent of McArdle patients and there also are data consistent with an abnormally large release of inorganic phosphate from active muscle (McArdle, 1951). Ammonia, which is produced primarily via the AMP deaminase reaction during muscular contraction and which increases excessively in the muscle venous effluent of McArdle patients (Haller, Lewis, Gunder, & Dennis,

1985), might be the "unknown mediator." It is more likely, however, that the increased ammonia production is only one consequence of an increased flux through AMP in McArdle patients. AMP may also be degraded to the vasodilator adenosine (Arch & Newsholme, 1978). Much less is known about the local metabolic state in other disorders of muscle energy metabolism but data is beginning to accumulate (Sabina et al., 1984).

CONCLUSIONS

The mechanisms involved in the coupling of circulatory responses to exercise with energy metabolism in active muscle are complex and our understanding is presently at a preliminary stage. Conventional approaches involving perfusion of animal hindlimbs with metabolites believed to participate in cardiovascular regulation have yielded a body of data favoring certain specific metabolites or metabolic states but no conclusive findings. The approach discussed in this paper involves the study of patients with certain specific defects in skeletal muscle energy metabolism, some of whom have normal and others abnormal responses to exercise. By comparing the circulatory and metabolic responses of these patients using a variety of specific exercise protocols, a novel picture of the critical local muscle metabolic state is beginning to develop. The distinctiveness of this approach derives in part from the ability to look, in a figurative sense, outward from within the muscle cell. Comparable animal models for many of these diseases do not exist but this situation might be modified in the foreseeable future pending advances in the field of molecular biology.

Acknowledgments

I am grateful to Ronald Haller for his collaboration in studying patients with neuromuscular diseases and to Gunnar Blomqvist for his support. Work related to this paper was supported in part by a grant-in-aid from the American Heart Association with funds contributed in part by the Texas Affiliate and by National Heart, Lung and Blood Institute Grants HL-17669 and HL-06296.

REFERENCES

Alam, M., & Smirk, F.H. (1937). Observations in man upon a blood pressure raising reflex arising from the voluntary muscles. *Journal of Physiology*, (London), **89**, 372-383.

Andersen, P., & Saltin, B. (1985). Maximal perfusion of skeletal muscle man. *Journal of Physiology,* (London), **366**, 233-249.

Arch, J.R.S., & Newsholme, E.A. (1978). The control of the metabolism and the hormonal role of adenosine. *Essays in Biochemistry,* **14**, 82-123.

Asmussen, E., & Nielsen, M. (1943). Experiments on nervous factors controlling respiration and circulation during exercise. *Acta Physiologica Scandinavica,* **60**, 103-111.

Barcroft, H., Greenwood, B., McArdle, B., McSwiney, R.R., Semple, S.J.G., Whelan, R.F., & Youlten, L.J.F. (1966). The effect of exercise on forearm blood flow and on venous blood pH, pCO_2 and lactate in the subject with phosphorylase deficiency in skeletal muscle (McArdle's syndrome). *Journal of Physiology,* (London), **189**, 44-46P.

Haller, R.G., Cook, J.D., Lewis, S., & Blomqvist, C.G. (1979). A "lipid myopathy" associated with a hyperkinetic circulatory response to exercise. *Transactions of the American Neurological Association,* **104**, 117-119.

Haller, R.G., Lewis, S.F., Cook, J.D., & Blomqvist, C.G. (1983). Hyperkinetic circulation during exercise in neuromuscular diseases. *Neurology,* **33**, 1283-1287.

Haller, R.G., Lewis, S.F., Estabrook, R.W., Nunnally, R., & Foster, D.W. (1985). A skeletal muscle disorder of electron transport associated with deficiency of cytochromes aa_3 and b and abnormal cardiovascular regulation in exercise. *Clinical Physiology,* **5**(Suppl. 4), 34.

Haller, R.G., Lewis, S.F., Gunder, M., & Dennis, M. (1985). Ammonia production during exercise in McArdle's syndrome—an index of muscle energy supply and demand. *Neurology,* **35**, 207.

Hilton, S.M., & Marshall, J.M. (1980). Dorsal root vasodilatation in cat skeletal muscle. *Journal of Physiology,* **299**, 277-288.

Hultman, E., & Sjoholm, H. (1982). Blood pressure and heart rate response to voluntary and nonvoluntary exercise in man. *Acta Physiologica Scandinavica,* **115**, 499-501.

Lewis, S.F., & Haller, R.G. (in press). The pathophysiology of McArdle's disease: Clues to regulation in exercise and fatigue. *Journal of Applied Physiology.*

Lewis, S.F., Haller, R.G., & Blomqvist, C.G. (1984). Neuromuscular diseases as models of cardiovascular regulation during exercise. *Medicine and Science in Sports and Exercise,* **16**, 466-471.

Lewis, S.F., Haller, R.G., Cook, J.D., & Blomqvist, C.G. (1984). Metabolic control of cardiac output response to exercise in McArdle's disease. *Journal of Applied Physiology,* **57**, 1749-1753.

Lewis, S.F., Haller, R.G., Cook, J.D., & Nunnally, R.L. (1985). Muscle fatigue in McArdle's disease studied by ^{31}P NMR: Effect of glucose infusion. *Journal of Applied Physiology,* **59**, 1991-1994.

Lewis, S.F., Taylor, W.F., Graham, R.M., Pettinger, W.A., Schutte, J.E., & Blomqvist, C.G. (1983). Cardiovascular responses to exercise as

functions of absolute and relative work load. *Journal of Applied Physiology,* **54**, 1314-1323.
Linderholm, H., Muller, R., Ringqvist, T., & Sornas, R. (1969). Hereditary abnormal muscle metabolism with hyperkinetic circulation during exercise. *Acta Medica Scandinavica,* **185**, 153-166.
McArdle, B. (1951). Myopathy due to a defect in muscle glycogen breakdown. *Clinical Science,* **10**, 13-33.
McCloskey, D.I. (1981). Centrally-generated commands and cardiovascular control in man. *Clinical and Experimental Hypertension,* **3**, 369-378.
Mitchell, J.H., & Schmidt, R.F. (1983). Cardiovascular reflex control by afferent fibers from skeletal muscle receptors. In J.T. Shepherd, F.M. Abboud, & S.P. Geiger (Eds.), *Handbook of physiology: The cardiovascular system III* (pp. 623-658). Bethesda, MD: American Physiological Society.
Pernow, B.B., Havel, R.J., & Jennings, D.B. (1967). The second wind phenomenon in McArdle's syndrome. *Acta Medica Scandinavica,* **472**(Suppl.), 294-307.
Rowell, L.B., Freund, P.R., & Hobbs, S.F. (1981). Cardiovascular responses to muscle ischemia in humans. *Circulation Research,* **48**(Suppl. I), 37-47.
Sabina, R.L., Swain, J.L., Olanow, C.W., Bradley, W.G., Fishbein, W.N., DiMauro, S., & Holmes, E.W. (1984). Myoadenylate deaminase deficiency: functional and metabolic abnormalities associated with the disruption of the purine nucleotide cycle. *Journal of Clinical Investigtion,* **73**, 720-730.
Shepherd, J.T. (1983). Circulation to skeletal muscle. In J.T. Shepherd, F.M. Abboud, & S.P. Geiger (Eds.) *Handbook of physiology: Sec. 2. The cardiovascular system III. Peripheral circulation and organ blood flow, Part I.* (pp. 319-370). Bethesda, MD: American Physiological Society.
Shepherd, J.T., Blomqvist, C.G., Lind, A.R., Mitchell, J.H., & Saltin, B. (1981). Static (isometric) exercise. Retrospection and introspection. *Circulation Research,* **48**(Suppl. I), 179-188.

On The Accuracy of Fuel Mobilization in Exercise

Henrik Galbo
Erik Arne Richter
Bente Sonne
University of Copenhagen
Copenhagen, Denmark

In the present paper such facts are emphasized that support the supposition that in exercise, fuel mobilization is not always—if ever—accurately adjusted to the energy needs of the working muscles.

Contractile activity per se directly elicits breakdown of intramuscular glycogen and triglyceride. The mobilization of intramuscular fuel is subjected to feed forward regulation and not accurately adjusted to fuel needs. Thus, at identical tension development, oxygen uptake and glycerol release, glycogen breakdown and lactate production are increased in in vitro stimulated perfused muscle, if preexercise glycogen levels are supranormal (Richter & Galbo, 1985). During stimulation glucose uptake is lower in perfused muscle with supranormal glycogen concentration than in muscle with normal glycogen concentration, but the difference is smaller than the difference in glycogen depletion (Richter & Galbo, 1985). It appears that mobilization of intramuscular fuel is not mainly called on when delivery of exogenous fuel is insufficient. Similarly, other experiments have shown that combustion of intramuscular fuels may increase with exercise intensity while muscular uptake of glucose and free fatty acids (FFA) decreases in spite of increased delivery of these blood-born fuels (Walker, Mickle, Tanner, Harding, & Romaschin, 1984).

HORMONAL CHANGES AS A RESULT OF EXERCISE

In vivo hormones influence fuel mobilization. The hormonal response to exercise is essentially nondiscriminating, promoting mobilization of both glycogen and triglyceride from extra- as well as intramuscular stores, and it is likely that hormone-mediated fuel mobilization to some extent is superimposed on mobilization of intramuscular stores by contractile activity per se. In favor of this interpretation the rapidity of the hormonal changes at the start of exercise indicates that the hormonal response probably is regulated partly by feed-forward mechanisms related intimately to motor activity rather than to substrate need (Galbo, 1983). Furthermore, the hormonal changes elicited by exercise are involved in regulation of circulation, body temperatures, the volume and osmolality of body fluids, in addition to metabolism, and feed-back from nonmetabolic error signals will influence the response of hormones having some metabolic effect (e.g., angiotensin, ADH, norepinephrine) as well as of hormones primarily influencing metabolism (e.g., increased sympathoadrenal activity elicited by decreasing intravascular volume will depress insulin levels). The finding of higher intramuscular glucose-6-phosphate and lactate concentrations during intense exercise in cool compared to normal conditions (Blomstrand, Bergh, Essén-Gustavsson, & Ekblom, 1984) probably illustrates an "irrelevant" enhancement of glycogenolysis mediated by epinephrine released in response to stimulation of cold receptors. In the regulation of nonmetabolic parameters circulatory changes influencing fuel mobilization may also be elicited. A decrease in splanchnic blood flow enhances hepatic glucose production while an increase in adipose tissue blood flow increases the fraction of FFA "mobilized" by lipolysis, which is released from adipose tissue, and diminishes the fraction that is directly reesterificated (Bülow & Madsen, in press).

In accordance with the view that mobilization of extramuscular fuel may be regulated in a "feed-forward" fashion rather than by "feed-back" mechanisms coupled to the minimal needs of the exercising muscles, it has been shown in running fed rats that hepatic glycogen is mobilized and glucose forced on the muscles at a time at which they are rich in endogenuous fuel (Sonne & Galbo, 1985a). Furthermore, studied at the same exercise intensity, oxygen uptake and muscular glycogen concentration, hepatic glycogenolysis and glucose production is higher in experiments in which preexercise hepatic glycogen stores are higher than in experiments in which they have been diminished (Sonne & Galbo, 1985b). Speaking against feed-back regulation, in the latter condition, glucose production did not increase with time during exercise of an intensity that did not elicit maximal glucose production (Sonne & Galbo, 1985b).

During exercise of a fixed intensity, the state of the organism before the studied moment of exercise (e.g., as regards nutrition [Miller, Bryce, & Conlee, 1984], degree of training, hormone levels in plasma, and level of physical activity) influences the induced hormonal changes, the fuel depots (in terms of size, hormone receptors and enzymatic capacity) and their sensitivity to stimulation, as well as the capacity of the recruited muscle fibers for metabolism of the different substrates (Galbo, 1983). Extra- and intramuscular fuels are burned in competition with each other, and the final choice of fuel depends on availability of substrates and on the capacity of the metabolizing, energy yielding enzymatic pathways (Galbo, 1983). Supply of extramuscular fuel depends on blood flow of a working muscle, and this does not exclusively depend on its metabolic rate, but also on the external environment and the work performed by other muscles (Klausen, Secher, Clausen, Hartling, & Trap-Jensen, 1982). Some feed-back inhibition is evidently exerted by the mobilized fuels on the initial enzymatic steps involved in mobilization of glycogen and triglyceride stores. However, this is not sufficient to allow accurate adjustment of fuel mobilization to energy demand. During exercise, fuel may be mobilized in excess and may be re-stored as evidenced by the finding of extracellular accumulation of FFA (Galbo, Holst, & Christensen, 1975) and glucose (Kjær, Farrell, Christensen, & Galbo, 1985; Sonne & Galbo, 1985a), reesterification of FFA in adipose tissue (Bülow & Madsen, in press), accumulation of triglyceride in liver (Górski, Nowacka, Namiot, & Kiryluk, 1985), and incorporation of infused radiolabelled glucose in muscular glycogen (Sonne & Galbo, in press).

NEED FOR FUEL MOBILIZATION

It might be argued that excess mobilization is necessary to allow optimal fuel delivery to the working muscles. However, during prolonged exercise the concentration of FFA in plasma and the supply of FFA to a working muscle group may increase without an accompanying decrease in whole body RQ or muscular RQ (Galbo et al., 1975; Kiens, Christensen, & Saltin, in press), indicating that mobilization of FFA may proceed beyond the point at which mobilization limits combustion. A small reservation has to be taken against this interpretation since changes may take place during exercise; for example, a reduction in mitochondrial capacity to oxidize FFA (Barakat, Kasperek, Dohm, Tapscott, & Snider, 1982), which have the effect that increasing FFA levels are necessary to maintain a constant FFA oxidation. From other experiments it can be concluded that fuel mobilization may be suboptimal. The evidence is that exhaustion may take place at a time at which triglyceride stores are plentiful, and may be delayed by exogenous administration of FFA. The quantitative importance of the mismatching between fuel mobilization and energy demand of the working muscles is not understood yet. However, since futile cycling is energy demanding, the fact that during dynamic exercise only slight variations in work efficiency have been found argues against marked malregulation.

Acknowledgment

The authors received support from the Danish Medical Research Council (12-5288).

REFERENCES

Barakat, H., Kasperek, G.J., Dohm, G.L., Tapscott, E.B., & Snider, R.D. (1982). Fatty acid oxidation by liver and muscle preparations of exhaustively exercised rats. *Biochemical Journal,* **208**, 419-424.

Blomstrand, E., Bergh, U., Essén-Gustavsson, B., & Ekblom, B. (1984). Influence of low muscle temperature on muscle metabolism during intense dynamic exercise. *Acta Physiologica Scandinavica,* **120**, 229-236.

Bülow, J., & Madsen, J. (In press). Regulation of fatty acid mobilization from adipose tissue during exercise. *Scandinavian Journal of Sports Science.*

Galbo, H. (1983). *Hormonal and metabolic adaptation to exercise.* Stuttgart & New York: Georg Thieme Verlag.

Galbo, H., Holst, J.J., & Christensen, N.J. (1975). Glucagon and plasma catecholamine responses to graded and prolonged exercise in man. *Journal of Applied Physiology,* **38**, 70-76.

Górski, J., Nowacka, M., Namiot, Z., & Kiryluk, T. (1985). Accumulation of triglycerides in the liver during exercise. *Clinical Physiology,* **5**(Suppl. 4), A71.

Kiens, B., Christensen, N.J., & Saltin, B. (In press). Skeletal muscle substrate utilization with exercise. Effect of training. *Journal of Applied Physiology.*

Kjær, M., Farrell, P., Christensen, N.J., & Galbo, H. (1985). Responsiveness of adrenal medullary secretion to exercise in trained and untrained humans. *Clinical Physiology,* **5**(Suppl. 4), A54.

Klausen, K., Secher, N.H., Clausen, J.P., Hartling, O., & Trap-Jensen, J. (1982). Central and regional circulatory adaptations to one-leg training. *Journal of Applied Physiology: Respiratory, Environmental, Exercise Physiology,* **52**, 976-983.

Miller, W.C., Bryce, G.R., & Conlee, R.K. (1984). Adaptations to a high-fat diet that increase exercise endurance in male rats. *Journal of Applied Physiology: Respiratory, Environmental, Exercise Physiology,* **56**, 78-83.

Richter, E.A., & Galbo, H. (1985). Rate of glycogen breakdown and lactate release in contracting, isolated skeletal muscle is dependent upon glycogen concentration. *Clinical Physiology,* **5**(Suppl. 4), A82.

Sonne, B., & Galbo, H. (1985a). Carbohydrate metabolism during and after exercise in rats. Studies with radioglucose. *Journal of Applied Physiology,* **59**, 1627-1639.

Sonne, B., & Galbo, H. (1985b). Regulation of hepatic glucose production in exercise. An alternative view. *Clinical Physiology,* **5**(Suppl. 4), A57.

Sonne, B., & Galbo, H. (In press). Carbohydrate metabolism in fructose fed and food restricted rats. *Journal of Applied Physiology.*

Walker, P.M., Mickle, D.A.G., Tanner, W.R., Harding, R., & Romaschin, A.D. (1984). Decreased uptake of exogenous substrates following graded muscle stimulation. *American Journal of Physiology,* **246**, H690-H695.

Discussion from the Session

Sex Differences in Metabolic Adaptation to Exercise

Ji Di Chen
Medical Sciences University of Beijing
Beijing, China

Claude Bouchard
Laval University
Ste-Foy, Quebec, Canada

This report constitutes the summary of a session held on the topic of sex differences in metabolic adaptation to exercise and training. The authors served as cochairpersons of the panel. Discussants included the following: Dr. T.E. Graham from Guelph, Canada, Dr. E. Jansson from Stockholm, Sweden, Dr. J.M. Lavoie from Montreal, Canada, Dr. E. Nygaard from Copenhagen, Denmark, Dr. P.K. Pedersen from Odense, Denmark, Dr. A. Tremblay, from Quebec, Canada, and Dr. C. Williams from Loughborough, England.

This summary will comprise two parts: (a) the abstracts submitted by each speaker on the panel, and (b) an overview of sex differences relevant to the topic.

ABSTRACT SUBMITTED BY EACH SPEAKER

Exercise Metabolic Responses in Men and Eumenorrheic and Amenorrheic Women **by T.E. Graham, J.P. Van Dijk, M. Viswanathan, K.A. Giles, A. Bonen, and J.C. George. University of Guelph, Ontario, and Dalhousie University, Halifax, Canada**

In the present study, we examined metabolic and thermal responses in men (M, n = 6) and women to progressive exercise at +21 °C. The women were either regularly menstruating (CW, n = 6) or amenorrheic (AW, n = 6). All subjects rested for 20 min. They then performed 20 min at 30% $\dot{V}O_2$max, 20 min at 60% $\dot{V}O_2$max and then rode to exhaustion at 90% of $\dot{V}O_2$max. There were no differences between groups for respiratory exchange ratio (RER), % $\dot{V}O_2max$ achieved at each workload and exhaustion times were not different (5.6 ± 0.6, 5.6 ± 0.9, and 7.6 ± 1.1 min for CW, M, and AW respectively).

In the heavy work, AW had a lower blood lactate level (5.6 ± 0.8 mM) than M (9.6 ± 1.2 mM) and the combination of AW and CW (6.9 ± 0.6 mM) were also lower than the M. The free fatty acids (FFA) rose with exercise and were not different between M and CW. However, the AW had higher FFA at rest, at 30% of max and at exhaustion. This, in part, may be correlated to the lower blood lactate levels.

Both female groups had lower noradrenaline levels at rest, at 30% VO_2max and at exhaustion. When these data are put into the context of those reported by Béliveau, Trudeau, Péronnet, and Brisson (1985), it appears that rather than concluding that women have less sympathetic nervous activity it is more reasonable to state that due to their smaller active muscle mass they have less noradrenaline "washed out" or released from muscle. Since active muscle appears to be the dominant source of noradrenaline, the blood level is lower. These findings agree with a previous report (Sanchez, Pequignot, Peyrin, & Monod, 1980) that men increase blood catecholamine levels during isometric contractions while women do not.

All three groups had similar (0.9 to 1.1 °C) rises in core temperature, but both the CW and AW had lower skin temperatures throughout the test.

The present study confirms that thermal and metabolic sexual dimorphism does exist and in addition it demonstrates that even within the female population there may be distinct subgroups that may be identified by menstrual status.

Sex Differences in Metabolic Response to Exercise **by E. Jansson. Department of Clinical Physiology, Karolinska Hospital, Stockholm, Sweden**

The aim of this presentation was to compare the sexes with respect to the relative proportion of muscle fiber types and the substrate metabolism at rest and during submaximal exercise. In a first study, leg muscle fiber types (m. quadriceps femoris vastus lateralis) were analyzed in a large group of 16-year-old Swedish boys and girls, representative of the 16-year-old population (Hedberg & Jansson, 1976). Ten years later, we have repeated the same tests on the same individuals, now at the age of 26. So far, 14 women and 27 men have been studied (Lundberg, Esbjörsson, Hedberg, & Jansson, 1985). In a second study, the metabolic response to diet and exercise was studied in 18 female and 15 male subjects (age 24 ± 3 years, mean ± SD). In this metabolic study, muscle fiber types were also analyzed (Jansson, 1980).

At the age of 16, the relative proportion of type 1 fibers was not significantly different between females and males (51.8 ± 9.1 vs. 53.9 ± 12.2 %, mean and SD). However, at the age of 26, females showed a higher percentage of type 1 fibers than males (56.5 ± 12.4 vs. 47.5 ± 11.3, $p < 0.05$). In the second study, the same results were obtained, that is, a higher percentage of type 1 fibers for the female subjects (56.5 ± 10.1 vs. 47.9 ± 8.0, $p < 0.05$).

At rest, the metabolic study showed that females tended to have a higher heart rate, lower RER and lower blood and muscle lactate concentrations than males. During exercise (25 min cycle exercise at 65% of maximal oxygen uptake), females had a higher heart rate and a lower RER, but no differences in blood and muscle lactate concentrations were found between the sexes. No sex differences were found for blood glucose, plasma FFA or muscle glycogen concentrations, either at rest or during exercise. The arterial-femoral venous difference for FFA was measured in 5 females and 5 males (^{3}H-labeled palmitate) after 25 min of exercise (65% of VO_2max) and was not significantly different between the sexes.

In conclusion, women might have a greater relative proportion of type 1 fibers in leg muscles than men. No statistically significant sex differences were found in the metabolic response to submaximal exercise, although the women tended to have a greater relative proportion of fat oxidation (estimated from the whole body respiratory quotient). Diet and training status seemed to influence the metabolic response to exercise to a larger extent than sex of subject.

Sex Difference in Epinephrine and Blood Glucose Response to Exercise

by J.M. Lavoie. Department of Physical Education, University of Montreal, Canada.

This summary deals with a study in which we investigated the metabolic and hormonal effects of a 24-hr low CHO diet during a period of prolonged exercise, both during the follicular and the luteal phases of the menstrual cycle. A significant decrease in blood glucose levels during the luteal but not the follicular phase of the menstrual cycle was observed. This decrease was particularly evident after 70 min of exercise, and it was consistent for all eight subjects.

Our purpose in submitting these women to a 24-hr low CHO diet the day before exercise was to generate a hypoglycemic challenge and test whether they could maintain blood glucose level. There is no doubt that this 24-hr low CHO diet, by reducing the liver glycogen content, has contributed to the reduction of the blood glucose level during exercise.

Since this study was a part of a series of experiments on the same topic, data for a group of men of approximately the same age and physical fitness level, under similar experimental conditions, were also available. Comparing the blood glucose response of women and men, we found that men responded to exercise and dietary conditions in a way similar to that found for women in the luteal phase. Since blood glucose had decreased during the luteal phase, the question becomes, What caused the blood glucose level to be maintained during the follicular phase?

There is very little information on the effects of ovarian hormones on the metabolic response to exercise in humans. It is not known whether ovarian hormone levels influence muscle glycogen concentration at rest in women. Differences in blood glucose metabolism during exercise between the follicular and luteal phases could also be accounted for either by a change in glucose uptake or by a reduction in hepatic glucose release.

In the first case, there have been reports of a decrease in insulin binding on erythrocytes and monocytes during the luteal phase of the menstrual cycle. It must be kept in mind, however, that insulin binding to circulating blood cells in vitro does not always reflect insulin action in vivo. Accordingly, a recent study has indicated that insulin-mediated glucose metabolism, as determined by the euglycemic clamp technique, is unaffected by the phase of the menstrual cycle in normal women (Yki-Järvinen, 1984). As for the second explanation, related to a possible decrease in liver glucose release, there have been consistent reports in rats and mice of a decrease in gluconeogenesis when the levels of estradiol and progesterone were elevated during the estrous cycle.

Since in our study the liver glycogen content was probably very low due to the 24-hr low CHO diet, one would expect gluconeogenesis to be an important metabolic pathway during prolonged exercise. It is therefore possible to hypothesize that the higher levels of ovarian hormones during the luteal phase may have decreased gluconeogenesis, thus contributing to the reduction in blood glucose level. Androgen hormones in men might have a similar action on gluconeogenesis as the ovarian hormones in women, thus explaining the observed decrease in blood glucose. From these observations, one can conclude that, under the dietary and exercise condition described, women in the follicular phase of the menstrual cycle can better maintain blood glucose levels than men.

***Sex Differences in Adaptation to Exercise* by E. Nygaard. Department of Clinical Physiology, Rehabilitation Institute at the University Hospital, Copenhagen, Denmark**

There is a sex difference in the areas of cross-sectioned muscle fibers as fibers are generally smaller in females than in males, the difference being most pronounced for the fast-twitch fibers (Nygaard, 1981). Since the relative occurrence of slow- and fast-twitch fibers is similar in males and females, slow-twitch fibers constitute a larger fractional volume of the lateral vastus muscle in females than in comparative male subjects because of the size difference. Parallel to these histochemical observations it has been shown that the ratio between the activities of oxidative and glycolytic enzymes are higher in females than in males (Bass, Vondra, Rath, & Vitek, 1975; Nikkilä, Taskinen, Rehunen, & Härkonen, 1978; Nygaard, 1981) indicating a higher potential for oxidative phosphorylation in women.

During a 1-hr continuous exercise on a cycle ergometer, 20 min at each of 3 loads equivalent to 50%, 60%, and 75% of maximal oxygen uptake, RER values were lower in females than in males at the 60% and 75% exercise levels. To further assess carbohydrate and lipid metabolism, concentrations of metabolic substrates were determined in blood collected from a cubital vein, and in muscle tissue obtained by the needle biopsy technique from the lateral head of m. quadriceps femoris. Low lactate, high glycerol, and less decrease of muscle glycogen in women than in men generally supported the results on RER.

A recent series of experiments further supported these findings. The subjects exercised on a cycle ergometer for 60 min at 60% of maximal oxygen uptake. Glycerol levels elevated to a greater extent in women than in men, further supporting the conclusion that women were able to rapidly adjust fat metabolism to the caloric needs of the work, while in general men required the immediate use of alternative substrates.

Fasting insulin plasma concentrations correlated inversely with the relative volume of slow-twitch fibers of the lateral vastus muscle. Plasma catecholamines increased gradually during prolonged exercise of moderate intensity, reaching relatively high levels toward the end of an exercise bout. Some studies have indicated a difference between males and females (a lower adrenergic reactivity in females) working at the same relative load (Sanchez et al., 1980; Vendsalu, 1960). In our study, lower epinephrine concentrations were seen in women during the high work load.

In summary, as evaluated from respiratory and metabolic reactions to exercise, fat combustion is higher in sedentary, normal-weight, healthy young females than in males. The relative body fat content was not directly related to metabolic and hormonal reactions to exercise. A relatively high volume of slow-twitch fibers in skeletal muscle of females compared to males appeared to be of significance for the choice of fat as a fuel, but exercise training led to increased fat combustion in both sexes.

Evidence for Sex Related Differences in Metabolic Response to Heavy Exercise by P.K. Pedersen. Department of Physical Education, Odense University, Denmark

In a recent study (Froberg & Pedersen, 1984), we exposed young women (n = 6) and men (n = 7) to exhaustive cycle exercise at 80% and 90% of maximal oxygen uptake. The subjects were selected in order to be comparable with respect to physical activity patterns. Thus, they were physical education students, aged 25 to 35 years, who had been coeducated for 1 year. Furthermore, their leisure time activity habits, as determined by questionnaire, were not significantly different.

Midexercise and terminal RER were significantly lower in women than in men at 80% of $\dot{V}O_2max$, 0.91 ± 0.01 versus 0.97 ± 0.01 (mean ± SE) ($p < 0.01$). The same trend was observed in the 90% experiment, 0.96 ± 0.02 versus 1.00 ± 0.01, but in this case the difference did only approach statistical significance ($p < 0.1$). We interpreted the lower RER values in these experiments as evidence for a relatively larger rate of fat utilization in women. The blood lactate values in women were lower by about 1.5 to 2.5 mM. Estimates of the possible influence of this phenomenon upon the CO_2 washout suggest, however, that this could only account for a minor part of the observed difference in RER values.

These observations are in conflict with those of Costill, Fink, Getchell, Ivy, and Witzmann (1979) and Powers, Riley, and Howley (1980). The discrepancy may be the result of the use of lower relative work loads in those studies, or of different modes of exercise, that is, running as compared to cycling, or of selection of subjects. We compared groups that were similar with respect to physical activity. In doing so, the $\dot{V}O_2max$ per kg body weight turned out to be 15% to 20% lower in women than in men, which is typical of existing sex difference. The other two studies compared men and women with similar $\dot{V}O_2max$ per kg body weight. This would imply that the women of these studies were relatively more fit than the men.

The present study offers no explanation for the difference in metabolic response between men and women. Komi and Karlsson (1978) have reported lower skeletal muscle glycolytic enzyme activities in women. At the same time, the difference in oxidative enzymes was not significant. This altered balance between glycolytic and oxidative enzymes could be related to the relative preference of fat as an energy source in women.

Sex Differences in the Effects of Exercise-Training on Adipose Tissue and Weight Regulation **by A. Tremblay and C. Bouchard. Laval University, Quebec, Canada**

Several investigators have shown that exercise-training can induce a low to moderate loss in body weight without strict control over food intake (Tremblay, Després, & Bouchard, 1985). Even though this effect had often been noted in both males and females, we thought it would be of interest to consider sex differences in weight and fat loss in response to exercise-training. During the course of a 20-week aerobic exercise program, the reduction in weight and fatness was found to be more pronounced in males than in females (Després et al., 1984a; Tremblay, Després, Leblanc, & Bouchard, 1984). This effect, which remained essentially unchanged even when taking into account their respective level of exercise-induced energy expenditure (Tremblay et al., 1984), was accompanied by sex differences in the response of fat cell metabolism. Thus, the increments in epinephrine-stimulated lipolysis (Després et al., 1984a, 1984b) and in basal and insulin-stimulated glucose conversion into triglycerides in isolated suprailiac fat cells (Savard, Després, Marcotte & Bouchard, 1985) were higher in males than in females.

From an energetic standpoint, we reported sex differences in the relationship between energy intake and energy expenditure associated with daily physical activity (Tremblay, Leblanc, Sévigny, Savoie, & Bouchard, 1983). For instance, the correlation between intake and expenditure was found to be significantly higher in males than in females. Furthermore, studies performed in animals have shown that females submitted to training tended to preserve their energy reserves mainly by increasing energy intake (Applegate, Upton, & Stern, 1982; Nance, Bromley, Barnard, & Gorski, 1977). In an attempt to document this phenomenon in humans, we assessed the acute effect of a prolonged vigorous exercise on energy, protein, lipid, and carbohydrate intake. Five healthy lean individuals of each sex were submitted to one bout of exercise (60 min, 68% $\dot{V}O_2max$) and, thereafter, had free access to food during 5 hr. This protocol was repeated without the exercise period. Both experimental conditions were administered in a random order. In agreement with results obtained in animals, these preliminary data indicate that during the hours following exercise, energy intake in females increased to a larger extent over the caloric cost of exercise in comparison with males. Interestingly, this compensation was solely achieved by an increment in carbohydrate intake.

***Maximum Oxygen Uptake, Muscle Fiber Composition and Running Performance* by C. Williams, R. Ramsbottom, L. Boobis, and W. Freeman. Department of Physical Education and Sports Science, University of Technology, Loughborough, England**

Twenty-six recreational runners (14 males and 12 females) volunteered for this study. The maximum oxygen uptake and treadmill running speeds equivalent to blood lactic acid concentration of 2 mM and 4 mM were determined for each individual as well as their time to complete 5 km on a running track under race conditions. In addition, needle biopsy samples of the vastus lateralis were obtained from each subject for the histochemical determination of fiber composition. There were only poor correlations between 5 km running times and the percentage of type I fibers of the male (r = 0.20, ns) and female (r = 0.55, ns) subjects but better correlations with their VO_2max value ($r = 0.83$, $p < 0.01$: females $r = 0.89$, $p < 0.01$). The strongest correlations were found between 5 km performance times and the running speeds equivalent to 4 mM lactate concentrations for both the male ($r = 0.90$, $p < 0.01$) and the female ($4 = 0.92$, $p < 0.01$) subjects. The differences in 5 km performance times between the male and female runners, in this study, are best explained by the difference in their $\dot{V}O_2max$ values.

SUMMARY OF CHAIRPERSONS

Sex differences are known for a variety of biological traits and more were uncovered at this symposium as suggested by the above short reviews. It is commonly recognized that, on the average, females live longer, have lower blood lipids but higher HDL-cholesterol concentrations, mature sexually earlier than males, have more relative body fat than males and a different pattern of fat distribution over the body, are less affected in terms of longevity and morbidity by the same amount of excess body fat as males, have a lower maximal oxygen uptake per kg of body weight or kg of fat free weight from puberty onward, have a lesser anaerobic capacity and power per unit of weight, exhibit quite a different pattern of sex hormone concentration in the blood, and others as well. One must, however, keep in mind that these sex differences were generally reported following the comparison of male versus female mean values. They do not imply that all males are strikingly different from females for a given characteristic. Indeed, there is a great deal of overlap between the distributions of male and female scores for any biological trait that one may want to consider.

Sex Differences in Skeletal Muscle

It is well established that, for a similar body mass, males will on the average have more muscle mass than females. More recently, it has been suggested that females may exhibit for a given muscle (m. vastus lateralis) a higher proportion of type I fibers than males, particularly when adult sedentary individuals are compared (Jansson, 1980, and this panel report; Simoneau et al., 1985). Nygaard has, however, pointed out that this finding may be caused by sex difference in fiber areas (see Nygaard above), a finding consistent with the data reported by Simoneau et al. (1985). It is important to note that this trend for a sex difference in fiber type distribution has been observed only in sedentary adults and not in more active teenagers or endurance-trained males and females.

In addition, it has been shown that glycolytic enzyme activities were higher in adult males than in females while oxidative enzyme markers were comparable in both sexes (Bass et al., 1975; Komi & Karlsson, 1978; Nikkilä et al., 1978; Nygaard, 1981; Simoneau et al., 1985). In other words, the ratio of oxidative to glycolytic enzyme activities is higher, suggesting perhaps that oxidative phosphorylation may be a preferred metabolic pathway in sedentary females.

Sex Difference in Fat Utilization During Exercise

Some data presented in the symposium and others in the literature suggest that women have a lower respiratory exchange ratio at rest (Jansson, 1980) and during exercise at various intensities (Froberg & Pedersen, 1984; Jansson, 1980; Nygaard, this panel report). It has also been reported that females have lower muscle or blood lactate levels at a given exercise intensity (Froberg & Pedersen, 1984; Jacobs, Tesch, Bar-Or, Karlsson, & Dotan, 1983; Nygaard, this panel report), less decrease in muscle glycogen (Froberg & Pedersen, 1984; Nygaard, this panel report) but the data are not always entirely supportive of these concepts (Jansson, this panel report).

The general trend from these studies is that sedentary adult women are on the average capable of utilizing more fat as a substrate during prolonged submaximal exercise than men. However, this sex difference progressively disappears with endurance training and is completely reversed in endurance athletes (Costill et al., 1979). These observations are coherent with the recent report by Lortie et al., 1984, indicating that after 5 months of training the response of previously sedentary adult males and females were identical for maximal oxygen uptake but endurance increased 50% more in male subjects.

Sex Difference in Response to Exercise and Menstrual Status

This is an area where good experimental research is needed. The effects of exercise and training have been reviewed recently from the point of view of reproductive hormones and training related menstrual cycle irregularities (Bonen, 1984; Loucks & Horvath, 1985). It has been reported that blood lactate during heavy exercise was higher in the follicular phase, when levels of estradiol and progesterone are low, but not in the luteal phase. In addition, performance time to exhaustion at 90% W_{max} was decreased in the follicular phase (see Jurkowski, 1982, for a review). The studies reported above by Graham and coworkers and by Lavoie suggest that the menstrual status and the phase of the menstrual cycle may sometimes be associated with the variation in metabolic adaptation to prolonged exercise. Of particular interest is the report that after a 24-hr low CHO diet, blood glucose levels decreased after 70 min of exercise in men, and in women in the luteal but not in the follicular phase. On the other hand, Graham and coworkers have shown that amenorrheic women had a lower blood lactate level than men after work to exhaustion at 90% $\dot{V}O_2max$.

REFERENCES

Applegate, E.A., Upton, D.E., & Stern, J.S. (1982). Food intake, body composition and blood lipids following treadmill exercise in male and female rats. *Physiology and Behaviour,* **28**, 917-920.

Bass, A., Vondra, K., Rath, R., & Vitek, V. (1975). M. quadriceps femoris of man, a muscle with an unusual enzyme activity pattern of energy supplying metabolism in mammals. *Pflügers Archiv,* **354**, 249-255.

Béliveau, L., Trudeau, F., Péronnet, F., & Brisson, G. (1985). Dynamics of circulating catecholamines during mild exercise in dog. *Clinical Physiology,* **5**(Suppl. 4), 27.

Bonen, A. (1984). Effects of exercise and training on reproductive hormones. *International Journal of Sports Medicine,* **5**, 195-197.

Costill, D., Fink, W.J., Getchell, L.H., Ivy, J.L., & Witzmann, F. (1979). Lipid metabolism in skeletal muscle of endurance-trained males and females. *Journal of Applied Physiology,* **47**, 787-791.

Després, J.P., Bouchard, C., Savard, R., Tremblay, A., Marcotte, M., & Thériault, G. (1984a). The effect of a 20-week endurance program on adipose tissue morphology and lipolysis in men and women. *Metabolism,* **33**, 235-239.

Després, J.P., Bouchard, C., Savard, R., Tremblay, A., Marcotte, M., & Thériault, G. (1984b). Effects of exercise-training and detraining on fat cell lipolysis in men and women. *European Journal of Applied Physiology,* **53**, 25-30.

Froberg, K., & Pedersen, P.K. (1984). Sex differences in endurance capacity and metabolic response to prolonged, heavy exercise. *European Journal of Applied Physiology,* **52**, 446-450.

Hansen, F.M., Fahmy, N., & Nielsen, J.H. (1980). The influence of sexual hormones on lipogenesis and lipolysis in rat fat cells. *Acta Endocrinologica Copenhagen,* **95**, 566-570.

Hedberg, G., & Jansson, E. (1976). Skelettmuskelfiberkomposition, kapacitet och intresse för olika fysiska aktiviteter bland elever i gymnasieskolan. *Pedagogiska rapporter, Umeå, nr* **54**, [English Summary].

Jacobs, I., Tesch, P.A., Bar-Or, O., Karlsson, J., & Dotan, R.. (1983). Lactate in human skeletal muscle after 10 s and 30 s of supramaximal exercise. *Journal of Applied Physiology,* **55**, 365-368.

Jansson, E. (1980). Diet and muscle metabolism in man with reference to fat and carbohydrate utilization and its regulation. *Acta Physiologica Scandinavica,* (Suppl. 487)[thesis].

Jurkowski, J.E.H. (1982). Hormonal and physiological responses to exercise in relation to the menstrual cycle. *Canadian Journal of Applied Sport Sciences,* **7**, 85-89.

Komi, P., & Karlsson, J. (1978). Skeletal muscle fibre types, enzyme activities and physical performance in young males and females. *Acta Physiologica Scandinavica,* **103**, 210-218.

Lortie, G., Simoneau, J.A., Hamel, P., Boulay, M.R., Landry, F., & Bouchard, C. (1984). Responses of maximal aerobic power and capacity to aerobic training. *International Journal of Sports Medicine,* **5**, 232-236.

Loucks, A.B., & Horvath, S.M. (1985). Athletic amenorrhea: A review. *Medicine and Science in Sports and Exercise,* **17**, 56-72.

Lundberg, B., Esbjörnsson, M., Hedberg, G., & Jansson, E. (1985). Skeletal muscle fibre types and physical performance. A 10 year follow-up study. *Clinical Physiology,* **5**(Suppl. 4), 167.

Nance, D.M., Bromley, B., Barnard, R.J., & Gorski, R.A. (1977). Sexually dimorphic effects of forced exercise on food intake and body weight in the rat. *Physiology and Behaviour,* **19**, 155-158.

Nikkilä, E.A., Taskinen, M.R., Rehunen, J., & Härkonen, M. (1978). Lipoprotein lipase activity in adipose tissue and skeletal muscle of runners: relation to serum lipoproteins. *Metabolism,* **27**, 1661-1671.

Nygaard, E. (1981). Skeletal muscle fibre characteristics in young women. *Acta Physiologica Scandinavica,* **112**, 299-304.

Powers, S.K., Riley, W., & Howley, E.T. (1980). Comparison of fat metabolism between trained men and women during prolonged aerobic work. *Research Quarterly,* **51**, 427-431.

Sanchez, J., Pequignot, J.M., Peyrin, L., & Monod, H. (1980). Sex differences in the sympatho-adrenal response to isometric exercise. *European Journal of Applied Physiology,* **45**, 147-154.

Savard, R., Després, J.P., Marcotte, M., & Bouchard, C. (1985). Endurance training and glucose conversion into triglycerides in human fat cells. *Journal of Applied Physiology,* **58**, 230-235.

Simoneau, J.A., Lortie, G., Boulay, M.R., Thibault, M.C., Thériault, G., & Bouchard, C. (1985). Skeletal muscle histochemical and biochemical characterics in sedentary male and female subjects. *Canadian Journal of Physiology and Pharmacology,* **63**, 30-35.

Tremblay, A., Després, J.P., & Bouchard, C. (1985). The effects of exercise-training on energy balance and adipose tissue morphology and metabolism. *Sport Medicine,* **2**, 223-233.

Tremblay, A., Després, J.P., Leblanc, C., & Bouchard, C. (1984). Sex dimorphism in fat loss in response to exercise-training. *Journal of Obesity and Weight Regulation,* **3**, 193-203.

Tremblay, A., Leblanc, C., Sévigny, J., Savoie, J.P., & Bouchard, C. (1983). The relationship between energy intake and expenditure: A sex difference. In F. Landry (Ed.), *Health risk estimation, risk reduction and health promotion* (pp. 115-119). Ottawa: Canadian Public Health Association.

Vendsalu, A. (1960). Studies on adrenaline and noradrenaline in human plasma. *Acta Physiologica Scandinavica,* **49**(Suppl. 173), 1-123.

Yki-Järvinen, H. (1984). Insulin sensitivity during the menstrual cycle. *Journal of Clinical Endocrinology and Metabolism,* **59**, 350-353.

SECTION E

DIABETES—CARDIOVASCULAR DISORDERS

Acute and Long-Term Effects of Exercise in Type 1 Diabetes

Bernard Zinman
University of Toronto
Toronto, Ontario, Canada

Exercise is said to be an important component of the treatment of patients with type 1 diabetes. However, demonstration of its utility in achieving improved diabetes control has been lacking (Wallberg-Henriksson et al., 1982; Zinman, Zuniga-Guajardo, & Kelly, 1983; Zinman, Zuniga-Guajardo, & Kelly, 1984). Indeed, more attention has been directed at avoiding the major acute complication in exercising type 1 diabetics, namely exercise-induced hypoglycemia. Recent studies (Caron, Poussier, Marliss, & Zinman, 1982; Koivisto & Felig, 1978; Vranic, Kemmer, Berchtold, & Berger, 1983; Zinman, Vranic, Albisser, & Marliss, 1979) have provided newer insights as to the mechanisms responsible for exercise-induced hypoglycemia and have led to more suitable exercise recommendations and guidelines for diabetics. In addition, experiments with newer methods of insulin replacement (e.g., insulin infusion pumps) indicate that more precise insulin replacement algorithms can be derived in order to normalize the metabolic responses to exercise both in the fasted and postprandial state (Nelson, Poussier, Marliss, Albisser, & Zinman, 1982; Poussier et al., 1983).

It is our aim in this paper to first address the acute response to exercise in type 1 diabetes as it relates to normal exercise physiology. The consequences of insulin deficiency and insulin excess on fuel flux will be reviewed and the potential for using exercise to acutely improve postprandial hyperglycemia will be examined. In the second part of this paper, the effects of exercise training on insulin sensitivity, glucoregulation, and nutrient intake recently studied in our laboratory (Zinman et al., 1984) will be described.

THE PHYSIOLOGIC, METABOLIC, AND HORMONAL RESPONSE TO EXERCISE

Exercise is a physiologic state requiring the rapid mobilization and redistribution of metabolic fuels to ensure an adequate energy supply for the work of muscle contraction (Felig & Wahren, 1975). These responses are orchestrated by a precise sequence of cardiovascular, neural and hormonal responses that have been well documented.

With the onset of exercise, muscle energy consumption immediately increases in order to provide high energy phosphate compounds necessary for the contractile process. Muscle glycogen serves as the source of energy in the first few minutes of exercise, since it is directly available to the contractile tissue and does not have to depend on a circulatory response for its mobilization. As exercise continues, circulating glucose supplied principally by the liver becomes a more prominent energy source. The increased uptake of glucose from the circulation by muscle is quickly and precisely repleted by a parallel increase in hepatic glucose production. Thus, despite a severalfold increase in glucose uptake by muscle during exercise, plasma glucose concentration remains remarkably constant. This is achieved primarily by hepatic glycogenolysis and gluconeogenesis. With more prolonged exercise, free fatty acids (FFA) mobilized from adipose tissue become a more significant energy yielding substrate. This is mediated by the process of lipolysis in adipose tissue, which results in the breakdown of triglyceride to FFA and glycerol. The FFA are transported in the plasma bound to albumin and are then taken up by actively exercising muscle. The glycerol released can also serve as a gluconeogenic precursor and is cleared by the liver. The sequence of metabolic fuel mobilization as outlined above can be significantly modified by several variables including the duration of exercise, the intensity of exercise, the fitness of the individual performing the exercise, and the previous nutritional state.

The hormonal responses to exercise have been well characterized and include a decrease in insulin secretion and a concomitant increase in the circulating concentration of the counterregulatory hormones. These include catecholamines, glucagon, growth hormone and cortisol. Several studies have recently been completed in order to evaluate the role of each of these hormones in contributing to the observed change in metabolic fuel flux (Christensen et al., 1979; Issekutz, 1978; Issekutz & Vranic, 1980; Wasserman, Lickley, & Vranic, 1984). The decrease in insulin secretion facilitates hepatic glucose production and the mobilization of FFA from adipose tissue (Zinman et al., 1979). At the same time, there is sufficient insulin present in the circulation to support the augmented muscle glucose uptake in response to exercise. As will be seen in the discussion of the metabolic response to exercise in patients with diabetes, insulin plays a central role in mediating these metabolic pathways. Glucagon and epinephrine also play an important role in maintaining glucose homeostasis during exercise. The main effect of glucagon is the stimulation and maintenance of increased hepatic glucose production with exercise in order to prevent hypoglycemia as a consequence of increased muscle glucose uptake. Epinephrine preserves circulating glucose concentrations by two mechanisms. First, it has a similar but less prominent effect on liver glucose production. Second, and perhaps more significant, epinephrine stimulates lypolysis in adipose tissue, which results in an increase in FFA production and thus provides an alternate fuel for exercising muscle with the conservation of circulating glucose. The metabolic and hormonal changes described above are summarized in Figure 1.

Considering the complexity of fuel flux during exercise, and the important regulatory role played by insulin and the counterregulatory hormones whose concentration and secretion are abnormal in diabetes, it is not surprising that patients with diabetes respond differently to exercise than normal controls. This, as expected, is more evident in patients with type 1 diabetes receiving exogenous insulin injections. The type of insulin used, the injection site, the time between insulin injection and the onset of exercise, and the time between exercise and the last meal are important variables in determining the metabolic response to exercise in patients with type 1 diabetes. In a similar vein, patients with type 2 diabetes characteristically have abnormalities in insulin sensitivity and secretion and thus can also be expected to demonstrate abnormal metabolic regulation during exercise.

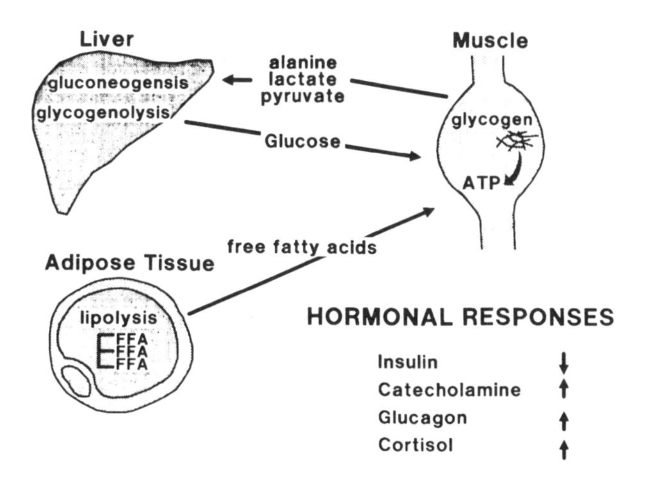

Figure 1 Metabolic fuel flux and hormonal response to exercise in normal man.

ACUTE RESPONSE TO EXERCISE IN TYPE 1 DIABETES

Standard Insulin Treatment

The standard treatment of patients with type 1 diabetes involves the injection of one or two doses of insulin subcutaneously, creating a slowly absorbable insulin depot. It is clear that this method of insulin replacement does not duplicate the normal secretion of insulin from the pancreas, which can vary acutely, depending on nutrient intake and physical activity. As a result, patients with type 1 diabetes commonly oscillate between states of insulin excess and insulin deficiency. Consequently, the metabolic responses to exercise have been shown to correlate with the metabolic state at the onset of exercise. When insulin deficiency and ketosis are present, exercise will predictably result in an increase in plasma glucose and accelerated ketone body formation. This occurs because exercise mediated muscle glucose uptake is insulin-dependent and that with insulin deficiency the usual increase in muscle glucose uptake during exercise will not occur. As well, insulin deficiency leads to an exaggerated increase in hepatic glucose production and thus, circulating plasma glucose concentrations increase significantly. In addition, insulin deficiency results in increased FFA mobilization and accelerated ketone body formation by the liver. It is thus clear that exercise performed by a patient who is severely insulin deficient will result in a further deterioration in metabolic control. In practical terms, it is evident that withholding insulin in anticipation of prolonged exercise can lead to undesirable metabolic consequences and should be discouraged.

The response to exercise performed with insulin deficiency can be contrasted with the more common clinical situation of exercise being performed at a time when there is a relative excess of insulin in the circulation. Under these circumstances, plasma glucose will predictably decrease during exercise and the well-known clinical observation of exercise-induced hypoglycemia occurs. The elevated insulin levels result in an inhibition of hepatic glucose production. Thus, although muscle glucose uptake increases with exercise, the liver is unable to increase glucose production in order to replenish the loss of glucose from the circulation and a fall in plasma glucose results. These metabolic events can be precipitated by the rapid absorption of depot insulin during exercise, which is likely to occur if the depot injection site used is an exercising extremity (Koivisto & Felig, 1978; Zinman et al., 1977; Zinman et al., 1979). The metabolic responses to exercise performed during standard insulin therapy are summarized in Table 1.

Table 1 Exercise and Subcutaneous Depot Insulin Treatment

With Insulin Excess		With Insulin Deficiency	
Hepatic Glucose Production	↓	Hepatic Glucose Production	↑
Muscle Glucose Utilization	↑	Muscle Glucose Utilization	→
Plasma Glucose Concentration	↓	Plasma Glucose Concentration	↑
Free Fatty Acid Production	↓	Blood Ketone Production	↑

Thus, it is clear from the above discussion that with standard depot insulin injections, it is extremely difficult to achieve a normal metabolic response to exercise in most insulin-dependent diabetic patients. Often, an adjustment in insulin dosage, or more commonly, the ingestion of carbohydrates before or during exercise is required to prevent exercise-induced hypoglycemia. It is also helpful to use a nonexercising injection site like the abdomen for insulin administration in order to avoid the rapid mobilization of depot insulin from an exercising extremity. The recent increased utilization of the technique of self blood glucose monitoring (SBGM) by many type 1 diabetic patients provides us with a useful and simple method by which individual responses to a particular exercise can be well documented. Thus, the need for changes in insulin and/or nutrient intake can be more precisely evaluated and the effectiveness of different intervention strategies in a particular patient can be accurately assessed.

Postprandial Exercise in Type 1 Diabetes

Type 1 diabetic patients characteristically have an abnormal glucose excursion with meals. This usually results from the inadequate matching of depot insulin absorption from the injection site with that of carbohydrate absorption from the gastrointestinal tract. Since exercise results in increased glucose utilization by muscle, a recent study was undertaken to determine whether exercise after a meal could significantly improve postprandial hyperglycemia in type 1 diabetes (Caron et al., 1982). The results of this study indicate that a significant improvement in meal-related glucose excursion can be achieved with postprandial exercise. However, the responses are somewhat variable and a marked improvement in glucose excursion with breakfast occurred in only five of the eight

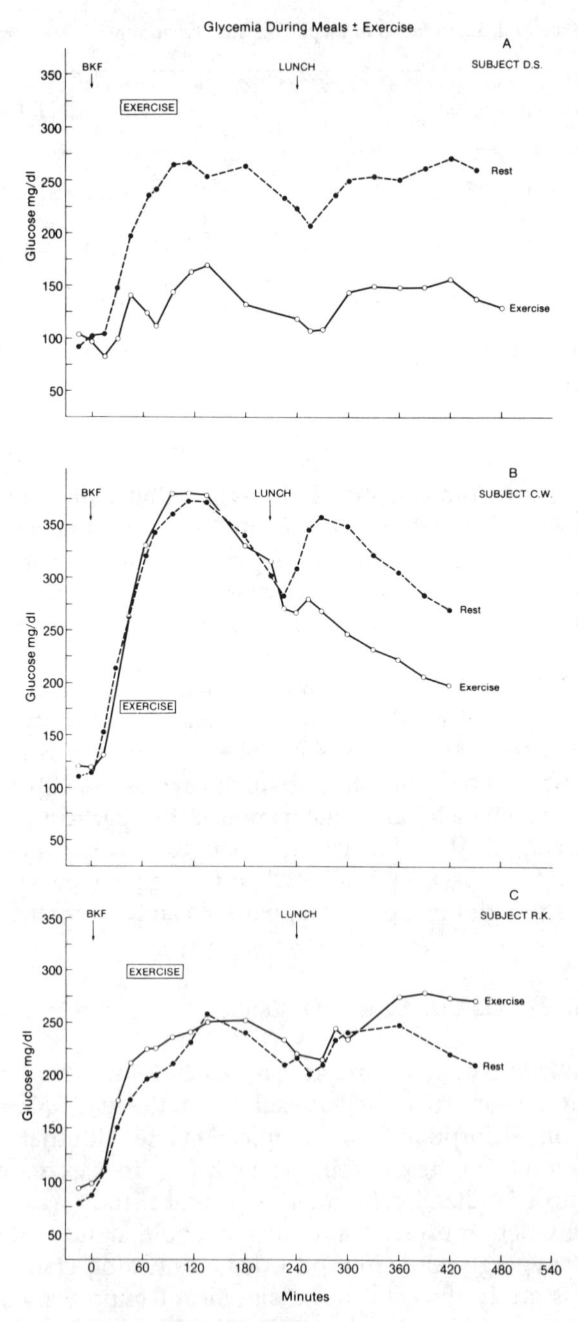

Figure 2 Glucose responses during breakfast (BKF) and lunch at rest and with 45 min of bicycle exercise beginning 30 min after BKF. The responses of three individuals are shown. From "The Effect of Postprandial Exercise on Meal-related Glucose Tolerance in Insulin-Dependent Diabetic Individuals" by D. Caron, P. Poussier, E.B. Marliss, and B. Zinman, 1982, *Diabetes Care,* **5**. Reprinted by permission.

subjects studied. Interestingly, in two subjects, there was no change in the glucose excursion with breakfast but a significant improvement in the glucose excursion with lunch was evident. In one subject, postprandial exercise did not improve the glucose response to either breakfast or lunch. An example of each of these three individual responses is shown in Figure 2. Thus, in most patients, postprandial exercise can significantly reduce meal glycemic excursions with the effect persisting for at least the duration of the next meal. However, it is also clearly evident that the responses to postprandial exercise are quite variable. To document and maximize the benefits in a particular patient, SBGM can provide valuable information.

Exercise and Insulin Infusion Pumps

There recently has been a great deal of interest in the use of insulin infusion pumps to treat diabetes, and with continued use, the advantages and disadvantages of these devices are becoming apparent. In a context of exercise, insulin infusion pumps appear to provide a distinct advantage over standard insulin therapy in normalizing the glycemic and metabolic responses to exercise. This appears to be the case for exercise performed in both the postabsorptive (overnight fasted) and postprandial (after meals) states. In contrast to the well-documented hypoglycemic effect of exercise during standard depot insulin therapy, patients receiving an infusion of basal insulin subcutaneously maintain steady state plasma glucose concentrations throughout exercise much like normal controls (Figure 3). Thus, insulin pump patients can exercise before breakfast with minimal risk of hypoglycemia while receiving sufficient insulin to promote increased muscle glucose uptake and permitting hepatic glucose production to respond appropriately. Adjustment in the basal insulin infusion rate will not usually be required, although for prolonged exercise, it is probably prudent to reduce the basal rate by 30% to 50%. Once again, the use of self-blood glucose monitoring can provide valuable information in order to accommodate for variations in individual metabolic responses. When exercise is performed after meals, insulin pump therapy may also provide increased flexibility in insulin treatment compared to conventional depot injections. The ability to adjust each premeal insulin bolus with insulin pump therapy provides the opportunity to modify meal insulin in anticipation of postprandial exercise. Depending on the timing and duration of exercise, the premeal bolus may be reduced to one half or one third of the usual amount. These changes can prevent exercise-induced hypoglycemia, but the normal physiological regulation of insulin with postprandial exercise cannot be fully achieved with subcutaneous insulin infusions. However, recent studies using a more physiologic route of insulin pump delivery, namely the intravenous route, have demonstrated

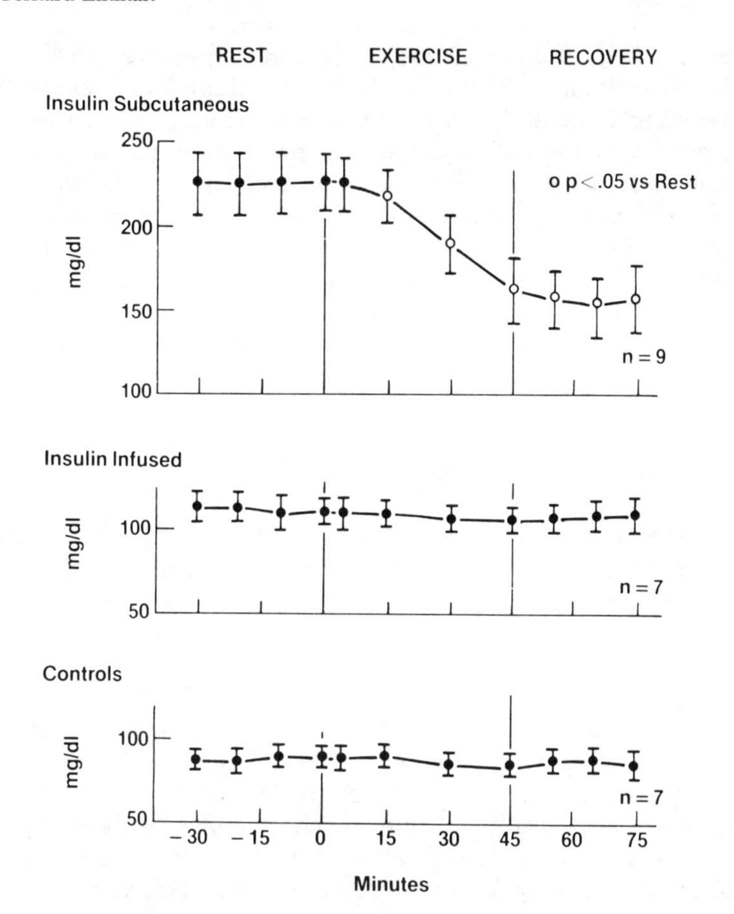

Figure 3 Glucose response to exercise in type 1 diabetes receiving a subcutaneous depo injection (top panel) and a constant basal insulin infusion (middle panel) as compared to normal controls (lower panel). From "Glucoregulation During Moderate Exercise in Insulin Treated Diabetes" by B. Zinman, F.T. Murray, M. Vranic, A.M. Albisser, B.S. Leibel, P.A. McClean, and E.B. Marliss, 1977, *Journal of Critical Endocrinology and Metabolism*, **45**. Reprinted with permission.

that specific insulin infusion waveforms for postprandial exercise can be formulated (Nelson et al., 1982; Poussier et al., 1983). Figure 4 illustrates the changes required in the open loop intravenous insulin infusion waveform in order to avoid postprandial hypoglycemia. Failure to reduce the increased insulin infusion to basal levels consistently resulted in hypoglycemia (Figure 4, Exercise 1). However, when basal rates of infusion were administered during exercise (Figure 4, Exercise 2), a normal postprandial exercise response was observed.

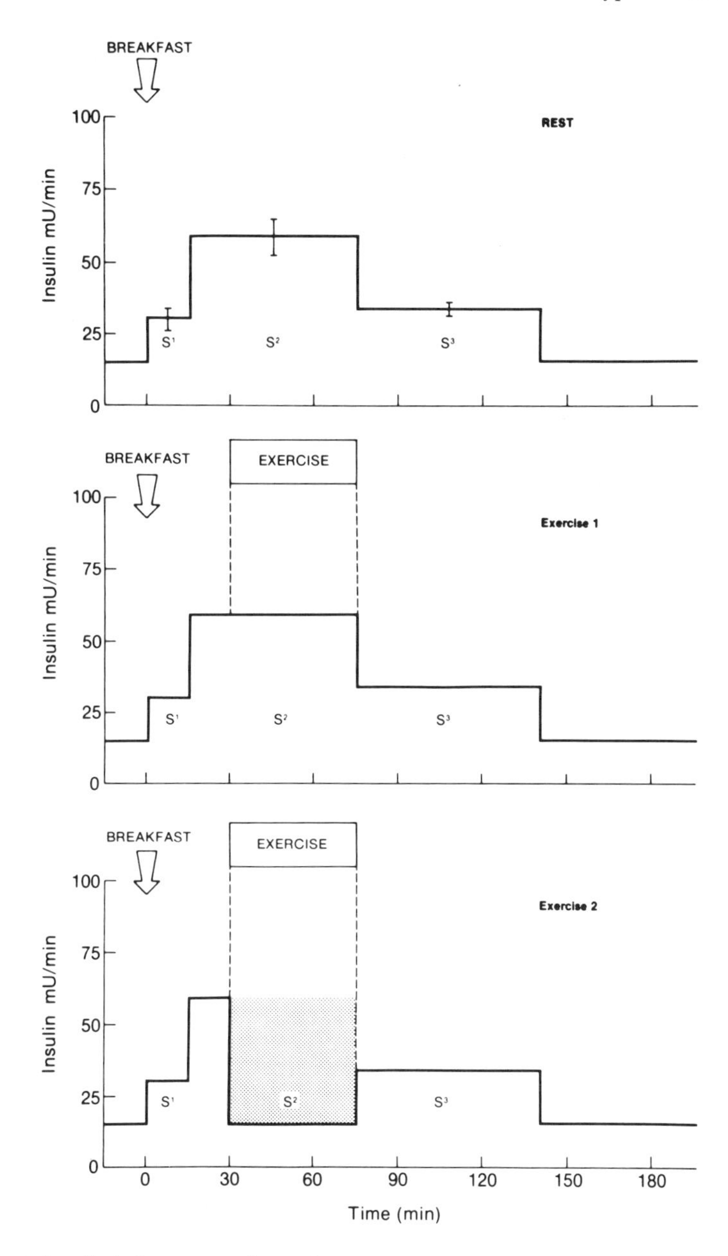

Figure 4 Insulin infusion waveforms during the 3 study days; breakfast insulin waveform at rest (rest) and breakfast insulin waveform with exercise (Exercise 1). Modified breakfast insulin waveform with exercise (Exercise 2). Means ± SEM are shown. From "Open Loop Intravenous Insulin Waveforms for Postprandial Exercise in Type I Diabetes" by P. Poussier, B. Zinman, E.B. Marliss, A.M. Albisser, K. Perlman, and D. Caron, 1983, *Diabetes Care*, **6**. Reprinted with permission.

LONG TERM EFFECTS OF EXERCISE TRAINING IN TYPE 1 DIABETES

Although exercise is thought to be useful in the treatment of diabetes, there is little evidence to support a beneficial effect of exercise training in type 1 diabetes. Indeed, a recent Scandinavian study (Wallberg-Henriksson et al., 1982) failed to demonstrate a significant change in glycosylated hemoglobin in nine type 1 diabetic subjects undergoing 16 weeks of exercise training despite an increase in peripheral insulin sensitivity.

The failure to demonstrate a beneficial effect of exercise on long-term glucose control appears to be inconsistent with the well-known acute hypoglycemic effect of exercise and the observation that exercise can improve postprandial glucose excursion (Caron et al., 1982). To examine the variables that might explain this apparent contradiction, the acute glucose responses to exercise, the effect of exercise on nutrient intake, and the long-term responses to exercise training were studied in 13 type 1 diabetic subjects and the responses compared to seven controls.

As shown in Table 2, fitness improved significantly in both control and diabetic subjects. As predicted, each exercise session was associated with an acute decrease in blood glucose. The magnitude of this change was similar throughout the study as seen in Figure 5. However, a long-term effect on glucoregulation was not evident. Fasting plasma glucose and glycosylated hemoglobin showed no significant change throughout the study (Table 3). Diet histories and food records indicated that total caloric intake, particularly carbohydrates, increased significantly on exercising days (Table 4). This observation was supported by constancy of weight before and after the training period (65.7 ± 5.2 kg vs. 65.1 ± 5.2 kg).

Table 2 Effect of Exercise Training on Maximal Oxygen Uptake ($\dot{V}O_2max$)(ml/min/kg)

Subjects	Pretraining (0 weeks)	Training		Posttraining (18 weeks)
		6 weeks	12 weeks	
Control Subjects	33.8 ± 1.7	40.0 ± 1.8*	43.2 ± 3.5*	40.0 ± 4.0
Diabetic Subjects	38.7 ± 3.3	44.6 ± 3.0*	46.5 ± 3.6*	43.1 ± 3.3*

*$p < 0.05$ as compared with pretraining

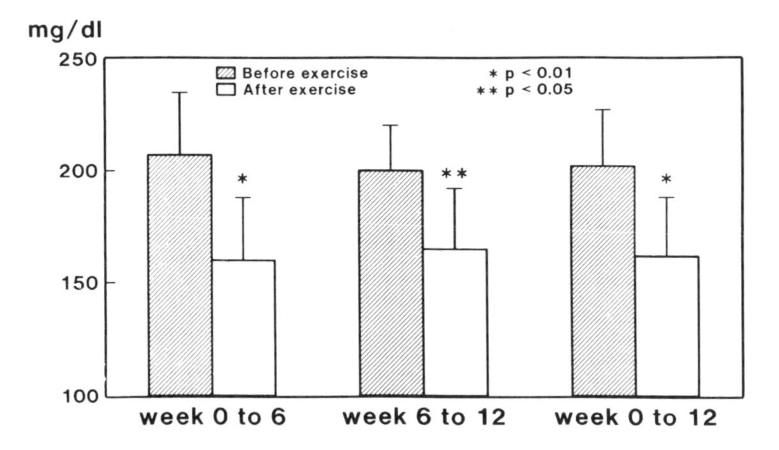

Figure 5 Blood glucose concentrations before (hatched bars) and after (open bars) each exercise session during the first 6 weeks of training, second 6 weeks of training, and over the entire training period. Mean ± SEM are shown for 13 subjects with type 1 diabetes. Reproduced with permisison from Zinman et al., 1983. From "The Effect of Exercise Training on Glucose Control in Type I Diabetes" by B. Zinman, S. Zuniga-Guajardo, and D. Kelly, 1983, *Clinical and Investigative Medicine,* **6**(Suppl. 2), p. 69. Reprinted with permission.

Table 3 Effect of Exercise Training on Fasting Plasma Glucose and Glycosylated Hemoglobin

Subjects	Pretraining (0 weeks)	Training 6 weeks	Training 12 weeks	Posttraining (18 weeks)
Fasting plasma glucose, mg/dl (mmol/L)				
Control Subjects	4.8 ± 0.2	4.8 ± 0.4	4.7 ± 0.2	4.5 ± 0.1
Diabetic Subjects	10.8 ± 1.5	10.7 ± 1.5	11.2 ± 1.7	10.5 ± 1.6
Hemoglobin Al (%)**				
Control Subjects	7.7 ± 0.5	7.5 ± 0.4	7.4 ± 0.2	7.0 ± 0.1
Diabetic Subjects	10.7 ± 0.3*	10.7 ± 0.3*	10.3 ± 0.8*	10.6 ± 0.3*

*$p < 0.005$ as compared with control subjects
**Normal, 6.5 % to 8.5%

Table 4 Effect of Exercise on Nutrient Intake

Nutrient Intake	Nonexercising day	Exercising day
Total calories (kcal)	2569 ± 273	2849 ± 330*
Carbohydrate (g)	265 ± 30	309 ± 38 *
Protein (g)	115 ± 11	125 ± 15 *
Fat (g)	115 ± 15	121 ± 17

* $p < 0.05$ as compared with nonexercising day

Thus, although plasma glucose decreased acutely with each exercise session, a long-term effect on overall glucose control could not be demonstrated. Increased caloric intake primarily as carbohydrate on exercising days likely accounts for the above observations.

Although exercise training per se does not have a significant effect on overall glucose control, diabetic patients should be encouraged and have the freedom to exercise for the same general reasons (primarily cardiovascular and physiological) that it is recommended for the population at large (Froelicher & Oberman, 1977; Kannel & Sorlie, 1979; Morgan, 1982; Paffenbarger & Hyde, 1980; Peterson, Jones, Esterly, Wantz, & Jackson, 1980). To demonstrate a beneficial metabolic effect of exercise training on diabetes control, more precise guidelines and recommendations as to exercise timing and nutrient intake based on self-monitoring of blood glucose data may be required.

REFERENCES

Caron, D., Poussier, P., Marliss, E.B., & Zinman, B. (1982). The effect of postprandial exercise on meal-related glucose tolerance in insulin-dependent diabetic individuals. *Diabetes Care*, **5**, 364-369.

Christensen, N., Galbo, H., Hansen, J.F., Hesse, B., Richter, E.A., & Trap-Jensen, J. (1979). Catecholamines and exercise. In M. Vranic, J. Wahren and S. Horvath (Eds.), Proceedings of a Conference on Diabetes and Exercise. *Diabetes*, **28**(Suppl. 1), 58-62.

Felig, P., & Wahren, J. (1975). Fuel homeostasis in exercise. *New England Journal of Medicine*, **293**, 1078-1084.

Froelicher, V.F., & Oberman, A. (1977). Analysis of epidemiologic studies of physical inactivity as risk factor for coronary artery disease. In E.H. Sonnenblick & M. Lesch (Eds.), *Exercise and heart disease* (pp. 209-227). New York: Grune & Stratton.

Issekutz, B. Jr. (1978). Role of beta-adrenergic receptors in mobilization of energy sources in exercising dogs. *Journal of Applied Physiology,* **44**, 869-876.

Issekutz, B. Jr., & Vranic, M. (1980). Significance of glucagon in the control of glucose production during exercise in dogs. *American Journal of Physiology,* **238**, E13-E20.

Kannel, W.B., & Sorlie, P. (1979). Some health benefits of physical activity. *Archives of Internal Medicine,* **139**, 857-861.

Koivisto, V., & Felig, P. (1978). Effects of leg exercise on insulin absorption in diabetic patients. *New England Journal of Medicine,* **298**, 77-83.

Morgan, W.P. (1982). Psychological effects of exercise. *Behavioral Medicine Update,* **4**, 25-30.

Nelson, J.D., Poussier, P., Marliss, E.B., Albisser, A.M., & Zinman, B. (1982). The metabolic responses of normal and insulin infused diabetics to postprandial exercise. *American Journal of Physiology,* **242**, E309.

Paffenbarger, R.S., Jr., & Hyde, R.T. (1980). Exercise as protection against heart attack. *American Journal of Physiology,* **302**, 1026-1027.

Peterson, C.M., Jones, R.L., Esterly, J.A., Wantz, G.E., & Jackson, R.L. (1980). Changes in basement membrane thickening and pulse volume concomitant with improved glucose control and exercise in patients with insulin-dependent diabetes mellitus. *Diabetes Care,* **3**, 586-589.

Poussier, P., Zinman, B., Marliss, E.B., Albisser, A.M., Perlman, K., & Caron, D. (1983). Open loop intravenous insulin waveforms for postprandial exercise in Type 1 diabetes. *Diabetes Care,* **6**, 129-134.

Vranic, M., Kemmer, F.W., Berchtold, P., & Berger, M. (1983). Hormonal interaction in control of metabolism during exercise in physiology and diabetes. In H. Ellenberg & H. Rifkin (Eds.), *Diabetes mellitus: Theory and practice* (pp. 567-590). New York: Medical Examination Publishing.

Wallberg-Henriksson, H., Gunnarsson, R., Henriksson, J., DeFronzo, R.A., Felig, P., Ostran, J., & Wahnen, J. (1982). Increased peripheral insulin sensitivity and muscle mitochondrial enzymes but unchanged blood glucose control in Type I diabetics after physical training. *Diabetes,* **31**, 1044-1050.

Wasserman, D.H., Lickley, H.L.A., & Vranic, M. (1984). Interactions between glucagon and other counterregulatory hormones during normoglycemic and hypoglycemic exercise in dogs. *Journal of Clinical Investigation,* **74**.

Zinman, B., Murray, F.T., Vranic, M., Albisser, A.M., Leibel, B.S., McClean, P.A., & Marliss, E.B. (1977). Glucoregulation during moderate exercise in insulin treated diabetes. *Journal of Clinical Endocrinology and Metabolism,* **45**, 641-652.

Zinman, B., Vranic, M., Albisser, A.M., & Marliss, E.B. (1979). The role of insulin in metabolic response to exercise in diabetic man. In M. Vranic, J. Wahren and S. Horvath (Eds.), Proceedings of the KROC Conference on Exercise and Diabetes. *Diabetes,* **28**(Suppl. 1), 76-81.

Zinman, B., Zuniga-Guajardo, S., & Kelly, D. (1983). The effect of exercise training on glucose control in Type 1 diabetes. *Clinical and Investigative Medicine,* **6**(Suppl. 2), 69.

Zinman, B., Zuniga-Guajardo, S., & Kelly, D. (1984). Comparison of the acute and long term effects of physical training on glucose control in Type 1 diabetes. *Diabetes Care,* **7**, 515-519.

Exercise in Type 2 Diabetes

Neil B. Ruderman
Boston University
Boston, Massachusetts, U.S.A.

Stephen H. Schneider
Rutgers Medical School
New Brunswick, New Jersey, U.S.A.

There are two major reasons for considering exercise in the treatment of type 2 (noninsulin-dependent) diabetes. First, it might be a useful adjunct to diet in improving glycemic control, and second, it might help prevent or retard the development of macrovascular complications. In this paper we will review the basis for these beliefs and describe some key relevant studies. In addition, we will examine the notion that exercise should be considered as a therapy for young individuals predisposed to type 2 diabetes and atherosclerosis.

GLUCOSE HOMEOSTASIS

Exercise, Insulin Sensitivity, and Glucose Tolerance

Hyperglycemia in the type 1 (insulin-dependent) diabetic is principally the result of an absolute deficiency of insulin. In contrast, in the type 2 diabetic insulin resistance, in part due to obesity, is often an important contributory factor; many type 2 diabetics often have higher plasma insulin levels than do normal weight individuals without diabetes (see DeFronzo, Delbert, Hendler, Felig, & Soman, 1979; DeFronzo, Ferranini, & Koivisto, 1983; Kolterman, Prince, & Olefsky, 1983). That exercise might overcome this insulin resistance was first suggested by the studies of Bjorntorp and his coworkers. In one of their earlier investigations (Bjorntorp et al., 1972) glucose tolerance and plasma insulin levels were compared in two groups of middle-aged Swedish men. The men were closely matched for age and weight; but, one group was relatively sedentary whereas the other consisted of life-long cross country skiers. As shown in Table 1, glucose tolerance was normal in both groups, but was better in the athletes despite initially lower plasma insulin levels and a smaller insulin response to the

Table 1 Glucose Tolerance and Serum Insulin in Trained and Untrained Middle Aged Men

Subjects	Time after oral glucose (min)		
	0	60	120
Glucose(mg/dl)			
Untrained	64	108	69
Trained	73	79*	75
Insulin(uU/ml)			
Untrained	10	95	55
Trained	2*	34*	21*

From "Carbohydrate and Lipid Metabolism in Middle Aged, Physically Well-Trained Men" by P. Bjorntorp, M. Fahlen, G. Grimby, A. Gustafson, J. Holm, P. Renstrom, and T. Schersten, 1972, *Metabolism*, **21**, 631-638. See text for details.
*$p < 0.05$ versus untrained group.

glucose load. Such an increase in insulin sensitivity in highly trained individuals has since been described by others (Lohmann, Liebold, Helmann, Stenger, & Pohl, 1978; Seals et al., 1984) as has the better maintenance of glucose tolerance in middle-aged and elderly athletes (Seals et al., 1984).

Bjorntorp and his coworkers also examined the effect of brief periods of physical training on individuals who had not been exercising regularly. In their orginal study (Bjorntorp, DeJounge, Sjostrom, & Sullivan, 1970) nondiabetic obese subjects participated in a supervised exercise program for several months while continuing to eat *ad libitum*. Body weight was maintained and blood glucose levels and glucose tolerance were unchanged; however, plasma insulin was diminished. Thus, like trained athletes, they showed an increase in insulin sensitivity, but unlike the athletes, glucose tolerance was not improved. Similar findings have been reported in patients undergoing a physical training program after a myocardial infarction and in other patient groups (reviewed by Bjorntorp, 1981). Somewhat in contrast to these findings, impaired glucose tolerance as well as insulin resistance has been observed in normal volunteers after several days of bed rest (Lipman et al., 1972).

Exercise and Glycemic Control in the Type 2 Diabetic

Studies by Ruderman, Ganda, and Johansen (1979) and by Saltin et al. (1979) suggested that physical training produces a modest improvement in glucose tolerance in patients with type 2 diabetes and chemical diabetes (impaired glucose tolerance) respectively. In the former study an improvement in intravenous glucose tolerance was noted 6 days after the cessation of training, (K = 0.75 vs. 0.59 initially). The improvement was not evident 8 days later, even though the training-induced increase in $\dot{V}O_2max$ was maintained. Serum insulin levels also tended to increase during this period. Thus the effect of training on glucose tolerance and insulin sensitivity appeared to be relatively short-lived and did not correlate closely with $\dot{V}O_2max$.

The effect of physical training on glycemic control in type 2 diabetics has recently been reexamined by Schneider, Amorosa, Khachadurian, and Ruderman (1984). Twenty sedentary type 2 diabetic men and 11 nondiabetics matched for age, weight and prior physical activity were studied before and after 6 weeks of thrice weekly training. Glycosylated hemoglobin (HbA_1) diminished significantly in the diabetics ($12.2 \pm 0.5\%$ to $10.7 \pm 0.4\%$; $p < 0.02$). Despite this, oral and intravenous glucose tolerance tests performed 72 hr after the last bout of exercise showed only a small improvement (see Table 3). On the other hand, both fasting plasma glucose levels and oral glucose tolerance were significantly better at 12 hr than at 72 hr after the last bout of exercise in eight trained subjects tested at both times (Table 2). The differences were especially marked in four patients in whom the fasting plasma glucose concentration was less than 200 mg/dl. These results suggest that a physical training program can improve glycemic control in the type 2 diabetic (as judged by the decrease in HbA_1) and that it does so in great measure due to the cumulative effect of improvements in glucose tolerance that follow each individual bout of exercise. The data also suggest that patients with milder forms of type 2 diabetes may be likely to benefit. A similar decrease in HbA_1 in type 2 diabetics, attributed to residual effects of individual exercise bouts has been reported in a preliminary study by Skor, Gavin, Hagberg, Goldberg, and Holloszy (1983). Likewise, profound and relatively long-lasting effects of a single bout of exercise on muscle glucose utilization in the rat and glucose tolerance in nondiabetic humans have been described (reviewed by Ruderman, Balon, Zorzano, & Goodman, 1986). Details of recent investigations in which the effect of physical training were examined in type 2 diabetics are given in Table 3. In general, glucose tolerance tests and other studies were performed several days after the cessation of training and the results were similar to those reported by

Table 2 Comparison of Glucose Tolerance in Trained Type 2 Diabetics 12 and 72 hr Post-Exercise

Time after glucose (min)	Group I(4)		Group II(4)	
	Glucose(mg/dl)			
	12h	72h	12h	72h
0	137	167**	225	235
30	167	223**	312	320
60	258	297**	367	380
120	269	310**	354	383*

The symbols * and ** indicate values significantly different from that of the 12 hr test at $p < 0.05$ and $p < 0.01$ levels respectively. Numbers of individuals in each group are in parentheses. Adapted from "Studies on the Mechanism of Improved Glucose Control During Regular Exercise in Type 2 (non insulin-dependent) Diabetes" by S.H. Schneider, L.F. Amorosa, A.K. Kachadurian, and N.B. Ruderman, 1984, *Diabetologia*, **26**, pp. 355-360.

Schneider et al. (1984). As in the latter study considerable interpatient variation was observed. There is remarkably little information concerning the effect of a single bout of exercise on glucose homeostasis in the type 2 diabetic. In the only published study, Minuk et al. (1981) observed that 45 min of moderately intense exercise caused 35 and 37 mg/dl decreases in fasting plasma glucose levels in obese type 2 diabetics treated with diet and sulfonylureas respectively. The decreases in plasma glucose tended to persist after exercise, especially in the sulfonyurea-treated group. We have observed a decrease in plasma of 19 ± 4 mg/dl in 16 type 2 diabetics after 30 min of exercise at 70% to 75% $\dot{V}O_2$max. The duration of such decreases in plasma glucose and their relation to the training status of the patient and the intensity and duration of the exercise remains to be determined.

Diet Versus Exercise

Diet is the principal therapeutic mainstay in the type 2 diabetic. As recently demonstrated by Bogardus et al. (1984), type 2 diabetics who lose weight on a hypocaloric diet show little added improvement in glycemic

Table 3 Effects of Physical Training on Patients With Type 2 Diabetes: Recent Studies

References	*n*	Age (yr)	IBW (%)	Training (wks)	HbA_1 (%) Init	Final	IVGT(K) Init	Final	→OGT
Ruderman et al. (1979)	6	52	120	24			0.59	0.75(6)* 0.65(14)	(8)
DeFronzo et al. (1983)	5	49		6					
Schneider et al. (1984)	20	51	< 115	6	12.2	10.7*	0.57	0.67(3)*	↑(0.5)* S1↑(3)
Trovati et al. (1984)	5	54	120	6	9.7	8.0*	0.80	0.90(>2)*	S1↑(>2)
Reitman et al.	6	26	170	6 to 10					↑(1.5)*

Results are means with statistically significant differences between initial and final values indicated by asterisk. Numbers in parentheses indicate days after last bout of exercise study was performed. Fasting plasma glucose decreased in Reitman study from 142 ± 13 to 108 ± 6 mg/dl. Insulin sensitivity as judged by either a euglycemic clamp study or insulin response during a glucose tolerance test was increased in all studies after training. IBW = ideal body weight; IVGT = intravenous glucose tolerance test.

control when exercise is added to their therapeutic regimen. On the other hand, weight loss is often not achieved in such individuals and many in whom diet is initially successful regain both their previous weight and hyperglycemia after reinstituting a supposedly eucaloric diet. Exercise may assist such individuals in achieving and maintaining weight loss (reviewed by Bjorntorp, 1982; Ruderman et al., 1986), although this remains controversial (Garrow, in press). Because of this and because of its independent effects on glycemic control and coronary risk factors (see below) it is our view that for the present exercise should be considered as an adjunct to diet therapy in motivated patients with type 2 diabetes in whom it is not contraindicated.

Exercise Prescription

Schneider and his coworkers (1982, 1984) have suggested that endurance type exercise involving large muscle groups be performed at least 3 to 4 times per week to improve glycemic control. Ideally patients should exercise for 30 to 60 min at 50% to 75% of $\dot{V}O_2max$, although even less intense exercise, for example, brisk walking, may produce surprising improvement in poorly conditioned individuals. A target pulse can be estimated using the formula

$$\text{Basal pulse} + 0.75\ (\text{maximal pulse} - \text{basal pulse})$$

In practice this may not be possible because certain patients develop significant systolic hypertension ($>$ 180 mm Hg) even with relatively light work loads. Another difficulty is that calculation of $\dot{V}O_2max$ from heart rate at submaximal work loads is often inaccurate in the type 2 diabetic. One reason for this is that $\dot{V}O_2max$ (and maximum heart) rate can be diminished in the type 2 diabetic even though heart rate at a submaximal workload is the same as in a nondiabetic (Schneider et al., 1984).

Precautions

Special problems encountered in type 2 diabetics who embark on an exercise program have been reviewed elsewhere (Richter, Ruderman, & Schneider, 1981; Schneider et al., 1984; Schneider & Ruderman, 1982). Suffice it to say because of such potential problems as occult coronary artery disease, hypoglycemia, proliferative retinopathy, and sensory and autonomic neuropathy, previously sedentary diabetics should not initiate an exercise program without first consulting a physician.

PREVENTION OF MACROVASCULAR DISEASE

Atherosclerotic vascular disease affecting arteries in the heart, brain, and periphery is accelerated in patients with all forms of diabetes (Kannel & McGee, 1979; Ruderman & Haudenschild, 1984). Epidemiological data (Froelicher, 1978; Paffenberger, Wing, & Hyde, 1978), animal studies (Kramsch, Aspen, Abramowitz, Kreimendahl, & Hood, 1981) and analysis of exercise effects on atherosclerotic risk factors all suggest that physical training might retard macrovascular disease in the general population (reviewed by Schneider, Vitug, & Ruderman, 1986). There is little direct information concerning the effect of exercise in the diabetic (see Schneider et al., 1986); however, it is of interest that a number of risk factors affected by exercise are both more prevalent in diabetics (Table 4) and are thought to contribute to this higher prevalence of macrovascular disease.

A systematic investigation of the effect of training on these factors in the type 2 diabetic has not yet been reported. In their 1979 study,

Table 4 Atherogenic Risk Factors That May Be Improved by Regular Exercise

More common in diabetic	Not more common in diabetic
Hypertension	Cigarette smoking
Hypercholesterolemia	Inactivity
Hypertriglyceridemia	
Diminished HDL cholesterol	
Hyperinsulinemia	
Disturbances in hemostasis (fibrinolysis)	
Disturbances in vascular metabolism (ACE)	
Tachycardia	

ACE = acid cholesterol esterase activity.
Adapted from "Diabetes as an Atherogenic Factor" by N.B. Ruderman and C. Haudenschild, 1984, *Progress in Cardiovascular Diseases*, **26**, pp. 373-412, and "Atherosclerosis and Physical Activity" by S.H. Schneider, A. Vitung, and N.B. Ruderman, 1986, *Diabetes and Metabolism Reviews*, **1**, 513-553.

Ruderman, Ganda, and Johansen observed substantial decreases in plasma triglycerides and cholesterol in 4 out of 5 patients. Schneider et al. (1986) also observed a decrease in plasma triglycerides, but found that triglyceride levels had returned to pretraining values within 3 days of the cessation of exercise. Of the other risk factors they examined the most noteworthy effect of training was an increase in fibrinolytic activity that occurred in all subjects (Schneider et al., 1982; 1986). Initially, diminished values in the diabetics approached those of sedentary controls, but were still considerably lower than those of nondiabetics who had undergone the same training regimen.

PROPHYLACTIC USE OF EXERCISE IN CLINICALLY UNAFFECTED POPULATIONS

Prevention of Diabetes

We have already alluded to several studies in which glucose tolerance was shown to be better in middle-aged athletes than in age-matched sedentary controls (Bjorntorp et al., 1972; Seals et al., 1984). Likewise, we have pointed out that physical training of briefer duration in untrained individuals might attenuate the insulin resistance that contributes to hyperglycemia in people genetically predisposed to type 2 diabetes. In this context the relationship between physical activity and diabetes prevalence has recently been examined by Taylor, Ram, Zimmet, Raper, and Ringrose (1984). They found that in Melanesian and Indian men in the Fiji islands, diabetes was twice as common in those graded as sedentary or undertaking light activity as in those performing moderate or heavy exercise. The difference was observed in both ethnic groups and it was still evident when age, obesity and urban/rural status were taken into account. The authors concluded that physical inactivity is an independent risk factor for type 2 diabetes.

Prevention of Atherosclerosis in the Diabetic

At the time of diagnosis type 2 diabetics are usually over 40 years of age and many of them very likely have established atherosclerotic vascular disease. Although exercise might be useful in improving glucose tolerance and retarding atherogenesis, middle aged type 2 diabetics are often resistant to embarking on a lifelong exercise program. Furthermore, some of them have medical problems that preclude all but the mildest exercise regimen. For this reason exercise may ultimately prove to be of most use in younger individuals at risk for these disorders. Such individuals are less likely to have established disease that would limit their ability to exercise and they are more likely to integrate exercise into their daily activities. Offspring of patients with premature atherosclerosis and type 2 diabetes would appear to be a particularly good target group. Many of these individuals demonstrate some of the risk factors found in their parents, including glucose intolerance and hyperinsulinemia (Schneider et al., 1986) and presumably they would be highly motivated. Genetic markers such as the class 3/3 (U/U) genotype (Jowett, Williams, Hitman, & Galton, 1984; Mandroup-Poulson et al., 1984) may further assist in delineating young subpopulations in whom exercise and other preventative measures; for example, dietary regulation and cessation of cigarette smoking are likely to prove beneficial.

Acknowledgments

Supported in part by USPHS grants PO1-HL-26895 and AM-19514. The authors thank Ms. Gretchen Fox for typing the manuscript.

REFERENCES

Bjorntorp, P. (1981). Effects of exercise on plasma insulin. *International Journal of Sports Medicine,* **2**, 125-129.

Bjorntorp, P. (1982). Interrelation of physical activity and nutrition on obesity. In P. White & T. Mondeika (Eds.), *Diet and exercise: Synergism in health maintenance* (pp. 91-98). Chicago: American Medical Association.

Bjorntorp, P., DeJounge, K., Sjostrom, L., & Sullivan, L. (1970). The effect of physical training on insulin production in obesity. *Metabolism,* **19**, 631-638.

Bjorntorp, P., Fahlen, M., Grimby, G., Gustafson, A., Holm, J., Renstrom, P., & Schersten, T. (1972). Carbohydrate and lipid metabolism in middle-aged, physically well-trained men. *Metabolism,* **21**, 1037-1044.

Bogardus, C., Ravussin, E., Robbins, D.C., Wolfe, R.R., Horton, E.S., & Sims, E.A.H. (1984). Effects of physical activity and diet therapy on carbohydrate metabolism in patients with glucose intolerance and non-insulin-dependent diabetes mellitus. *Diabetes,* **33**, 311-318.

DeFronzo, R.A., Delbert, D., Hendler, R., Felig, P., & Soman, V. (1979). Insulin sensitivity and insulin binding to monocytes in maturity onset diabetes. *Journal of Clinical Investigation,* **63**, 939-946.

DeFronzo, R.A., Ferrannini, E., & Koivisto, V. (1983). New concepts in the pathogenesis and treatment of non-insulin dependent diabetes. *American Journal of Medicine,* **74**, 1A, 52-81.

Froelicher, V.F. (1978). Exercise and the prevention of atherosclerotic heart disease. *Cardiovascular Clinics,* **9**, 13-23.

Garrow, J.S. (in press). Diet and thermogenesis. In M. Winick & S.J. Rozovski (Eds.), *Advances in clinical nutrition: VII. Nutrition and exercise.*

Jowett, N.I., Williams, L.G., Hitman, G.A., & Galton, D.J. (1984). Diabetic hypertriglyceridemia and related 5′ flanking polymorphism of the human insulin gene. *British Medical Journal,* **V228**, 96.

Kannel, W.B., & McGee, D.L. (1979). Diabetes and cardiovascular disease—the Framingham study. *Journal of the American Medical Association,* **241**, 2035-2038.

Kolterman, O.G., Prince, M.J., & Olefsky, J.M. (1983). Insulin resistance in non insulin-dependent diabetes. *American Journal of Medicine,* **74**, 1A, 82-101.

Kramsch, D.M., Aspen, A.J., Abramowitz, B.M., Kreimendahl, T., & Hood, W. (1981). Reduction of coronary atherosclerosis by moderate conditioning exercise in monkeys on an atherogenic diet. *New England Journal of Medicine,* **305**, 1483-1491.

Lipman, R., Raskin, P., Love, T., Triewasser, J., LeCoq, F.R., & Sojnure, J.J. (1972). Glucose tolerance during decreased physical activity in man. *Diabetes,* **21**, 101-107.

Lohmann, D.F., Liebold, W., Helmann, J., Stenger, J., & Pohl, A. (1978). Diminished insulin response in highly trained athletes. *Metabolism,* **27**, 521-524.

Mandroup-Poulsen, T., Owerbach, D., Mortensen, S.A., Johansen, K., Meinertz, H., Sorensen, H., & Nerup, J. (1984). DNA sequences flanking the insulin gene on chromosome 11 confer risk of atherosclerosis. *Lancet,* **1**(8371), 250-252.

Minuk, H.L., Vranic, M., Marliss, E.B., Hanna, A.K., Albisser, A.M., & Zinman, B. (1981). Glucoregulatory and metabolic response to exercise in obese non insulin-dependent diabetes. *American Journal of Physiology,* **240**, E458-E464.

Paffenbarger, R.S., Wing, A.L., & Hyde, R.T. (1978). Physical activity as an index of heart attack risk in college alumni. *American Journal of Epidemiology,* **108**, 161-175.

Reitman, J.S., Vasquez, B., Klimes, I., & Nagulesparan, M. (1984). Improvement of glucose homeostasis after exercise training in non insulin-dependent diabetes. *Diabetes Care,* **7**, 434-441.

Richter, E.A., Ruderman, N.B., & Schneider, S.H. (1981)1. Diabetes and exercise. *American Journal of Medicine,* **70**, 201-209.

Ruderman, N.B., Balon, T., Zorzano, A., & Goodman, M. (1986). The postexercise state: Altered effects of insulin in skeletal muscle and their physiological relevance. In *Diabetes and Metabolism Reviews,* **1**, 425-444.

Ruderman, N.B., Ganda, O.P., & Johansen, K. (1979). Effects of physical training on glucose tolerance and plasma lipids in maturity onset diabetes mellitus. *Diabetes,* **28** (Suppl. 1), 89-92.

Ruderman, N.B., & Haudenschild, C. (1984). Diabetes as an atherogenic factor. *Progress in Cardiovascular Diseases,* **26**, 373-412.

Saltin, B., Lindgarde, F., Houston, M., Horlin, R., Nygaard, E., & Gad, P. (1979). Physical training and glucose tolerance in middle aged men with chemical diabetes. *Diabetes,* **28**(Suppl. 1), 30-32.

Schneider, S.H., & Ruderman, N.B. (1982). Diabetes and exercise. In B.N. Brodoff & S.J. Bleicher (Eds.), *Diabetes mellitus and obesity* (pp. 185-191). Baltimore, MD: Williams and Wilkins.

Schneider, S.H., Ruderman, N.B., Amorosa, L.F., & Khachadurian, A.V. (1981). Physical training of non insulin-dependent diabetics. *Diabetes,* **30** (Suppl. 1), 74A.

Schneider, S.H., Amorosa, L.F., Khachadurian, A.K., & Ruderman, N.B. (1984). Studies on the mechanism of improved glucose control during regular exercise in type 2 (non insulin-dependent) diabetes. *Diabetologia,* **26**, 355-360.

Schneider, S.H., Vitug, A., & Ruderman, N.B. (1986). Atherosclerosis and physical activity. *Diabetes and Metabolism Reviews,* **1**, 513-553.

Seals, D.R., Hagberg, J.M., Allen, W.K., Hurley, B.F., Dalsky, G.P., Ersani, A.A., & Holloszy, J.O. (1984). Glucose tolerance in young and older athletes and sedentary men. *Journal of Applied Physiology,* **56**, 1521-1525.

Skor, D., Gavin, J., Hagberg, J., Goldberg, A.P., & Holloszy, J.O. (1983). The effects of acute and chronic exercise on insulin sensitivity in non insulin-dependent diabetes mellitus. *Diabetes,* **32** (Suppl. 1), 64A.

Taylor, R., Ram, P., Zimmet, P., Raper, L.R., & Ringrose, H. (1984). Physical activity and prevalence of diabetes in Melanesian and Indian men in Fiji. *Diabetologia*, **27**, 578-582.

Trovati, M., Carta, Q., Cavalot, F., Vitali, S., Banaldi, C., Lucchina, P.G., Fiocchi, F., Emanuelli, G., & Lenti, G. (1984). Influence of physical training on blood glucose control, glucose tolerance, insulin secretion and insulin action in non-insulin-dependent diabetic patients. *Diabetes Care*, **1**, 416-420.

Central and Peripheral Adaptations to Training in Patients with Coronary Artery Disease

James M. Hagberg
Washington University
St. Louis, Missouri, U.S.A.

As recently as 25 years ago the standard treatment for patients recovering from acute myocardial infarction was a prolonged period of bed rest to minimize hemodynamic demands on their compromised myocardium and to reduce the likelihood of cardiac rupture. This resulted in marked deconditioning, a further reduction in these patients' functional capacity, and dramatic orthostatic intolerance when the person finally left the bed. The first attempts at exercise rehabilitation of these patients were intended to counteract the deconditioning and orthostatic intolerance effects of bed rest. However, it quickly became obvious that these patients could actually develop adaptations in response to exercise training that allowed them to return to their usual lifestyle and work more rapidly. The first studies documenting the physiological and psychological improvements brought about by programs of coronary rehabilitation appeared in the mid-1960s (Hellerstein et al., 1963); numerous studies over the past 20 years have confirmed these results and exercise training is now generally accepted as an integral component of the rehabilitation program of patients with coronary artery disease (CAD). In fact, the numerous benefits derived from exercise training in patients with CAD have led to the current practice of initiating low-level physical activity soon after their infarction.

Exercise training in healthy individuals has been shown to elicit central and peripheral adaptations with both contributing approximately equally to the increase in maximal O_2 consumption ($\dot{V}O_2max$) induced by training. On the other hand, the majority of exercise training studies in patients with CAD have not found any evidence for central cardiovascular adaptations, indicating that their increase in $\dot{V}O_2max$ is the result of adaptations in the periphery, that is, skeletal muscles and the autonomic nervous system (Clausen, 1976). However, a number of recent reports have indicated that central cardiovascular adaptations may also be elicited by training in these patients. The purpose of this review is to summarize the peripheral adaptations and to critically analyze the recent reports of central cardiovascular adaptations elicited by training in patients with CAD.

PERIPHERAL TRAINING ADAPTATIONS IN PATIENTS WITH CAD

One of the first demonstrations of a training effect in patients with CAD was a reduction in heart rate at the same absolute work rate after training. A reduction in heart rate at the same absolute work rate has been found subsequently in virtually every training study in patients with CAD, even those taking beta-receptor blocking agents. These studies indicate that patients with CAD show 6 to 22 beat/min reductions in heart rate at submaximal work rates with training; this reduction in heart rate is similar to that elicited by training in healthy individuals (Åstrand & Rodahl, 1977).

In the past 10 years, a number of studies have demonstrated blunted plasma norepinephrine and epinephrine responses to a standard submaximal work rate after exercise training in patients with CAD (Cousineau et al., 1977; Ehsani, Heath, Martin, Hagberg, & Holloszy, 1984; McCrimmon, Cunningham, Rechnitzer, & Griffiths, 1976). This reduction in plasma catecholamines has previously been reported to occur in healthy individuals (Winder, Hagberg, Hickson, Ehsani, & McLane, 1978). This blunting of sympathetic nervous system activity is one of the major causes of the reduction in heart rate during submaximal exercise following training.

Another training adaptation that is the result of altered autonomic nervous system activity is the reduction in heart rate at rest. Patients with CAD generally decrease their heart rate at rest by 4 to 12 beat/min with training; this reduction is the same as that elicited by training in healthy individuals (Åstrand & Rodahl, 1977). The reduction in heart rate at rest is generally attributed to an increase in parasympathetic tone and possibly also a reduction in the intrinsic rate of the sinus node. These adaptations may also play a role in eliciting the training-induced reduction in heart rate at lower exercise intensities.

In addition to these effects of training on heart rate, a number of metabolic and ventilatory adaptations have been reported in patients with CAD. Reports as early as 1969 indicated that patients with CAD have lower blood lactate levels during submaximal exercise after training, an adaptation known to occur in healthy individuals (Bergman & Varnauskas, 1971; Bjernulf, Boberg, & Froberg, 1974; Clausen, Larsen, & Trap-Jensen, 1969; Varnauskas, Houk, & Bjorntorp, 1966). Other investigators have also reported that patients with CAD respond to training with an increased utilization of fat, a lower plasma FFA level, and a lower ventilatory response during exercise at a standard submaximal work rate (Bjernulf et al., 1974); these training adaptations are also known to occur in healthy individuals (Åstrand & Rodahl, 1977).

All of these adaptations are generally attributed to the increase in skeletal muscle oxidative capacity elicited by training in healthy individuals. While this has not yet been proven, numerous studies have provided evidence that this may be the case. The evidence supporting this hypothesis comes from studies comparing responses during trained and untrained limb exercise. In these studies a diminished increase in heart rate from rest to exercise is evident only during exercise with the trained musculature; exercise with the untrained limb elicits a lower heart rate than before training but the increase in heart rate from rest is unchanged (Clausen, Trap-Jensen, & Larsen, 1970; Saltin, Nazar, & Costill, 1976). The adaptive capacity of skeletal muscle oxidative enzyme systems to training has been demonstrated repeatedly in healthy individuals (Holloszy, 1976; Saltin et al., 1976).

The same hypothesis is also proposed to mediate the heart rate, autonomic nervous system, metabolic and ventilatory adaptations that occur in patients with CAD with training. Recent evidence has demonstrated that patients with CAD also exhibit these training adaptations only when they exercise with their trained limbs (Thompson, Cullinane, Lazarus, & Carleton, 1981). However, very little data are available to demonstrate the enzyme and capillarization adaptations to training within the trained skeletal muscle of patients with CAD. The single report available in the literature indicates that patients with CAD and exertional angina increased their succinate dehydrogenase (SDH) activity by nearly 100% with a 3 day per week, 6-month training program (Ferguson et al., 1982). The initial muscle SDH activity of these patients was very low, something that cannot be attributed to the age of the patients, and the absolute increase in SDH activity was generally below that elicited in younger individuals by training.

CENTRAL TRAINING ADAPTATIONS IN PATIENTS WITH CAD

The initial exercise training studies on patients with CAD provided evidence that ST segment depression, a crude index of myocardial ischemia, was improved at a standard work rate after training (Detry & Bruce, 1971). Upon first inspection this would appear to be evidence for improved myocardial function. However, in this case the decreased ST segment depression was likely to be the result of a decreased myocardial O_2 demand at the same external work rate. When the degree of ST segment depression was related to the rate pressure product (RPP), an index of myocardial O_2 demand, the responses were virtually identical before and after training. This result has since been reported numerous times and new techniques including echocardiography, systolic time intervals, and nuclear cardiology had until 1980 provided essentially the same conclusion: All adaptations to exercise training in patients with CAD are peripheral in nature and no evidence indicated that improved myocardial function could result from training in these patients. The exercise training programs in these studies were, in general, relatively moderate with respect to intensity, frequency, and duration—the factors that determine the magnitude of the training stimulus and the adaptive responses to it. The patients generally underwent three 30 to 40 min training sessions per week at an intensity from 50% to 70% $\dot{V}O_2$max for 3 months. True-measured $\dot{V}O_2$max was increased by approximately 10% to 15% by this program.

A number of animal models of CAD have been reported to develop improvements in myocardial blood flow, oxygenation, and performance in response to exercise training (Heaton, Marr, Capurro, Goldstein, & Epstein, 1978; McElroy, Gissen, & Fishbein, 1978; Wyatt & Mitchell, 1978). These studies used training programs much more intense than those conventionally used in the rehabilitation of patients with CAD. Our studies were initiated to test the hypothesis that more prolonged, intense, and frequent exercise training might be capable of eliciting central adaptations in patients with CAD similar to those found in experimental animals.

The first 3 months of training in our studies used the conventional cardiac rehabilitation program; the patients exercised for 30 to 40 min 3 times per week at 50% to 70% $\dot{V}O_2$max. Thereafter the training intensity, duration, and frequency were gradually increased so that in the final 6 months of the year of training they were exercising for approximately 1 hr at 70% to 90% $\dot{V}O_2$max 5 times per week. The increase in $\dot{V}O_2$max elicited by this program has averaged 38% in the five studies we have published.

To assess the possibility that this more intensive training program might elicit improvements in myocardial oxygenation and therefore, function, we utilized a number of noninvasive techniques. Each of these techniques has certain inherent limitations; the strength of these techniques is that they are independent of each other. Therefore, we have a number of methods to assess potential changes in myocardial responses to increases in O_2 demand.

Our first study indicated that the RPP at which 0.1 mV of ST segment depression occurred increased by 22% with training; the heart rate at this degree of ST segment depression increased by 19 beat/min (16%) with training while systolic blood pressure was only slightly higher (Ehsani, Heath, Hagberg, Sobel, & Holloszy, 1981). After training, the ST segment depression at the same RPP was reduced and the ST segment depression at maximal exercise was unchanged despite the attainment of a higher RPP. Changes in left ventricular radius, wall thickness, and contractility can alter the RPP-myocardial $\dot{V}O_2$ relationship, especially over a year-long training program, which could confound our interpretation of an improved O_2 supply. However, we have demonstrated with radionuclide and echocardiographic measurements that left ventricular volumes are larger after training, thereby actually increasing the O_2 demand at a given RPP. We have also shown that plasma norepinephrine levels at maximal exercise are increased after training, making the O_2 demand actually higher at the same RPP; despite this, electrocardiographic manifestations of myocardial ischemia did not change (Ehsani, Heath, Martin, Hagberg, & Holloszy, 1984).

Another report from our laboratory used echocardiographic measurements to assess myocardial function during graded increases in afterload induced by static handgrip exercise, a limb not involved in our training program (Ehsani, Martin, Heath, & Coyle, 1982). Before training the experimental and control groups both exhibited decreases in mean velocity of circumferential fiber shortening (mV_{CF}) with increases in mean blood pressure. Following training the experimental group maintained their mV_{CF} at resting levels despite similar increases in blood pressure as before training; the control group continued to exhibit a reduced mV_{CF} after the 12-month period.

We have also used a noninvasive CO_2 rebreathing technique to assess cardiac output and stroke volume during submaximal exercise in these patients before and after training (Hagberg, Ehsani, & Holloszy, 1983). Using this technique we found an 18% increase in stroke volume during submaximal exercise in patients with CAD after training. This increase in stroke volume appeared, in part, to be the result of adaptations within the myocardium because afterload was not changed by training and stroke volume was greater at any level of vascular resistance after training. Stroke work also increased by 18%.

We have also used systolic time intervals to assess myocardial function since the duration of the pre-ejection period normalized for heart rate (PEPI) has been shown to be inversely related to the maximal left ventricular dP/dt and other isovolumic phase indices of contractility. The 13 patients we studied had a more rapid PEPI and an improvement in the PEP/LV ejection time ratio after 22 months of training (Martin et al., 1984).

We have also used ECG-gated blood pool radionuclide ventriculography to assess myocardial performance in patients before and after our year-long training program (Ehsani, Biello, Bloomfield, & Holloszy, 1982). Our preliminary results show that the patients increased their left ventricular ejection fraction (EF) from rest to maximal supine cycle ergometer exercise after but not before training, despite a higher mean blood pressure and RPP after training. The EF at maximal exercise was significantly higher after than before training. In addition, during isometric handgrip exercise, a limb not involved in the training program, EF decreased from rest before training but did not change after training and was higher at the same mean blood pressure. We are continuing to accumulate more data to determine if these trends persist.

Thus, we believe these 5 studies using different procedures suggest that our more prolonged, intensive, and frequent exercise training program does elicit physiologically significant improvements in myocardial oxygenation and function in some patients with CAD. It is important to note that none of the patients with previous infarctions were studied until at least 4 months after their infarction. The average interval between their infarction and admission to the study was 14 ± 10 months. Control subjects included in all studies showed no improvement in myocardial function across the year, though in some cases deterioration in function was evident.

While our studies were in progress, other investigators published data that offer further evidence that central adaptations do, in fact, occur in patients with CAD in response to exercise training. Raffo et al. (1980) reported a higher heart rate and RPP was necessary to elicit 0.1 mV of ST segment depression in patients with CAD after training. In the same year Jensen et al. (1980) reported that after training EF was modestly increased during submaximal exercise at the same RPP and was unchanged at maximal exercise though RPP was higher. Vanhees, Fagard, Grauwels, DeGeest, and Amery (1984), using systolic time intervals, found a decreased PEP and PEP/LV ejection time ratio in patients with CAD after training. Recently, Laslett, Paumer, and Amsterdam (1985) also demonstrated an increased heart rate and RPP at 0.1 mV ST segment depression after training. Thus, further evidence is available suggesting that some patients with CAD can develop central adaptations in response to training.

In addition to these studies that provide evidence for central training adaptations in patients with CAD, others have reported suggestive but inconclusive data. Froelicher et al. (1984) recently completed a randomized trial of exercise training; they found no evidence of myocardial adaptations with respect to ECG responses, though thallium perfusion studies showed modest improvement in myocardial ischemia. Kavanagh, Shephard, Doney, and Pandit (1973) reported that exercise training in patients with CAD elicited improved ST segment responses during submaximal exercise testing after training; however, the degree of ST segment depression at the heart rate used for comparison before and after training ranged from only 0.05 to 0.09 mV initially. Sidney and Shephard (1977) also reported improved ST segment responses in elderly subjects after training; however, only 13 of 39 subjects had evidence of CAD before training, and the RPP at which the subjects were compared before and after training elicited only 0.03 mV of depression initially. Finally, Paterson, Shephard, Cunningham, Jones, and Andrew (1979) reported an increase in stroke volume during submaximal exercise after training in patients with CAD, however, no blood pressure data were reported; therefore, the increase could have been elicited by peripheral mechanisms, that is, a decrease in afterload due to a decrease in blood pressure.

A question that has arisen in the past 2 years is whether the year-long intensive training program we have utilized is necessary to elicit the central adaptations in patients with CAD or if a somewhat less intensive program might elicit these adaptations. To attempt to answer this question, we have analyzed the data from 26 studies on the effects of exercise training on patients with CAD. We divided these studies into 2 groups—one containing the 13 studies that provide evidence of central adaptations and a second containing 13 studies that elicited only peripheral adaptations (Table 1). It is evident from this compilation that the studies that provide some evidence of central adaptations utilized exercise programs that provide a greater training stimulus and elicit larger changes in measured $\dot{V}O_2max$ than those that elicit only peripheral adaptations. These studies trained their patients for nearly twice as long at a higher percentage of $\dot{V}O_2max$ and more frequently than those studies eliciting no central adaptations. However, one study did elicit central adaptations with a 3-month training program (Vanhees et al., 1984) while three other studies that trained their patients for 1 year elicited only peripheral adaptations.

SUMMARY

Conventional cardiac rehabilitation exercise training programs have been shown to result in peripheral adaptations in patients with coronary artery disease that allow them to undergo less myocardial ischemia during their daily activities. However, recent studies that have applied training programs more intense and prolonged than those used previously have demonstrated improvements in myocardial oxygenation and left ventricular function using electrocardiographic, echocardiographic, and radionuclide techniques and measurement of exercise hemodynamics. Further studies are needed to substantiate these findings, though it seems reasonable to conclude, even at this point, that in some patients with coronary artery disease more prolonged and intense exercise training can elicit improvements in left ventricular function.

Acknowledgments

This research was supported by National Institutes of Health research grant HL 22215. The authors would like to thank Joan Schultz for her contributions to this research.

Table 1 Comparison of Studies Reporting Evidence of Central Training Adaptations in Patients with CAD and Studies Reporting Only Peripheral Training Adaptations

Studies	Training Index†	% Change in Measured $\dot{V}O_2max$‡	Length of Training (mo)	% $\dot{V}O_2max$ During Training	Length of Sessions (min)	Training Sessions/week
With evidence for central adaptations	105 ± 82 (18-290)	34 ± 12 (9-46)	10.8 ± 6.2 (3-24)	78 ± 4 (70-80)	45 ± 21 (12-75)	4.3 ± 1.0 (2.3-5)
With evidence only for peripheral adaptations	34 ± 36* (9-117)	21 ± 2* (20-22)	5.2 ± 4.1* (1.5-13)	72 ± 4* (65-77)	40 ± 14 (20-60)	3.5 ± 0.7* (3-5)

Data are presented as means ± SD. Numbers in parentheses are ranges.
*Comparison between groups significantly different at $p < 0.05$.
†Calculated as (hr/session) × number of sessions × adherence × (%$\dot{V}O_2max$/100).
‡Since not all studies measured $\dot{V}O_2max$, the Central Adaptations group includes seven studies and the Peripheral Adaptations group includes four studies.

REFERENCES

Åstrand, P.-O., & Rodahl, K. (1977). *Textbook of work physiology*. New York: McGraw-Hill.

Bergman, H., & Varnauskas, E. (1971). Placebo effect in physical training of coronary heart disease patients. In O.A. Larsen & R.O. Malmborg (Eds.), *Coronary heart disease and physical fitness* (pp. 48-52). Baltimore, MD: University Park Press.

Bjernulf, A., Boberg, J., & Froberg, S. (1974). Physical training after myocardial infarction. *Scandinavian Journal of Clinical and Laboratory Investigation,* **33**, 173-185.

Clausen, J.P. (1976). Circulatory adjustments to dynamic exercise and effect of physical training in normal subjects and in patients with coronary artery disease. *Progress in Cardiovascular Diseases,* **18**, 459-495.

Clausen, J.P., Larsen, O.A., & Trap-Jensen, J. (1969). Physical training in the management of coronary artery disease. *Circulation,* **40**, 143-154.

Clausen, J.P., Trap-Jensen, J., & Larsen, O.A. (1970). Effects of training on the heart rate during arm and leg exercise. *Scandinavian Journal of Clinical and Laboratory Investigation,* **26**, 295-301.

Cousineau, D., Ferguson, R.J., deChamplain, J., Gauthier, P., Cote, P., & Bourassa, M. (1977). Catecholamines in coronary sinus during exercise in man before and after training. *Journal of Applied Physiology,* **43**, 801-806.

Detry, J.M., & Bruce, R.A. (1971). Effects of physical training on exertional ST segment depression in coronary heart disease. *Circulation,* **44**, 390-396.

Ehsani, A.A., Biello, D.R., Bloomfield, S.A., & Holloszy, J.O. (1982). Exercise training improves intrinsic left ventricular performance in ischemic heart disease. *Clinical Research,* **30**, 480A.

Ehsani, A.A., Heath, G.W., Hagberg, J.M., Sobel, B.E., & Holloszy, J.O. (1981). Effects of 12 months of intense exercise training on ischemic ST segment depression in patients with coronary artery disease. *Circulation,* **64**, 1116-1124.

Ehsani, A.A., Heath, G.W., Martin, W.H., Hagberg, J.M., & Holloszy, J.O. (1984). Effects of intense exercise training on plasma catecholamines in coronary patients. *Journal of Applied Physiology,* **57**, 154-159.

Ehsani, A.A., Martin, W.H., Heath, G.W., & Coyle, E.F. (1982). Cardiac effects of prolonged and intense exercise training in patients with coronary artery disease. *American Journal of Cardiology,* **50**, 246-254.

Ferguson, R.J., Taylor, A.W., Cote, P., Charlebois, J., Dinelle, Y., Peronnet, F., deChamplain, J., & Bourassa, M. (1982). Skeletal muscle and cardiac changes with training in patients with angina pectoris. *American Journal of Physiology,* **243**, H830-H836.

Froelicher, V., Jensen, D., Genter, F., Sullivan, M., McKirnan, M.D., Witztum, K., Scharf, J., Strong, M.L., & Ashburn, W. (1984). A randomized trial of exercise training in patients with coronary heart disease. *Journal of the American Medical Association*, **252**, 1291-1297.

Hagberg, J.M., Ehsani, A.A., & Holloszy, J.O. (1983). Effect of 12 months of intense exercise training on stroke volume in patients with coronary artery disease. *Circulation*, **67**, 1194-1199.

Heaton, W.H., Marr, K.C., Capurro, N.L., Goldstein, R.E., & Epstein, S.E. (1978). Beneficial effect of physical training on blood flow to myocardium perfused by chronic collaterals in the exercising dog. *Circulation*, **57**, 575-581.

Hellerstein, H.K., Hirsch, E.Z., Cumber, W., Allen, L., Polster, S., & Zucker, N. (1963). Reconditioning of the coronary patient. In W. Likoff & J.H. Moyer (Eds.), *Coronary heart disease* (pp. 448-454). New York: Grune and Stratton.

Holloszy, J.O. (1976). Adaptations of muscular tissue to training. *Progress in Cardiovascular Diseases*, **18**, 445-458.

Jensen, D., Atwood, J.E., Froelicher, V., McKirnan, M.D., Buttler, A., Ashburn, W., & Ross, J. (1980). Improvement in ventricular function during exercise studied with radionuclide ventriculography after cardiac rehabilitation. *American Journal of Cardiology*, **46**, 770-777.

Kavanagh, T., Shephard, R.J., Doney, H., & Pandit, V. (1973). Intensive exercise in coronary rehabilitation. *Medicine and Science in Sports*, **5**, 34-39.

Laslett, L., Paumer, L., & Amsterdam, E.A. (1985). Increase in myocardial oxygen consumption indexes by exercise training at onset of ischemia in patients with coronary artery disease. *Circulation*, **71**, 958-962.

Martin, W.H., Heath, G.W., Coyle, E.F., Bloomfield, S.A., Holloszy, J.O., & Ehsani, A.A. (1984). Effect of prolonged intense endurance training on systolic time intervals in patients with coronary disease. *American Heart Journal*, **107**, 75-81.

McCrimmon, D.R., Cunningham, D.A., Rechnitzer, P.A., & Griffiths, J. (1976). Effect of training on plasma catecholamines in post myocardial infarction patients. *Medicine and Science in Sports*, **8**, 152-156.

McElroy, C.L., Gissen, S.A., & Fishbein, M.C. (1978). Exercise-induced reduction in myocardial infarct size after coronary occlusion in the rat. *Circulation*, **57**, 958-962.

Paterson, D.H., Shephard, R.J., Cunningham, D., Jones, N.L., & Andrew, G. (1979). Effects of physical training on cardiovascular function following myocardial infarction. *Journal of Applied Physiology*, **47**, 482-487.

Raffo, J.A., Luksic, I.Y., Kappagoda, C.T., Mary, D.A.S.G., Whitaker, W., & Linden, R.J. (1980). Effects of physical training on myocardial ischemia in patients with coronary artery disease. *British Heart Journal*, **43**, 262-269.

Saltin, B., Nazar, K., Costill, D.L., Stein, E., Jansson, E., Essén, B., & Gollnick, P.D. (1976). The nature of the training response. Peripheral and central adaptations to one-legged exercise. *Acta Physiologica Scandinavica,* **96**, 289-305.

Sidney, K.H., & Shephard, R.J. (1977). Training and electrocardiographic abnormalities in the elderly. *British Heart Journal,* **39**, 1114-1120.

Thompson, P.D., Cullinane, E., Lazarus, B., & Carleton, R.A. (1981). Effect of exercise training on the untrained limb exercise performance of men with angina pectoris. *American Journal of Cardiology,* **48**, 844-850.

Vanhees, L., Fagard, R., Grauwels, R., DeGeest, H., & Amery, A. (1984). Changes in systolic time intervals during physical training in patients with ischemic heart disease. *Cardiology,* **71**, 207-214.

Varnauskas, E., Houk, P., & Bjorntorp, P. (1966). Hemodynamic effects of physical training in coronary patients. *Lancet* **II**, 8-12.

Winder, W.W., Hagberg, J.M., Hickson, R.C., Ehsani, A.A., & McLane, J.A. (1978). Time course of sympathoadrenal adaptation to endurance exercise training. *Journal of Applied Physiology,* **45**, 370-374.

Wyatt, H.L., & Mitchell, J.H. (1978). Influences of physical conditioning and deconditioning on coronary vasculature in dogs. *Journal of Applied Physiology,* **45**, 619-625.

Lipoprotein Metabolism and Physical Training in Normal Man and Diabetic and Cardiac Patients

Hans O.L. Lithell
Uppsala University
Uppsala, Sweden

The hydrophobic lipids (triglycerides and cholesterol esters) are transported in blood plasma in the core of lipoprotein particles, the surface of which is coated with polypeptides (apolipoproteins) and hydrophilic lipids (phospholipids and cholesterol) (Brewer, 1981; Jackson, Morrisett, & Gotto, 1976). To cover energy requirements in different tissues fatty acids are transported either in nonesterified form, bound to plasma albumin, or in esterified form as triglycerides, transported in chylomicrons (secreted from the gut) and in very low density lipoproteins (VLDL, secreted from the liver). Factors known to influence the rate of secretion of VLDL particles are the plasma insulin (Olefsky, Farquhar, & Reaven, 1974) and the plasma free fatty acids (Kissebah, Alfarsi, Adams, & Wynn, 1976). In the postprandial state most of the plasma triglycerides are directed towards the adipose tissue for storage, whereas in the fasting state about 50% are taken up by skeletal muscle tissue (Rössner, 1974). Lipoprotein lipase is the key enzyme in this process. It was first described as a ''clearing factor'' about 40 years ago, when it was found that injection of heparin was followed by clearance of postprandial dog plasma that was opalescent due to the presence of numerous chylomicrons (Hahn, 1943). Lipoprotein lipase is synthesized in adipocytes and myocytes, from which it is secreted by an energy-requiring process (Cryer, McDonald, Williams, & Robinson, (1975). It is thought to be picked up by heparan sulphate, which is a constituent of the endothelial cells, and the lipoprotein lipase molecule is bound to this glucosaminoglycan (Olivecrona, Bengtsson, Marklund, Lindahl, & Höök, 1977). Lipoprotein lipase also has an affinity for other glucosaminoglycans (Olivecrona et al., 1977). Heparin can effectively compete with the binding of lipoprotein lipase to heparan sulphate. The chylomicrons in the circulation are therefore efficiently hydrolized after injection of heparin, as a result of the release of numerous lipoprotein lipase molecules from different tissues.

The factors regulating the transport of triglycerides to different tissues are the distribution of the blood and the diurnal variation of lipoprotein lipase in different tissues. In adipose tissue the lipoprotein lipase activity has been found to be increased about 3 to 6 hr after repeated meals (Lithell, Boberg, Hellsing, Lundqvist, & Vessby, 1978; Pagano Mirani-Oostdijk et al., 1983; Pykälistö, Smith, & Bruznell, 1975) and insulin seems to be one important hormonal regulator (Sadur & Eckel, 1982). After several meals the muscle lipoprotein lipase activity was found to be down-regulated in one study (Lithell, Boberg, Hellsing, Lundqvist, & Vessby, 1978), but not in another (Pagano Mirani-Oostdijk et al., 1983). A variation in enzyme activity in opposite directions in adipose and muscle tissue will effectively influence the direction of fat transport to these two tissues (by a factor of 7) (Lithell, Boberg, Hellsing, Lundqvist, & Vessby, 1978).

After hydrolysis of most of the triglycerides of the chylomicrons, these particles end up as "chylomicron remnants," which are efficiently removed from the circulation by a specific receptor-mediated mechanism in the liver. The receptors recognize a specific apolipoprotein pattern on the surface of these particles (Brewer, 1981). Following hydrolysis of the triglyceride load of the VLDL particles, these end up as low density lipoprotein (LDL) particles (Brewer, 1981). This end product is also removed from the circulation by means of specific receptors, which recognize the apolipoprotein pattern on the surface of the particles (Brewer, 1981). The physiological function of LDL particles is probably to distribute cholesterol to the cells in the body, which is an energy-saving way of providing cholesterol to the tissues compared with the process by which cells can synthesize cholesterol themselves. A feedback mechanism controls the density of the receptors and the uptake can thus be limited to prevent overload (Brewer, 1981). A person who eats a Western diet with a high dietary fat content has a high plasma level of LDL particles. This leads to a down-regulation of the LDL receptors. However, the LDL particles can also be taken up in the cells by a nonreceptor mediated process, the rate of which is proportional to the plasma concentration of LDL. This may lead to an overstorage of cholesterol in the cells. Furthermore, when the uptake of LDL particles by the specific receptor is down-regulated, this will lead to prolonged circulation of these particles in the blood plasma (Brewer, 1981), which in turn may result in a change in their surface physicochemical properties (Steinberg, 1983). Such altered particles can be taken up by macrophages via receptors that recognize only "modified" LDL particles (Steinberg, 1983). It has been suggested that it is these cholesterol-loaded macrophages that constitute the initial phase in the development of the atheromatous process (Steinberg, 1983). In subjects with low lipoprotein lipase activity this is associated with a decrease in the hydrolysis of the triglyceride core of the VLDL particles. This will lead to prolonged circulation in the blood stream of particles with a density between that of the VLDL and LDL (Kissebah, Alfarsi, Evans, & Adams, 1982). Particles that are relatively rich in triglycerides are not as readily recognized by the specific LDL receptors (Hiramatsu, Bierman, & Chait,

1985). As a consequence of this, a larger proportion of the VLDL articles will be removed by non-LDL-receptor pathways than when the lipoprotein lipase activity is normal (Kissebah et al., 1982). An uptake via such scavenger pathways may initiate and promote atherosclerosis (Hiramatsu et al., 1985; Steinberg, 1983). This may possibly explain why the plasma triglyceride concentration has been found to constitute an independent risk factor for coronary heart disease in several population studies (Åberg, Lithell, Selinus, & Hedstrand, 1985; Carlson, Böttiger, & Åhfeldt, 1979; Pelkonen, Nikkilä, Koskinen, Penttinen, & Sarna, 1977; Peterson, Henningsen, & Hood, 1984).

The high density lipoproteins (HDL) seem to be involved in the transport of cholesterol from peripheral tissues to the liver (Brewer, 1981). HDL are secreted from the gut and from the liver as discoidal particles, rich in phospholipids and polypeptides, but poor in cholesterol (Brewer, 1981); these particles have a high density (the HDL_3 subclass). The polypeptides specific for these particles are the apolipoproteins A-I and A-II (Brewer, 1981; Jackson et al., 1976; Schaefer, Zech, et al., 1982). Apoliprotein A-I has a very high affinity for cholesterol. This means that wherever these particles come into contact with surfaces containing cholesterol, they are able to pick up some of it. This cholesterol is then converted to a cholesterol ester by the enzyme lecithin-cholesterol-acyl-transferase (LCAT). The cholesterol ester is carried in the central part of the particles, which become spherical. During these processes the density of HDL_3 particles decreases and the subclass HDL_2 develops. During hydrolysis of the triglycerides of the VLDL particles, the surface components (cholesterol, phospholipids and peptides) become detached. In studies in vitro VLDL cholesterol has been recovered within the HDL_2 fraction after hydrolysis by lipoprotein lipase (Schaefer, Wetzel et al., 1982). Thus, when plasma triglycerides are vigorously hydrolyzed, much of the surface component is transferred to HDL and, as one result, the concentration of HDL_2 cholesterol increases. The plasma level of the HDL_2 particles is also highly dependent on the activity of hepatic lipase. This is a phospholipase that is present on the surface of endothelial cells of the liver sinusoids (Jansen, Van Tol, & Hülsmann, 1980; Kuusi, Kinnunen, & Nikkilä, 1979; Kuusi, Saarinen, & Nikkilä, 1980). This enzyme is probably attached to the cells by a mechanism similar to that by which the lipoprotein lipase becomes attached to the endothelium of capillaries. Hepatic lipase is released by heparin and after heparin injections it can be recognized and quantified in peripheral blood plasma by specific methods (Huttunen, Ehnholm, Kinnunen, & Nikkilä, 1975). The hepatic lipase activity is decreased after administration of exogenous estrogens (Tikkanen, Nikkilä, Kuusi, & Sipinen, 1982) and increased after administration of gestagens derived from testosterone (Tikkanen et al., 1982). Women have lower hepatic lipase activity than men (Huttunen, Ehnholm, Kekki, & Nikkilä, 1976) and this has been regarded as the main reason for the higher plasma concentrations of HDL in women than in men (identified as elevated HDL_2 levels). In childhood, boys and girls have similarly high levels of HDL, but during puberty the HDL levels in boys decrease, so that adult men have HDL cholesterol concentrations that are about 0.2 to 0.3 mmol/l lower than women during the rest of life (Heiss, Johnson, Reiland, Davis, & Tyroler, 1980). HDL cholesterol is recognized as a strong negative risk factor for atherosclerotic complications (Castelli et al., 1977; Gordon, Castelli, Hjortland, Kannel, & Dawber, 1977). It is well known that women generally develop coronary heart disease complications about 10 years later than men (Castelli, 1984) and the difference in lipoprotein patterns which is most pronounced for HDL levels, has been regarded as one important explanation of the later cardiac manifestations in women.

THE LIPOPROTEIN PATTERN IN WELL-TRAINED HEALTHY SUBJECTS

In many of the early studies the different lipoprotein classes were not separated and differences in plasma cholesterol levels between sedentary and well-trained subjects could not be detected (for reviews, Wood & Haskell, 1979; Moffatt & Gilliam, 1979). In more recent investigations in which lipoprotein concentrations have been measured, elevated HDL cholesterol levels in well-trained subjects have been consistently found. Long-distance runners, skiers, and joggers, both men and women, have higher HDL cholesterol concentrations than comparable groups of sedentary subjects (Adner & Castelli, 1980; Christie, Bloore, & Logan, 1980; Clarkson, Hintermister, Fillyaw, & Stylos, 1981; Enger, Herbjørnsen, Eriksson, & Fretland, 1977; Hartung, Foreyt, Mitchell, Vlasek, & Gotto, 1980; Kiens, Lithell, & Vessby, 1984; Lehtonen & Viikari, 1978a; Lehtonen & Viikari, 1978b; Lehtonen, Viikari, & Ehnholm, 1979; Moore, Hartung, Mitchell, Kappus, & Hinderlitter, 1983; Nikkilä, Taskinen, Rehunen, & Härkönen, 1978; Sady, Cullinane, Herbert, Kantor, & Thompson, 1984; Stamford et al., 1984; Thompson, Cullinane, Eshleman, Kantor, & Herbert, 1984). In tennis players practicing four to five times a week, increases equal to those found in long-distance runners have been found (Vodak, Wood, Haskell, & Williams, 1980). In studies in which HDL cholesterol levels were determined in 260 well-trained sportsmen of different sports categories (Schnabel & Kindermann, 1982), those groups with the most aerobic training showed the highest values, and the HDL cholesterol was also significantly correlated to $\dot{V}O_2max$ in several studies (Carlson & Mossfeldt, 1964; Farrell et al., 1982; Masarei, Pyke, & Pyke, 1982; Schnabel & Kinderman, 1982; Thorland & Gilliam, 1981). Cardiorespiratory fitness, as indicated by treadmill test duration, showed a significantly positive correlation to HDL cholesterol (Schwane & Cundiff, 1979), but other indications of fitness had a lower discriminating capacity (Masarei et al., 1982; Schwane & Cundiff, 1979). Furthermore, the plasma triglyceride concentrations and LDL cholesterol were lower in well-trained subjects than in sedentary controls in some studies (Hartung, Foreyt, Mitchell, Vlasek, & Gotto, 1980; Moore et al., 1983; Nikkilä et al., 1978; Sady et al., 1984) though not in others (Adner & Castelli, 1980; Farrell et al., 1982). Therefore, the balance between the cholesterol concentration in atherogenic lipoproteins (LDL and VLDL) and anti-atherogenic lipoproteins (HDL) is more favorable in well-trained than in sedentary subjects.

A number of factors, however, such as adiposity, smoking, alcohol intake, quality of dietary fat and use of exogenous sex hormones are known to affect the HDL cholesterol levels (Tyroler, 1980). Well-trained subjects are usually less obese and smoke less, for example, than sedentary ones (Adner & Castelli, 1980; Clarkson et al. 1981; Farrell et al., 1982; Lehtonen & Viikari, 1978b; Moore et al., 1983). Such differences in characteristics might partly explain the higher HDL cholesterol concentration in well-trained subjects. After such confounding factors have been taken into account in statistical analyses, an independent effect of exercise on the HDL cholesterol concentration has been found in many studies (Adner & Castelli, 1980; Hartung et al., 1980; Moore et al., 1983; Vodak et al., 1980), but not all (Farrell et al., 1982; Masarei et al., 1982; Sady et al., 1984). In one study, however, the effect of exercise on HDL cholesterol seemed to be less pronounced in women than in men (Vodak et al., 1980).

ACUTE EFFECTS OF PHYSICAL EXERCISE ON LIPOPROTEINS

In view of these confounding factors, it is important to confirm the results of cross-sectional studies in longitudinal investigations in which all factors except the degree of physical training are kept constant. One crucial point to be kept in mind when evaluating the effect of regular, physical training on the lipoprotein pattern is the fact that an acute bout of physical exercise changes the lipoprotein pattern for varying lengths of time. A decrease in the plasma triglyceride concentration by about 50% occurs immediately after a prolonged bout of heavy exercise and this concentration is regularly reduced during the 1st day after exercise to approximately equal degree (Enger, Strømme, & Refsum, 1980; Kantor, Cullinane, Herbert, & Thompson, 1984; Lithell, Cedermark, Fröberg, Tesch, & Karlsson, 1981; Lithell, Schéle, Vessby, & Jacobs, 1984; Thompson, Cullinane, Henderson, & Herbert, 1980). In some studies these triglyceride values were found to be restored to normal on the 2nd day (Enger et al., 1980; Lithell et al., 1984) but in others they were still decreased by about one-third after 2 (Kantor et al., 1984; Thompson et al., 1980) and 3 (Thompson et al., 1980) days after the exercise. Increases in HDL cholesterol by about 10% have been demonstrated 1 day after heavy exercise (Dufaux, Assmann, Schachten, & Hollman, 1982; Enger et al., 1980; Kantor et al., 1984; Lithell et al., 1984; Thompson et al., 1980), but in some studies more prolonged elevations have been observed (for 2 days—Dufaux et al., 1982; Kantor et al., 1984; and 4 days—Enger et al., 1980). This rise in HDL seems to be largely attributable to an increase in HDL_2 cholesterol (Kantor et al., 1984; Kuusi et al., 1984). A decrease in the atherogenic lipoprotein cholesterol concentration has been observed after heavy exercise (Dufaux et al., 1982; Enger et al., 1980; Kantor et al., 1984; Lithell et al., 1984; Thompson et al., 1980). The HDL apolipoproteins do not seem to be affected by a single bout of heavy exercise (Kantor et al., 1984), but after repeated heavy bouts for 10 (Lithell et al., 1984) to 21 (Nestel, Podkolinski, & Fidge, 1979) days apolipoproteins A-I and A-II have been reported to be still elevated 5 days after exercise (Lithell et al., 1984). It seems as if the degree and duration of the lipoprotein changes after a single bout of exercise are dependent upon such factors as the degree of exertion (Lithell, Cedermark, Fröberg, Tesch, & Karlsson, 1981), the time spent exercising (Kantor et al., 1984) and the subject's physical fitness (Lithell, Örlander, Schéle, Sjödin, & Karlsson, 1979).

In long-term studies it is therefore important to state whether the final evaluation is made on a morning after a day when exercise was allowed or not. It seems advisable to wait for 48 to 72 hr before assessing the "chronic" effects of regular exercise training. On the other hand, it may be argued that in subjects who exercise every day the acute effects, which last for about 1 day, contribute to the lipoprotein pattern that is typical for that individual training each day, and in such populations the evaluation may take place 24 hr after the last bout of exercise.

RESULTS OF LONG-TERM STUDIES

Many longitudinal studies have now demonstrated that plasma HDL cholesterol increases with regular physical exercise (Brownell, Bachorik, & Ayerle, 1982; Danner et al., 1984; Farrell & Barboriak, 1980; Goldberg, Elliot, Schultz, & Kloster, 1984; Higuchi et al., 1984; Huttunen et al., 1979; Kiens et al., 1979; Kiens et al., 1984; Myhre, Mjøs, Bjørsvik, & Strömme, 1981; Peltonen, Marniemi, Hietanen, Vuori, & Enhnolm, 1981; Rauramaa et al., 1984; Rotkis, Boyden, Pamenter, Stanforth, & Wilmore, 1981; Seals, Hagberg, Hurley, Ehsani, & Holloszy, 1984; Stubbe, Hansson, Gustafsson,

& Nilsson-Ehle, 1983; Thompson, Cullinane, Eshleman, Sady, & Herbert, 1984; Thompson, Thomas, Araujo, Albers, & Decedue, 1985; Williams et al., 1983; Wood et al., 1983). In a few studies this effect was not confirmed (Bassett Frey, Doerr, Laubach, Mann, & Glueck, 1982; Després, Bouchard, Savard, Tremblay, & Allard, 1985; Moll, Williams, Lester, Quarfordt, & Wallace, 1979; Ready & Quinney, 1982; Wynne, Bassett Frey, Laubach, & Glueck, 1980). With regular training sessions three to four times a week, the effect in terms of an increased HDL cholesterol value by about 10% was evident after about 6 to 8 weeks of training. The levels were unchanged or even decreased after the first 2 to 6 weeks of training (Basset Frey et al., 1982; Farrell & Barboriak, 1980; Kiens et al., 1984; Rotkis et al., 1981). In some studies (Danner et al., 1984; Higuchi et al., 1984; Nestel et al., 1979) fairly pronounced elevations of HDL cholesterol (or apolipoprotein A-I) were evident after only 2 to 4 weeks, but in these studies there were at least five training sessions per week and therefore some of the effects observed may have been acute effects of the last bout of exercise. In one investigation (Huttunen et al., 1979) HDL cholesterol increased even more during the 3rd and 4th months than during the 1st and 2nd months, but in another study (Rauramaa et al., 1984) there was no further increase between weeks 3 and 15 beyond that which took place during the first 3 weeks. However, in a 1-year study (Wood et al., 1983), an even stronger association between mileage (run per week) and change in HDL cholesterol during the last 6 months than during the first 6 months of the study was observed.

The intensity of the training is probably of importance for the effect on lipoproteins. In 63-year-old subjects training for 6 months at 60% of the maximum heart rate (walking 27 min per day; $\dot{V}O_2max$ increased by 12%), the HDL cholesterol did not change (Seals et al., 1984). In contrast, when the same group trained for an average of 3.6 times per week, each session about 30 to 45 min long at 80% to 90% of the maximum heart rate, the HDL cholesterol level increased by about 14%. When long-distance skiers had trained for 4 months at a submaximal intensity, their HDL cholesterol was 2.1 mmol/l, but it decreased to 1.7 mmol/l during the following 3 months when the training was of a high-intensity type (Myhre et al., 1981). Training at 65% of $\dot{V}O_2max$ for 15 weeks produced more pronounced increases in HDL_2 cholesterol than training at 80% of $\dot{V}O_2max$ (Ledoux, Lanoue, Cacan, Brisson, & Péronnet, 1985). Thus, both high-intensity and very-low-intensity training models have less pronounced effects on the lipoproteins than medium-intensity training (about 65%). A change of the quantity of exercise per week has been found to show a relationship to an increase of HDL cholesterol in several studies (Myhre et al., 1981; Rotkis et al., 1981; Wood et al., 1983).

In all studies the training was of endurance type (jogging, swimming, bicycling, skiing), with one exception, namely weightlifting in regular sessions three times per week for 4 months, which was also associated with an increase in HDL cholesterol (Goldberg et al., 1984). However, in the latter case a change in body composition was found, with less adipose tissue and a larger muscle mass after the training period than before, which also might have contributed to the lipoprotein changes.

An increase in $\dot{V}O_2max$ or in endurance time at a fixed submaximal work load is usually regarded as indicating a training effect. In most studies showing improvement of either of these variables an increase in HDL cholesterol has been found. In some studies, however, an improved $\dot{V}O_2max$ was not associated with any change in HDL cholesterol (Bassett Frey et al., 1982; Brownell et al., 1982; Després et al., 1985; Moll et al., 1979; Ready & Quinney, 1982; Seals et al., 1984; Wynne et al., 1980). Four of these were performed in women (Bassett Frey et al., 1982; Brownell et al., 1982; Moll et al., 1979; Wynne et al., 1980). A rise in HDL cholesterol with increased training has also been demonstrated in women, however (Goldberg et al., 1984; Rotkis et al., 1981). There are several possible reasons for the poorer results in women: They had higher HDL cholesterol values than men before the training, the intensity was rather high (70%), and the sessions lasted for only 30 min in most of the studies, which ran for 6 to 8 weeks. Women may respond more slowly than men (cf. Bassett Frey et al., 1982; Farrell & Barboriak, 1980; Kiens et al., 1984; Rotkis et al., 1981) and therefore studies of longer duration than 6 to 8 weeks may be necessary. In one of these programs the HDL cholesterol in the men improved (Brownell et al., 1982). The adaptability of adipose tissue to training seems different or less pronounced in women than in men, which provides one further possible explanation to the different responses in plasma HDL cholesterol in men and women (Després et al., 1984). Two of the studies showing no change in HDL despite improvements of $\dot{V}O_2max$ were carried out on 24- to 25-year-old men (Després et al., 1985; Ready & Quinney, 1982) who trained at rather high intensity (80% of $\dot{V}O_2max$), which may explain the negative findings (cf. Ledoux et al., 1985; Stubbe, Hansson, Gustafsson, & Nilsson-Ehle, 1983).

The age of the training subject is probably of importance. Younger persons have greater trainability and may improve their $\dot{V}O_2max$ by 40% when starting from low pretraining values, whereas people at the age of 60 to 70 years may improve their $\dot{V}O_2max$ by only 10% to 20%, even when starting from a low pretraining $\dot{V}O_2max$ (Saltin & Rowell, 1980). Thus, smaller effects on lipoproteins should be expected in older people. However, a training-associated improvement of HDL has also been demonstrated in 63-year-old people (Seals et al., 1984).

There are indications that in those who carry on with regular exercise sessions over some years the lipoprotein profile may continue to improve with time (Wood et al., 1983). Some long-term follow-ups have indicated that exercise habits may be difficult to change over a 3- to 5-year period

(Ilmarinen & Fardy, 1977; Sedgwick, Brotherhood, Harris-Davidson, Taplin, & Thomas, 1980), but other authors have found that habits have changed even under unsupervised conditions and that the new habits have lasted for at least 1-1/2 years (Lampman et al., 1978).

This review of longitudinal studies has focused on the effects on HDL cholesterol. However, most investigators have also analyzed serum cholesterol and triglycerides, and in many cases VLDL and LDL. In many of the studies serum triglycerides decreased by 10% to 30% (Dufaux et al., 1982; Farrell & Barboriak, 1980; Goldberg et al., 1984; Huttunen et al., 1979; Rauramaa et al., 1984) and LDL cholesterol decreased about 5% to 10% (Brownell et al., 1982; Goldberg et al., 1984; Peltonen et al., 1981; Wood et al., 1983) and thus the balance between atherogenic and antiatherogenic lipoproteins improved. In fact, the index expressing the balance between atherogenic and antiatherogenic lipoproteins was the variable best associated with the improvement in fitness (Brownell et al., 1982; Myhre et al., 1981; Peltonen et al., 1981; Seals et al., 1984; Wood et al., 1983). Furthermore, people with elevated levels of serum triglycerides (who often have subnormal HDL cholesterol values) seemed to respond to exercise with a pronounced fall in the absolute triglyceride level (Lampman et al., 1977; Lampman et al., 1978). Unfortunately, in the latter studies changes in HDL cholesterol were not evaluated.

In summary, the findings in the large majority of longitudinal investigations conform well with the pattern observed in cross-sectional studies—that a changed lifestyle with regard to physical training results in an improved lipoprotein pattern. Thus, serum triglycerides and LDL cholesterol decrease and HDL cholesterol (confined to the HDL_2 subfraction) increases. Endurance-type training of moderate intensity results in more pronounced changes than high-intensity training. The effects are more evident in men than in women and are related to the amount of training performed.

MECHANISMS INFLUENCED BY REGULAR TRAINING AND AFFECTING THE LIPOPROTEIN PATTERN

Lipoprotein Lipase Activity

The activity of lipoprotein lipase constitutes a key-enzyme function in the hydrolysis of triglycerides in chylomicrons and VLDL particles. Tissue lipoprotein lipase activity is higher in long-distance runners (both men and women) than in control subjects both in adipose tissue and in skeletal muscle (Nikkilä et al., 1978). In acute experiments in which heavy physical work was performed for several hours, this was associated with an increase in lipoprotein lipase activity in skeletal muscle tissue on the morning after the day of heavy exercise (Lithell, Cedermark, et al., 1981). It appears that these acute elevations of muscle lipoprotein lipase activity may be long-standing under certain conditions, since in another study the muscle lipoprotein lipase activity was still increased 3 days after the work (Lithell et al., 1984). The elevation may be related to the increased levels of plasma catecholamines during exercise, as indicated by the positive relationship observed between the 24-hr excretion of epinephrine in urine and muscle lipoprotein lipase activity (Lithell, Cedermark, et al., 1981); in fact, the variation in urine epinephrine excretion accounted for more than 70% of the variation in muscle lipoprotein lipase activity. Such increases in the latter variable may probably explain the simultaneous decreases in serum triglycerides and at least part of the HDL increases that occur after a bout of heavy exercise.

Other mechanisms, however, may explain the elevated muscle lipoprotein lipase activity in well-trained subjects. This activity in skeletal muscle tissue is directly correlated to the capillary density of the muscle (Lithell, Lindgärde, Hellsing, Lundqvist, Nygaard, Vessby, & Saltin, 1981). As mentioned earlier, the lipoprotein lipase molecule involved in the hydrolysis of plasma triglycerides is attached by heparan sulphate to the endothelial surface of arteries and capillaries (Kjellén, Bielefeld, & Höök, 1983; Kjellén, Oldberg, & Höök, 1980). It therefore follows that the denser capillary network in the muscles of long-distance runners (Andersen & Henriksson, 1977; Saltin, Henriksson, Nygaard, Adnersen, & Jansson, 1977) may partly explain the muscle lipoprotein lipase activity. These cross-sectional results were confirmed in a long-term study (where any influence of the preceding bout of exercise was avoided) in which increases in muscle lipoprotein lipase activity and capillary density were found after 2 months of regular training with three 45-min sessions per week (Svedenhag, Lithell, Juhlin-Dannefelt, & Henriksson, 1983). However, the improved capacity for triglyceride hydrolysis does not seem to be confined to skeletal muscle alone. Thus, in two studies the lipoprotein lipase activity in adipose tissue also increased (by about 50%) (Peltonen et al., 1981; Stubbe, Hansson, Gustafsson, & Nilsson-Ehle, 1983). In both of these studies postheparin lipoprotein lipase activity was enhanced after regular training.

The improvements in lipoprotein lipase activity in adipose and skeletal muscle tissue may have different relevance for different pathways in the lipoprotein metabolism. Thus, in the fasting state about 50% of the hydrolysis of circulating triglycerides takes place in skeletal muscle and only about 25% in adipose tissue (Rössner, 1974). This may explain the negative relationship between fasting serum triglyceride concentration and skeletal muscle lipoprotein lipase activity and the absence of a significant relationship between serum triglyceride concentration and lipoprotein lipase activity in adipose tissue (Lithell, Boberg, Hellsing, & Vessby, 1978). The increase in capillary density per mm^2 is not evident until after the first 4 to 6 weeks of training, which fits well with the time course of triglyceride and HDL cholesterol changes. It may also explain the lack of alteration in muscle lipoprotein lipase activity in one training study of 6 weeks duration (Stubbe et al., 1983). After repetitive meals the greater part of the triglycerides are transported in the form of chylomicrons. Relatively more of the hydrolysis of circulating triglycerides is now taking place in adipose than in skeletal muscle tissue. The surface components of the chylomicrons contain apolipoprotein A-I, which during hydrolysis is transferred to the HDL fraction. Apolipoprotein A-I is important for the cholesterol-carrying capacity of HDL and the fact that more chylomicrons are hydrolyzed in adipose than in skeletal muscle tissue may explain the good correlation between adipose tissue lipoprotein lipase activity and HDL cholesterol in well-trained men and women (Nikkilä et al., 1978).

Hepatic Lipase Activity

In cross-sectional studies an inverse relationship between $\dot{V}O_2max$ and hepatic lipase activity has been observed (Kuusi, Nikkilä, Saarinen, Varjo, & Laitinen, 1982). Thus, those subjects with the highest maximal oxygen uptake capacity had the lowest hepatic lipase activity. Such low hepatic lipase activity may partly explain the increased HDL cholesterol in well-trained persons. Acute exercise does not cause a reduction in hepatic lipase activity (Kantor et al., 1984), but we have found that after heavy exercise for several days this activity is decreased (unpublished results).

In long-term studies different results have been obtained. In one study no change in hepatic lipase activity was noted in association with regular training (Marniemi, Peltonen, Vuori, & Hietanen, 1980), in another the activity was decreased (Stubbe et al., 1983), and in a third study (Sutherland, Woodhouse, Nye, & Gerard, 1984) it was increased. Thus it is unlikely that this latter increase would have explained the significant increase in HDL cholesterol in the same study.

DISCUSSION

Is it the training in itself or other simultaneous lifestyle modifications or metabolic effects that explain the changes in lipoprotein metabolism? Alterations in dietary habits, cigarette smoking, alcohol intake, body weight and body composition have been taken into account in several studies (Brownell et al., 1982; Huttunen et al., 1979; Kiens et al., 1979; Rotkis et al., 1981). However, the relatively small sample size in these studies has meant that the statistical ability to detect minor changes in such factors as body weight has been weak. It seems rather unlikely, however, that the fairly small reductions in adipose tissue mass of 1 to 3 kg that might occur would cause the rather pronounced lipoprotein modifications, as judged from results of other studies on body-weight reduction by reduced energy intake. This assumption is supported by observations in the control (nontraining) group in a long-term training study, in which changes in body weight were weakly positively association with a variation in HDL cholesterol (Williams et al., 1983). In contrast, in the training group there was a strong negative association between change in body weight and change in HDL cholesterol concentration (Williams et al., 1983). The body-weight reduction was strongly associated with the mileage run per week and occurred despite an increase in dietary energy intake. The strong association between metabolic responses and body-weight reduction with physical training has been confirmed in another study (Blair et al., 1983). In view of the difference between (a) the relationship of body-weight reduction with exercise to lipoprotein changes and (b) that of body-weight reduction after caloric restriction to lipoprotein changes, it seems more relevant to regard both the body-weight reduction and the lipoprotein changes as metabolic consequences of physical training rather than to regard the lipoprotein changes as consequences of both the body weight reduction and the training. Physical training is associated with increased adrenergic sensitivity (Krotkiewski et al., 1983), as reflected in enhanced epinephrine-stimulated lipolysis in adipose tissue in trained subjects (Deprés et al., 1984). This means that fat in adipose tissue is more easily mobilized after regular training. It might be speculated that if this effect were also related to mileage per week, then fatty acids from the adipose tissue might more readily cover some of the energy costs during training, owing to the greater sensitivity and flexibility of adipose tissue. The higher adrenergic sensitivity associated with training may also explain the lower insulin response to glucose (Krotkiewski et al., 1983) after training, which, in turn, may lead to a lower rate of synthesis of VLDL particles from the liver. Such mechanisms may thus be operative and contribute to the reductions in VLDL and LDL and the increase in HDL concentration with training. Furthermore, the lower response in adipose tissue in women than in men (Després et al., 1984) might partly explain the less pronounced changes in lipoprotein levels in women than in men during training. On the other hand, women have a better lipoprotein pattern from the beginning. It is quite possible that they have a higher threshold for lipoprotein changes than men. It has been found in most studies, in fact, that in women moderate training does not cause lipoprotein alterations. However, a great increase in training (by about 50 km per week) caused a significant increase in HDL cholesterol in women. The magnitude of the change was similar to that observed during increased training in well-trained men with initial HDL cholesterol levels equal to those in the women (Kiens et al., 1984; Myhre et al., 1981).

Thus, it seems as if the training-induced alterations in key-enzyme functions occur both in adipose tissue and in skeletal muscle (and possibly in the liver) and might all contribute to changing both the production and the removal of lipoproteins, leading to a less atherogenic lipoprotein pattern.

In such a complex system it is difficult to estimate the actual relevance of each individual alteration. However, in a one-leg training study it was shown that a larger part of the arterial concentration of VLDL triglycerides was hydrolyzed over the trained leg than over the untrained one and that this arterio-venous (a-v) difference was associated with an increased v-a difference in HDL cholesterol (Kiens & Lithell, 1985). A denser capillary network and increased lipoprotein lipase activity in the muscle with training was confirmed. The systemic venous blood concentration of HDL cholesterol was increased despite absence of a change in systemic $\dot{V}O_2max$ and in the insulin and adrenergic hormone concentrations in the blood stream. These observations prove that alterations in the skeletal muscle are of importance for the lipoprotein changes observed during training.

Effect of Physical Training on Lipoprotein Metabolism in Cardiac Patients

As part of the National Exercise and Heart Disease Project, 223 postcoronary men, aged 30 to 64, were randomly assigned to moderate exercise or control groups (LaRosa et al., 1982). After 1 year of regular training no changes in lipid or lipoprotein levels were seen either in the training or in the control group. A statistical analysis revealed no predictable effect of work capacity or change in work capacity on changes in lipid values.

In another study on postcoronary men over a 1-year period (Kavanagh, Shephard, Lindley, & Pieper, 1983), one group of men (n = 35) was recruited 2 to 3 months after the myocardial infarction, whereas the other group (n = 27) had had their myocardial infarction 2 to 3 years earlier and had adopted regular jogging habits after the cardiac event. The first group was subjected to a training program including regular walking or jogging on an average of 16.9 km per week. After 1 year this was associated with a small increment of HDL cholesterol (< 2%). In the second group some subjects increased and some decreased their weekly training (averaging (67.7 km). The statistical analysis revealed that HDL cholesterol correlated well with the weekly running distance and that the ''dose'' of exercise necessary for inducing any ''substantial'' increase in HDL cholesterol was about 20 km per week.

In a small group (n = 10) of postmyocardial infarction patients (aged 46 to 62 years) Heath, Ehsani, Hagberg, Hinderliter, and Goldberg (1983) found that after 29 weeks of training three to five times per week, 40 to 60 min each session, there was an increase in $\dot{V}O_2max$ by 50% to 85%. This was associated with increases in HDL cholesterol (20%) and the HDL cholesterol/LDL cholesterol ratio (25%).

Ballantyne, Clark, Simpson, and Ballantyne (1982) reported that post-myocardial infarction patients (n = 19) who were subjected to a training program for 6 months showed significant decreases in serum triglycerides and low density lipoprotein cholesterol concentrations and increases in both HDL cholesterol and apolipoprotein A-I. The HDL increase was restricted to the subfraction HDL_2. However, there was no relationship between the changes in lipoproteins and those in treadmill exercise test performance.

In a study on a small group (n = 14) of patients with severe angina pectoris it was found that their physical performance was improved by 40% after a 9-week in-hospital training period (training two 30-min sessions each day) (Stubbe, Gustafson, Nilsson-Ehle, & Ågren, 1983). During the training program there was an improvement in both glucose tolerance and the insulin values during a glucose tolerance test, and in addition, both the serum triglycerides and LDL cholesterol concentration decreased, but there was no change in HDL cholesterol. However, some of the metabolic improvements may have been effects of the change to hospital diet.

In a study of 18 patients with coronary artery disease, Erkelens, Albers, Hazzard, Frederich, & Bierman (1979) found that their HDL cholesterol increased from 35.2 to 40.0 mg/dl during a 6-month training period. However, the increase was achieved after only 1 week of training. In one further study (Streja & Mymin, 1979) an increase in HDL cholesterol was found in a similar group of patients (n = 32) studies over a 13-week training period. This increase was not associated with any change in plasma triglyceride concentration.

Cardiac Disease, Physical Training and Lipoprotein Changes in Perspective

Of people who die of coronary heart disease, about 50% die suddenly. Of those who receive hospital care, about one-third die during the hospital stay or in the 1st year of follow-up, whereas one-third leave the hospital with angina pectoris and only one-third become free of complications after their myocardial infarction. It is promising that even among patients with severely disabling angina pectoris metabolic improvements have been seen after a 9-week training program. However, only cardiac patients with well-preserved cardiac function can be expected to perform a training program of such brisk exercise that it will result in clinically important changes in the lipoprotein pattern. In groups in which a major improvement in maximal oxygen uptake can be achieved, this is associated with an improvement in the balance between the atherogenic and antiatherogenic lipoproteins that is as great as those achieved in the Lipid Research Clinics Intervention Trial in which cholestyramine was used to reduce LDL cholesterol (National Heart, Lung, and Blood Institute, 1984a, 1984b). In that trial the change in the lipoprotein profile was associated with a 19% reduction in coronary heart disease over a 7- to 9-year period (National Heart, Lung, and Blood Institute, 1984a). The results of the study showed that the occurrence of coronary heart disease complications was not reduced until after 2 to 3 years of treatment (National Heart, Lung, and Blood Institute, 1984a). This delayed effect is in accordance with the results of epidemiological studies that have indicated that the incubation period between a change in exposure to major coronary risk factors and the maximum effect on mortality may be 10 years or more (Rose, 1982). The average life expectancy of patients who have survived the 1st year after their myocardial infarction is about 14 years and serum cholesterol is a risk factor for reinfarction (Coronary Drug Project Research Group, 1978). In the long-term perspective the influence of regular physical training on the lipoprotein profile may therefore be of great importance, together with a prudent diet and other lifestyle alterations such as reduction of body weight, stopping cigarette smoking, and a change from high to moderate alcohol intake (World Health Organization [WHO] Expert Committee, 1982). It also follows from the above considerations that clinically significant lipoprotein improvements due to physical training are limited to only a minority of the cardiac patients and that the most important place for training is as a primary preventive measure.

Lipoprotein Metabolism in Type 1 Diabetes Mellitus

The lipoprotein pattern in young insulin-treated diabetic patients is normal (Walden, Knopp, Wahl, Beach, & Strandness, 1984). The better the degree of diabetes control, the more favorable the lipoprotein pattern (Lopes-Virella, Wohltmann, Loadholt, & Buse, 1981). Even increased levels of HDL cholesterol have been demonstrated (Nikkilä & Harmila, 1978). It is therefore not the lipoprotein pattern per se that accounts for the increased frequency of coronary heart disease in this patient group (Bradley, 1971). However, there are some specific conditions in this form of diabetes, of which some may explain the apparently normal lipoprotein pattern and others may explain the increased atherogenesis. Thus, insulin is important for regulation of the lipoprotein lipase activity in adipose tissue (Sadur & Eckel, 1982; Yki-Järvinen, Taskinen, Koivisto, & Nikkilä,

1984). After withdrawal of insulin treatment for 12 hr, an 8-hr intravenous infusion of insulin has been found to be associated with an increase in this activity in adipose tissue of 36% (Taskinen, Nikkilä, Nousiainen, & Gordin, 1981). The high plasma free-insulin concentrations after a subcutaneous insulin injection are probably of significance for the high post-heparin plasma lipoprotein lipase activity in this group of patients (Nikkilä, Huttunen, & Ehnholm, 1977). Furthermore, insulin stimulates LDL catabolism. After a 4-hr insulin infusion using the euglycemic-insulin clamp technique, isolated mononuclear cells degraded more I^{125} labelled LDL than did cells isolated after a saline infusion in control subjects (Mazzone, Foster, & Chait, 1984). Thus, insulin-induced stimulation of LDL catabolism might account for the reduction in LDL cholesterol levels observed in intensively treated type 1 diabetics (Walden et al., 1984). However, when the disease is less well regulated, the LDL particles become glycosylated. This changes the LDL particle so that it is not taken up and degraded by the high-affinity LDL pathway in normal fibroblasts (Witztum et al., 1982). Furthermore, its uptake and degradation are not accompanied by the the normal feedback effects preventing any further uptake. If the uptake by such a pathway proves to be important, this could explain the finding of increased cellular uptake of cholesterol despite normal LDL concentrations.

Training Studies

In several different studies of type 1 diabetics, regular training sessions, three times a week for 8 to 16 weeks, have been found not to be associated with changes in fasting blood glucose concentrations, HbA_1C levels or insulin requirements (Wallberg-Henriksson et al., 1982; Wallberg-Henriksson et al., 1984). In one of these studies (Wallberg-Henriksson et al., 1982) a 16-week training program was associated with a 14% decrease in plasma cholesterol resulting from a decrease in the atherogenic lipoproteins, whereas HDL cholesterol remained constant. The response of muscle tissue of type 1 diabetics to training seems to differ in some respect from that of controls. In one study, for example, the expected increase in capillary density did not take place (Wallberg-Henriksson et al., 1984). In addition, abnormally low muscle lipoprotein lipase activity in relation to capillary density has been observed in type 1 diabetics (Lithell et al., 1985). Whether this is due to nonfunctioning capillaries in the diabetic patient or to an altered affinity of lipoprotein lipase molecules for heparan sulphate due to glycosylation of the latter (Kjellén et al., 1980; Kjellén et al., 1983) cannot be determined.

In summary, the present knowledge suggests that increased atherosclerosis in type 1 diabetics may be related to abnormal metabolism of lipoproteins of normal concentration. This may improve with better glucose control. So far, the training studies have not proved that a schedule with three training sessions per week can help to improve glucose homeostasis. Other training schedules, for example, one session each day, may possibly give a better result.

Diabetes Mellitus of Type 2

Diabetes mellitus of type 2 (noninsulin-dependent diabetes mellitus) differs in several epidemiological and clinical respects from that of type 1 (Mann & Houston, 1983; Spencer & Gudworth, 1983). Thus, the hereditary influence is stronger in type 2 than in type 1 diabetes and the incidence of the former increases with increasing age; type 2 diabetes is fairly infrequent below the age of 40 to 45 years in most populations. There are exceptions; for example, among the Pima Indians the incidence curve is shifted toward the left, so that the incidence starts to increase already during the 2nd and 3rd decades of life. The Pima Indians are characterized by a very high frequency of pronounced obesity and a sedentary lifestyle, characteristics that are regarded as the most important exogenous factors for precipitation of type 2 diabetes in individuals with positive heredity (Bennett, 1983; Mann & Houston, 1983).

The lipoprotein pattern in obese patients with newly detected type 2 diabetes differs from that in weight-matched controls, independent of sex. Thus, in one study the VLDL triglyceride concentration was found to be about 3 times higher in the diabetics than in the controls, and the LDL triglyceride concentration was also higher in the diabetics (Taskinen, Nikkilä, Kuusi,& Harno, 1982). Furthermore, HDL cholesterol was lower in the diabetic than in the control group (Taskinen et al., 1982; Taylor et al., 1981). Among treated patients a similar lipoprotein pattern, but less pronounced, has been observed (Walden, Knopp, Wahl, Beach, & Strandness, 1984). However, the lipoprotein abnormalities were more marked in women than in men, a finding which was regarded as one possible explanation for the fact that diabetes is a more pronounced risk factor for cardiovascular complications among women than among men (Walden et al., 1984).

Hypertriglyceridemia in type 2 diabetes seems to be a result from increased synthesis in and/or secretion of VLDL particles from the liver. In normolipidemic, mildly diabetic subjects this increase is accompanied by increased removal of these particles. In hyperlipidemic diabetic patients the fractional turnover rates are significantly reduced, and the increase in VLDL removal is therefore not sufficient to compensate for the high production. In such patients a 5-fold increase in the removal of VLDL "remnants" via a non-LDL pathway has been found (Kissebah et al.,

1982). An abnormal lipid composition of the LDL particles has been observed in type 2 diabetes (Taskinen et al., 1982), which may explain the abnormal LDL catabolism. In one study (Kraemer, Chen, Cheung, & Reaven, 1982), normal uptake and degradation of LDL from type 2 diabetic patients by normal fibroblasts was observed. This was not the case with LDL from diabetics with more pronounced triglyceride elevations (Hiramatsu et al., 1985). Their LDL particles failed to suppress the LDL-receptor activity as efficiently as LDL from healthy persons (Hiramatsu et al., 1985). The ability of LDL from hypertriglyceridemic subjects, whether diabetic or not, to suppress LDL binding was inversely related to the ratio of triglyceride to protein in LDL. Hypertriglyceridemia is a prominent feature of type 2 diabetes (Taskinen et al., 1982). Since hypertriglyceridemia and type 2 diabetes are inherited as separate entities, it is likely that this hypertriglyceridemia is secondary to diabetes and obesity (Brunzell, Hazzard, Motulsky, & Bierman, 1975). A decrease in lipoprotein lipase activities have been demonstrated in adipose tissue in patients with newly detected type 2 diabetes as compared with weight-matched control subjects (Taskinen et al., 1982). It therefore seems likely that in type 2 diabetes low lipoprotein lipase activity may be one important cause of the elevated plasma triglyceride concentrations and abnormal LDL composition, and may prove to be contributory to the accelerated atherogenesis.

Effect of Physical Training on the Lipoprotein Pattern in Type 2 Diabetes

Improvement of glucose homeostasis resulting from treatment with sulphonylurea (Greenfield, Doborne, Rosenthal, Vreman, & Reaven, 1982), or from dietary therapy or body-weight reduction (Kennedy, Walshe, Hadden, Weaver, & Buchanan, 1982; Lindgärde, Eriksson, Lithell, & Saltin, 1982; Vessby, Boberg, Karlström, Lithell, & Werner, 1984; Vessby, Selinus, & Lithell, 1985) is associated with a beneficial effect on the lipoprotein pattern. The effect of physical training on glucose homeostasis is reviewed elsewhere in these proceedings. Some of these short-term studies have shown improvement, but all studies have been performed on small, selected, relatively young populations. Thus, both fasting blood glucose and oral glucose tolerance improved in six obese patients (age 19 to 41 years) (Reitman, Vasquez, Klimes, & Nagulesparan, 1984), in five patients aged 54 $\pm$ 4 years (Trovati et al., 1984) and in a group of nine males (age 48 years) (Lindgärde, Malmquist, & Balke, 1983), some of whom were treated with drugs. In two of these investigations euglycemic hyperinsulinemic clamp studies indicated an improved rate of insulin-induced glucose disposal after the training period. In none of these studies were serum lipids or lipoproteins analyzed. In a recent study in 10 obese and 10 sulphonylurea-treated diabetics, 10 weeks of regular physical training two to three times a week did not cause any significant decreases in serum triglyceride concentrations (Lithell et al., 1985). It should be noted that neither the capillary density nor the lipoprotein lipase activity in skeletal muscle increased with training in these patients. As discussed earlier, both these factors generally increase with regular physical training for such a long period, at least in young healthy subjects of normal body weight.

Physical Training in Type 2 Diabetic Patients—in Perspective

Improvements in the lipoprotein pattern, particularly in the HDL cholesterol concentrations, are generally related to the improvement in maximal oxygen uptake. However, trainability is much lower in older than in younger subjects and type 2 diabetes is more frequent in older people with relatively low trainability. Therefore, results of mode-of-action studies in relatively young persons with type 2 diabetes may have little relevance for the large majority of type 2 diabetics. Furthermore, other diseases and complications are abundant among older type 2 diabetics. Thus, we found that among 1,800 60-year-old men who were screened for diabetes, 46 had developed this disease during the last decade (unpublished data).

Thirty-four men had diseases that made them unsuitable for participation in a long-term training study. Of 12 available men, only 8 wanted to take part. These eight men followed a schedule with regular 45-min training sessions two to three times per week. After 2 years three patients remained in the study group. Two had dropped out and three had developed myocardial infarction or angina pectoris. The three remaining patients had improved their $\dot{V}O_2max$ but only one showed improvement in glucose tolerance but not in HDL cholesterol. This shows that the larger majority of type 2 diabetics cannot or are unwilling to participate in regular physical training. This fact underlines the need for physical training to be a preventive measure with regard to type 2 diabetes mellitus. The target group could be, for example, women with gestational diabetes, who frequently develop permanent type 2 diabetes later on, or middle-aged men with impaired glucose tolerance and positive heredity for diabetes. In such groups regular training may be effective in improving the glucose tolerance (Lindgärde et al., 1982; Ruderman, Ganda, & Johansen, 1979) at a lower insulin requirement (LeBlanc, Nadeau, Richard, & Tremblay, 1981; Lindgärde et al., 1982; Ruderman et al., 1979), which may hopefully postpone the development of diabetes (Hellerström, 1984) and thereby also the deterioration of lipoprotein metabolism associated with diabetes of type 2.

REFERENCES

Åberg, H., Lithell, H., Selinus, I., & Hedstrand, H. (1985). Serum triglycerides are a risk factor for myocardial infarction but not for angina pectoris. Results from a 10-year follow-up of Uppsala Primary Preventive Study. *Atherosclerosis*, **54**, 89-97.

Adner, M.M., & Castelli, W.P. (1980). Elevated high-density lipoprotein levels in marathon runners. *Journal of the American Medical Association*, **243**, 534-536.

Andersen, P., & Henriksson, J. (1977). Capillary supply of the quadriceps femoris muscle of man: Adaptive response to exercise. *Journal of Physiology*, **270**, 677-691.

Ballantyne, F.C., Clark, R.S., Simpson, H.S., & Ballantyne, D. (1982). The effect of moderate physical exercise on the plasma lipoprotein subfractions of male survivors of myocardial infarction. *Circulation*, **65**, 913-918.

Bassett Frey, M.A., Doerr, B.M., Laubach, L.L., Mann, B.L., & Glueck, C.J. (1982). Exercise does not change high-density lipoprotein cholesterol in women after ten weeks of training. *Metabolism*, **31**, 1142-1146.

Bennett, P.H. (1983). Diabetes in developing countries and unusual populations. In J.I. Mann, K. Pyörälä, & A. Teuscher (Eds.), *Diabetes in epidemiological perspective* (pp. 43-57). Edinburgh, London, Melbourne, New York: Churchill Livingstone.

Blair, S.N., Cooper, K.H., Gibbons, L.W., Gettman, L.R., Lewis, S., & Goodyear, N. (1983). Changes in coronary heart disease risk factors associated with increased treadmill time in 753 men. *American Journal of Epidemiology*, **118**, 352-359.

Bradley, R.F. (1971). Cardiovascular disease. In A. Markte, R. White, R.F. Bradley, & L.D. Krall (Eds.), *Diabetes mellitus* (pp. 417-477). Philadelphia: Lea and Febiger.

Brewer, J.B., Jr. (1981). Current concepts of the molecular structure and metabolism of human apoliproteins and lipoproteins. *Klinische Wochenschrift*, **59**, 1023-1035.

Brownell, K.D., Bachorik, P.S., & Ayerle, R.S. (1982). Changes in plasma lipid and lipoprotein levels in men and women after a program of moderate exercise. *Circulation*, **65**, 477-484.

Brunzell, J.D., Hazzard, W.R., Motulsky, A.G., & Bierman, E.J. (1975). Evidence for diabetes mellitus and genetic forms of hypertriglyceridemia as independent entities. *Metabolism*, **24**, 1115-1121.

Carlson, L.A., Böttiger, L.E., & Åhfeldt, P.-E. (1979). Risk factors for myocardial infarction in the Stockholm Prospective Study—a 14-year follow-up focusing on the role of plasma triglycerides and cholesterol. *Acta Medica Scandinavica*, **206**, 351-360.

Carlson, L.A., & Mossfeldt, A. (1964). Acute effects of prolonged, heavy exercise on the concentration of plasma lipids and lipoproteins in man. *Acta Physiologica Scandinavica,* **62**, 51-59.

Castelli, W.P. (1984). Epidemiology of coronary heart disease: The Framingham study. *The American Journal of Medicine,* **76**, 4-12.

Castelli, W.P., Doyle, J.T., Gordon, T., Hames, C.G., Hjortland, M.C., Hulley, S.B., Kagan, A., & Zukel, W.J. (1977). HDL cholesterol and other lipids in coronary heart disease. The cooperative lipoprotein phenotyping study. *Circulation,* **55**, 767-772.

Christie, R.J., Bloore, H.G., & Logan, R.L. (1980). High-density lipoprotein (HDL) cholesterol in middle-aged joggers. *The New Zealand Medical Journal,* **91**, 39-40.

Clarkson, P.M., Hintermister, R., Fillyaw, M., & Stylos, L. (1981). High density lipoprotein cholesterol in young adult weight lifters, runners, and untrained subjects. *Human Biology,* **53**, 251-257.

Coronary Drug Project Research Group (1978). Natural history of myocardial infarction in the coronary drug project: Long-term prognostic importance of serum lipid levels. *The American Journal of Cardiology,* **42**, 489-498.

Cryer, A., McDonald, A., Williams, E.R., & Robinson, D.S. (1975). Colchicine inhibition of the heparin-stimulated release of clearing-factor lipase from isolated fat-cells. *Biochemical Journal,* **152**, 717-720.

Danner, S.A., Wieling, W., Havekes, L., Leuven, G.J., Smit, E.M., & Dunning, A.J. (1984). Effect of physical exercise on blood lipids and adipose tissue composition in young healthy men. *Atherosclerosis,* **53**, 83-90.

Després, J.-P., Bouchard, C., Savard, R., Tremblay, A., & Allard, C. (1985). Lack of relationship between changes in adiposity and plasma lipids following endurance training. *Atherosclerosis,* **54**, 135-143.

Després, J.-P., Bouchard, C., Savard, R., Tremblay, A., Marcotte, M., & Thériault, G. (1984). The effect of a 20-week endurance training program on adipose-tissue morphology and lipolysis in men and women. *Metabolism,* **33**, 235-239.

Dufaux, B., Assmann, G., Schachten, H., & Hollman, W. (1982). The delayed effects of prolonged physical exercise and physical training on cholesterol level. *European Journal of Applied Physiology,* **48**, 25-29.

Enger, S.C., Herbjørnsen, K., Eriksson, J., & Fretland, A. (1977). High density lipoproteins (HDL) and physical activity: The influence of physical exercise, age, and smoking on HDL-cholesterol and the HDL-/total cholesterol ratio. *Scandinavian Journal for Clinical and Laboratory Investigation,* **37**, 251-255.

Enger, S.C., Strømme, S.B., & Refsum, H.E. (1980). High density lipoprotein cholesterol, total cholesterol and triglycerides in serum after a single exposure to prolonged heavy exercise. *Scandinavian Journal of Clinical and Laboratory Investigation,* **40**, 341-345.

Erkelens, D.W., Albers, J.J., Hazzard, W.R., Frederich, R.C., & Bierman, E.L. (1979). High-density lipoprotein-cholesterol in survivors of myocardial infarction. *Journal of the American Medical Association,* **242**, 2185-2189.

Farrell, P.A., & Barboriak, J. (1980). The time course of alterations in plasma lipid and lipoprotein concentrations during eight weeks of endurance training. *Atherosclerosis,* **37**, 231-238.

Farrell, P.A., Maksud, M.G., Pollock, M.L., Foster, C., Anholm, J., Hare, J., & Leon, A.S. (1982). A comparison of plasma cholesterol, triglycerides, and high density lipoprotein-cholesterol in speed skaters, weightlifters and non-athletes. *European Journal of Applied Physiology,* **48**, 77-82.

Goldberg, L., Elliot, D.L., Schultz, R.W., & Kloster, F.E. (1984). Changes in lipid and lipoprotein levels after weight training. *Journal of the American Medical Association,* **252**, 504-506.

Gordon, T., Castelli, W.P., Hjortland, M.C., Kannel, W.B., & Dawber, T.R. (1977). High density lipoprotein as a protective factor against coronary heart disease. The Framingham study. *The American Journal of Medicine,* **62**, 707-714.

Greenfield, M.S., Doborne, L., Rosenthal, M., Vreman, H.J., & Reaven, G.M. (1982). Lipid metabolism in non-insulin-dependent diabetes mellitus. Effect of glipizide therapy. *Archives of Internal Medicine,* **142**, 1498-1500.

Hahn, P.E. (1943). Abolishment of alimentary lipemia following injection of heparin. *Science,* **98**, 19-26.

Hartung, G.H., Foreyt, J.P., Mitchell, R.E., Vlasek, I., & Gotto, A.M., Jr. (1980). Relation of diet to high-density-lipoprotein cholesterol in middle-aged marathon runners, joggers and inactive men. *The New England Journal of Medicine,* **302**, 357-361.

Haskell, W.L., Taylor, H.L., Wood, P.D., Schrott, H., & Heiss, G. (1980). Strenuous physical activity, treadmill exercise test performance and plasma high-density lipoprotein cholesterol. The Lipid Research Clinics Program Prevalence Study. *Circulation,* **62**(Suppl. IV), 53-61.

Heath, G.W., Ehsani, A.A., Hagberg, J.M., Hinderliter, J.M., & Goldberg, A.P. (1983). Exercise training improves lipoprotein lipid profiles in patients with coronary artery disease. *American Heart Journal,* **105**, 889-895.

Heiss, G., Johnson, N.J., Reiland, S., Davis, C.E., & Tyroler, H.A. (1980). The epidemiology of plasma high-density lipoprotein cholesterol levels. The Lipid Research Clinics Program Prevalence Study. *Circulation,* **62**(Suppl. IV), 116-136.

Hellerström, C. (1984). The life story of the pancreatic B cell. *Diabetologia,* **26**, 393-400.

Higuchi, M., Hashimoto, I., Yamakawa, K., Tsuji, E., Nishimuta, M., & Suzuki, S. (1984). Effect of exercise training on plasma high-density lipoprotein cholesterol level at constant weight. *Clinical Physiology*, **4**, 125-133.

Hiramatsu, K., Bierman, E.L., & Chait, A. (1985). Metabolism of low-density lipoprotein from patients with diabetic hypertriglyceridemia by cultured human skin fibroblasts. *Diabetes*, **37**, 8-14.

Huttunen, J.K., Ehnholm, C., Kekki, M., & Nikkilä, E.A. (1976). Post-heparin plasma lipoprotein lipase and hepatic lipase in normal subjects and in patients with hypertriglyceridemia—correlations to sex, age and various parameters of triglyceride metabolism. *Clinical Science and Molecular Medicine*, **50**, 249-260.

Huttunen, J.K., Ehnholm, C., Kinnunen, P.K.J., & Nikkilä, E.A. (1975). An immunochemical method for the selective measurement of two triglyceride lipases in human postheparin plasma. *Clinical Chimica Acta*, **63**, 335-347.

Huttunen, J.K., Länsimies, E., Voutilainen, E., Ehnholm, C., Hietanen, E., Penttilä, I., Siitonen, O., & Raurmaa, R. (1979). Effect of moderate physical exercise on serum lipoproteins. A controlled clinical trial with special reference to serum high-density lipoproteins. *Circulation*, **60**, 1220-1229.

Ilmarinen, J., & Fardy, P.S. (1977). Physical activity intervention for males with high risk of coronary heart disease. *Preventive Medicine*, **6**, 416-425.

Jackson, R.L., Morrisett, J.D., & Gotto, A.M., Jr. (1976). Lipoprotein structure and metabolism. *Physiological Reviews*, **56**, 259-316.

Jansen, H., Van Tol, A., & Hülsmann, W.C. (1980). On the metabolic function of heparin-releasable liver lipase. *Biochemical and Biophysical Research Communications*, **92**, 53-59.

Kantor, M.A., Cullinane, E.M., Herbert, P.N., & Thompson, P.D. (1984). Acute increase in lipoprotein lipase following prolonged exercise. *Metabolism*, **33**, 454-457.

Kavanagh, T., Shephard, R.J., Lindley, L.J., & Pieper, M. (1983). Influence of exercise and life-style variables upon high density lipoprotein cholesterol after myocardial infarction. *Arteriosclerosis*, **3**, 24-27.

Kennedy, L., Walshe, K., Hadden, D.R., Weaver, J.A., & Buchanan, K.D. (1982). The effect of intensive dietary therapy on serum high density lipoprotein cholesterol in patients with type 2 (non-insulin-dependent) diabetes mellitus: A prospective study. *Diabetologia*, **23**, 24-27.

Kiens, B., Jørgensen, I., Lewis, S., Jensen, G., Lithell, H., Vessby, B., Hoe, S., & Schnohr, P. (1979). Increased plasma HDL-cholesterol and apo A-I in sedentary middle-aged men after physical conditioning. *European Journal of Clinical Investigation*, **10**, 203-209.

Kiens, B., & Lithell, H. (1985). Lipoprotein metabolism related to adaptations in human skeletal muscle. *Clinical Physiology*, **5**(Suppl. 4), Abstract No. 108.

Kiens, B., Lithell, H., & Vessby, B. (1984). Further increase in high density lipoprotein in trained males after enhanced training. *European Journal of Applied Physiology*, **52**, 426-430.

Kissebah, A.H., Alfarsi, S., Adams, P.W., & Wynn, V. (1976). Role of insulin resistance in adipose tissue and liver in the pathogenesis of endogenous hypertriglyceridemia in man. *Diabetologia*, **12**, 563-571.

Kissebah, A.H., Alfarsi, S., Evans, D.J., & Adams, P.W. (1982). Integrated regulation of very low density lipoprotein triglyceride and apolipoprotein-B kinetics in non-insulin-dependent diabetes mellitus. *Diabetes*, **31**, 217-225.

Kjellén, L., Bielefeld, D., & Höök, M. (1983). Reduced sulfation of liver heparin sulfate in experimentally diabetic rats. *Diabetes*, **32**, 337-342.

Kjellén, L., Oldberg, Å., & Höök, M. (1980). Cell surface heparin sulfate; mechanisms of proteoglycan-cell association. *Journal of Biological Chemistry*, **225**, 10407-10413.

Kraemer, F.B., Chen, Y-D.I., Cheung, R.M.C., & Reaven, G.M. (1982). Are the binding and degradation of low density lipoprotein altered in type 2 (non-insulin-dependent) diabetes mellitus? *Diabetologia*, **23**, 28-33.

Krotkiewski, M., Mandroukas, K., Morgan, L., William-Olsson, T., Feurle, G.E. von Schenck, H., Björntorp, P., Sjöström, L., & Smith, U. (1983). Effects of physical training on adrenergic sensitivity in obesity. *Journal of Applied Physiology: Respiratory, Environmental, Exercise Physiology*, **55**, 1811-1817.

Kuusi, T., Kinnunen, P.K.J., & Nikkilä, E.A. (1979). Hepatic endothelial lipase antiserum influences rat plasma low and high density lipoproteins in vivo. *Federation of the European Biochemistry Society Letters*, **104**, 384-388.

Kuusi, T., Kostiainen, E., Vartiainen, E., Pitkänen, L., Ehnholm, C., Korhonen, H.J., Nissinen, A., & Puska, P. (1984). Acute effects of marathon running on levels of serum lipoproteins and adrogenic hormones in healthy males. *Metabolism*, **33**, 527-531.

Kuusi, T., Nikkilä, E.A., Saarinen, P., Varjo, P., & Laitinen, L.A. (1982). Plasma high density lipoproteins HDL_2, HDL_3 and postheparin plasma lipases in relation to parameters of physical fitness. *Atherosclerosis*, **41**, 209-219.

Kuusi, T., Saarinen, P., & Nikkilä, E.A. (1980). Evidence for the role of hepatic endothelial lipase in the metabolism of plasma high density lipo-$protein_2$ in man. *Atherosclerosis*, **36**, 589-593.

Lampman, R.M., Santinga, J.T., Bassett, D.R., (MonDragon) Mercer, N., Block, W.D., Flora, J.D., Jr., Foss, M.L., & Thorland, W.G. (1978). Effectiveness of unsupervised and supervised high intensity physical training in normalizing serum lipids in men with type IV hyperlipoproteinemia. *Circulation*, **57**, 172-180.

Lampman, R.M., Santiaga, J.T., (LaValley) Hodge, M.F., Block, W.D., Flora, J.D., Jr., & Bassett, D.R. (1977). Comparative effects of physical training and diet in normalizing serum lipids in men with type IV hyperlipoproteinemia. *Circulation,* **55**, 652-659.

LaRosa, J.C., Cleary, P., Muesing, R.A., Gorman, P., Hellerstein, H.K., & Moughton, J. (1982). Effect of long-term moderate physical exercise on plasma lipoproteins. The National Exercise and Heart Disease Project. *Archives of Internal Medicine,* **142**, 2269-2274.

LeBlanc, J., Nadeau, A., Richard, D., & Tremblay, A. (1981). Studies on the sparing effect of exercise on insulin requirements in human subjects. *Metabolism,* **30**, 1119-1124.

Ledoux, M., Lanoue, L., Cacan, S., Brisson, G., & Péronnet, F. (1985). Effect of two intensities of exercise on lipids and lipoproteins after a 15 week training program. *Clinical Physiology,* **5**(Suppl. 4), Abstract No. 109.

Lehtonen, A., & Viikari, J. (1978a). The effect of vigorous physical activity at work on serum lipids with a special reference to serum high-density lipoprotein cholesterol. *Acta Physiologica Scandinavica,* **104**, 117-121.

Lehtonen, A., & Viikari, J. (1978b). Serum triglycerides and cholesterol in highly physically active men. *Acta Medica Scandinavica,* **204**, 111-114.

Lehtonen, A., & Viikari, J. (1980). Serum lipids in soccer and ice-hockey players. *Metabolism,* **29**, 36-39.

Lehtonen, A., Viikari, J., & Ehnholm, C. (1979). The effect of exercise on high density (HDL) lipoprotein apoproteins. *Acta Physiologica Scandinavica,* **106**, 487-488.

Lindgärde, F., Eriksson, K.-F., Lithell, H., & Saltin, B. (1982). Coupling between dietary changes, reduced body weight, muscle fibre size and improved glucose tolerance in middle-aged men with impaired glucose tolerance. *Acta Medica Scandinavica,* **212**, 99-106.

Lindgärde, F., Malmquist, J., & Balke, B. (1983). Physical fitness, insulin secretion, and glucose tolerance in healthy males and mild type-2 diabetes. *Acta Diabetologia Latina,* **20**, 33-40.

Lithell, H., Boberg, J., Hellsing, K., Lundqvist, G., & Vessby, B. (1978). Lipoprotein-lipase activity in human skeletal muscle and adipose tissue in the fasting and the fed states. *Atherosclerosis,* **30**, 89-94.

Lithell, H., Boberg, J., Hellsing, K., & Vessby, B. (1978). Relationships between the lipoprotein lipase activities of human adipose and skeletal-muscle tissue and the elimination rate of i.v.-injected intralipid. In H. Peeters (Ed.), *Proteins and related subjects: Vol. 25* (pp. 389-392). Oxford: Pergamon Press.

Lithell, H., Cedermark, M., Fröberg, J., Tesch, P., & Karlsson, J. (1981). Increase of lipoprotein-lipase activity in skeletal muscle during heavy exercise. Relation to epinephrine excretion. *Metabolism,* **30**, 1130-1134.

Lithell, H., Krotkiewski, M., Kiens, B., Wroblewski, Z., Holm, G., Strömblad, G., Grimby, G., & Björntorp, P. (1985). Non-response of muscle capillary density and lipoprotein-lipase activity to regular training in diabetic patients. *Diabetes Research,* **2**, 17-21.

Lithell, H., Lindgärde, F., Hellsing, K., Lundqvist, G., Nygaard, E., Vessby, B., & Saltin, B. (1981). Body weight, skeletal muscle morphology, and enzyme activities in relation to fasting serum insulin concentration and glucose tolerance in 48-year-old men. *Diabetes,* **30**, 19-25.

Lithell, H., Örlander, J., Schéle, Sjödin, B., & Karlsson, J. (1979). Changes in lipoprotein-lipase activity and lipid stores in human skeletal muscle with prolonged heavy exercise. *Acta Physiologica Scandinavica,* **107**, 257-261.

Lithell, H., Schéle, R., Vessby, B., & Jacobs, I. (1984). Lipoproteins, lipoprotein lipase, and glycogen after prolonged physical activity. *Journal of Applied Physiology: Respiratory, Environmental, Exercise Physiology,* **57**, 698-702.

Lopes-Virella, M.F., Wohltmann, H.J., Loadholt, C.B., & Buse, M.G. (1981). Plasma lipids and lipoproteins in young insulin-dependent diabetic patients: Relationship with control. *Diabetologia,* **21**, 216-223.

Mann, J.I., & Houston, A.C. (1983). The aetiology of non-insulin dependent diabetes mellitus. In J.I. Mann, K. Pyörälä, & A. Teuscher (Eds.), *Diabetes in epidemiological perspective* (pp. 122-164). Edinburgh, London, Melbourne, New York: Churchill Livingstone.

Marniemi, J., Peltonen, P., Vuori, I., & Hietanen, E. (1980). Lipoprotein lipase of human postheparin plasma and adipose tissue in relation to physical training. *Acta Physiologica Scandinavica,* **10**, 131-135.

Masarei, J.R.L., Pyke, J.E., & Pyke, F.S. (1982). Physical fitness and plasma HDL cholesterol concentrations in male business executives. *Atherosclerosis,* **42**, 77-83.

Mazzone, T., Foster, D., & Chait, A. (1984). In vivo stimulation of low-density lipoprotein degradation by insulin. *Diabetes,* **33**, 333-338.

Moffatt, R.J., & Gilliam, T.B. (1979). Serum lipids and lipoproteins as affected by exercise: A review. *Artery,* **6**, 1-19.

Moll, M.E., Williams, R.S., Lester, R.M., Quarfordt, S.H., & Wallace, A.G. (1979). Cholesterol metabolism in non-obese women. Failure of physical conditioning to alter levels of high density lipoprotein cholesterol. *Athersclerosis,* **34**, 159-166.

Moore, C.E., Hartung, G.H., Mitchell, R.E., Kappus, C.M., & Hinderlitter, J. (1983). The relationship of exercise and diet on high-density lipoprotein cholesterol levels in women. *Metabolism,* **32**, 189-196.

Myhre, K., Mjøs, O.D., Bjørsvik, G., & Strömme, S.B. (1981). Relationship of high density lipoprotein cholesterol concentration to the duration and intensity of endurance training. *Scandinavian Journal of Clinical and Laboratory Investigation,* **41**, 303-309.

National Heart, Lung, and Blood Institute. (1984a). The lipid research clinics coronary primary prevention trial results. I. Reduction in incidence of coronary heart disease. *Journal of the American Medical Association,* **251**, 351-364.

National Heart, Lung, and Blood Institute (1984b). The lipid research clinics coronary primary prevention trial results. II. The relationship of reduction in incidence of coronary heart disease to cholesterol lowering. *Journal of the American Medical Association,* **251**, 365-374.

Nestel, P.J., Podkolinski, M., & Fidge, N.H. (1979). Marked increase in high density lipoproteins in mountaineers. *Atherosclerosis,* **34**, 193-196.

Nikkilä, E.A., & Harmilam, P. (1978). Lipids and lipoproteins in insulin treated diabetes. Demonstration of increased high density lipoprotein concentrations. *Diabetes,* **27**, 1078-1086.

Nikkilä, E.A., Huttunen, J.K., & Ehnholm, C. (1977). Postheparin plasma lipoprotein lipase and hepatic lipase in diabetes mellitus. Relationship to plasma triglyceride metabolism. *Diabetes,* **26**, 11-21.

Nikkilä, E.A., Taskinen, M.R., Rehunen, S., & Härkönen, M. (1978). Lipoprotein lipase activity in adipose tissue and skeletal muscle of runners: Relation to serum lipoproteins. *Metabolism,* **27**, 1661-1667.

Olefsky, J.M., Farquhar, J.W., & Reaven, G.M. (1974). Reappraisal of the role of the insulin in hypertriglyceridemia. *American Journal of Medicine,* **57**, 551-560.

Olivecrona, T., Bengtsson, G., Marklund, S.-E., Lindahl, U., & Höök, M. (1977). Heparin-lipoprotein lipase interactions. *Federation Proceedings,* **36**, 60-65.

Pagano Mirani-Oostdijk, C., Havekes, L., Terpstra, J., Frölich, M., van Gent, C.M., & Jansen, H. (1983). Diurnal changes in serum triglycerides as related to changes in lipolytic enzymes, (apo) lipoproteins and hormones in normal subjects on a carbohydrate-rich diet. *European Journal of Clinical Investigation,* **13**, 301-309.

Pelkonen, R., Nikkilä, E.A., Koskinen, S., Penttinen, K., & Sarna, S. (1977). Association of serum lipids and obesity with cardiovascular mortality. *British Medical Journal,* **II**, 1185-1187.

Peltonen, P., Marniemi, J., Hietanen, E., Vuori, I., & Ehnholm, C. (1981). Changes in serum lipids, lipoproteins, and heparin releasable lipolytic enzymes during moderate physical training in man: A longitudinal study. *Metabolism,* **30**, 518-526.

Peterson, B., Henningsen, N.-C., & Hood, B. (1984). Risk factors for premature death in middle aged men. *British Medical Journal,* **288**, 1264-1268.

Pykälistö, O.J., Smith, P.H., & Brunzell, J.D. (1975). Determinants of human adipose-tissue lipoprotein lipase—effect of diabetes and obesity on basal- and diet-induced activity. *Journal of Clinical Investigation,* **56**, 1108-1117.

Rauramaa, R., Salonen, J.T., Kukkonen-Harjula, K., Seppänen, K., Seppälä, E., Vapaatalo, H., & Huttunen, J.K. (1984). Effects of mild physical exercise on serum lipoproteins and metabolites of arachidonic acid: A controlled randomised trial in middle aged men. *British Medical Journal,* **288**, 603-606.

Ready, E.A., & Quinney, H.A. (1982). The response of serum lipids and lipoproteins to high intensity endurance training. *Canadian Journal of Applied Sports Sciences*, **7**, 202-208.

Reitman, J.S., Vasquez, B., Klimes, I., & Nagulesparan, M. (1984). Improvement of glucose homeostasis after exercise training in non-insulin-dependent diabetes. *Diabetes Care*, **7**, 434-441.

Rose, G. (1982). Incubation period of coronary heart disease. *British Medical Journal*, **284**, 1600-1601.

Rotkis, T., Boyden, T.W., Pamenter, R.W., Stanforth, P., & Wilmore, J. (1981). High density lipoprotein cholesterol and body composition of female runners. *Metabolism*, **30**, 994-995.

Ruderman, N.B., Ganda, O.P., & Johansen, K. (1979). The effect of physical training on glucose tolerance and plasma lipids in maturity-onset diabetes. *Diabetes*, **28**(Suppl. 1), 89-92.

Rössner, S. (1974). Studies on an intravenous fat-tolerance test. Methodological, experimental and clinical experiences with Intralipid. *Acta Medica Scandinavica*, (Suppl. 564).

Sadur, C.N., & Eckel, R.H. (1982). Insulin stimulation of adipose tissue lipoprotein lipase. Use of the euglycemic clamp technique. *Journal of Clinical Investigation*, **69**, 1119-1125.

Sady, S.P., Cullinane, E.M., Herbert, P.N., Kantor, M.A., & Thompson, P.D. (1984). Training, diet, and physical characteristics of distance runners with low or high concentrations of high density lipoprotein cholesterol. *Atherosclerosis*, **53**, 273-281.

Saltin, B., Henriksson, J., Nygaard, E., Andersen, P., & Jansson, E. (1977). Fiber types and metabolic potentials of skeletal muscles in sedentary man and endurance runners. *Annals of the New York Academy of Sciences*, **301**, 3-29.

Saltin, B., & Rowell, L.B. (1980). Functional adaptations to physical activity and inactivity. *Federal Proceedings*, **39**, 1056-1513.

Schaefer, E.J., Wetzel, M.G., Bengtsson, G., Scow, R.O., Brewer, H.B., Jr., & Olivecrona, T. (1982). Transfer of human lymph chylomicron constituents to other lipoprotein density fractions during in vitro lipolysis. *Journal of Lipid Research*, **23**, 1259-1273.

Schaefer, E.J., Zech, L.A., Jenkins, L.L., Bronzert, T.J., Rubalcaba, E.A., Lindgren, F.T., Aamodt, R.L., & Brewer, H.B., Jr. (1982). Human apolipoprotein A-I and A-II metabolism. *Journal of Lipid Research*, **23**, 850-862.

Schnabel, A., & Kindermann, W. (1982). Effect of maximal oxygen uptake and different forms of physical training on serum lipoproteins. *European Journal of Applied Physiology*, **48**, 263-277.

Schwane, J.A., & Cundiff, D.E. (1979). Relationships among cardiorespiratory fitness, regular physical activity, and plasma lipids in young adults. *Metabolism*, **28**, 771-776.

Seals, D.R., Hagberg, J.M., Hurley, B.F., Ehsani, A.A., & Holloszy, J.O. (1984). Effects of endurance training on glucose tolerance and plasma lipid levels in older men and women. *Journal of the American Medical Association,* **252**, 645-649.

Sedgwick, A.W., Brotherhood, J.R., Harris-Davidson, A., Taplin, R.E., & Thomas, D.W. (1980). Long-term effects of physical training programme on risk factors for coronary heart disease in otherwise sedentary men. *British Medical Journal,* **281**, 7-10.

Spencer, K.M., & Gudworth, A.G. (1983). The aetiology of insulin-dependent diabetes mellitus. In J.I. Mann, K. Pyörälä, & A. Teuscher (Eds.), *Diabetes in epidemiological perspective* (pp. 99-121). Edinburgh, London, Melbourne, New York: Churchill Livingstone.

Stamford, B.A., Matter, S., Fell, R.D., Sady, S., Papanek, P., & Cresanta, M. (1984). Cigarette smoking, exercise and high density lipoprotein cholesterol. *Atherosclerosis,* **52**, 73-83.

Steinberg, D. (1983). Lipoproteins and atherosclerosis. A look back and a look ahead. *Arteriosclerosis,* **3**, 283-301.

Streja, D., & Mymin, D. (1979). Moderate exercise and high-density lipoprotein-cholesterol. Observations during a cardiac rehabilitation program. *Journal of the American Medical Association,* **242**, 2190-2192.

Stubbe, I., Hansson, P., Gustafsson, A., & Nilsson-Ehle, P. (1983). Plasma lipoproteins and lipolytic enzyme activities during endurance training in sedentary men: Changes in high-density lipoprotein subfractions and composition. *Metabolism,* **32**, 1120-1128.

Sutherland, W.H., Woodhouse, S.P., Nye, E.R., & Gerard, D.F. (1984). Post-heparin hepatic lipase activity and plasma high density lipoprotein levels in men during physical training. *Biochemical Medicine,* **31**, 31-35.

Svedenhag, J., Lithell, H., Juhlin-Dannefelt, A., & Henriksson, J. (1983). Increase in skeletal muscle lipoprotein lipase following endurance training in man. *Atherosclerosis,* **59**, 203-207.

Taskinen, M-R., Nikkilä, E.A., Kuusi, T., & Harno, K. (1982). Lipoprotein lipase activity and serum lipoproteins in untreated type 2 (insulin-independent) diabetes associated with obesity. *Diabetologia,* **22**, 46-50.

Taskinen, M-R., Nikkilä, E.A., Nousiainen, R., & Gordin, A. (1981). Lipoprotein lipase activity in adipose tissue and skeletal muscle of human diabetics during insulin deprivation and restoration. *Scandinavian Journal of Clinical and Laboratory Investigation,* **41**, 263-268.

Taylor, K.G., Wright, A.D., Carter, T.J.N., Valente, A.J., Betts, S.A., & Matthews, K.A. (1981). High-density lipoprotein cholesterol and apolipoprotein A-I levels at diagnosis in patients with non-insulin dependent diabetes. *Diabetologia,* **20**, 535-539.

Thompson, C.E., Thomas, T.R., Araujo, J., Albers, J.J., & Decedue, C.J. (1985). Response of HDL cholesterol, apoprotein A-I, and LCAT to exercise withdrawal. *Atherosclerosis,* **54**, 65-73.

Thompson, P.D., Cullinane, E., Henderson, L.O., & Herbert, P.N. (1980). Acute effects of prolonged exercise on serum lipids. *Metabolism,* **29**, 662-665.

Thompson, P.D., Cullinane, E.M., Eshleman, R., Kantor, M.A., & Herbert, P.N. (1984). The effects of high-carbohydrate and high-fat diets on the serum lipid and lipoprotein concentrations of endurance athletes. *Metabolism,* **33**, 1003-1010.

Thompson, P.D., Cullinane, E.M., Eshleman, R., Sady, S.P., & Herbert, P.N. (1984). The effects of caloric restriction or exercise cessation on the serum lipid and lipoprotein concentrations of endurance athletes. *Metabolism,* **33**, 943-950.

Thorland, W.G., & Gilliam, T.B. (1981). Comparison of serum lipids between habitually high and low active preadolescent males. *Medicine and Science in Sports and Exercise,* **13**, 316-321.

Tikkanen, M.J., Nikkilä, E.A., Kuusi, T., & Sipinen, S. (1982). High density lipoprotein-2 and hepatic lipase: Reciprocal changes produced by estrogen and norgestrel. *Journal of Clinical Endocrinology and Metabolism,* **54**, 1113-1117.

Trovati, M., Carta, Q., Cavalot, F., Vitali, S., Banaudi, C., Lucchina, P.G., Fiocchi, F., Emanuelli, G., & Lenti, G. (1984). Influence of physical training on blood glucose control, glucose tolerance, insulin secretion, and insulin action in non-insulin-dependent diabetic patients. *Diabetes Care,* **7**, 416-420.

Tyroler, H.A. (1980). Epidemiology of plasma high-density lipoprotein cholesterol levels. The lipid research clinics program prevalence study. *Circulation,* **62**(Suppl. IV), 1-3.

Vessby, B., Boberg, M., Karlström, B., Lithell, H., & Werner, I. (1984). Improved metabolic control after supplemented fasting in overweight type II diabetic patients. *Acta Medica Scandinavica,* **216**, 67-74.

Vessby, B., Selinus, I., & Lithell, H. (1985). Serum lipoprotein and lipoprotein lipase in overweight, type II diabetes during and after supplemented fasting. *Arteriosclerosis,* **5**, 93-100.

Vodak, P.A., Wood, P.E., Haskell, W.L., & Williams, P.T. (1980). HDL-cholesterol and other plasma lipid and lipoprotein concentrations in middle-aged male and female tennis players. *Metabolism,* **29**, 745-752.

Walden, C.E., Knopp, R.H., Wahl, P.W., Beach, K.W., & Strandness, E., Jr. (1984). Sex differences in the effect of diabetes mellitus on lipoprotein triglyceride and cholesterol concentrations. *The New England Journal of Medicine,* **311**, 953-959.

Wallberg-Henriksson, H., Gunnarsson, R., Henriksson, J., Defronzo, R., Felig, P., Östman, J., & Wahren, J. (1982). Increased peripheral insulin sensitivity and muscle mitochondrial enzymes but unchanged blood glucose control in type I diabetics after physical training. *Diabetes,* **31**, 1044-1050.

Wallberg-Henriksson, H., Gunnarsson, R., Henriksson, J., Östman, J., & Wahren, J. (1984). Influence of physical training on formation of muscle capillaries in type I diabetes. *Diabetes,* **33**, 851-857.

WHO Expert Committee. (1982). *Prevention of coronary heart disease* (Technical Report Series 678). Geneva: World Health Organization.
Williams, P.T., Wood, P.D., Krauss, R.M., Haskell, W.L., Vranizan, K.M., Blair, S.N., Terry, R., & Farquhar, J.W. (1983). Does weight loss cause the exercise-induced increase in plasma high density lipoproteins? *Atherosclerosis,* **47**, 173-185.
Wilson, W.R., & Geraci, J.E. (1983). Antibiotic treatment of infective endocarditis. *Annual Review of Medicine,* **34**, 413-427.
Witztum, J.L., Mahoney, E.M., Branks, M.J., Fisher, M., Elam, R., & Steinberg, D. (1982). Nonenzymatic glucosylation of low-density lipoprotein alters its biologic activity. *Diabetes,* **31**, 283-291.
Wood, P.D., & Haskell, W.L. (1979). The effect of exercise on plasma high density lipoproteins. *Lipids,* **14**, 417-427.
Wood, P.E., Haskell, W.L., Blair, S.N., Williams, P.T., Krauss, R.M., Lindgren, F.T., Albers, J.J., Ho, P.H., & Farquhar, J.W. (1983). Increased level and plasma lipoprotein concentrations: A one-year, randomized, controlled study in sedentary, middle-aged men. *Metabolism,* **32**, 31-39.
Wynne, T.P., Bassett Frey, M.A., Laubach, L.L., & Glueck, C.J. (1980). Effect of a controlled exercise program on serum lipoprotein levels in women on oral contraceptives. *Metabolism,* **29**, 1267-1271.
Yki-Järvinen, H., Taskinen, M.R., Koivisto, V.A., & Nikkilä, E.A. (1984). Response of adipose tissue lipoprotein lipase activity and serum lipoproteins to acute hyperinsulinemia in man. *Diabetologia,* **27**, 364-369.

Discussion from the Session

Exercise as Therapy in Diabetic and Cardiac Patients

Michael Berger
Düsseldorf University
Düsseldorf, West Germany

This article reviews the areas covered by the special panel discussion session dealing with the therapeutic implications of exercise/training programs for patients with diabetes mellitus and with hypertension, as other cardiovascular disorders were not addressed in detail. Panelists included Thorsten Hansen (Copenhagen, Denmark), Bernhard Zinman (Toronto, Canada), Neil B. Ruderman (Boston, MA, USA), James Hagberg (St. Louis, MO, USA), and Hans Lithell (Uppsala, Sweden); in addition, a selected number of colleagues were asked to present their studies that had been displayed during the poster session and there was active participation from the floor that included well-known authorities in the fields of exercise physiology and metabolic diseases. The discussion was divided into attempts to address the therapeutic implications of exercise and training programs in patients with type 1 (insulin-dependent) diabetes mellitus, type 2 (noninsulin-dependent) diabetes mellitus and hypertension. Throughout, the difficulties of differentiating between the consequences of (repeated bouts of) acute physical exertion and long-term physical training on metabolic and cardiovascular parameters were addressed; and the potential relevance of various data from clinical research studies for patient care was discussed.

THERAPEUTIC ROLE OF PHYSICAL EXERCISE IN TYPE 1 DIABETES MELLITUS

Consequences of Exercise

According to historic as well as present textbooks of clinical medicine and diabetology, physical exercise has always been regarded, along with insulin and diet, as one of the three cornerstones of diabetes therapy.

On a closer look, however, this paradigm needs to be qualified. It seems as if the propagation of physical exercise in the treatment of diabetic patients dates back, to a large extent, to the times of the preinsulin era and reflects mostly the conditions of noninsulin dependent diabetes. Zinman has summarized the potential consequences of physical exercise and training in type 1 diabetic patients for the session. He recalled the well-known potentiation of insulin's hypoglycemic action by physical exercise, a phenomenon so perfectly described by Lawrence some 60 years ago. On one hand, this effect can be used therapeutically to decrease hyperglycemia, for example in the postprandial state; on the other hand, exercise-induced hypoglycemia has become one of the most feared side-effects of insulin treatment—a complication well-known to every insulin-treated diabetic and his physician. Another, obviously less frequent complication of physical exertion in type 1 diabetic patients is the additional deterioration of metabolic parameters precipitated in situations of insulin deficiency, that is, unsatisfactory degrees of metabolic control with fasting glycemia of > 350 mg/dl and ketosis of > 2.5 mmol/l. Under such circumstances, physical exercise may well induce a rapid further worsening, even to the precipitation of severe ketoacidotic states. Recent advances in the development of clinical diabetology based upon the introduction of self-blood glucose monitoring, the efforts to intensify insulin substitution strategies, and, most importantly, the renewed emphasis on patient education programs, have made it possible to prevent the complications of exercise in type 1 diabetic patients quite efficiently. Thus, well trained diabetic patients should be capable of avoiding the precipitation of hypoglycemia and ketoacidosis by appropriate preventive measures even when engaging in most strenuous physical activities, such as competitive sports. In this context, it should be helpful to mention to young diabetic patients interested in sports and games that a growing number of type 1 diabetics is successfully running the marathon and participating in the triathlon; insulin-dependent diabetic patients have also been most successful during recent Olympic Games in various disciplines.

Avoiding Exercise Risks

Thus, it was the consensus of the panelists, when Zinman concluded that any diabetic patient who is interested and determined to engage in physical activities, sports, and games should be enabled to do so without running the risk of hypoglycemia and other metabolic complications. For diabetic patients free of vascular or neuropathic complications of their disease this should be a primary goal of diabetes care. Patient education, systematic training of blood glucose self-monitoring and insulin dosage adaptation by the patients must remain the basis of such efforts. In particular, the patients have to be trained to effectively reduce their insulin dosages before (and after) physical exercise of longer duration and intensity to avoid hypoglycemia. Only for short-term exercise does the additional consumption of carbohydrates seem recommendable. In fact, Zinman pointed out that many diabetic patients are used to consuming excessive amounts of fast absorbable carbohydrates before physical exercise, which may not only interfere with the ability to perform (due to a full stomach) but represents very often many more extra calories than will be disposed of by the physical activity. Another misconception relates to the habit of diabetic patients changing the insulin injection site before physical exercise in order to prevent exercise-induced hypoglycemia, although it has been documented amply and repeatedly that such measures are rather unreliable as safeguards against excessive falls of glycemia during and after physical exertion. In any case, it was felt unanimously that diabetic patients who wanted to exercise should be given all the education and training to do so under the optimal conditions for good performance.

Special recommendations, however, need to be put forward for patients who have already developed diabetic late complications. In this context, Ruderman pointed to the particular risks associated with diabetic neuropathy and the syndrome of the diabetic foot. The loss of peripheral sensory functions should represent a major hazard in connection with particular sportive activities, such as jogging and other disciplines in which the occurrence of (multiple, even minor) trauma to the foot is a frequent event.

Other particularly relevant risk factors for exercising diabetic patients include proliferative retinopathy and autonomic neuropathy. Thus, in diabetic patients with autonomic neuropathy, especially when associated with (a deterioration of metabolic control resulting in) dehydration, quite serious states of hypotension may occur during, or in particular, following, exercise. For patients with proliferative retinopathy, any (abrupt) increase in blood pressure may lead to hemorrhages with further deteriorations of vision. Thus, these patients should be advised not to exercise intensely, and to avoid physical exertions that are known to raise the blood pressure in particular (such as isometric exercises) at least until the risk of the development of hemorrhages has been eliminated by appropriate (laser) treatment. These warnings against exercise-induced elevations of blood pressure should be particularly important for those patients with proliferative retinopathy who suffer from hypertension, as well. Diabetic patients who ask their physicians for advice on whether to participate at all or which type of sport they may participate in, should be thoroughly screened for neuropathic and vascular complications and often a collaborative effort of the physician, the cardiologist, ophthalmologist and podiatrist may be necessary to offer the patient thorough recommendations. Finally, Zinman led the audience into a discussion on the subject whether or not in type 1 diabetic patients exercise could be used in order to systematically improve improve glycemic control. Such an attempt would have to include the daily performance of physical exertion with a defined intensity and duration at a fixed time, for example, postprandially. It is obvious that such a regimen would represent an additional burden to the patient whose quality of life is already compromised by having to abide by certain restrictions regarding nutrition and in connection with metabolic self-monitoring and insulin injections. As Zinman pointed out, a number of more recent studies have actually shown that the participation of type 1 diabetic patients has not led to the improvement of metabolic control that might have been expected. What seems more important, however, is the fact that well trained type 1 diabetic patients may very well achieve (near-) normoglycemic control without having to subject themselves to regular exercise regimens.

Exercise Benefits

Nevertheless, it was expressed that the long-term benefits of habitual physical activity that are being claimed for the general population should be equally relevant for patients with type 1 diabetes mellitus. In addition, high degrees of physical fitness should (such as in the nondiabetic population) be associated with particularly high degrees of insulin-sensitivity and, hence, with low insulin requirements. Thus it might be possible to reduce the hyperinsulinemia that results from subcutaneous insulin substitution, at least to a certain extent. Recent evidence from epidemiological studies in middle-aged men might indicate that such a reduction of hyperinsulinemia could be of potential benefit with regard to the alleged, but so far never conclusively documented, risk of type 1 diabetic patients to develop macroangiopathy. While any particular benefits of physical training concerning the morbidity and mortality in type 1 diabetes mellitus have never been proven, the possibility of such influences on the prognosis and natural history should be kept in mind.

In conclusion of this part of the discussion, it was felt that exercise/training could hardly be considered one of the three cornerstones of the treatment in type 1 diabetes mellitus. Since physical exercise and sports do play an increasingly important role in the lives of our patients and in our societies, it has become an important task for diabetologists to enable their insulin-dependent diabetic patients to participate in sports and games whenever they want to.

THERAPEUTIC ROLE OF PHYSICAL EXERCISE IN TYPE 2 DIABETES MELLITUS

In contrast to type 1 diabetes mellitus, which represents a disease caused by the deficiency of a single hormone (before the development of secondary complications of chronic hyperglycemia), type 2 (non-insulin-dependent) diabetes mellitus is a syndrome of metabolic abnormalities, diseases, and risks for atherosclerosis, probably related to a strong genetic disposition. Thus, to a very high percentage type 2 diabetic patients are also overweight, hyperlipidemic, hypersensitive, hyperuricemic, and physically inactive. Furthermore, the majority of them belongs to the elderly segments of our populations and have already developed cardiovascular disease at the time when diabetes is diagnosed, and many of the patients are in fact suffering from multimorbidity. These many facets of the syndrome of type 2 diabetes (often called the ''dia-besity'' syndrome) need to be thoroughly considered when the various potential benefits and hazards of physical exercise and training in these patients are discussed.

Consequences of Exercise

At first, the issue of *acute effects* of physical exercise in type 2 diabetic patients were briefly reviewed. Zinman described an earlier study from his group (Minuk, Vranic, Marliss, Hanna, Albisser, & Zinman, 1981) delineating the influence of a 45-min exercise challenge on glucose homeostasis and insulinemia in obese type 2 diabetic patients treated with sulfonylureas or with diet alone. In these experiments, exercise resulted in a substantial diminution of the initially marked hyperglycemia, mainly due to an increase of peripheral glucose utilization with a comparatively small rise in hepatic glucose production, and a failure of serum insulin levels to decrease. The latter finding was, however, more likely due to the persisting hyperglycemia during the experiments rather than due to a perturbation of neurohormonal regulation of insulin secretion. In an unpublished study on healthy volunteers, Berger et al. (Düsseldorf) was able to demonstrate that the glibenclamide-induced hyperinsulinemia remained unaffected by bicycle ergometer exercise associated with the development of hypoglycemia. Thus the sulfonylurea-induced stimulation of insulin secretion can not be overridden by the inhibitory effects of physical exercise and of hypoglycemia. This phenomenon might be helpful in characterizing the pathophysiological events responsible for the exercise-induced hypoglycemia in sulfonylurea treated type 2 diabetic patients.

In fact, these observations should call for the explicit advice to decrease the dosage of sulfonylurea in anticipation of physical exercise for type 2 diabetic patients in good to reasonable metabolic control.

Secondly, the clinically most relevant issue of *physical training* as a primary therapeutic approach in type 2 diabetes mellitus was discussed. A number of impressive studies carried out with various animal models of non-insulin-dependent diabetes (with and without concomitant obesity) have indicated quite strongly that physical training programs might be instrumental in reversing glucose intolerance and diabetes. During this section of the panel discussion, various investigations, most of them as yet unpublished, of ongoing intervention studies in type 2 diabetic patients were presented. A number of problems became repeatedly apparent when discussing these investigations.

Thus, controversy prevails with regard to the question of how one might be able to differentiate between genuine (metabolic and other) effects of training and the direct consequences of the last bout(s) of exercise carried out in the process of such training programs. Contrasting data were presented with regard to the duration of the increase in insulin-sensitivity, as assessed by euglycemic clamp techniques resulting from intensive physical exercise challenges. Over and over, the question of the time course of the so-called ''detraining'' process was addressed. The clinical relevance of these, as yet unresolved, questions is rather obvious: If most of the effects of increased physical activity, for example, on glucose and lipid metabolism, are merely the cumulative results of the repeated exercise challenges, the expected long-term benefits associated with such effects would disappear within days after discontinuation of the training program. On the other hand, those benefits would be expected to persist for much longer, if they would represent genuine long-term effects of the training process.

Second, a number of participants in the session expressed their concern as to what extent the various changes observed in the course of a training program could actually be directly related to the increase of physical activity at all. Confounding factors might include alterations of nutrition (even if statistically significant changes in body weight and lean body mass can be excluded), alcohol consumption, smoking habits, and other areas of health and behavior.

Third, the possibility of dissociating among the various consequences of physical training was delineated. Thus, Hagberg pointed out that training intensities of around 40% to 50% $\dot{V}O_2max$, which are usually insufficient to increase the maximal work capacity, except when performed for extended periods of time, seem to be quite effective in reducing blood pressure readings. Furthermore, suggestive evidence was presented that more intensive workloads would be required for a training program to improve glucose tolerance than to increase maximal work capacity. Obviously, these interesting issues would need to be addressed by further studies in different populations of type 2 diabetic patients, before final conclusions for the practice of exercise therapies can be drawn.

Finally, it was pointed out that a main problem in applying exercise programs to type 2 diabetic patients was the advanced age, the considerable overall morbidity and the apparent lack of motivation in these patient populations. These latter difficulties, relevant to both clinical research and practice, were highlighted in a fascinating presentation by Lithell.

During a follow-up investigation of approximately 2,330 male individuals originally entered as 50-year-olds in an epidemiological survey between 1980 and 1983, 46 subjects were identified as type 2 diabetics. These patients were considered for a trial of exercise/training as the basis for the treatment of their diabetes. After patients with significant degrees of coronary heart disease, chronic medications, hypertension and degenerative disorders of the musculoskeletal system had been excluded, 14 patients remained as potential candidates for the treatment program. Of those, six subjects were unresponsive to any motivation attempt and declined to participate, and another two dropped out after 1 year. At the end, three individuals finished the investigation protocol that had called for 2 years of structured physical training sessions three times weekly. Only in one of the three patients, significant improvements of glucose tolerance and circulating lipids were observed; but even this singular success could not be directly and exclusively related to the exercise program since the patient had stopped drinking alcohol during the experimental period.

Benefits of Exercise

As lively and ironic as Lithell's presentation was, it was also relevant and truthful in imaging the real world of clinical medicine. During the discussion of Lithell's study, it was repeatedly argued that for the majority of type 2 diabetic patients it might in fact be too late to subject them to physical training programs, whereas much more energy should be spent to motivate individuals with high risk profiles for the development of type 2 diabetes mellitus (i.e., patients with obesity and a family history of diabetes, individuals with glucose intolerance, or with [as yet not clearly defined] genetic markers for type 2 diabetes) to participate in physical training programs in a prophylactic attempt to prevent the manifestation of the disease.

More reason for optimism could be derived from the presentation made by Hagberg, who reported on a collaborative effort carried out in St. Louis together with Holloszy in the documentation of various metabolic and cardiovascular effects of long-term intensive physical training of patients (several weekly sessions supervised by an exercise physiologist over the course of 1 year) included in a cardiovascular rehabilitation program. This program led invariably to a substantial improvement of insulin-sensitivity (lower levels of insulinemia during unchanged or even improved oral glucose tolerance). In fact, in a limited number of clinically manifest type 2 diabetic patients, glucose tolerance was shown to be normalized following the rehabilitation program, and metabolic profiles had reached the standards characteristic for the famous St. Louis cohort of elderly ''master athletes.'' Unfortunately, no HbA_{Ic} data are as yet available for these type 2 diabetic patients, and because any documentation of an improvement of glycemic control would have to be based upon glycosylated hemoglobin levels, as the so-called gold standard of clinical diabetology, further data from this promising study need to be collected before definitive statements can be made.

Another rather positive set of conclusions was presented by Krotkiewski on behalf of the most experienced group of investigators in the area of exercise and metabolic diseases working in Göteborg, Sweden. Krotkiewski summarized a recent series of long-term studies on the effects of a 3-month physical exercise/training program in obese glucose-intolerant women. In accordance with earlier studies from Göteborg, training intensities that were associated with a significant increase in maximal work capacity resulted in an improvement of glucose tolerance. In their latest investigation, however, Krotkiewski et al. were able to differentiate the effect of physical training according to the initial degree of insulin secretion. Those patients with initially high postglucose-challenges levels of circulating insulin and C-peptide (high insulin secretors, HIS) respond quite differently from those with initially low serum insulin and C-peptide levels (low insulin secretors, LIS). Whereas in both groups, an improvement of glucose tolerance was observed following intensive physical training for 3 months, the LIS patients exhibited increased insulin secretory capacity on the oral glucose challenge, whereas the HIS individuals decreased their serum insulin levels following the training period. Further detailed experimentation led the Göteborg group to conclude that the physical training program resulted primarily in an increase in peripheral insulin sensitivity in the HIS group, whereas the beneficial effects of the physical activity in the LIS group were primarily related to an increase in (the β-adrenergic sensitivity) of the pancreatic B cells. For both groups of patients, an increased removal of insulin, that is, an increase of insulin's metabolic clearance rate due to the physical training program was postulated. These data presented by Krotkiewski in all its wealth, detail, and complexity were discussed in detail. Problems seem to have arisen from difficulties in the characterization of the patients studied; thus, a subgroup of Hagberg's patients from St. Louis that might, at first glance, have been identical to the Göteborg LIS patients, exhibited a totally different response to the training program. In fact, in St. Louis, only HIS-like patients would respond with an improvement of glucose homeostasis, whereas LIS-like type 2 diabetics tended not to show any improvement of glucose tolerance following the exercise program at all. Obviously, further details on the selection process and a truly prospective analysis must be performed before relevant differentiations between subgroups of type 2 diabetic patients, with regard to their suitability for training therapy, can be formulated.

Further Considerations

Despite the many studies carried out in recent years to document the improvement of glucose tolerance and glycemic control in type 2 diabetic patients by a physical training program, the book cannot yet be closed. A definitive proof of the benefit of training programs, and even more urgently, the characterization of the subgroups of patients that might benefit from such efforts in particular and a specification of the detailed methodologies (intensity, frequency, sports disciplines) that are most suitable, must still be forthcoming.

More unequivocal information appeared to be available concerning the beneficial effects of training programs on circulating lipid levels, and so-called atherogenic profiles. Much of the relevant data in this area had already been published by Holloszy some 15 years ago. Lithell had communicated a most detailed review to the Symposium earlier on, and thus the discussion of this subject was kept relatively brief. Ruderman pointed out that while no one would neglect the benefits of exercise related to the improvement of circulating lipid profiles it should be noted that the prevention of cardiovascular morbidity by physical exercise in monkeys kept on an atherogenic diet (Kramsch, Aspen, Abramowitz, Kreimendahl, & Hood, 1981) had not been mediated by any lipid lowering effect of physical training. Therefore, factors other than lipid-lowering effects, for example, potential effects in the area of fibrinolysis, must be considered as possible mechanisms for a diminution of coronary and atherosclerotic morbidity by physical training programs.

In a separate presentation, G. Annuzi (Stockholm) provided some interesting data as to the possible mechanism by which physical training might reduce circulating lipids, and triglyceride levels in particular. Again, the issue of whether the lipid-lowering, resulting from physical training, was an acute effect of the last exercise bout(s), possibly due to an increase of triglyceride removal rates, or whether and to what extent it was a genuine consequence of long-term physical training was discussed, and had to be left open.

Finally, the efficacy of physical training programs to treat hypertension was introduced in a presentation by T. Bennett (Nottingham). The controversy as to whether the long-term lowering of blood pressure by acute physical exercise and/or training was discussed in detail. Bennett presented some elegant studies which demonstrated the possibility that exercise might be instrumental to reset baro-reflexes that are disturbed in primary hypertension. Inasmuch as these studies were impressive in demonstrating the fall of blood pressure following exercise in hypertensive patients for at least up to 8 hours, the question of the long-term efficacy of training programs seems to remain controversial at present. Again, it was the consensus of the participants of the program session that physical activity should be helpful as a preventive and as a therapeutic measure in hypertension, but the final proofs and the characterization of the patients and training methods for most likely successes remained to be elucidated.

CONCLUSIONS

The session was concluded by the formulation of a general consensus according to which physical training, along with other measures of so-called healthy living and prudent nutrition, should be advocated, primarily as a preventive measure with regard to the increasing tendencies of the populations of our Western industrialized nations to develop type 2 diabetes, obesity, hyperlipoproteinemia, hypertension and their various sequelae. It was, however, acknowledged that the practical use of exercise programs in the treatment of these disorders, as helpful and beneficial it may be, needed to be substantiated by more detailed studies—with particular need to identify the subgroups of patients and the methods of physical training that would be expected to allow for most likely successes.

REFERENCES

Kramsch, D.M., Aspen, A.J., Abramowitz, B.M., Kreimendahl, T., & Hood, W.B., Jr. (1981). Reduction of coronary atherosclerosis by moderate conditioning exercise in monkeys on an atherogenic diet. *New England Journal of Medicine,* **305**(25): 1483-1489.

Minuk, H.L., Vranic, M., Marliss, E.B., Hanna, A.K., Albisser, A.M., & Zinman, B. (1981). Glucoregulatory and metabolic response to exercise in obese and non-insulin-dependent diabetes. *American Journal of Physiology,* **240**, E458-E464.

Part IV
Exercise-Induced Muscle Fatigue

Metabolic Changes Limiting Muscle Performance

Kent Sahlin
Karolinska Institute
Huddinge, Sweden

Contracting muscle converts stored chemical energy into static and kinetic energy and heat. Skeletal muscle has a remarkable ability to adjust its energy production to meet an increase in the energy demand. Energy expenditure can increase several times within a fraction of a second, which sets very high demands on the regulation of ATP production. Different biochemical pathways are available for the production of ATP; that is, oxidation of fat and carbohydrates, lactic acid (LA) formation and phosphocreatine (PCr) breakdown. The energy producing processes are characterized by their capacity (the amount of ATP that can be produced) and by their power (the rate of ATP production). The limitations in capacity and power for the different energy producing processes will be discussed in this review.

When the rate of ATP production is insufficient to meet the demands the muscle becomes fatigued. Muscle fatigue is always relative to a certain work intensity. If the work intensity and thus the energy demand is decreased the exercise can continue. The metabolic changes in muscle is dependent upon the work intensity at which fatigue occurs and will be quite different at a low intensity (glycogen depletion) than at a high intensity (LA accumulation and PCr depletion). It is, however, in this review suggested that muscular fatigue under both of these conditions is caused by the same metabolic factor—transient and local increases of ADP.

CAPACITY AND POWER OF THE DIFFERENT ENERGY SOURCES

The immediate energy source for muscular contraction is ATP. The concentration of ATP within the muscle cell is, however, limited, and for continuous exercise ATP must be resynthesized at the same rate as it is utilized. This can be achieved by three mechanisms (Figure 1): (a) by the creatine kinase reaction whereby the storage of the high-energy phos-

$$ATP \rightarrow ADP + P_i + Energy$$

Cytoplasm:

$$ADP + PCreatine \rightarrow Creatine + ATP$$
$$ADP + Glucose\ (Glycogen) \rightarrow Lactate + ATP$$

Mitochondria:

$$ADP + Substrate + O_2 \rightarrow CO_2 + ATP$$

Figure 1 Energy producing processes in muscle.

Table 1 Fuel Storage in Man

Process	Available Energy (mol ATP)	Work time at 70% $\dot{V}O_2max$ (min)
Anaerobic Processes:		
ATP	0.02	0.03
PCr	0.34	0.5
CHO → Lactate	0.7 to 5.2	0.9 to 6.9
Aerobic processes:		
CHO → CO_2 + H_2O	70	93
FFA → CO_2 + H_2O	8000	10600

The available energy was calculated from 20 kg muscle with a glycogen content of 70 mmol/kg w.wt., from a liver glycogen store of 500 mmol and from a fat depot of 15 kg. The work time was calculated from a $\dot{V}O_2max$ of 4.0 l and with the hypothetical assumption that the specific energy process is the sole source of ATP.

phate compound phosphocreatine (PCr) is utilized, (b) through glycolysis or glycogenolysis resulting in lactic acid (LA) formation, and (c) through complete oxidation of carbohydrates (CHO) or free fatty acids (FFA) within the mitochondria.

It is evident from Table 1 that the amount of energy that is available from the ATP store (10% to 30% of the ATP content) is very limited, and it thus seems more adequate to regard ATP as a mediator of energy conversion than as an energy source. The PCr store in skeletal muscle can be utilized completely during exercise and the capacity is sufficient to maintain the ATP production for about 0.5 min during exercise at 70% of $\dot{V}O_2max$ (Table 1). The amount of ATP that can be produced in the leg muscles through LA formation is about 0.7 mol ATP if all of the LA is accumulated within the muscle (Table 1). Accumulation of H^+ ion will in this situation reach an inhibitory level that will prevent further LA formation (see below). However, if LA can be removed from the working muscle, H^+ ion concentration will not be limiting for performance and the whole carbohydrate store can, in theory, be utilized for anaerobic ATP production, which then would amount to about 5.2 mol ATP.

Exercise for longer periods necessitates complete oxidation of CHO or FFA in the mitochondria. Complete oxidation of the whole CHO store would give 70 moles of ATP and would allow 93 min of exercise at 70% of $\dot{V}O_2max$ (Table 1). The storage of fat has a capacity for sustaining ATP production for several days and is not limiting for exercise.

The rate of ATP production (the power) that can be derived from oxidation of fat is, however, low (Table 2) and will limit its usage as a main

Table 2 Power, Acceleration Time, and O_2 Requirements of the Different Energy Sources

Process	Max Power (mmol ATP/kg d.m./s)	Time to Reach Max Power	O_2 requirement (mmol O_2/ATP)
Anaerobic Processes:			
ATP	11.2	< 1 s	0
PCr	8.6	< 1 s	0
CHO → Lactate	5.2	< 5 s	0
Aerobic Processes:			
CHO → $CO_2 + H_2O$	2.7	3 min	0.167
FFA → $CO_2 + H_2O$	1.4	30 min	0.177

The maximal power of the anaerobic energy sources was calculated from Hultman and Sjöholm (1983). The maximal aerobic power was calculated from an assumed $\dot{V}O_2max$ of 4.0 l of which 72% is utilized by the working legs (Jorfeldt & Wahren, 1971) and working muscle mass of 20 kg (= 4.7 kg d.m.). The maximal power of FFA oxidation was assumed to correspond to 50% of the total aerobic power, which seems to be the upper limit (Davies & Thompson, 1979). A relative long time for acceleration to the maximal power of the FFA oxidation is expected due to the necessity of mobilizing FFA from the fat depots into the blood.

energy source to low intensity exercise. If the exercise intensity exceeds 30% to 50% of $\dot{V}O_2$max, additional oxidation of CHO (which has a higher power) must occur. If the exercise intensity is further increased additional ATP will be produced from glycolysis and PCr. The anaerobic production of ATP can accelerate from a low baseline level to the maximal power within a few seconds. The aerobic ATP production requires a longer time to reach the maximal power. This is due to the necessity of adjusting the circulation and respiration to the demands. Anaerobic ATP production thus has three advantages over aerobic energy utilization: (a) no requirements for O_2, (b) higher power, and (c) more rapid acceleration from a low rate of ATP production to the maximal power.

The rate of ATP production from the different energy sources at different exercise intensities has been estimated in Figure 2. The aerobic energy

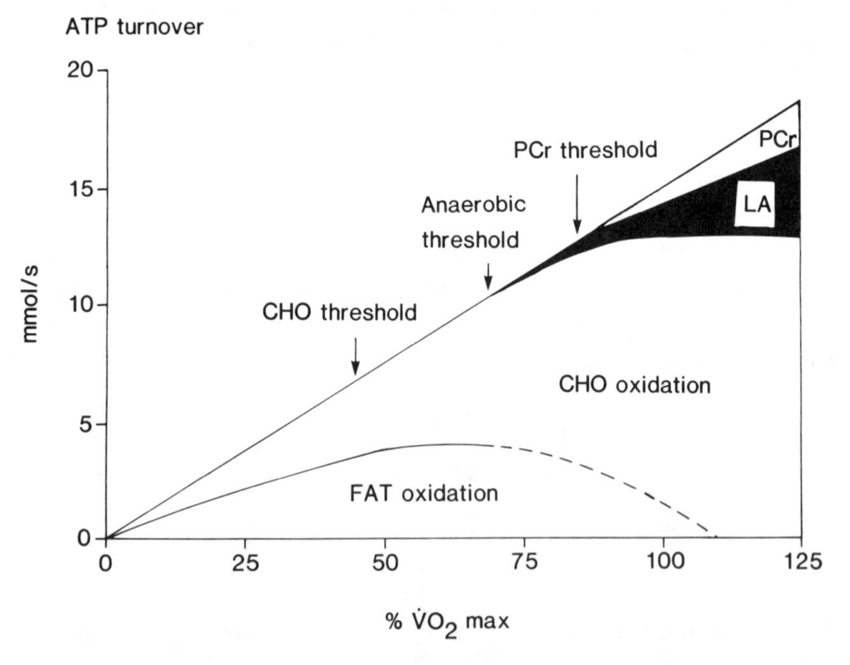

Figure 2 Estimated rate of ATP production from different energy sources in the working legs. The values have been calculated for a subject with a VO_2max of 4.5 l and an anaerobic work capacity of 19 kJ corresponding to 850 mmol ATP (1 mol ATP = 53 kJ; 42% efficiency). At submaximal work 72% of the whole body oxygen uptake was considered to be utilized by the legs (Jorfeldt & Wahren, 1971). The ATP turnover was assumed to increase linearly with the work load, and endurance at 100% VO_2max was assumed to be 6 min, which gives an anaerobic energy turnover of 2.4 mmol ATP/s (i.e., 16% of total). The CHO threshold denotes the work load where the maximal power of fat oxidation is sufficient to produce all of the required ATP. The anaerobic threshold denotes the work load, when blood LA exceeds 2 mmol/l. The PCr threshold denotes the work load where the whole PCr store is depleted in the working muscle.

production dominates when the intensity is below 150% of $\dot{V}O_2$max and anaerobic ATP production dominates when the work intensity exceeds 150% of $\dot{V}O_2$max. Anaerobic energy production does, however, occur already at 50% to 60% of $\dot{V}O_2$max and seems necessary for achieving full utilization of the aerobic capacity.

Substrate utilization during exercise at different intensities has three important breakpoints where the metabolism is changed. The first breakpoint (the carbohydrate threshold) occurs when the energy requirement exceeds the maximum power for FFA oxidation, which therefore must be complemented by CHO oxidation (Figure 2). If available, CHO will also be oxidized when the exercise intensity is below the CHO threshold. The proportion of fat and CHO oxidation will be dependent on the muscle glycogen level and the concentration of FFA in blood. The storage of CHO is, however, limited and the first breakpoint will thus signify an exercise intensity, which when exceeded, will be limited in time.

The second breakpoint (the anaerobic threshold) occurs when anaerobic energy utilization is initiated (Figure 2). LA formation will provide a small increment in the ATP production but at a high price: rapid depletion of the local glycogen store and thus a decrease in work time.

The third breakpoint (the PCr threshold) occurs when the formation of LA exceeds its removal (Figure 2). At this high exercise intensity (80% to 95% $\dot{V}O_2$max) LA and H^+ will continuously accumulate in the muscle and PCr will decrease until a level is reached where anaerobic energy production is insufficient to meet the demand and muscle contraction ceases. The position of the three breakpoints is highly dependent upon the training status. In an endurance-trained subject the breakpoints will occur at a higher relative work intensity than for an untrained subject.

AEROBIC ENERGY UTILIZATION

FFA Oxidation and the Carbohydrate Threshold

FFA are stored as triacylglycerols, both in muscle and fat depots. The muscle triacylglycerol constitutes an important fuel reserve and a reduction of its size has been observed during prolonged exercise (Essén, Hagenfeldt, & Kaijser, 1977). Little is known about the mechanisms regulating the use of the fat store in muscle. Although the storage of FFA is not limiting for exercise (provided the fat depots are not too big), the power of oxidation is low. The power of FFA oxidation is partly determined by the rate of FFA transport into the mitochondria, which is dependent upon the FFA concentration in plasma and the blood flow. Mobilization of FFA from the adipose tissue is regulated by hormonal factors (adrenaline, insulin) and by the plasma glucose concentration. It has been shown that increases of plasma FFA by infusion of caffeine (Costill, Dalsky, & Fink, 1978) increases the exercise performance. Inhibition of FFA mobilization by beta-receptor blockade has been shown to increase the rate of glycogen degradation (Juhlin-Dannfeldt, Terblanche, Fell, Young, & Holloszy, 1982) and result in decreased performance (Nazar, Brezezinska, & Kowalski, 1972). The level of FFA in plasma is thus an important factor for exercise performance. The rate of FFA transport from plasma into mitochondria is, in addition to the plasma FFA level, dependent upon the capillary density, the mitochondrial density and the activity of carnitine-palmitoyl transferase. These factors are all known to increase with aerobic training, which also increases the power of FFA oxidation (see Saltin & Gollnick, 1983). The maximum power of FFA oxidation is, in addition to the availability of FFA, dependent upon the enzymatic activity for beta-oxidation, which also increases with training (Saltin & Gollnick, 1983).

The power of FFA oxidation is also dependent upon the availability of O_2. The ATP yield per mole of O_2 is lower when FFA is oxidized (5.65) than when glycogen is oxidized (6.0). Under conditions where O_2 tension in the muscle becomes limiting, it would thus be of advantage for the muscle to oxidize CHO instead of FFA. The increase in the respiratory quotient ($RQ = \dot{V}CO_2/\dot{V}O_2$) that occurs at increasing work loads show an increased degree of CHO oxidation and is in accordance with this concept. Another approach is to study substrate utilization when exercise is performed at the same intensity but at different inspired O_2 concentrations. With this experimental protocol Linnarsson (1974) found that bicycle exercise at about 65% VO_2max required less O_2 when performed under hypoxic ($FIO_2 = 14\%$) than under normoxic ($FIO_2 = 21\%$) or hyperoxic ($FIO_2 = 30\%$) conditions although the output of CO_2 was the same under all conditions. The calculated RQ values (14% O_2: $RQ = 0.965 \pm 0.031$; 21% O_2: $RQ = 0.889 \pm 0.027$; 30% O_2: $RQ = 0.874 \pm 0.028$) suggested increased CHO oxidation when exercise was performed under hypoxic conditions and thus supported the hypothesis of oxygen dependence in the choice of substrate. The exercise intensity corresponding to the first breakpoint in metabolism (carbohydrate theshold) (Figure 2) denotes the maximal intensity for which all of the required ATP can be produced from FFA oxidation. When the exercise intensity is higher than the carbohydrate threshold the performance time will be limited in time. The limiting factor can either be the muscle glycogen store or the liver glycogen store resulting in hypoglycemia. The latter is probably most important during long-term exercise at lower work intensities. The carbohydrate threshold will probably vary from about 30% for untrained subjects to about 50% in elite marathon runners (Davies & Thompson, 1979). In summary, the carbohydrate threshold, that is, the maximal power for FFA oxidation, will be determined by the inflow of FFA to the muscle, the aerobic training status of the subject, and the availability of O_2.

Oxidation of CHO and the Anaerobic Threshold

The body storage of CHO (mainly muscle and liver glycogen) is in contrast to fat limited in size and can theoretically sustain the whole ATP production for about 90 min at an exercise intensity of 70% $\dot{V}O_2max$ (Table 1). It is well known that the glycogen storage of both muscle and liver can be increased by a combination of exercise and diet (Bergström, Hermansen, Hultman, & Saltin, 1967; Nilsson & Hultman, 1973) and that the work time can be increased accordingly. The technique is frequently used by athletes to increase performance during long-term exercise.

The maximal power of CHO-oxidation is about two-fold higher than for fat oxidation and is dependent upon the availability of O_2 at the cellular level and by the local capacity for aerobic metabolism (the mitochondrial enzyme activities). The exercise intensity corresponding to the second breakpoint in metabolism denotes where anaerobic utilization of CHO becomes important and has previously been termed anaerobic threshold, lactate threshold, OBLA (Onset of Blood Lactate Acid), or Owle's point. The importance of the anaerobic threshold for exercise performance is that glycogen utilization increases rapidly at this exercise intensity. The limiting factor for performance between the second and the third breakpoint is the same as between the first and second breakpoint, that is, the CHO storage. The difference is the accelerating rate of muscle glycogen depletion due to LA formation, which occurs after the anaerobic threshold, and which will decrease the work time considerably. The pattern of glycogen depletion will vary between different fiber types. At an exercise intensity of 50% to 60% of $\dot{V}O_2max$ the slow-twitch (ST) fibers will first be depleted of glycogen, and some of the fast-twitch (FT) fibers will then gradually become glycogen depleted when the exercise continues to fatigue (Gollnick, Piehl, & Saltin, 1974). At higher exercise intensities the same pattern occurs but at a higher rate. The muscle could thus still contain an appreciable amount of glycogen at fatigue although unevenly distributed between the muscle fibers.

The total aerobic capacity ($\dot{V}O_2max$) cannot be utilized (by unknown reasons) without LA formation. Full activation of oxidative phosphorylation might require highly increased cellular levels of ADP and inorganic phosphate (P_i), which are both associated with activation of glycolysis and depletion of PCr ($PCr \rightarrow Cr + P_i$). Other possibilities are an imbalance in the formation and oxidation of NADH (i.e., cytoplasmic NADH accumulation) or differences in the oxidative capacity between adjacent muscle fibers. Further research is required to explore these possibilities.

The work intensity corresponding to the anaerobic threshold is dependent upon the muscle fiber type composition (Ivy, Withers, VanHandel, Elger, & Costill, 1980) and the training status of the subject. It is known that a trained individual can work at a high relative work load (60% to

65% of $\dot{V}O_2max$) before LA accumulation in blood occurs, whereas an untrained subject starts to accumulate lactate at about 50% of $\dot{V}O_2max$ (See Åstrand & Rodahl, 1970). If the O_2 content of inspired air is decreased, accumulation of LA in blood occurs at a lower work intensity (Hughes, Clode, Edwards, Goodwin, & Jones, 1968) than under normoxic conditions. The anaerobic threshold is thus also dependent upon the availability of O_2.

ANAEROBIC ENERGY UTILIZATION

Glycolysis

During intense exercise anaerobic energy utilization increases in importance. The maximal ATP production from glycolysis will vary between 0.7 and 5.2 mol (Table 1) depending upon if the lactic acid can escape from the muscle (intact circulation) or if it is trapped within the muscle (restricted circulation and/or high production rate) thus reaching inhibitory levels. The concentration of lactate in muscle can increase 20 to 30 times during exercise and the equimolar release of H^+ ions results in a decrease of muscle pH of 0.4 to 0.5 units (Sahlin, 1978). The acidification of muscle interferes with both the energy production (Sahlin, 1983) and the contraction process itself (Donaldsson, Hermansen, & Bolles, 1978) and has been suggested for a long time to be the limiting factor for performance in short-term exercise. The magnitude of the decrease in muscle pH is determined both by the accumulation of lactic acid and by the ability of the muscle to buffer the H^+ ions. Recent studies have shown that the buffering capacity of muscle can be increased by training (Sahlin & Henriksson, 1984; Sharp, Costill, Fink, & King, 1983).

When the rate of LA formation exceeds the removal of LA from the working muscle the concentration of LA and H^+ will continuously increase (the third breakpoint). The third breakpoint in metabolism is here also called the PCr threshold due to the depletion of the PCr content in muscle that occurs parallel to the increase of LA. The PCr threshold occurs at about 80% to 95% of $\dot{V}O_2max$ and work time will here be limited by an inhibitory level of H^+ ions and by a low PCr content (see below).

The power of glycolysis is determined by the activity of the glycolytic and the glycogenolytic enzymes in the muscle, which in some studies have been shown to increase with anaerobic training but not in other studies (see Saltin & Gollnick, 1983). The maximal activities in vitro of the glycolytic enzymes are about two-fold higher in the fast-twitch muscle fibers than in the slow-twitch muscle fibers (see Saltin & Gollnick, 1983). It has also been shown in isolated muscles from rat that the activation of phosphorylase by transformation of the *b* form into the more active *a* form and by increase of P_i occurs to a much greater extent in the fast-twitch glycolytic muscles than in the slow-twitch oxidative muscle (Chasiotis, Edström, Sahlin, & Sjöholm, 1985). The higher enzyme activities and the greater activation of phosphorylase will provide a higher glycolytic power in the fast-twitch muscle.

Utilization of PCr

The muscle content of PCr is three to four times higher than that of ATP. The whole store of PCr can be utilized but will still only provide a small amount of ATP. It has been shown in rats that muscle with a high glycolytic capacity also has a high PCr content (Edström, Hultman, Sahlin, & Sjöholm, 1982) whereas muscles with a low glycolytic capacity have a low PCr content. The PCr content in human skeletal muscle is, however, similar in different types of muscles (Edström et al., 1982).

A decrease of PCr can be observed already at 50% $\dot{V}O_2max$ (22% decrease, Katz, Broberg, Sahlin, & Wahren, in press) and as exercise intensity increases, a progressive decrease of PCr occurs (Hultman, Bergström, & McLennan Andersson, 1967). A relationship between the content of PCr and LA has been observed in muscle samples taken after exercise and long-term ischemia (Figure 3). The relationship was found to be independent of exercise intensity, duration, or type of exercise (Harris, Sahlin, & Hultman, 1977). The observed relationship between increased LA and decreased PCr has been regarded to be the consequence of increased H^+ ion concentration (Harris et al., 1977). H^+ ions are directly involved in the creatine kinase reaction and an increased concentration will displace the equilibrium towards PCr breakdown: $H^+ + ADP + PCr \rightarrow ATP + Cr$.

An increase of H^+ will also inhibit phosphofructokinase (PFK), the key regulatory enzyme of glycolysis. During exercise glycolysis is, however, constant despite a decrease in muscle pH (Sahlin, Harris, & Hultman, 1975). The inhibition of PFK by H^+ is obviously adequately overcome, probably by increased concentration of the activators AMP, ADP and fructose 6-P. The increased concentration of ADP will affect the creatine kinase reaction and cause a further breakdown of PCr. A decrease of intracellular pH will thus cause a decrease of the PCr level in two ways: a direct effect on the creatine kinase equilibrium and an indirect effect through increased ADP.

PCr is the energy source with the highest power (Table 2) and is generally regarded as an easily available reservoir of high-energy phosphates, which will buffer the limited ATP store when fluctuations occur in the energy requirement. Recent studies have also shown that changes in the PCr content are likely to be an important regulator for glycogenolysis

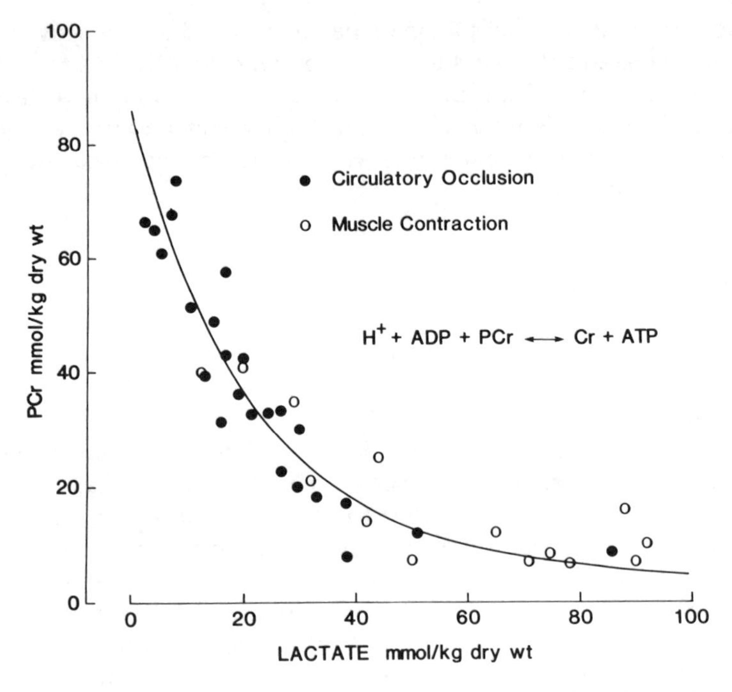

Figure 3 PCr content versus lactate content in human quadriceps femoris muscle. Values for circulatory occlusion are from "The Effects of Long-term Circulatory Occlusion on Intracellular pH and Energy Metabolism" by H. Sjöholm, A. Gidlöf, J. Larsson, and K. Sahlin, 1985, *Clinical Science*, **68**, pp. 597-600. Values for muscle contraction (induced by electrical stimulation) are from "Quantitative Estimation of Anaerobic and Oxidative Energy Metabolism and Contraction Characteristics in Intact Human Skeletal Muscle During and After Electrical Stimulation" by H. Sjöholm, K. Sahlin, L. Edström, and E. Hultman, 1983, *Clinical Physiology*, **3**, pp. 227-239.

(Chasiotis, Sahlin, & Hultman, 1983). A decrease in PCr will activate glycogen phosphorylase through the corresponding increase in P_i, which is present in a limiting amount to the enzyme. P_i is also one of the substrate for oxidative phosphorylation and an increase of its concentration is therefore expected to enhance the aerobic metabolism.

ACIDOSIS AND MUSCLE FATIGUE

Muscle fatigue at high exercise intensities is often considered to be due to the accumulation of an inhibitory level of H^+ within the muscle. A series of experiments have been performed in order to study the relation between acid-base status and work capacity. Alkalosis has been induced by administration of $NaHCO_3$ and acidosis by administration of NH_4Cl (see Hultman & Sahlin, 1981). Generally, no effect of the treatment on the work performance has been observed when the exercise is of short duration (Katz, Costill, King, Hargreaves, & Fink, 1984; Kindermann, Keul, & Huber, 1977). However, when the exercise period was extended in time by using two 20 min periods of exercise at submaximal intensities (33% and 66% of $\dot{V}O_2max$) prior to the maximal work bout at 95% of $\dot{V}O_2max$ a significant improvement in performance and a higher muscle and blood LA content was obtained when alkalosis was induced (Jones, Sutton, Taylor, & Toews, 1977; Sutton, Jones, & Toews, 1981). Similar results were obtained by Costill, Verstappen, Kuipers, Janssen, and Fink (1984), employing an intermittent exercise protocol prior to the final maximal work bout.

Although muscle fatigue at short intensive exercise under many situations is related to acidosis, there is yet no conclusive evidence that it is the H^+ ion per se that inhibits the contraction process. The effect of acidosis could as well be an indirect effect due to a decreased capacity to generate ATP under acidotic conditions. In a recent study, acidosis was induced by incubation of isolated rat muscle in an atmosphere of high CO_2 tension (30% CO_2) (Sahlin, Edström, & Sjöholm, 1983). Both tetanic tension and twitch tension decreased compared to the control muscles (5% CO_2). The PCr content was, however, also decreased in acidosis and it was concluded that increased H^+ ion concentration inhibited the force generation, but it was uncertain whether the effect was due to H^+ ion per se or by high-energy phosphate depletion induced by the acidosis.

During isometric contraction tension decline has been shown to be related to the increase of ADP, to the decrease of PCr and to the decrease in muscle pH (Dawson, Gadian, & Wilkie, 1978). We have, in a preliminary experiment (Sahlin & Katz, unpublished observations), investigated the time course of tension recovery following an isometric contraction to fatigue (i.e., sustained maximal knee extension until tension decreased to 50% of the maximal voluntary contraction force = MVC). With intact circulation the tension recovered, rapidly reaching over 80% of MVC after about 30 s (Figure 4) and 100% of MVC after 4 min recovery. Similar data have previously been observed after isometric contraction with the forearm muscle, where the half-time for strength recovery was 30 to 40 s (Stull & Clark, 1971). Recovery in force is similar to the time course of PCr recovery (Figure 4) but considerably faster than the recovery of LA which has a half-time of about 3 to 4 min. Recovery of pH has been measured by phosphorous NMR after isometric contraction (Taylor, Bore, Styles, Gadian, & Radda, 1983) and seemed to follow the time course of LA except that a further decrease of pH occurred during the first min of recovery. The postcontraction decrease in pH is probably due to the fast resynthesis of PCr, which produces H^+ ions. Force generation during recovery is thus

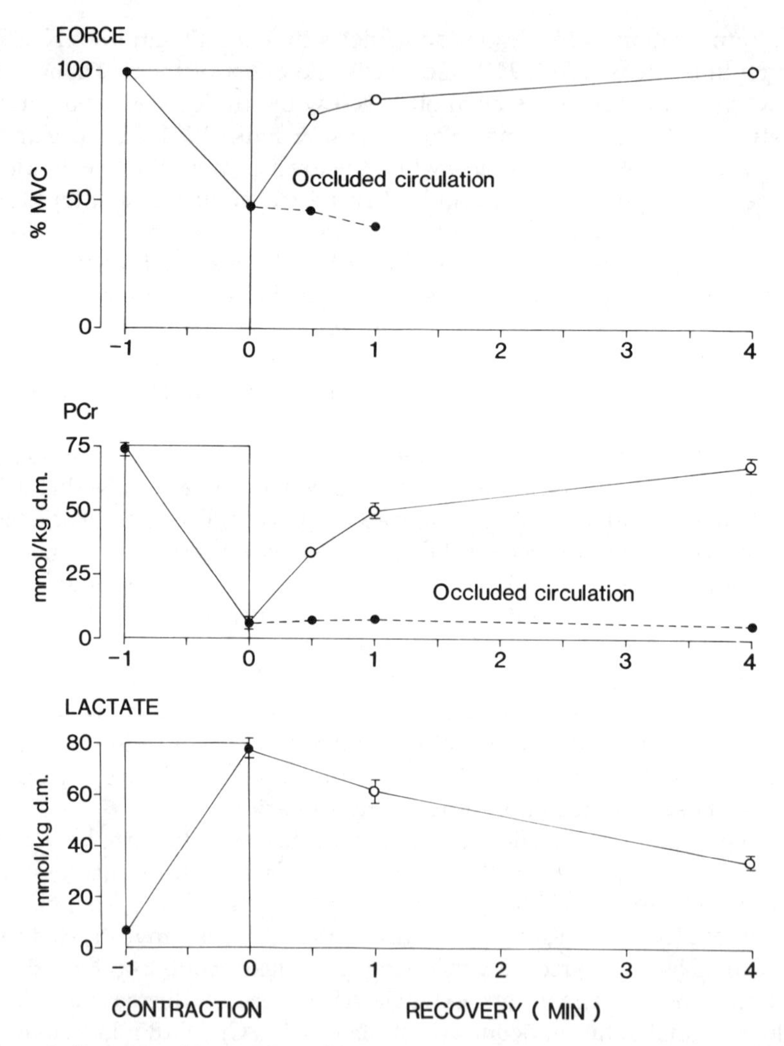

Figure 4 Recovery of force, PCr and lactate after isometric contraction (knee extension) to fatigue. Values for force recovery are the means from two subjects. Values for PCr and lactate recovery are from Harris et al., 1976, and Katz, Sahlin, and Henriksson (unpublished data, 1984).

not related to intracellular pH but rather to the PCr content. When the circulation to the muscle was occluded, no recovery in tension or PCR occurred (Figure 4), which supports the relationship between tension and PCr.

CAPACITY TO GENERATE ATP AND MUSCLE FATIGUE

The maximal work time at different exercise intensities has been estimated in Figure 5. When the exercise intensity is below the PCr threshold but above the anaerobic threshold (i.e., 65% to 85% $\dot{V}O_2$max) the work time is limited by the muscle glycogen content (Figure 5) and when the

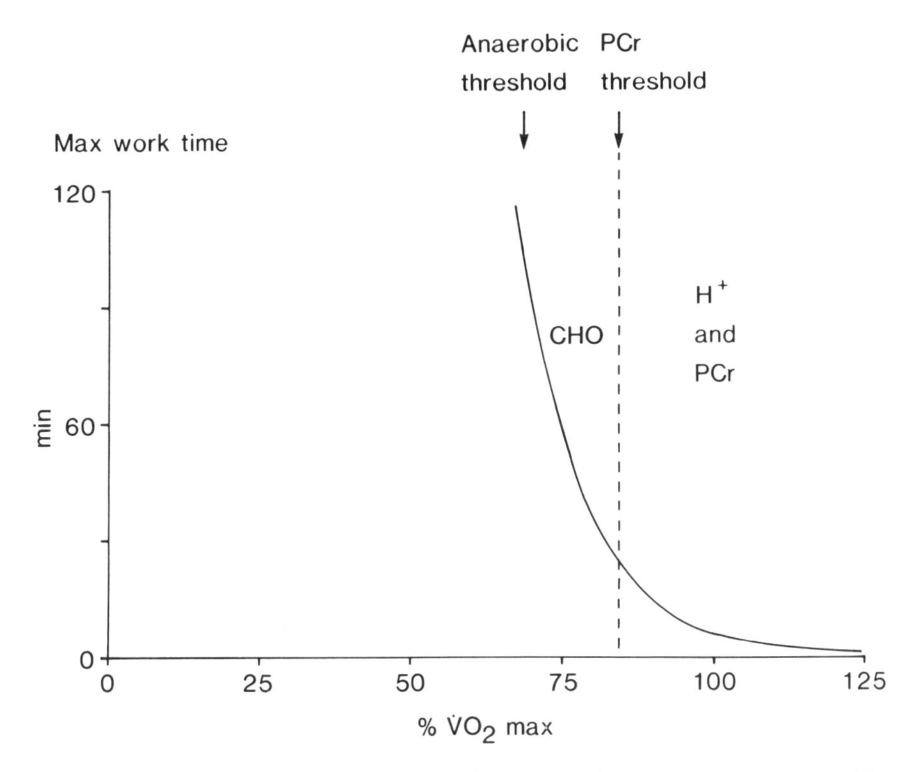

Figure 5 Estimated maximal work time at different work loads. The work time at 100% $\dot{V}O_2$max was assumed to correspond to 6 min and at 68% $\dot{V}O_2$max to 116 min (Björkman, Sahlin, Hagenfeldt, & Wahren, 1984). The curve is highly dependent on the training status, being transferred to the right for an endurance-trained athlete and to the left for an untrained subject. The limiting factor for performance, when exercise intensity is above the anaerobic threshold but below the PCr threshold (i.e., 65% to 85% $\dot{V}O_2$max) is the muscle glycogen store. Above the PCr threshold muscle, PCr store or H^+ ion accumulation limits the work (see text).

exercise intensity is above the PCr-threshold work time is limited by LA accumulation or the PCr content. In both of these situations, muscle fatigue occurs when the capacity to generate ATP (through oxidation of glycogen or through breakdown of PCr) is lower than the demands required by the exercise intensity. If the exercise intensity is decreased, the energy demand will decrease and exercise can continue.

What then is the mechanism whereby the inability to generate ATP results in muscle fatigue? It has been known for a long time that the muscle content of ATP decreases only slightly at fatigue (10% to 30% decrease, Harris et al., 1977). Studies on skinned muscle fibers have shown that force generation is not dependent on the ATP concentration down to 0.03 mM (Donaldson, Bond, Seeger, Niles, & Bolles, 1981), which is only 0.5% of the value observed in fatigued muscle. It has been speculated that ATP is compartmentalized in the cell making only a small part available for muscle contraction. This appears unlikely, as a decrease of ATP down to 10% to 20% was observed in IAA poisoned rat skeletal muscle during muscle contraction (Dudley & Terjung, 1985). It is concluded that the ATP content as such can hardly be the limiting factor for performance.

The products of ATP hydrolysis (ADP, P_i, and H^+) increases when the PCr store is depleted. A large amount of the ADP in the cell (50% to 95%) has been suggested to be protein bound (Wilkie, 1981, and the discussion following the paper). The increase in ADP is believed to occur only in the free pool. The increase of calculated free ADP and of H^+ has been found to be linearly related to the decrease in force in stimulated frog muscle (Dawson et al., 1978).

To fully understand the dynamics of the adenine nucleotides during exercise one must, however, consider the time delay that occurs before freezing of muscle samples. With the muscle biopsy technique, the time delay between end of contraction and sampling is about 2 to 5 s. It is quite clear that changes can occur in the adenine nucleotide content of the muscle sample during this time and obtained values will therefore reflect the steady-state concentration and not the metabolic state during the actual contraction. In a recent study on skinned muscle preparation, an elaborate technique involving laser-induced release of ATP from chemically trapped ATP ("caged" ATP) was developed (Ferenczi, Homsher, & Trentham, 1984). It was possible to increase the ATP concentration from zero to the physiological range (5 mM) within 1 ms and to study the kinetics of ATP hydrolysis by myosin ATPase. When ATP was released by laser pulses, the muscle relaxed from its rigor tension and MgATP was rapidly hydrolyzed to ADP. The rapid initial burst of ADP formation amounted to about 152 uM and was complete within 50 ms, with a half-time of less than 20 ms. This study emphasized the rapid changes of the adenine nucleotides that occur during muscular contraction. The most rapid technique for freezing contracting muscle utilizes a hammer precooled in liquid nitrogen, which flattens the muscle to a thin layer before freezing. With this freeze-clamp technique the freezing time is about 80 ms (Gilbert, Kretzschmar, Wilkie, & Woledge, 1971), which is likely too slow to measure the rapid changes in adenine-nucleotides occurring in contracting muscle.

It is suggested that transient increases of ADP occurs locally in the muscle during muscle contraction. When the capacity to rephosphorylate ADP at a sufficient rate is decreased (glycogen depletion and/or PCr depletion) the transient increases of ADP will be extended in amplitude and time.

The hypothesis of cyclic variations in the concentrations of the adenine nucleotides during the contraction is supported by a study on rat heart, where PCr, ATP and P_i were measured during the cardiac contraction cycle with NMR (Fossel, Morgan, & Ingwall, 1980). By synchronizing the collection of data with the heartbeat it was possible to obtain values during the cardiac cycle (214 ms). PCr and ATP decreased to a minimum during systole but increased during diastole, whereas the contrary was observed for P_i.

The hypothesis is also supported by the increase of inosine monophosphate (IMP) and of NH_3 that occurs in fatigued muscle. AMP deaminase catalyzes the deamination of AMP to IMP and is present in skeletal muscle. It has a high Km value for AMP 0.5 mM (Ronca-Testoni, Raggi, & Ronca, 1970), which makes the activity very sensitive to increases in AMP. Exercise to fatigue results in increased levels of IMP in muscle

Table 3 IMP formation in human skeletal muscle at different conditions of anaerobic energy utilization.

Formation	Rest[c]	Bicycle Exercise[a] to fatigue at 100% $\dot{V}O_2max$	Isometric Contr.[b] to fatigue 66% MVC	Long-term[c] ischemia
IMP or - Δ TAN[d]	0	3.8 ± 0.8	3.6 ± 0.4	0
ADP	2.7 ± 0.1	3.5 ± 0.2	4.2 ± 0.3	4.0 ± 0.3
AMP	0.08 ± 0.02	0.19 ± 0.02	0.26 ± 0.04	0.27 ± 0.07
Lactate	4	100 ± 4	79 ± 3	46 ± 6

Values are $\bar{x}$ ± SE and are expressed as mmol/kg d.m.
[a]Values are from Sahlin, Palmskog, & Hultman (1978)
[b]Values are from Katz, Sahlin, & Henriksson (unpublished data)
[c]Values are from Larsson & Hultman (1979)
[d]Δ TAN = (ATP + ADP + AMP) - $(ATP + ADP + AMP)_{Rest}$

simultaneously as ADP, AMP and LA increase (Table 3). During long-term ischemia the muscle utilizes the anaerobic energy sources and after 2 hr of ischemia the levels of ADP and AMP are similar to that of a fatigued muscle (Table 3). In spite of this similarity, no increase of IMP or decrease of TAN (ATP + ADP + AMP) (Larsson & Hultman, 1979) occur. This supports the theory of transient increases of ADP and AMP above the increased steady-state level in the contracting muscle.

It has also been reported recently that IMP increases in glycogen depleted muscle at fatigue. When individual muscle fibers were analyzed it was found that IMP accumulation occurred only in the glycogen depleted fibers (Norman, Jansson, Sollevi, & Kaijser, 1984). It thus appears that AMP deamination occurs when the capacity to rephosphorylate ADP is diminished either by depletion of glycogen and/or depletion of PCr together with high lactate and H^+ ions, which will inhibit PFK. Under these circumstances, it is expected that the ADP and AMP transients will have a longer duration and a larger amplitude, which will activate AMP deaminase. The IMP level in muscle can thus be regarded as a reflection of the AMP transients (and thereby indirectly the ADP transients) that occur during exercise in a fatigued muscle. The increase in ADP in the contracting muscle fibers will decrease the free-energy change during ATP hydrolysis and might therefore interfere with the energetics of contraction.

The ATP utilizing processes involved in muscular contraction are catalyzed by myosin ATPase, Ca-transporting ATPase and Na-K-ATPase. The release of Ca from the SR-system and the formation of cross-bridges are processes that do not require ATP. The relaxation decrease of cytosolic Ca-concentration and release of cross-bridges are, however, energy-dependent (i.e., ATP utilizing) process. An impaired function of the first two of these enzymes (myosin ATPase and Ca-transporting ATPase) will therefore primarily affect the detachment of cross-bridges but not the force-generating process. A slowing of relaxation is observed in fatigued muscle (Sjöholm, Sahlin, Edström, & Hultman, 1983) and is probably a sign of impaired function of one or both of these reactions. In extreme situations of energy deficiency, the muscle remains in a contractile state and cannot relax (rigor). Rigor formation does not occur normally in fatigued muscle but can occur under conditions when glycolysis is inhibited (Iodoacetate-poisoned muscles or glycogen-phosphorylase-deficient muscle).

A decreased function of Na-K-ATPase would, however, affect the ion balance over the muscle cell membrane, with increased extracellular K^+ concentration and increased intracellular $Na+$. A change of the ionic composition in this direction has been observed in fatigued muscle (Sahlin, Alvestrand, Brandt, & Hultman, 1978; Sjögaard, Adams, & Saltin, 1985). The resulting decrease of membrane potential is likely to prevent activation of the contraction process.

CONCLUSIONS

1. The different biochemical pathways for generation of ATP are characterized by their capacity (amount of ATP produced) and by their power (rate of ATP production). The capacity of the different energy producing processes are in the following order: FFA oxidation > CHO oxidation > LA formation > PCr breakdown, while the power is in the opposite direction (i.e., highest power for PCr breakdown and lowest power for FFA oxidation).
2. Anaerobic energy utilization occurs when: (a) the energy demand is high, (b) rapid fluctuations occur in the energy requirement and (c) O_2 is available in a limiting amount.
3. Substrate utilization during exercise at different intensities has three important breakpoints. The first breakpoint (the carbohydrate threshold) occurs when the energy demand exceeds the maximum power of FFA oxidation (30% to 50% of $\dot{V}O_2max$). The second breakpoint (the anaerobic threshold) occurs when anaerobic energy production accelerates and accumulation of LA occurs in muscle and blood (55% to 75% of $\dot{V}O_2max$). The third breakpoint (the PCr threshold) occurs when LA continuously increases in muscle and PCr is completely depleted in the working muscle (80% to 95% $\dot{V}O_2max$).
4. Muscle fatigue occurs when the PCr store is depleted in the working muscle (work load > PCr threshold), muscle glycogen is depleted (work load > anaerobic threshold), or when the carbohydrate store of the body (muscle glycogen or liver glycogen) is depleted (work load > carbohydrate threshold).
5. It is suggested that muscle fatigue during both high intensity exercise (PCr depletion) and moderate intensity exercise (muscle glycogen depletion) is caused by the same metabolic factor; that is, transient and local increases of ADP, which affect the ionic balance over the muscle cell membrane and prevents activation of the contraction process.

Acknowledgments

Financial support from the Swedish Research Council of Sports Medicine is gratefully acknowledged.

REFERENCES

Åstrand, P.-O., & Rodahl, K. (1971). *Textbook of work physiology* (p. 305). New York: McGraw Hill.

Bergström, J., Hermansen, L., Hultman, E., & Saltin, B. (1967). Diet, muscle glycogen and physical performance. *Acta Physiologica Scandinavica,* **71**, 140-150.

Björkman, O., Sahlin, K., Hagenfeldt, L., & Wahren, J. (1984). Influence of glucose and fructose ingestion on endurance performance in well-trained athletes. *Clinical Physiology,* **4**, 483-494.

Chasiotis, D., Edström, L., Sahlin, K., & Sjöholm, H. (1985). Activation of glycogen phosphorylase by electrical stimulation of isolated fast-twitch and slow-twitch muscles from rat. *Acta Physiologica Scandinavica,* **123**, 43-48.

Chasiotis, D., Sahlin, K., & Hultman, E. (1983). Regulation of glycogenolysis in human muscle in response to epinephrine infusion. *Journal of Applied Physiology,* **54**, 45-50.

Costill, D.L., Dalsky, G.P., & Fink, J.W. (1978). Effects of caffeine ingestion on metabolism and exercise performance. *Medicine and Science in Sports,* **10**, 155-158.

Costill, D.L., Verstappen, F., Kuipers, H., Janssen, E., & Fink, W. (1984). Acid-base balance during repeated bouts of exercise: Influence of $NaHCO_3$. *International Journal of Sports Medicine,* **5**, 228-231.

Davies, C.T.M., & Thompson, M.W. (1979). Aerobic performance of female marathon and male ultramarathon athletes. *European Journal of Applied Physiology,* **41**, 233-245.

Dawson, M., Gadian, D.G., & Wilkie, D.R. (1978). Muscular fatigue investigated by phosphorus nuclear magnetic resonance. *Nature,* **274**, 861-866.

Donaldson, S.K.B., Bond, E., Seeger, L., Niles, N., & Bolles, L. (1981). Intracellular pH vs. MgATP concentration: Relative importance as determinants of Ca activated force generation of disrupted rabbit cardiac cells. *Cardiovascular Research,* **15**, 268-275.

Donaldson, S.K.B., Hermansen, L., & Bolles, L. (1978). Differential, direct effects of H^+ on Ca^{2+} activated force of skinned fibers from the soleus, cardiac and adductor magnus muscles of rabbits. *Pflügers Archiv,* **376**, 55-65.

Dudley, G.A., & Terjung, R.L. (1985). Influence of acidosis on AMP deaminase activity in contracting fast-twitch muscle. *American Journal of Physiology,* **248**, C43-C50.

Edström, L., Hultman, E., Sahlin, K., & Sjöholm, H. (1982). The contents of high-energy phosphates in different fibre types in skeletal muscle from rat, guinea-pig and man. *Journal of Physiology* (London), **332**, 47-58.

Essén, B., Hagenfeldt, L., & Kaijser, L. (1977). Utilization of blood-borne and intramuscular substrates during continuous and intermittent exercise in man. *Journal of Physiology* (London), **265**, 489-506.

Ferenczi, M.A., Homsher, E., & Trentham, D.R. (1984). The kinetics of magnesium adenosine triphosphate cleavage in skinned muscle fibres of the rabbit. *Journal of Physiology* (London), **352**, 575-599.

Fossel, E.T., Morgan, H.E., & Ingwall, J.S. (1980). Measurement of changes in high energy phosphates in the cardiac cycle by using gated ^{31}P nuclear magnetic resonance. *Proceedings of the National Academy of Science, USA*, **77**, 3654-3658.

Gilbert, C., Kretzschmar, K.M., Wilkie, D.R., & Woledge, R.C. (1971). Chemical change and energy output during muscular contraction. *Journal of Physiology* (London), **218**, 163-193.

Gollnick, P.D., Piehl, K., & Saltin, B. (1974). Selective glycogen depletion pattern in human skeletal muscle fibres after exercise of varying intensity and at varying pedalling rates. *Journal of Physiology* (London), **241**, 45-47.

Harris, R.C., Edwards, R.H.T., Hultman, E., Nordesjö, L.-O., Nylind, B., & Sahlin, K. (1976). The time course of phosphorylcreatine resynthesis during recovery of the quadriceps muscle in man. *Pflügers Archiv*, **367**, 137-142.

Harris, R.C., Sahlin, K., & Hultman, E. (1977). Phosphagen and lactate contents of m. quadriceps femoris of man after exercise. *Journal of Applied Physiology*, **43**, 852-857.

Hughes, R.L., Clode, M., Edwards, R.H.T., Goodwin, T.J., & Jones, N.L. (1968). Effect of inspired O_2 on cardiopulmonary and metabolic responses to exercise in man. *Journal of Applied Physiology*, **24**, 336-347.

Hultman, E., Bergström, J., & McLellan-Andersson, N. (1967). Breakdown and resynthesis of phosphorylcreatin and adenosine-triphosphate in connection with muscular work in man. *Scandinavian Journal of Clinical and Laboratory Investigation*, **19**, 56-66.

Hultman, E., & Sahlin, K. (1981). Acid-base balance during exercise. In R.S. Hutton & D.I. Miller (Eds.), *Exercise and Sport Sciences Reviews* (Vol. 8, pp. 41-128). Boston: The Franklin Institute Press.

Hultman, E., & Sjöholm, H. (1983). Substrate availability. In H.G. Knuttgen, J.A. Vogel, & J. Poortmans (Eds.), *Biochemistry of Exercise* (Vol. 13, pp. 63-75). Champaign, IL: Human Kinetics.

Ivy, J.L., Withers, R.T., VanHandel, P.J., Elger, D.E., & Costill, D.L. (1980). Muscle respiratory capacity and fiber type as determinants of the lactate threshold. *Journal of Applied Physiology*, **48**, 523-527.

Jones, N.L., Sutton, J.R., Taylor, R., & Toews, C.J. (1977). Effect of pH on cardiorespiratory and metabolic responses to exercise. *Journal of Applied Physiology*, **43**, 959-964.

Jorfeldt, L., & Wahren, J. (1971). Leg blood flow during exercise in man. *Clinical Science*, **41**, 459-473.

Juhlin-Dannfeldt, A., Terblanche, S.E., Fell, R.D., Young, J.C., & Holloszy, J.O. (1982). Effects of β-adrenergic receptor blockade on glycogenolysis during exercise. *Journal of Applied Physiology*, **53**, 549-554.

Katz, A., Broberg, S., Sahlin, K., & Wahren, J. (in press). Leg glucose uptake during maximal dynamic exercise. *American Journal of Physiology*.

Katz, A., Costill, D.L., King, D.S., Hargreaves, M., & Fink, W.J. (1984). Maximal exercise tolerance after induced alkalosis. *International Journal of Sports Medicine,* **5**, 107-110.

Kindermann, W., Keul, J., & Huber, G. (1977). Physical exercise after induced alkalosis (bicarbonate or tris-buffer). *European Journal of Applied Physiology,* **37**, 197-204.

Larsson, J., & Hultman, E. (1979). The effect of long-term arterial occlusion on energy metabolism of the human quadriceps muscle. *Scandinavian Journal of Clinical and Laboratory Investigation,* **39**, 257-264.

Linnarsson, D. (1974). Dynamics of pulmonary gas exchange and heart rate changes at start and end of exercise. *Acta Physiologica Scandinavica,* (Suppl. 415), 5-68.

Nazar, K., Brzezinska, Z., & Kowalski, W. (1972). Mechanism of impaired capacity for prolonged muscular work following beta-adrenergic blockade in dogs. *Pflügers Archiv,* **336**, 72.

Nilsson, H. & Hultman, E. (1973). Liver glycogen in man—the effect of total starvation or a carbohydrate-poor diet followed by carbohydrate refeeding. *Scandinavian Journal of Clinical and Laboratory Investigation,* **32**, 325-330.

Norman, B., Jansson, E., Sollevi, A., & Kaijser, L. (1984). IMP and muscle glycogen during exercise in man. *Acta Physiologica Scandinavica,* **120**, 50A.

Ronca-Testoni, S., Raggi, A., & Ronca, G. (1970). Muscle AMP aminohydrolase. III. A comparative study on the regulatory properties of skeletal muscle enzyme from various species. *Biochimica and Biophysica Acta,* **198**, 101-112.

Sahlin, K. (1978). Intracellular pH and energy metabolism in skeletal muscle of man. With special reference to exercise. *Acta Physiologica Scandinavica,* (Suppl. 455), 1-56. Thesis. Stockholm.

Sahlin, K. 1983. Effect of acidosis on energy metabolism and force generation in skeletal muscle. In H.G. Knuttgen, J.A. Vogel, & J. Poortmans (Eds.), *Biochemistry of Exercise* (Vol. 13, pp. 151-161). Champaign, IL: Human Kinetics.

Sahlin, K., Alvestrand, A., Brandt, R., & Hultman, E. (1978). Intracellular pH and bicarbonate concentration in human muscle during recovery from exercise. *Journal of Applied Physiology,* **45**, 474-480.

Sahlin, K., Edström, L., & Sjöholm, H. (1983). Fatigue and creatine phosphate depletion during CO_2 induced acidosis in rat muscle. *American Journal of Physiology,* **245**, C15-C20.

Sahlin, K., Harris, R.C., & Hultman, E. (1975). Creatine kinase equilibrium and lactate content compared with muscle pH in tissue samples obtained after isometric exercise. *Biochemical Journal,* **152**, 173-180.

Sahlin, K., & Henriksson, J. (1984). Buffer capacity and lactate accumulation in skeletal muscle of trained and untrained men. *Acta Physiologica Scandinavica,* **122**, 331-339.

Sahlin, K., Palmskog, G., & Hultman, E. (1978). Adenine nucleotide and IMP contents of the quadriceps muscle in man after exercise. *Pflügers Archiv*, **374**, 193-198.

Saltin, B., & Gollnick, P.D. (1983). Skeletal muscle adaptability: Significance for metabolism and performance. In L.D. Peachey, R.H. Adrian, & S.R. Geiger (Eds.), *Handbook of physiology* (pp. 555-632). Baltimore, MD: Waverly Press.

Sharp, R.L., Costill, D.L., Fink, W.J., & King, D.S. (1983). The effects of eight weeks of sprint training on the buffer capacity of muscle in man. *Medicine and Science in Sports and Exercise*, **15**, 116.

Sjögaard, G., Adams, R.P., & Saltin, B. (1985). Water and ion shifts in skeletal muscle of humans with intense dynamic knee extension. *American Journal of Physiology*, **248**, R190-R196.

Sjöholm, H. Gidlöf, A., Larsson, J., & Sahlin, K. (1985). The effect of long-term circulatory occlusion on intracellular pH and energy metabolism of the quadriceps muscle in man. *Clinical Science*, **68**, 597-600.

Sjöholm, H., Sahlin, K., Edström, L., & Hultman, E. (1983). Quantitative estimation of anaerobic and oxidative energy metabolism and contraction characteristics in intact human skeletal muscle during and after electrical stimulation. *Clinical Physiology*, **3**, 227-239.

Stull, G.A., & Clarke, D.H. (1971). Patterns of recovery following isometric and isotonic strength decrement. *Medicine and Science in Sports*, **3**, 135-139.

Sutton, J.R., Jones, N.L., & Toews, C.J. (1981). Effect of pH on muscle glycolysis during exercise. *Clinical Science*, **61**, 331-338.

Taylor, D.J., Bore, P.J., Styles, P., Gadian, D.G., & Radda, G.K. (1983). Bioenergetics of intact human muscle. A ^{31}P nuclear magnetic resonance study. *Molecular Biological Medicine*, **1**, 77-94.

Wilkie, D.R. (1981). Shortage of chemical fuel as a cause of fatigue: Studies by nuclear magnetic resonance and bicycle ergometry. In R. Porter & J. Whelan (Eds.), *Human muscle fatigue: Physiological mechanisms* (pp. 102-119). London: Pitman Medical.

Work-Induced Potassium Loss From Skeletal Muscles and Its Physiological Implications

Pavel Hník
František Vyskočil
Evžen Ujec
Richard Vejsada
Czechoslovak Academy of Sciences
Prague, Czechoslovakia
Helga Rehfeldt
Zentralinstitut für Arbeitsmedizin der DDR
Berlin, German Democratic Republic

Potassium, as one of the most important cations in excitable tissues, has been extensively studied, namely in the nervous system and the skeletal musculature. It was almost 50 years ago that Fenn and his collaborators (e.g., Fenn, 1936; Fenn & Cobb, 1934) reported a postexercise decrease of K^+ in frog muscles.

This, and analogous approaches (for review, see Conway, 1957), could only provide rough estimates of the K^+ changes induced by muscle activity. A more promising approach was the finding that increased potassium concentrations were found in venous effluent blood from working muscles of cats (Kjellmer, 1965) and man (Costill & Saltin, 1975; Haralambie, 1975; Lind, McNicol, & Donald, 1966). However, not even muscle biopsies can provide more exact data about the changes occurring in extracellular potassium concentrations (K_e^+) during muscle activity.

Ion-selective glass microelectrodes first made it possible to measure intracellular Na^+ and K^+ activities in crab and lobster muscle fibers (Hinke, 1961) and in frog skeletal muscle fibers (Sorokina, 1964). This type of electrode was also employed by Gebert (1970) for assessing changes in extracellular K^+ and Na^+ concentrations in rabbit skeletal muscles.

The introduction of liquid ion-exchanger microelectrodes (ISMs) by Walker (1971) meant a further step forward in obtaining a higher selectivity for individual cations (namely K^+ as compared with Na^+). Comprehensive reviews and monographs have previously appeared on this subject (cf. Koryta, 1980; Syková, Hník, & Vyklický, 1981; Walker & Brown, 1977; Zeuthen, 1981).

RESULTS

Measurements of K_e^+ Changes in Contracting Rabbit and Cat Muscles

A new type of microelectrode was developed for measuring changes in extracellular K_e^+ during muscle tetanic contractions of the rabbit and cat gastrocnemius muscle in response to indirect stimulation. This is the sidepore electrode (Vyskočil & Kříž, 1972), the preparation of which was also described in detail by Hník and Vyskočil (1981). The external diameter of the tip of this electrode is 30 to 100 μm. The sidepore is siliconed according

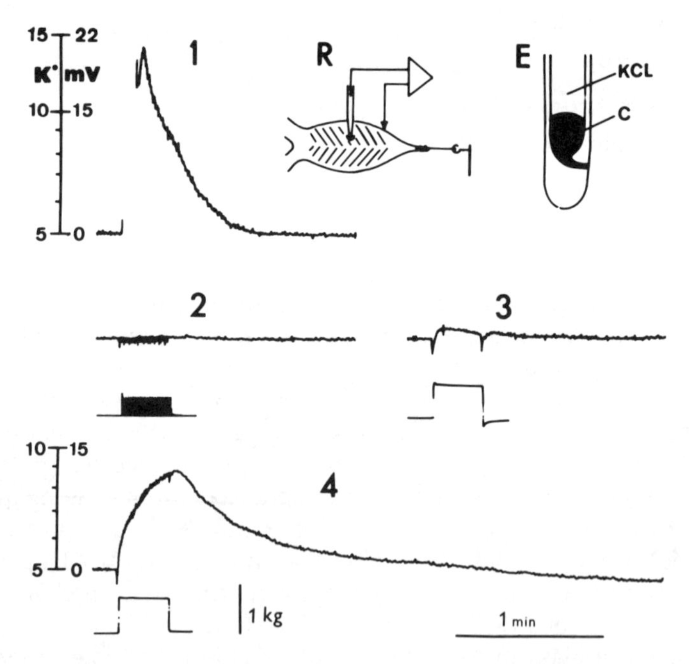

Figure 1 Changes in extracellular concentrations (K_e^+) in a rabbit gastrocnemius muscle. R—recording arrangement. E—sidepore electrode tip filled with Corning ion-exchanger (C). (1) K_e^+ changes after insertion of the electrode into the muscle. (2) No changes in K_e^+ (upper trace) in response to single twitches (1 Hz) for 20 s (lower trace), or to passive muscle stretch. (3) Tension on lower trace. (4) Increase and decay of K_e^+ in the muscle (upper trace) during and after an isometric tetanus (50 Hz) lasting 20 s. Time calibration 1 min applies to all records, myograph tension 1 kg. Ordinate: on left scale mmol/l K_e^+, on right scale actual changes in mV for upper records in 1 to 4. From "Work Induced Increase of Extracellular Potassium Concentration in Muscle Measured by Ion-Specific Electrodes" by P. Hník, F. Vyskočil, N. Kříž, and M. Holas, 1972, *Brain Research*, **40**, pp. 559-562. Copyright 1972 by Elsevier. Reprinted with permission.

to the procedure first proposed by Walker (1971) and the tip filled with a 200 to 300 μm column of potassium specific Corning ion-exchanger (No. 477317). The space above this column is filled with a 0.5 mmol/l KCl solution. The selectivity constant $K_{K, Na}$ is higher by one to two orders of magnitude than the electrodes made of potassium-specific glass.

The experiments were performed on gastrocnemius muscles of rabbits (2 to 3.5 kg body weight) and cats (2 to 4 kg body weight). Under anesthesia, the hind limbs were firmly fixed in the knee and ankle, a pool was made of the skin flaps, the muscle freed from surrounding tissues, and the sciatic nerve was dissected high up in the thigh and transected ready for stimulation. All other muscle nerve branches to the hind limb were sectioned. The pool was filled with a solution of the following composition (in mmol/l): 137.0 NaCl, 5.0 KCl, 2.0 $CaCl_2$, 1.0 $MgCl_2$, 11.9 $NaHCO_3$, 0.32 NaH_2PO_4, and 5.54 glucose. The temperature of the pool was maintained at 36.0° to 37.5 °C by radiant heat. The muscles were stimulated indirectly with 0.3 ms pulses at 50 Hz and supramaximal intensity (1 to 5 V) for 1, 5, 10, or 20 s.

When the ISM sidepore electrode (Figure 1E) is introduced into the rabbit gastrocnemius (Figure 1R), there is a transient increase of K_e^+ which is apparently due to leakage of K^+ from damaged muscle fibers (Figure 1.1). As shown in Figure 1.4, a 20 s isometric tetanus causes an increase from 5 to 8 to 9 mmol/l K^+ with half-time of decay of 1 min or more. Control experiments eliminating the possibility that this increase in K_e^+ levels is due to further damage of hitherto intact muscle fibers during the tetanus is shown in Figure 1.2 and 1.3 (Hník, Vyskočil, Kříž, & Holas, 1972). A set of representative records obtained in the rabbit gastrocnemius is shown in Figure 2. It is obvious that the longer the tetanic concentration, the greater the increase of K^+ concentration and the longer the decay time (Hník et al., 1976).

It has been suggested by several authors that the loss of K^+ from contracting muscles could be due to hemolysis (Cier, Lacour, & Cier, 1960; Haralambie, 1975). We therefore repeated these experiments with cats because there is an interesting difference between this species and the rabbit. According to Prankerd (1961), for example, the concentration in rabbit erythrocytes is about 100 mmol/l K^+ while feline red blood cells only have around 6 mmol/l K^+. It was therefore assumed that, if similar results were obtained in cats as in rabbits, the increased K_e^+ could hardly be ascribed to hemolysis occurring in working muscles.

The results obtained in contracting cat muscles are shown in Figure 3 (Hník et al., 1976). As may be seen, the increase in K^+ is closely similar to that obtained in rabbit muscles and shows that K_e^+ again rose up to analogous values as in the rabbit, the erythrocytes of which contain a high concentration of K^+.

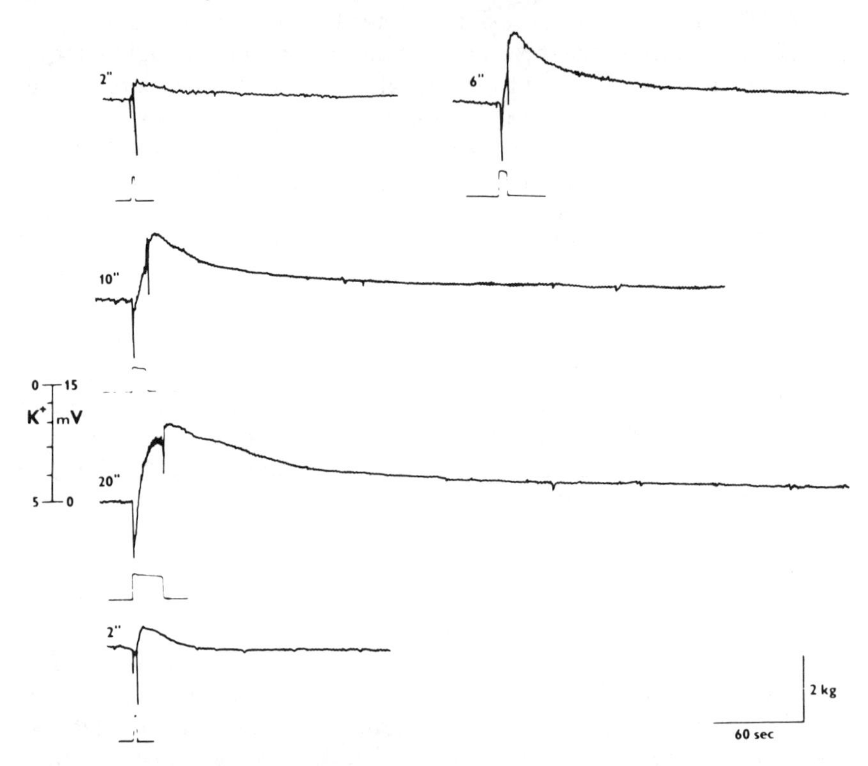

Figure 2 Changes of K_e^+ in rabbit gastrocnemius muscle before, during, and after isometric contractions lasting 2, 6, 10 and 20 s. The corresponding contraction curve is shown below each record. Calibration for myograph on the right. K_e^+ concentrations are given on the left. Unretouched records showing stimulus artifacts at the beginning and end of stimulation. From "Work Induced Potassium Changes in Skeletal Muscle and Effluent Venous Blood Assessed by Liquid Ion-Exchanger Microelectrodes" by P. Hník, M. Holas, I. Krekule, N. Kříž, J. Mejsnar, V. Smieško, E. Ujec, and F. Vyskočil, 1976, *Pflügers Archiv,* **362**, pp. 85-94. Copyright 1976 by Springer Verlag. Reprinted with permission.

It naturally appeared of interest to employ these sidepore ISMs for assessing the K^+ losses from the working muscles; that is, to measure the K^+_{ven} changes in venous effluent blood and to calculate the amount of K^+ lost from working muscles by computing the K^+ changes in venous blood with the changes in blood flow. The animal species of choice was, of course, the cat, which has the low K^+ concentration in its red blood platelets.

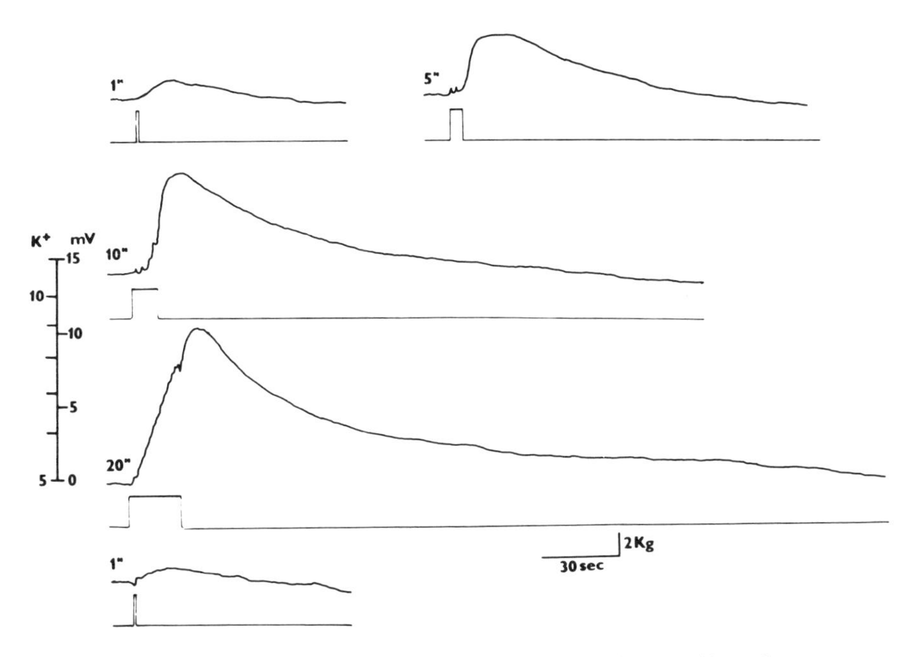

Figure 3 Time course of K_e^+ changes in cat gastrocnemius muscle evoked by indirect tetanic stimulation of the sciatic nerve (50 Hz) lasting 1, 5, 10 and 20 s. For further details see text to Figure 2. From "Work Induced Potassium Changes in Skeletal Muscle and Effluent Venous Blood Assessed by Liquid Ion-Exchanger Microelectrodes" by P. Hník, M. Holas, I. Krekule, N. Kříž, J. Mejsnar, V. Smieško, E. Ujec, and F. Vyskočil, 1976, *Pflügers Archiv,* **362**, pp. 85-94. Copyright 1976 by Springer Verlag. Reprinted with permission.

K^+_{ven} Changes in Venous Effluent Blood From Working Cat Muscle

A sidepore ISM was inserted into a side branch of a Y-shaped cannula through which blood was flowing from the cat gastrocnemius muscle. Considerable care was taken to ligate all accessory veins from neighboring muscles and tissues (Hník et al., 1973; Hník et al., 1976), so that the blood flowing from the lower leg was exclusively drained from the stimulated muscle. After passing through a photoelectric drop-counter, the blood was returned into the central stump of the contralateral femoral vein.

Figure 4 illustrates the changes in K^+_{ven} and blood flow in a typical experiment. It is clear that the concentration of K^+ in the venous blood rises with a slight delay (apparently due to reduced flow through the muscle vascular bed during maximum tetanic contractions) and that the loss of K^+ into venous blood is related to the duration of muscle activity. A more

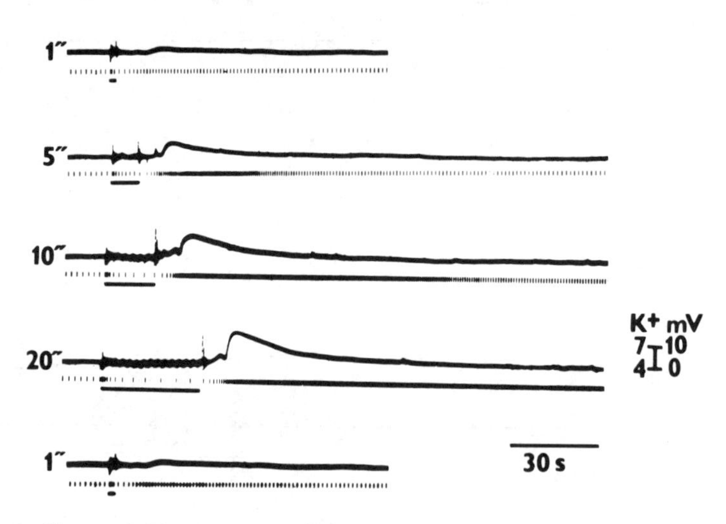

Figure 4 Changes in K^+_{ven} in venous effluent blood (upper records) and blood flow (lower records) after isometric tetanic contractions of various durations (1 to 20 s). Stimulation is indicated by horizontal bars. From "Work Induced Potassium Changes in Skeletal Muscle and Effluent Venous Blood Assessed by Liquid Ion-Exchanger Microelectrodes" by P. Hník, M. Holas, I. Krekule, N. Kříž, J. Mejsnar, V. Smieško, E. Ujec, and F. Vyskočil, 1976, *Pflügers Archiv,* **362**, pp. 85-94. Copyright 1976 by Springer Verlag. Reprinted with permission.

precise relationship was obtained by computing K^+_{ven} changes with blood flow occurring after tetanic contractions of the cat gastrocnemius muscle of various durations (Hník et al., 1976; Hník & Vyskočil, 1981) (Figure 5).

It appeared to be of interest to assess the speed of reuptake of K^+ in working muscles, if the loss of K^+ from the working muscle is prevented by arteriovenous occlusion during muscle activity. Figure 6 shows that the reuptake of K^+ is relatively slow. After a 10 s isometric tetanus, almost no K^+ is released into venous blood from the previously occluded working muscle until 45 to 60 s. This means that K^+ reuptake into previously active muscle fibers is relatively slow and that there is a considerable time lag between extrusion of K^+ into the interstitial muscle phase and its reuptake into previously active muscle fibers (Hník et al., 1976).

Two aspects of the K^+ problem appear to be intriguing; first, whether the loss of K^+ is dependent upon the type of muscle contraction, that is, whether the muscle is working under isometric or isotonic conditions. The records in Figure 7 indicate that, irrespective of the type of contraction, the K^+ losses into venous effluent blood are closely analogous (Hník

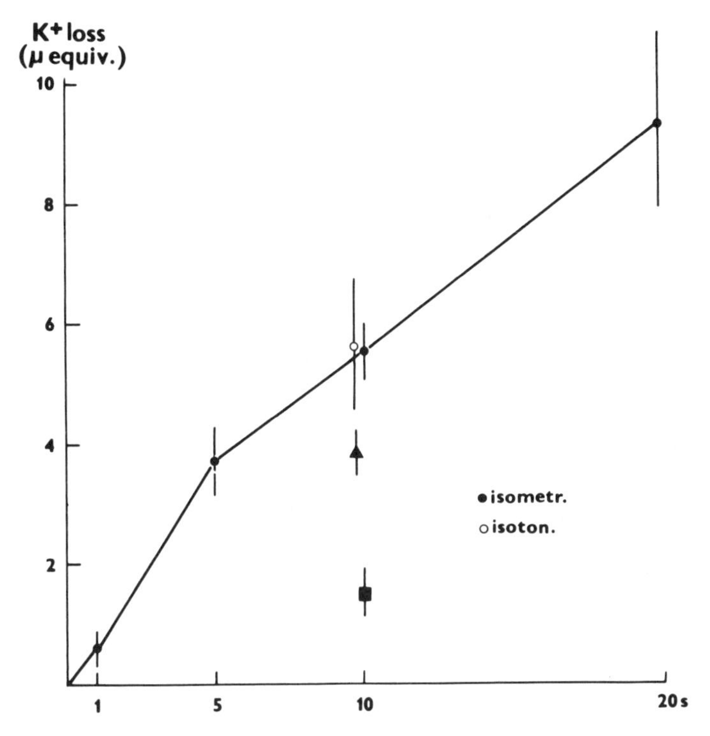

Figure 5 The relation between loss of K^+_{ven} in effluent venous blood and duration of isometric tetanus (full line, black circles). Open circle: loss of K^+ after 10 s isotonic tetanic contraction. Values denoted by ▲ and ■ indicate K^+ loss when the 10 s tetanus was performed under conditions of 20 to 25 s and 40 to 60 s arteriovenous occlusion, respectively. Vertical bars are standard errors of the mean. From "Work Induced Potassium Changes in Skeletal Muscle and Effluent Venous Blood Assessed by Liquid Ion-Exchanger Microelectrodes" by P. Hník, M. Holas, I. Krekule, N. Kříž, J. Mejsnar, V. Smieško, E. Ujec, and F. Vyskočil, 1976, *Pflügers Archiv,* **362**, pp. 85-94. Copyright 1976 by Springer Verlag. Reprinted with permission.

et al., 1976). Second, perhaps the K^+ changes are not dependent so much upon the process of muscle shortening per se, but that the electrical events occurring along the muscle membrane may be decisive.

K^+ Released From Single Frog Muscle Fibers

For this reason, measurements were performed in frogs, when a stimulating intracellular microelectrode was inserted into a single sartorius muscle fiber and the effects of K_e^+ changes were recorded with a double-barrel ISM close by (Figure 8). These experiments were performed in vitro

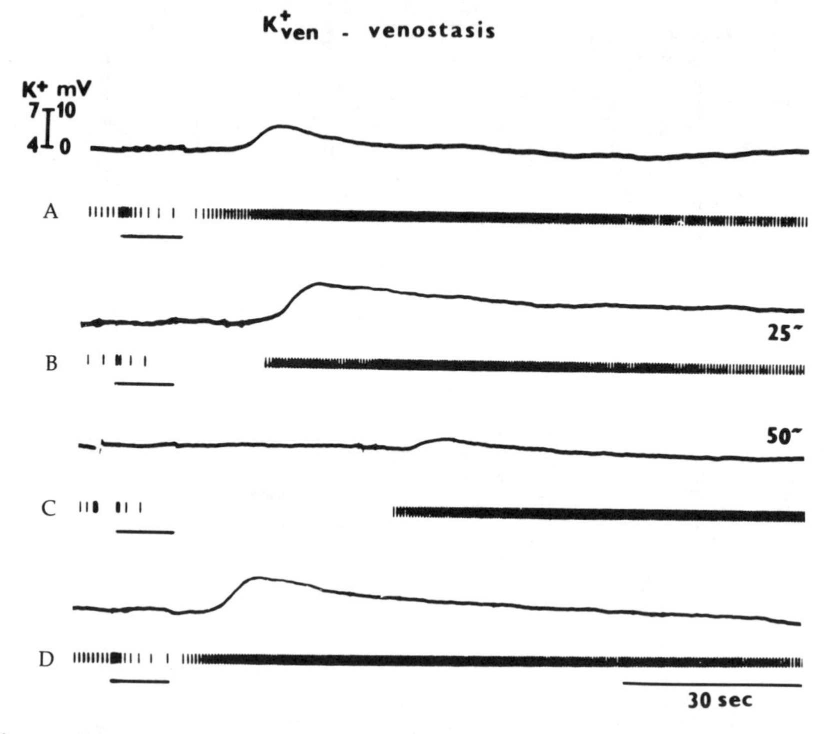

Figure 6 Representative records of the effect of arteriovenous occlusion upon K^+_{ven} released by the cat gastrocnemius after a 10 s isometric tetanus (50 Hz). A and D—control 10 s isometric tetani without occlusion. B and C—stimulation plus occlusion lasting 25 and 50 s respectively. Note the small rise in K^+_{ven} in the longer-lasting experiment. From "Work Induced Potassium Changes in Skeletal Muscle and Effluent Venous Blood Assessed by Liquid Ion-Exchanger Microelectrodes" by P. Hník, M. Holas, I. Krekule, N. Kříž, J. Mejsnar, V. Smieško, E. Ujec, and F. Vyskočil, 1976, *Pflügers Archiv,* **362**, pp. 85-94. Copyright 1976 by Springer Verlag. Reprinted with permission.

and the muscles were immersed in a hyperosmotic Ringer solution that prevented the muscle preparation from twitching (Hodgkin & Horowicz, 1957). More details may be found in the review by Hník and Vyskočil (1981). As may be seen in Figure 9, K^+ changes even after a single action potential from one muscle fiber, which can be detected when a double-barrel ISM is applied in the close proximity of the stimulated muscle fiber (Figure 9A). There appears to be temporal summation on repetitive stimulation, although muscle twitches are eliminated by the hyperosmotic composition of the bath. It is possible to conclude from these results that muscle shortening (i.e., muscle contractions) is not a prerequisite for the release of K^+ from activated muscle fibers.

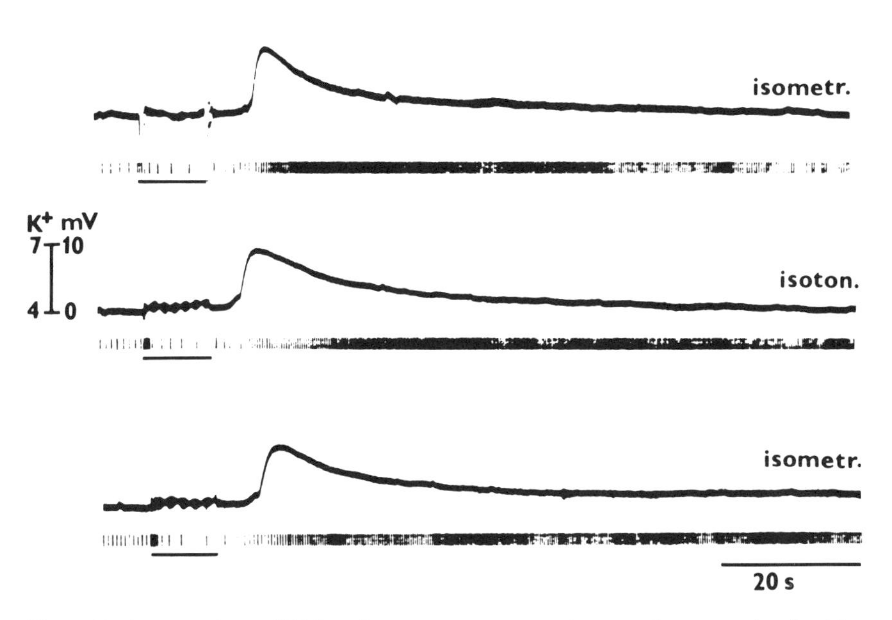

Figure 7 A comparison of K^+ loss from a cat gastrocnemius muscle contracting for 10 s under isometric (top and bottom records) and isotonic conditions (middle record). Horizontal bars indicate the duration of tetanic stimulation. For further details see text to Figure 4. From "Work Induced Potassium Changes in Skeletal Muscle and Effluent Venous Blood Assessed by Liquid Ion-Exchanger Microelectrodes" by P. Hník, M. Holas, I. Krekule, N. Kříž, J. Mejsnar, V. Smieško, E. Ujec, and F. Vyskočil, 1976, *Pflügers Archiv*, **362**, pp. 85-94. Copyright 1976 by Springer Verlag. Reprinted with permission.

K_e^+ Changes in Working Human Muscles

In order to make full use of the ISMs, it appeared to be of eminent interest to modify this method for use in man.

More than 20 years ago, Beránek (1964, 1965) published a procedure for introducing a conventional glass microelectrode into human forearm muscles through a steel intramuscular injection needle as a protective trocar. We substituted an ISM with a sidepore for the nonselective glass electrode (Vyskočil, Hník, Rehfeldt, Vejsada, & Ujec, 1983). We employed the holder devides by Beránek (1964), which consists of a heavy stand and a horseshoe-shaped holder movable in the vertical plane (Figure 10). An intramuscular injection needle (1.2 mm external and 1.0 mm internal diameters) is firmly held in this holder. A sidepore ISM is inserted into the needle, introduced into the brachioradialis muscle through the skin. The

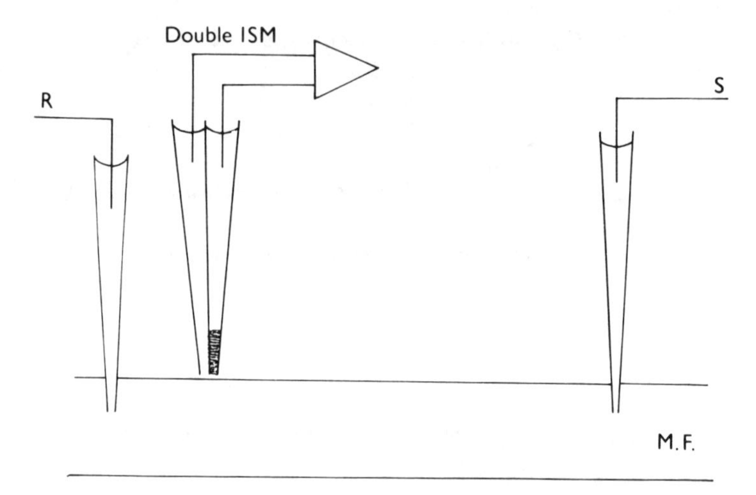

Figure 8 Schema of experimental set-up for measuring K_e^+ changes from stimulated single frog sartorius muscle fibers (F) immersed in a hypertonic solution. S and R—single conventional glass micropipettes used for intracellular stimulation and recording respectively. Double-barrel ISM is brought into the close vicinity of the impaled muscle fiber. M.F.—muscle fiber. (Vyskočil, F., Ujec, E., & Keller, O., 1978, unpublished results).

microelectrode can then be extruded from the steel needle by means of a micrometer screw. The general set up and block schema of the apparatus is shown in Figure 10.

So far, only coauthors of this paper have been impaled by these trocar ISMs. In fact, one of us had more than 20 insertions into one muscle in the course of a week without any aftereffects. The insertion only causes minor discomfort even during volitional contractions.

Representative records of K^+ changes are shown in Figure 11. Isometric volitional contractions were performed at three different levels of intensity (lower curves in Figures 11A, B, C). Corresponding changes in K_e^+ were recorded by a trocar ISM. When a sidepore electrode was filled with a 5 mmol/l KCl solution solution only (without the Corning ion-exchanger), no potassium transient was recorded (Figure 11D).

As we pointed out in the original paper (Vyskočil et al., 1983), this attractive method of employing trocar ISMs has, as yet, several drawbacks: (a) For routine use in man, experience with microelectrodes is essential; (b) in view of the relatively high resistance of these electrodes (50-200 MΩ) a high-impedance amplifier input is essential; and (c) because the indifferent electrode was placed in these experiments on the skin of the forearm, the conditions for recording and those during calibration were not identical. This means that, hitherto, the initial levels of K^+ are not as reliable as should be the case when employing such a sensitive method. For this reason, we are trying out double-barrel sidepore electrodes that should

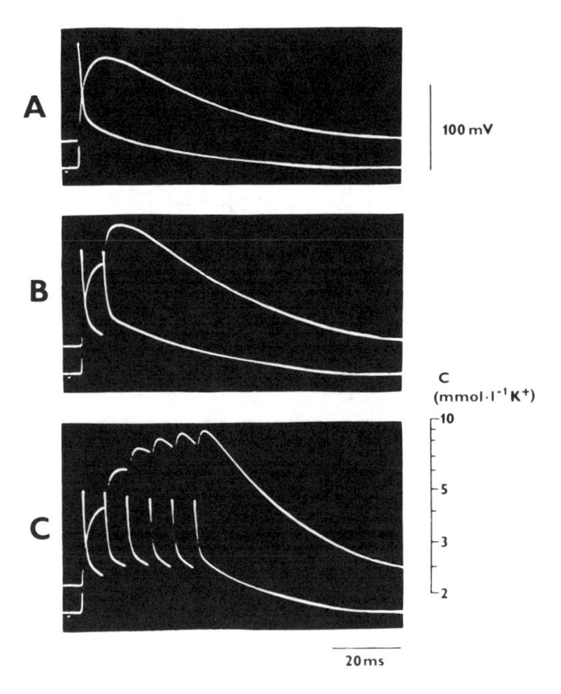

Figure 9 Extracellularly recorded changes in K_e^+ (upper traces in each record) during passage of individual action potentials (lower traces, intracellular recordings) along a single muscle fiber (Sartorius muscle of *Rana esculenta*). The Ringer solution was of the following composition (in mmol/l): Na^+ 115.0, K^+ 2.5, Ca^{2+} 1.8, $NaHCO_3$ 2.0, sucrose 300.0, and pH 7.1. A, B and C present K_e^+ changes in response to one, two and six action potentials, respectively. Temperature of the bath was 22 °C. The tip resistance of the K^+ selective electrode and reference channel was 95 and 100 MO respectively. From ''Ion-selective Microelectrodes—A New Tool for Studying Ionic Movements in Working Muscles'' by P. Hník and F. Vyskočil in T. Zeuthen (Ed.), *The Application of Ion Selective Microelectrodes*, pp. 157-172. Amsterdam: Elsevier. Copyright 1981 by Elsevier/North Holland Biomedical Press. Reprinted with permission.

make the measurement of resting and working K^+ in human muscles more accurate.

DISCUSSION

Physiological Implications of K_e^+ Changes in Skeletal Muscles at Rest, During and After Activity

The fact that it is now possible to directly measure changes in K_e^+ in the muscle during and after activity necessarily leads to a number of sig-

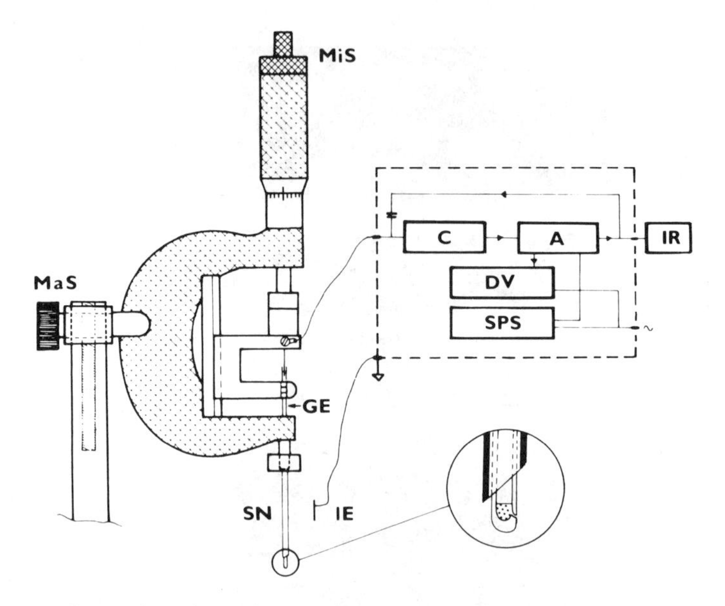

Figure 10 Schema of the device for introducing a steel trocar needle into human muscle. Horseshoe holder fixed to a solid bar may be moved by a macroscrew (MaS). Glass capillary (GE) inserted into a steel intramuscular needle (SN) may be protruded out of the needle tip by means of a micrometer screw (MiS). The tip of the sidepore electrode is shown in the inset. A block diagram of the recording set-up is shown on the right. C—floating calibrator, A—DC amplifier, IR—ink recorder, DV—digital voltmeter, SPS—stabilized power supply, IE—indifferent reference electrode. From "The Measurement of K_e^+ Concentration Changes in Human Muscles During Volitional Contractions" by F. Vyskočil, P. Hník, H. Rehfeldt, R. Vejsada, and E. Ujec, 1983, *Pflügers Archiv*, **399**, pp. 235-237. Copyright 1983 by Springer Verlag. Reprinted with permission.

nificant physiological implications. These implications were pointed out in a previous review (Hník & Vyskočil, 1981) and are only listed here with a few additional comments.

It seems a very attractive hypothesis to assume that the transient accumulation of K^+ in the interstitial space during muscle activity is of considerable further physiological significance for tissue elements coming within the scope of these concentration changes. The elements to be considered include presynaptic motor nerve terminals, the muscle cell itself and its metabolism, effect upon the contractile apparatus, smooth vascular musculature and sensory nerve terminals (whether from encapsulated muscle receptors, free myelinated or nonmyelinated endings).

Nerve presynaptic terminals. Both quantal (Cooke, Okamoto, & Quastel, 1973; Parsons, Hofmann, & Feigin, 1965; Vizi & Vyskočil, 1979) and nonquantal acetylcholine release (Vizi & Vyskočil, 1979) are enhanced when K_e^+ is increased. This is in agreement with the finding of Takeuchi and

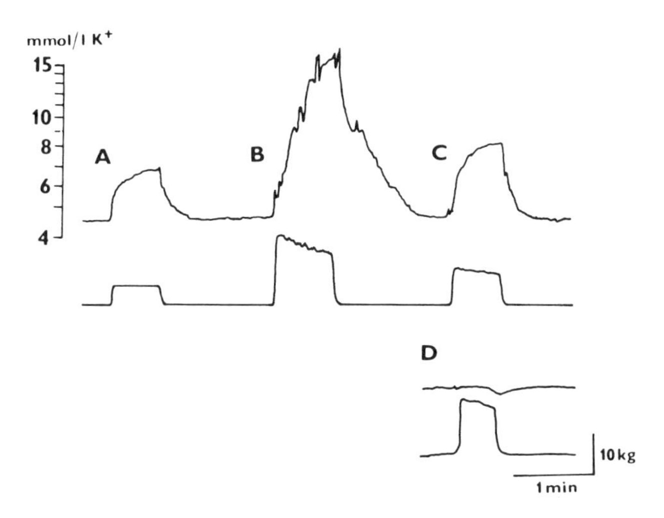

Figure 11 Representative records of K_e^+ changes in human bracioradialis muscle. Upper traces—K_e^+ changes, lower traces—myographic records of muscle contractions. A—slight voluntary effort, B—maximum contraction, C—intermediate effort, D—control record with sidepore electrode without ion-exchanger. Scale on the left—K^+ concentration calibration. Myograph calibration and time scale on the right. From "The Measurement of K_e^+ Concentration Changes in Human Muscles During Volitional Contractions" by F. Vyskočil, P. Hník, H. Rehfeldt, R. Vejsada, and E. Ujec, 1983, *Pflügers Archiv*, **399**, pp. 235-237. Copyright 1983 by Springer Verlag. Reprinted with permission.

Takeuchi (1961) about the increased frequency of miniature end-plate potentials when the extracellular K^+ concentration is elevated. It may thus be expected that, within a certain range, higher K^+ concentrations may enhance neuromuscular transmission.

Influence of elevated K_e^+ on the muscle membrane, metabolism and contraction properties. As has been pointed out in more detail in our previous article (Hník & Vyskočil, 1981), physiological levels of K_e^+ attained during muscle activity (usually from about 5 to 10 to 15 mmol/l K^+) are significant enough to enhance the activity of a number of enzymes apparently involved in membrane transport characteristics. These include the Mg^{2+} dependent neutral phosphatase (alias p-nitrophenylphosphatase) and others. A highly increased excitability of the of the muscle fiber membrane has been shown by Vyskočil (1974, 1977) under conditions when K_e^+ was elevated and the muscle was being bathed in a chloride-free medium. Higher K_e^+ also increases the turnover of membrane phosphatidylinositol and phosphatidylserine (Novotný, Živný, & Saleh, 1978).

Furthermore, elevated K^+ concentrations undoubtedly affect muscle metabolism, for example, increased oxygen consumption (Fenn & Cobb, 1934) and heat production (Solandt, 1936). An interesting aspect was brought up by Boldyrev and Tverdislov (1978) who pointed out that the activity of more than 70 enzymes is dependent upon monovalent cations and that out of 33 named enzymes, 31 are activated by potassium ions.

Increased K_e^+ has also been reported to enhance muscle twitch tension (Chapman, 1969). Apparently, higher K_e^+ increases the availability of intracellular Ca^{2+} for release during activation of the muscle membrane.

All these results, reviewed in more detail by Hník and Vyskočil (1981), show that K^+ can play a contradictory role in striated muscle physiology according to whether there is accumulation or loss of K^+ from working muscles.

The loss of K^+ continuously rises during muscle activity, but the reuptake into muscle cells is relatively slow (Hník et al., 1976). This means that both enzymatic and contraction properties of working muscles will be greatly modified according to the intensity and duration of the work cycle and the possibilities of replenishing the muscle K^+ levels.

Vascular smooth musculature. Immediate functional hyperemia at the beginning of muscle activity is a generally known phenomenon. A number of phenomena are apparently involved—a major role is played again by increased K_e^+, which is considered to act locally upon smooth vascular muscles (Biamino & Wessel, 1973; Brecht, Konold, & Gebert, 1969; Kjellmer, 1965; Mohrman & Sparks, 1974; Tominaga, Suzuki, & Nakamura, 1973), although inorganic phosphate (Hilton, 1977) and other factors are, no doubt, also involved. The effect of local changes in the muscle induced by activity may serve as another example of the feedback mechanisms adapting the muscle to its function.

Muscle afferents. Increased concentrations of K^+ have convincingly been shown to affect the function of different types of sensory afferents in the muscle.

- The threshold of muscle spindles (Kidd, Kučera, & Vaillant, 1971) and Paciniform corpuscles (Akoyev & Elman, 1974) to mechanical stimuli is lowered when K_e^+ is increased. This means that the sensitivity of these encapsulated mechanoreceptors is enhanced.
- Small myelinated muscle afferents that terminate as free nerve endings in the muscle interstitial space (Barker, Ip, & Adal, 1962; Stacey, 1969; Zelená & Hník, 1963) were originally ascribed a pressure-pain function (Bessou & Laporte, 1960; Paintal, 1961). We have attempted to demonstrate that it is possible to activate these terminals by intra-arterial infusions of physiological concentrations of K^+ (Hník, Hudlická, Kučera,

& Payne, 1969). These experiments led to the conclusion that these nonproprioceptive myelinated afferents are part of a nonspecific chemoreceptor system signaling changes in the extracellular space occurring in working muscles (Hník, 1981). This could explain the mechanism triggering the cardiovascular and respiratory responses induced by muscle activity (Hník et al., 1969). This postulate has recently been confirmed by Rybicki, Waldrop, and Kaufman (1985) and Tallarida, Baldoni, Peruzzi, Raimondi, Di Nardo, Massaro, Vissigalli, Franconi, and San Giorgi (1985).

- The unmyelinated Group IV afferents, however, are apparently also activated by enhanced K_e^+. Kniffki, Mense, and Schmidt (1977) have shown that, besides bradykinin and 5-hydroxytryptamine, intra-arterial injections of potassium activate Group III and IV muscle afferents project into the spinocervical tract and may serve as a pathway for muscular nociception in the cat. This indicates that Group IV afferents may mediate muscle pain during contractions due to raised K_e^+ and that it is not only induced by muscle work performed under hypoxic or ischemic conditions (e.g., Bessou & Laporte, 1958).

Depletion of Potassium From Working Muscle

The accumulation of K_e^+ during muscle work is transient and, as has been pointed out above, may be of further physiological significance. However, long-term muscle activity also leads to K^+ depletion as the result of the relatively slow reuptake of K^+ by muscle fibers. According to our calculations based on computer evaluation, the cat gastrocnemius muscle loses about 0.3 nmol K^+/impulse per gram muscle weight after a 20 s isometric tetanus at 50 Hz (Hník & Vyskočil, 1981). This seems to be a fair estimate when compared with the results of Mohrman and Sparks (1974) who reported, in the dog tibialis anterior and extensor digitorum longus muscles, a loss of approximately 0.5 nmol K^+/impulse per g muscle weight as assessed by flame photometry.

An interesting comparison of these numerical values may be made when confronted with the results of Hirche, Schumacher, and Hagemann (1980). These authors stimulated the dog gastrocnemius muscle with 0.2 s trains at 100 Hz every 0.7 s. In order to express their results in comparable "units," the 148 μeq K^+/min per 100 g muscle weight may also be stated as 148 μeq K^+/1720 impulses per 100 g. This means that the muscles in their experiments lost 0.86 nmol/impulse per g muscle weight. It is thus obvious that muscles of different species and activated under different working conditions have a closely similar range of K^+ loss, that is, between 0.3 nmol/impulse per g (Hník & Vyskočil, 1981), 0.5 nmol/impulse per g (Mohrman & Sparks, 1974), and 0.86 nmol/impulse per g (Hirsche et al.,

1980). The calculations of Sjøgaard, Adams, and Saltin (1985) concerning the loss of K^+ in man during maximum exercise, although approximative, give surprisingly close values to those mentioned above. When recalculated per g muscle weight, the knee extensors performing one-legged dynamic knee extensions lose about 0.7 nmol/impulse per g muscle weight.

These results again indicate that irrespective of the type of muscle contractions (isotonic-isometric, tetanic or twitch-like contractions, short-term or long-term activity), one obtains closely analogous results as far as the loss of K^+ from contracting muscles is concerned. This conclusion, together with our finding that K^+ is being lost even when only action potentials are generated without muscle shortening, shows that it is the bioelectrical rather than the mechanical events that are responsible for K^+ extrusion and the eventual loss of potassium from working muscles.

Not much is known about the relationship between ionic equilibria and muscle fatigue. It seems quite clear, however, that ionic dysbalance lasting for up to 30 min after 12 min exercise, according to the regimen employed by Hirsche et al. (1980), will necessarily lower the working capacity of skeletal muscles. An intriguing problem arises from these conclusions. How does physical training modify this ionic dysbalance in the course of long-lasting muscle activity?

REFERENCES

Akoyev, G.N., & Elman, S.I. (1974). Rol' ionov kaliya v deyatelnosti telets Pachini. *Fiziologicheskii Zhurnal,* **60**, 55-61.

Barker, D., Ip, M.C., & Adal, M.N. (1962). A correlation between the receptor population of the cat's soleus muscle and the afferent fibre-diameter spectrum of the nerve supplying it. In D. Barker (Ed.), *Symposium on Muscle Receptors* (pp. 259-261). Hong Kong: Hong Kong University Press.

Beránek, R. (1964). Intracellular stimulation myography in man. *Electroencephalography and Clinical Neurophysiology,* **16**, 301-304.

Beránek, R. (1965). Intracellular Electromyography in Man. (In Czech., with English Summary). *Babákova Sbírka No. 39* (pp. 1-117). Prague: Avicenum.

Bessou, P., & Laporte, Y. (1958). Activation des fibres afférentes amyéliniquées d'origine musculaire. *Compte Rendu des Séances de la Société de Biologie,* **152**, 1587-1590.

Bessou, P., & Laporte, Y. (1960). Activation des fibres afférentes myéliniquées de petit calibre, d'origine musculaire (fibres du groupe III). *Compte Rendu des Séances de la Société de Biologie,* **154**, 1093-1096.

Biamino, G., & Wessel, H.-J. (1973). Potassium induced relaxation of vascular smooth muscle: A possible mechanism of exercise hyperaemia. *Pflügers Archiv,* **343**, 95-106.

Boldyrev, A.A., & Tverdislov, V.A. (1978). Molekularnaya organizatsiya i mekhanizm funktsionirovaniya Na-nasosa. *Biofizika,* **10**, 5-149.

Brecht, K., Konold, P., & Gebert, G. (1969). The effect of potassium and other vasoactive agents on isolated arterial segments of the muscular type. *Physiologia Bohemoslovaka,* **18**, 15-22.

Chapman, J.B. (1969). Potentiating effect of potassium on skeletal muscle twitch. *American Journal of Physiology,* **217**, 898-902.

Cier, J.F.,Lacour, J.R., & Cier, A. (1960). Travail musculaire et équilibres ioniques chez le Rat. *Pathologie et Biologie,* **8**, 1147-1154.

Conway, E.J. (1957). Nature and significance of concentration of potassium and sodium ions in skeletal muscle. *Physiological Reviews,* **37**, 84-132.

Cooke, J.D., Okamoto, K., & Quastel, D.M.J. (1973). The role of calcium in depolarization—Secretion coupling at the motor nerve terminal. *Journal of Physiology,* **228**, 459-497.

Costill, D.L., & Saltin, B. (1975). Muscle glycogen and electrolytes following exercise and thermal dehydration. In A. Howald & J.R. Poortmans (Eds.), *Metabolic adaptation to prolonged physical exercise* (pp. 352-360). Basel: Birkhaüser Verlag.

Fenn, W.O. (1936). Electrolytes in muscle. *Physiological Reviews,* **16**, 450-487.

Fenn, W.O., & Cobb, D.M. (1934). The potassium equilibrium in muscle. *Journal of General Physiology,* **17**, 629-656.

Gebert, G. (1970). Changes in K^+ and Na^+ activity in the extracellular space of skeletal muscle during muscular work. *Pflügers Archiv,* **319**, 162.

Haralambie, G. (1975). Changes in electrolytes and trace elements during long-lasting exercise. In H. Howald & J.R. Poortmans (Eds.), *Metabolic adaptation to prolonged physical exercise* (pp. 340-351). Basel: Birkhaüser Verlag.

Hilton, S.M. (1977). Evidence for phosphate as a mediator of functional hyperaemia in skeletal muscles. *Pflügers Archiv,* **369**, 151-159.

Hinke, J.A.M. (1961). The measurement of sodium and potassium activities in the squid axon by means of cations-selective glass microelectrodes. *Journal of Physiology,* **156**, 314-355.

Hirche, H., Schumacher, E., & Hagemann, H. (1980). Extracellular K^+ concentration and K^+ balance of the gastrocnemius muscle of the dog during exercise. *Pflügers Archiv,* **387**, 231-237.

Hník, P. (1981). Peripheral neural control of cardiovascular and respiratory responses to isometric exercise. In F. Obál & H. Benek (Eds.), *Advances in physiological sciences; 18, Environmental physiology* (pp. 219-227). Budapest: Pergamon Press—Akadémiai Kiadó.

Hník, P., Holas, M., Krekule, I., Kříž, N., Mejsnar, J., Smieško, V., Ujec, E., & Vyskočil, F. (1976). Work induced potassium changes in skeletal muscle and effluent venous blood assessed by liquid ion-exchanger microelectrodes. *Pflügers Archiv,* **362**, 85-94.

Hník, P., Hudlická, O., Kučera, J., & Payne, R. (1969). Activation of muscle afferents by non-proprioceptive stimuli. *American Journal of Physiology,* **217**, 1451-1457.

Hník, P., Kříž, N., Vyskočil, F., Smieško, V., Mejsnar, J., Ujec, E., & Holas, M. (1973). Work induced potassium changes in muscle venous effluent blood measured by ion-specific electrodes. *Pflügers Archiv,* **338**, 177-181.

Hník & Vyskočil, F. (1981). Ion-selective microelectrodes—a new tool for studying ionic movements in working muscles. In T. Zeuthen (Ed.), *The application of ion selective microelectrodes* (pp. 157-172). Amsterdam: Elsevier.

Hník, P., Vyskočil, F., Kříž, N., & Holas, M. (1972). Work-induced increase of extracellular potassium concentration in muscle measured by ion-specific electrodes. *Brain Research,* **40**, 559-562.

Hodgkin, A.L., & Horowicz, P. (1957). The differential action of hypertonic solutions on the twitch and action potential of a muscle fibre. *Journal of Physiology* (London), **136**, 17P-18P.

Kidd, G.L., Kučera, J., & Vaillant, C.H. (1971). The influence of the interstitial concentration of K^+ on the activity of muscle receptors. *Physiologica Bohemoslovenica,* **20**, 95-108.

Kjellmer, I. (1965). The potassium ion as vasodilator during muscular exercise. *Acta Physiologica Scandinavica,* **63**, 460-468.

Kniffki, K.D., Mense, S., & Schmidt, R.F. (1977). The spinocervical tract as a possible pathway for muscular nociception. *Journal of Physiology* (Paris), **73**, 359-366.

Koryta, J. (Ed.). (1980). *Medical and biological applications of electrochemical devices.* Chichester, England: John Wiley and Sons.

Lind, A.R., McNicol, G.W., & Donald, K.W. (1966). Circulatory adjustments to sustained (static) muscular activity. In K. Evang & K. Lange Andersen (Eds.), *Proceedings of the Beitostölen Symposium* (pp. 38-63). Baltimore, MD: Williams and Wilkins.

Mohrman, D.E., & Sparks, H.V. (1974). Role of potassium ions in the vascular response to a brief tetanus. *Circulation Research,* **35**, 384-390.

Novotný, I., Živný, A., & Saleh, F. (1978). The effect of potassium depolarization on ^{32}P-labelling of phosphatidylinositol and phosphatidylserine in frog sartorius muscle. *Physiologia Bohemoslovaca,* **27**, 477-483.

Paintal, A.S. (1961). Participation by pressure-pain receptors of mammalian muscles in the flexion reflex. *Journal of Physiology* (London), **156**, 498-514.

Parsons, R.L., Hofmann, W.W., & Feigin, G.A. (1965). Presynaptic effects of potassium ion on the mammalian neuromuscular junction. *Nature,* **208**, 590-591.

Prankerd, T.A.J. (1961). *The red cell. An account of its chemical physiology and pathophysiology*. Oxford, England: Blackwell.

Rybicki, K.J., Waldrop, T.G., Kaufman, M.P. (1985). Increasing gracilis muscle interstitial potassium concentrations stimulate group III and IV afferents. *Journal of Applied Physiology,* **58**, 936-941.

Sjøgaard, G., Adams, R.P., & Saltin, B. (1985). Water and ion shifts in skeletal muscle of humans with intense dynamic knee extension. *American Journal of Physiology,* **248**, R190-R196.

Solandt, D.Y. (1936). The effect of potassium on the excitability and resting metabolism of frog's muscle. *Journal of Physiology* (London), **86**, 162-170.

Sorokina, Z.A. (1964). Metod izmereniya aktivnosti ionov kaliya i natriya vnutri kletok. *Byulleten' éksperimental'noi biologii i meditsiny (Moskva),* **10**, 119-121.

Stacey, M.J. (1969). Free nerve endings in skeletal muscle of the cat. *Journal of Anatomy,* **105**, 231-254.

Syková, E., Hník, P., & Vycklický, V. (Eds.) (1981). *Ion-selective microelectrodes and their use in excitable tissues.* New York and London: Plenum Press.

Takeuchi, A., & Takeuchi, N. (1961). Changes in potassium concentration around motor nerve terminals, produced by current flow, and their effects on neuromuscular transmission. *Journal of Physiology* (London), **155**, 46-58.

Tallarida, G., Baldoni, F., Peruzzi, G., Raimondi, G., Di Nardo, P., Massaro, M., Visigalli, G., Franconi, G., & San Giorgi, M. (1985). Cardiorespiratory reflexes from muscles during dynamic and static exercise in the dog. *Journal of Applied Physiology,* **58**, 844-852.

Tominaga, S., Suzuki, T., & Nakamura, T. (1973). Evaluation of roles of potassium, inorganic phosphate, osmolarity, pH, pCO_2, and adenosine or AMP in exercise and reactive hyperaemias in canine hindlimb muscles. *Tohoku Journal of Experimental Medicine,* **109**, 347-373.

Vizi, E.S., & Vyskočil, F. (1979). Changes in total and quantal release of acetylcholine in the mouse diaphragm during activation and inhibition of membrane ATPase. *Journal of Physiology* (London), **286**, 1-14.

Vyskočil, F. (1974). Action potentials of the rat diaphragm and their sensitivity to tetrodotoxin during postnatal development and old age. *Pflügers Archiv,* **352**, 155-163.

Vyskočil, F. (1977). Diazepam blockade of repetitive action potentials in skeletal muscle fibres. A model of its possible control action. *Brain Research,* **352**, 315-328.

Vyskočil, F., & Kříž, N. (1972). Modification of single and double-barrel potassium-specific microelectrodes for various physiological experiments. *Pflügers Archiv,* **337**, 265-276.

Vyskočil, F., Hník, P., Rehfeldt, H., Vejsada, R., & Ujec, E. (1983). The measurement of K_e^+ concentration changes in human muscles during volitional contractions. *Pflügers Archiv,* **399**, 235-237.

Walker, J.L., Jr. (1971). Ion-specific liquid ion exchanger microelectrodes. *Analytical Chemistry*, **43**, 89A-92A.

Walker, J.L., Jr., & Brown, H.M. (1977). Intracellular ionic activity measurements in nerve and muscle. *Physiological Reviews*, **57**, 729-778.

Zelená, J., & Hník, P. (1963). Motor and receptor units in the soleus muscle after nerve regeneration in very young rats. *Physiologia Bohemoslovaca*, **12**, 277-290.

Zeuthen, T. (Ed.). (1981). *The application of ion-selective microelectrodes.* Amsterdam, New York, and Oxford: Elsevier/North Holland Biomedical Press.

Muscle Blood Flow-Fatigue Relationship

Robert B. Armstrong
M. Harold Laughlin
Oral Roberts University
Tulsa, Oklahoma, U.S.A.

In the Ciba Foundation Symposium on muscle fatigue that was held several years ago, Saltin discussed the apparent progressive recruitment of motor units during prolonged submaximal exercise and the possible role of this progression in the development of muscular fatigue (Saltin, 1981). Saltin stated that one important aspect in understanding the effects of progressive motor unit fatigue in a muscle during moderate exercise concerns the distribution of blood flow within the muscle. However, as he pointed out, the magnitude and distribution of blood flow in individual muscles during prolonged exercise was experimentally unresolved.

We (Armstrong & Laughlin, 1983, 1984; Laughlin & Armstrong, 1982, 1983) have been studying the distribution of blood flow within and among muscles during locomotion as a function of fiber types and recruitment patterns over the past several years in several animal models. We have not specifically designed our experiments to study the phenomenon of fatigue per se, but some of our results should be of interest in considering this topic. Unfortunately, the necessary techniques for mapping distribution of flow cannot be applied to human subjects, so the data presented are from studies on rats and miniature swine. There are some apparent differences in the blood flow responses to exercise between humans and these species of animals. Nonetheless, the striking differences in distribution of flow within the muscles that we have observed in the animals should be considered in fatigue models with a metabolic basis.

METHODS

Rat Experiments

In the rodent experiments, male Sprague-Dawley rats with body weights of 400 to 600 g were used. Following training of the animals on a treadmill, surgery was performed to implant Silastic catheters (Laughlin & Armstrong, 1982; Laughlin, Armstrong, White, & Rouk, 1982). One was placed in the ascending aorta via the right carotid artery for subsequent microsphere infusion, and one was placed in the descending aorta via the left renal artery for reference blood sample withdrawal. The rats were allowed to recover for 2 days postsurgery, and the blood flow experiments were performed. Typically, blood flows at two to three time points were measured in each rat using two to three different infusions of 15 μ microspheres labeled with different isotopes. Following exercise, the animals were sacrificed and about 32 hindlimb muscles or muscle parts plus a number of other tissues and organs were dissected free and analyzed for blood flows (Laughlin et al., 1982).

Pig Experiments

In the pig experiments, female Pitman-Moore miniature swine weighing 19 to 25 kg were used. During preliminary treadmill training, the animals' $\dot{V}O_2max$ was determined. Surgery was then performed to implant Silastic catheters in the left atrium for microsphere infusion, the descending aorta via the internal mammary artery for reference blood sample withdrawal, and the right atrium for mixed venous blood sampling. The pigs required about 3 to 4 weeks of recovery before they were able to perform at speeds eliciting the previously determined $\dot{V}O_2max$. On the day of the blood flow experiment, the animals performed on the treadmill and blood flow was measured at 5 time points with 15 μ microspheres labeled with different isotopes. $\dot{V}O_2$, colonic temperature, blood lactate and pH, heart rate, and arterial pressure were also monitored.

RESULTS AND DISCUSSION

Rat Muscle Blood Flows

When blood flows in rat muscles are plotted as a function of running speed, there is no evidence of a limitation in flow to the muscles (Figure 1) (Armstrong & Laughlin, 1985b; Laughlin & Armstrong, 1982). When the animal is standing on the treadmill prior to exercise (PE in Figure 1), blood flows among and within the hindlimb muscles are proportional to the slow-twitch-oxidative (SO) fiber type population. At the treadmill speeds from 15 through 105 m/min, blood flows are proportional to the fast-twitch-oxidative-glycolytic (FOG) fiber type populations in the muscles. At 105 m/min, which is the highest running speed reported in the literature for rats, flows in deep red portions of muscles are about 5-fold higher than in in the peripheral white portions (e.g., red vastus lateralis [VL_R] versus white vastus lateralis [VL_W] muscles in Figure 1). Even at the very

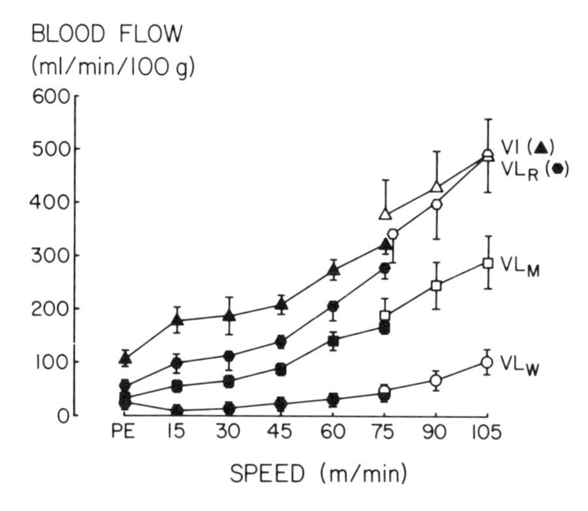

Figure 1 Blood flows in rat quadriceps femoris muscles during preexercise (PE) standing on the treadmill and at 1 min of treadmill locomotion at speeds of 15 through 105 m/min. Muscles are vastus intermedius (VI) and the red (VL_R), middle (VL_M), and white (VL_W) portions of vastus lateralis. Solid symbols are data from "Muscular Blood Flow Distribution Patterns as a Function of Running Speed in Rats" by M.H. Laughlin and R.B. Armstrong, 1982, *American Journal of Physiology*, **243**, pp. H296-H306. Copyright 1982 by the American Physiological Society. Adapted by permission. Open symbols are data from "Rat Muscle Blood Flows During High Speed Locomotion" by R.B. Armstrong and M.H. Laughlin, 1985, *Journal of Applied Physiology*, **59**, 1322-1328. Copyright 1985 by the American Physiological Society. Adapted by permission.

high running speeds used in these experiments, there is no evidence that there is a cardiovascular limitation in delivery of blood to the muscles, since the relationships of flow as a function of speed for the muscles are linear.

The progressive elevations in blood flow to the muscles apparently are due to increases in cardiac output, since shunting of flow from the viscera and other nonmuscular tissues does not change above speeds of 40 to 60 m/min (Figure 2). These data, and other observations from our laboratories (e.g., Armstrong, Laughlin, Rome, & Taylor, 1983), suggest that the major limitation to exercise in rats is motivational or behavioral. Most laboratory rats refuse to exercise at the high intensities used in these experiments, and even for low-intensity exercise experiments, their disposition makes them a questionable animal model for studies of fatigue.

Nonetheless, when rats undergo an endurance training program, there is a significant redistribution of flow within muscles during treadmill exercise (30 m/min), which suggests that training increases the efficiency of O_2 delivery to the oxidative fibers (Armstrong & Laughlin, 1984). As depicted in Figure 3, flow is maintained in the deep red parts of the trained muscles over time, whereas in the untrained animals there is a decline

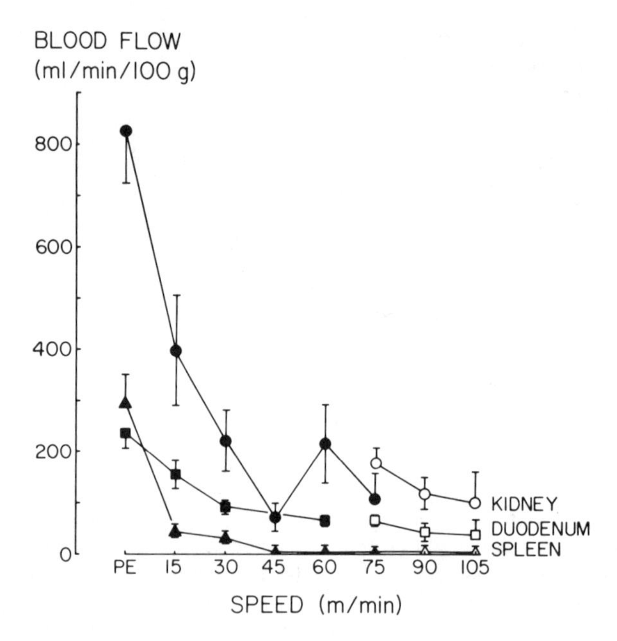

Figure 2 Visceral organ blood flows in rats during preexercise (PE) standing on the treadmill and at 1 min of treadmill locomotion at speeds of 15 through 105 m/min. Solid symbols are data from "Muscular Blood Flow Distribution Patterns as a Function of Running Speed in Rats" by M.H. Laughlin and R.B. Armstrong, 1982, *American Journal of Physiology*, **243**, pp. H296-H306. Copyright 1982 by the American Physiological Society. Adapted by permission. Open symbols are data from "Rat Muscle Blood Flows During High Speed Locomotion" by R.B. Armstrong and M.H. Laughlin, 1985, *Journal of Applied Physiology*, **59**, pp. 1322-1328. Copyright 1985 by the American Physiological Society. Adapted by permission.

in flow in the red muscles and concomitant elevation in flow in the white muscles. Total hindlimb muscle flow during exercise was not affected by training, so the alteration was in distribution of the available flow. It is not possible to determine from the experiments whether the untrained animals fatigue sooner because of declining blood flows, or whether blood flows in red muscle parts declined because of decreasing performance of their constituent fibers.

During prolonged, low-intensity treadmill exercise (15 m/min, a fast walk), blood flows in rat muscles show interesting patterns (Figure 4) (Laughlin & Armstrong, 1983). Blood flows in muscles with significant numbers of FOG fibers increase rapidly at the beginning of exercise, then remain elevated or decrease to a steady state level by about 5 to 15 min of walking (numbers 2 and 1 respectively, in Figure 4). However, in these muscles, flows then progressively increase with time of exercise for about 1 hr, and may attain very high levels (e.g., adductor longus muscle, Figure

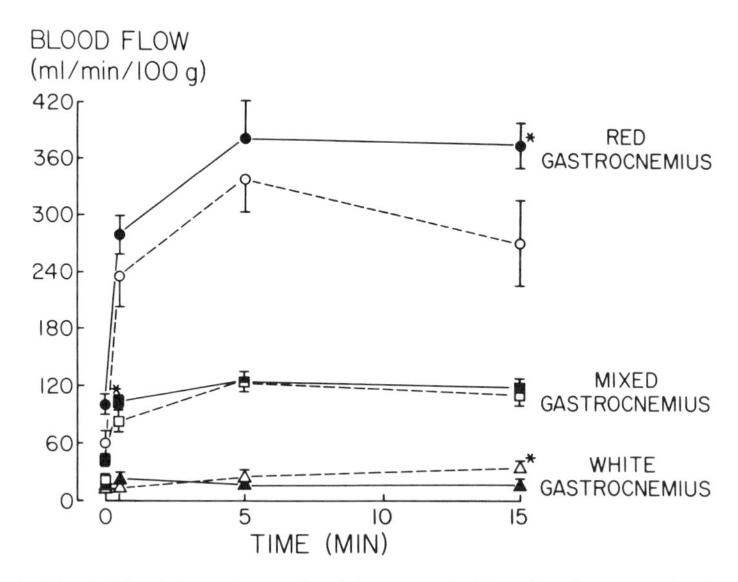

Figure 3 Muscle blood flows in untrained (open symbols) and endurance trained (closed symbols) rats during preexercise (0 min) and during 15 min of treadmill running at 30 m/min. Asterisk (*) indicates the mean value is different from the respective untrained or trained mean value ($p < 0.05$). From "Exercise Blood Flow Patterns Within and Among Rat Muscles After Training" by R.B. Armstrong and M.H. Laughlin, 1984, *American Journal of Physiology*, **246**, pp. H814-H824. Copyright 1984 by the American Physiological Society. Reprinted by permission.

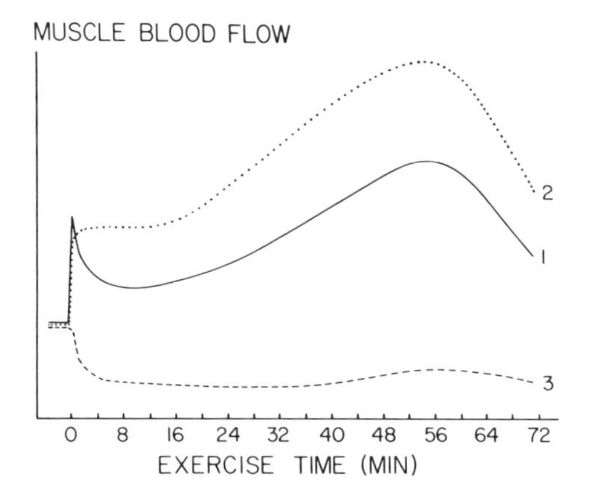

Figure 4 The 3 general blood flow patterns observed among the hindlimb muscles of rats during prolonged low-intensity treadmill exercise (15 m/min, a fast walk). From "Rat Muscle Blood Flows as a Function of Time During Prolonged Slow Treadmill Exercise" by M.H. Laughlin and R.B. Armstrong, 1983, *American Journal of Physiology*, **244**, pp. H814-H824. Copyright 1983 by the American Physiological Society. Reprinted by permission.

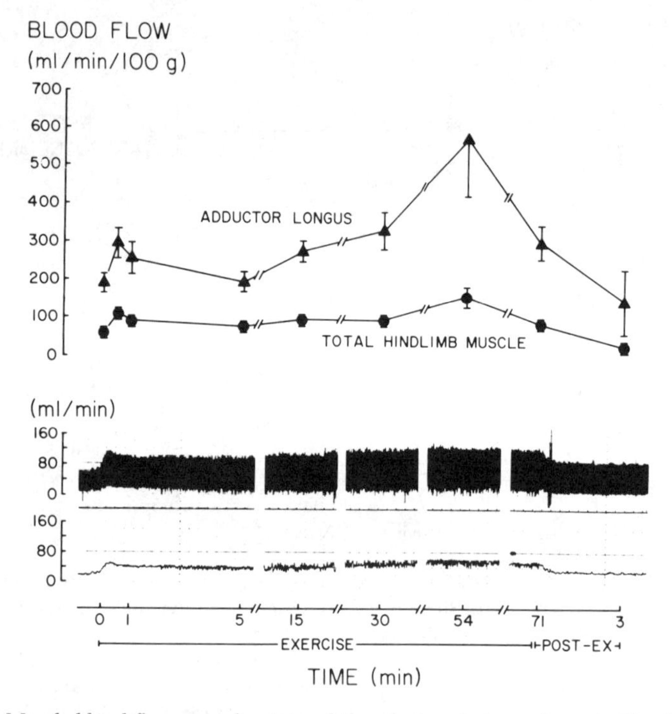

Figure 5 Muscle blood flows as a function of time during prolonged treadmill walking (15 m/min) as measured by radiolabeled microspheres (top panel) and by an electromagnetic flow probe positioned on the descending aorta just above the iliac bifurcation (bottom panel). For the flow probe recordings, the upper trace is the raw signal, and the lower trace is the average aortic flow. From "Metabolic Indicators of Fiber Recruitment in Mammalian Muscles During Locomotion" by R.B. Armstrong and M.H. Laughlin, 1985, *Journal of Experimental Biology*, **115**, pp. 201-213. Reprinted by permission.

5). Blood flows in these muscles then declines as the animal fatigues and does not keep a steady pace on the treadmill (Figures 4 and 5). This pattern of blood flow during prolonged slow exercise was independently verified with flow probes positioned on the descending aorta just above the bifurcation of the iliac arteries (Figure 5). We (Laughlin & Armstrong, 1983) hypothesized the progressive rise in blood flow in the muscles could be due to (a) progressive recruitment of new motor units as the initially recruited units fatigue; (b) gradual accumulation of a vasodilator substance; (c) progressive fatigue or withdrawal of sympathetic vasoconstrictor influences; or (d) progressive rise in body temperature. We have tested the first hypothesis with glycogen depletion and EMG experiments, and progressive recruitment does not appear to be the underlying mechanism. As discussed below, progressive hyperthermia may explain the phenomenon.

Pig Muscle Blood Flows

When muscle blood flows in pigs are measured as a function of exercise intensity, similar patterns to those described for rats are observed. Figure 6 shows the $\dot{V}O_2$s for miniature swine plotted against speed. For the 8 animals included in this study, all attained $\dot{V}O_2$max at speeds from 16 to 18 km/hr, so the highest experimental mean data point represents $\dot{V}O_2$max. Figure 7 depicts typical blood flows in the deep red and superficial white parts of the skeletal muscles. Flows in the red parts were generally 1.5- to 2-fold higher than in the white parts. In 2 animals, flows were measured at 14.5, 16.0, 17.7, and 19.4 km/hr to determine if muscle blood flows plateau as a function of speed at $\dot{V}O_2$max (the dashed line in Figure 7 shows the data for one pig). In muscles of varying fiber compositions, blood flows did level off at or before $\dot{V}O_2$max. These data support the notion that maximal oxygen consumption may be limited by muscle perfusion in this species. As has been described previously, nonmuscular tissues show decreases in blood flow as a function of speed (Figure 8).

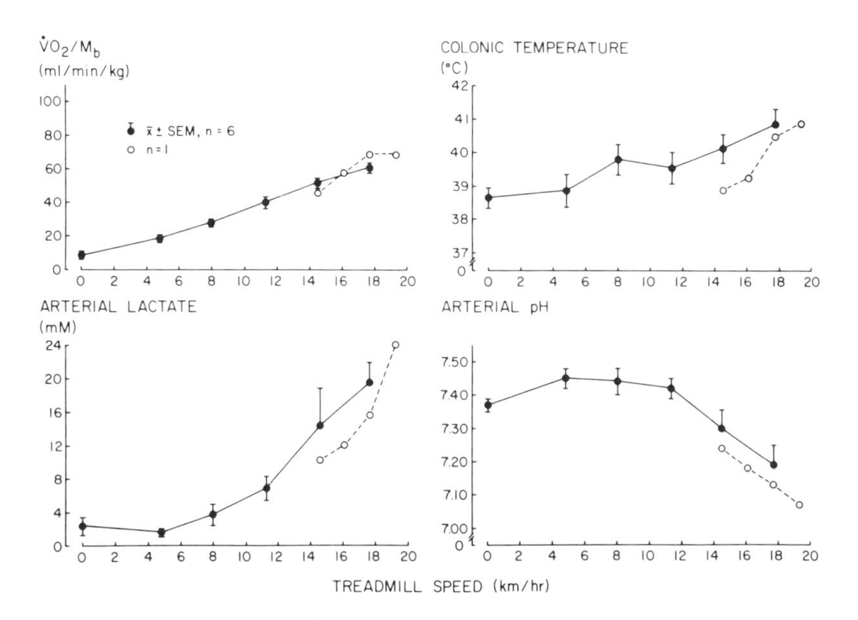

Figure 6 Oxygen consumption ($\dot{V}O_2$/Mb), colonic temperature, arterial lactate concentration, and arterial blood pH in female miniature swine during preexercise (0 km/hr) standing on the treadmill and at 3 to 5 min of treadmill locomotion at various speeds. At the highest running speed for the mean data (17.7 km/hr), all of the pigs were at or above $\dot{V}O_2$max as indicated by preliminary treadmill tests. Data are also shown for one pig that exercised at several speeds just below and just above $\dot{V}O_2$max.

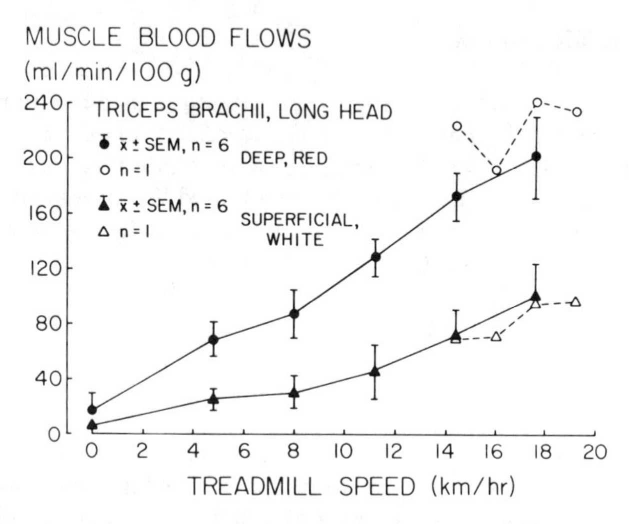

Figure 7 Blood flow data for red and white parts of the long head of triceps brachii in miniature swine as a function of treadmill speed. See caption of Figure 6 for further description.

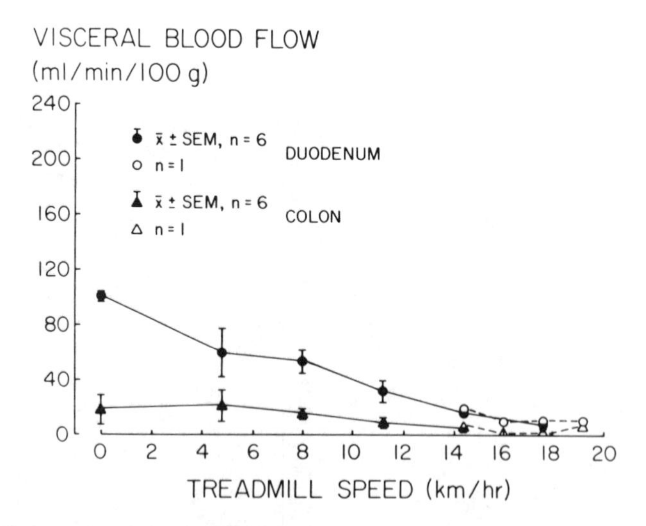

Figure 8 Representative visceral blood flows in miniature swine as a function of treadmill speed. See caption of Figure 6 for further description.

We have completed several experiments in which we followed muscle blood flows in pigs as a function of time at a treadmill speed that elicited about 60% of $\dot{V}O_2$max. Similar to what we previously observed in rats, muscle blood flows progressively rose with time to attain relatively high

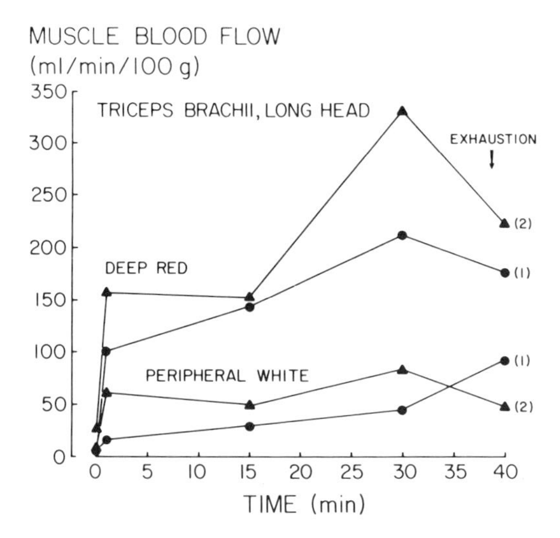

Figure 9 Muscle blood flows in two miniature swine as a function of time during treadmill exercise requiring about 60% of $\dot{V}O_2max$ (about 11.3 km/hr). Both pigs were beginning to falter by 30 to 35 min of exercise and were falling down at the time the 40 min flows were measured, so the 40 min flows do not represent steady running.

values (Figure 9). At this exercise intensity the animals were able to run steadily for about 35 min; as they began to lose the pace, muscle flows decreased (Figure 9). Similar patterns, that is, increases in flow with exercise time, were observed in the respiratory muscles (Figure 10) and visceral organs (Figure 11). $\dot{V}O_2$ increased gradually during the exercise bout, and there was a marked increase in body temperature (Figure 12). It is possible that the elevations in blood flow (and $\dot{V}O_2$) were a result of the increases in temperature. Also, the pig data suggest that the progressive elevations in flow over time that we observed in rats during low-intensity treadmill exercise may result from increasing body temperatures. We are planning experiments to test this hypothesis.

In summary, marked patterns of distribution of blood flow occur among and within the muscles of rats and pigs during locomotory exercise. Unfortunately, these measurements cannot presently be made in human subjects. Although our experiments have not been designed to study the fatigue process per se, the results have implications to the understanding of muscular fatigue.

Acknowledgments

Thanks are expressed to our technical staff, including Mike Delp, Debbie Jarrett, Ron Phelps, Ken Rouk, Robyn Stroup, and Judy White; to Judy

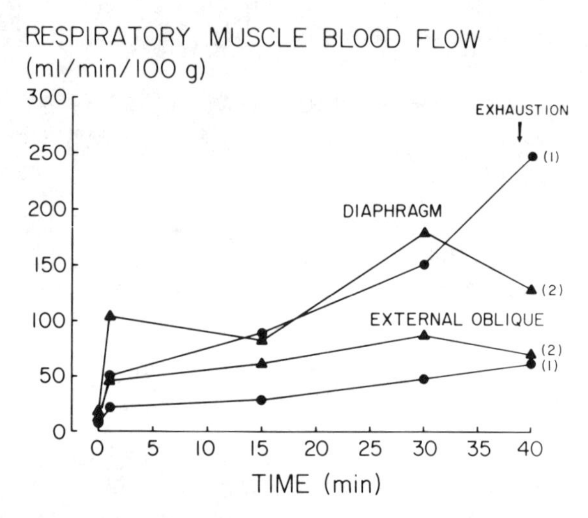

Figure 10 Respiratory muscle blood flows in two miniature swine as a function of time during treadmill exercise requiring about 60% of $\dot{V}O_2max$. See caption of Figure 9 for further explanation.

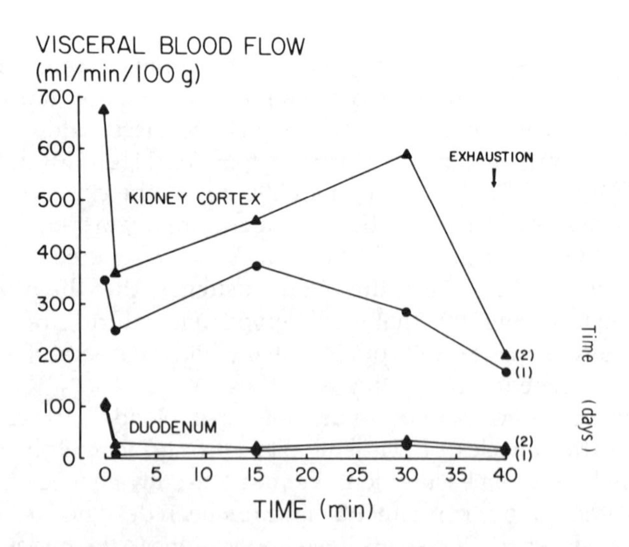

Figure 11 Representative visceral blood flows in two miniature swine as a function of time during treadmill exercise requiring about 60% of $\dot{V}O_2max$. See caption of Figure 9 for further explanation.

White for the artwork; and to Wanda Cuzick for her work on the manuscript. This research has been supported by NIH Grants AM25472, HL26963, and HL29428, AHA-Tulsa Chapter funds, and Oral Roberts University funds.

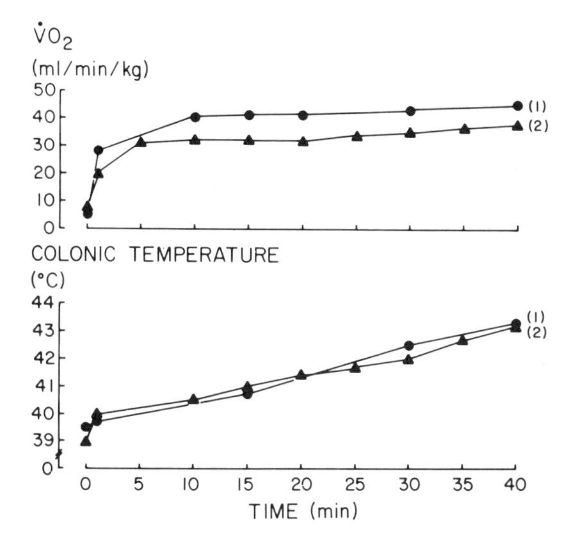

Figure 12 Oxygen consumption ($\dot{V}O_2$) and colonic temperature in two miniature swine as a function of time during treadmill exercise requiring about 60% $\dot{V}O_2max$. See caption of Figure 9 for further explanation.

REFERENCES

Armstrong, R.B., & Laughlin, M.H. (1983). Blood flows within and among rat muscles as a function of time during high speed treadmill exercise. *Journal of Physiology*, **344**, 189-208.

Armstrong, R.B., & Laughlin, M.H. (1984). Exercise blood flow patterns within and among rat muscles after training. *American Journal of Physiology*, **246**, H59-H68.

Armstrong, R.B., & Laughlin, M.H. (1985a). Metabolic indicators of fiber recruitment in mammalian muscles during locomotion. *Journal of Experimental Biology*, **115**, 201-213.

Armstrong, R.B., & Laughlin, M.H. (1985b). Rat muscle blood flows during high speed locomotion. *Journal of Applied Physiology*, **59**, 1322-1328.

Armstrong, R.B., Laughlin, M.H., Rome, L., & Taylor, C.R. (1983). Metabolism of rats running up and down an incline. *Journal of Applied Physiology*, **55**, 518-521.

Laughlin, M.H., & Armstrong, R.B. (1982). Muscular blood flow distribution patterns as a function of running speed in rats. *American Journal of Physiology*, **243**, H296-H306.

Laughlin, M.H., & Armstrong, R.B. (1983). Rat muscle blood flows as a function of time during prolonged slow treadmill exercise. *American Journal of Physiology*, **244**, H814-H824.

Laughlin, M.H., Armstrong, R.B., White, J., & Rouk, K. (1982). A method for using microspheres to measure muscle blood flow in exercising rats. *Journal of Applied Physiology*, **52**, 1629-1635.

Saltin, B. (1981). Muscle fiber recruitment and metabolism in prolonged exhaustive dynamic exercise. In R.H.T. Edwards (Ed.), *Human muscle fatigue: Physiological mechanisms* (pp. 41-58). London: Pitman Medical.

Electrical and Contractile Changes in Muscle Fatigue

David A. Jones
University College
London, England

Brenda Bigland-Ritchie
John B. Pierce Foundation
New Haven, Connecticut, U.S.A.

Everyone has experienced the feelings of fatigue and the increasing difficulty of continuing a given level of physical effort, while in sporting activities, fatigue, and how to avoid it, is of critical importance. Despite its importance, relatively little is known about the nature of the processes involved when fatigue is induced experimentally and even less is known of its causes in everyday life or during competitive activity.

For technical reasons the majority of studies, including our own, have been carried out on fatigue from isometric contractions. But in most sporting activities the muscles are moving, and it is power output, which comprises speed as well as force, that is of particular concern.

Here we discuss possible sites of failure in the neuromuscular system but will concentrate on two main aspects: (a) changes in electrical properties of the muscle fiber membrane during activity, and (b) alterations in muscle contractile characteristics and motor unit firing rates that appear to minimize the effects of changed electrical properties occurring during the first 60 s or so of a high force contraction. We will conclude by speculating on the relationship between the experimental findings for this type of contraction and the way muscles are used in real life.

FATIGUE OF CENTRAL ORIGIN

Central fatigue refers to conditions in which the force loss can be attributed to reduced motor drive failing to maintain muscle activation. It has been widely believed that even in the unfatigued state the central nervous system (CNS) is not capable of recruiting and maximally activating all motor units by voluntary effort. However, in 1954 Merton showed that the force of a maximum voluntary contraction (MVC) of the adductor pollicis muscle matched that from supramaximal tetanic stimulation of the ulnar nerve. Recently, Belanger and McComas (1981), using a somewhat different method, have confirmed that most human muscles can be fully activated by voluntary effort. Merton also concluded that for the adductor pollicis, full muscle activation was maintained during fatigue when the contraction was sustained with maximum effort for up to 3 min, since maximal nerve stimulation failed to increase the falling force. We have subsequently confirmed this observation in both large and small muscle groups but have found that maximum force can only be sustained by highly motivated and experienced subjects in the presence of visual feedback (Bigland-Ritchie, Jones, Hosking, & Edwards, 1978). Thus, for maximum contractions lasting 45 to 60 s, central fatigue does not seem to be an insurmountable problem despite up to 50% loss of overall force generating capacity. However, in exercise of long duration, when large muscle groups are involved or when the subject's whole attention is not concentrated on maintaining maximum force, declining motor drive may well limit force production. This topic requires further investigation.

FAILURE OF PERIPHERAL NEUROMUSCULAR TRANSMISSION

Even if the motor drive from the CNS remains adequate throughout each contraction, full muscle activation cannot be maintained if failure of neuromuscular transmission develops.

The effectiveness of electrical propagation across the neuromuscular junction can be assessed by recording the muscle mass action potential (M wave) evoked when single maximal shocks to the motor nerve are superimposed during voluntary contractions. If neuromuscular transmission or muscle membrane excitability is impaired, a reduction in M wave amplitude and area results. For the adductor pollicis, Merton (1954) observed no decline in the amplitude of the surface M wave evoked periodically during more than 3 min of isometric MVC despite almost total loss of force. He therefore concluded that no failure of electrical transmission had occurred.

Since then there has been controversy with Stephens and Taylor (1972) challenging Merton's conclusions while our own work (see Bigland-Ritchie & Woods, 1984) has supported the view that during the first 60 s of a sustained MVC there is little or no failure of neuromuscular transmission.

Metabolite Changes and Contractile Protein Function

Much attention has been paid to the influence of changes in metabolite levels on the function of actomyosin crossbridges, mainly the effects of reduced ATP or increased lactate concentrations. Although ATP is intimately involved in crossbridge function, the reduced concentrations seen in fatigued muscle may not necessarily affect force development. Work with skinned fibers has shown that maximum force can be developed at concentrations as low as 0.1 mM (Ferenczi, Goldman, & Summers, 1984).

Hydrogen ion accumulation can alter the affinity of troponin for calcium leading to reduced force (Fabiato & Fabiato, 1978), but while this may play some part in the development of fatigue, it cannot be the only factor, since fatigue develops even more rapidly than normal when glycolysis is absent, as in poisoned muscle or patients with myophosphorylase deficiency.

There is no doubt that the metabolic status of a muscle influences the rate of fatigue, but a number of observations suggest that the site of failure is not necessarily limited to the level of actin and myosin interactions.

Action Potential Propagation Over the Muscle Membrane

During a prolonged tetanus the time course of the force loss depends on the frequency of stimulation. At high frequencies (50 to 80 Hz for human muscle) force is maintained for only a few seconds before falling to between 10% to 20% of the initial value by about 30 s. In contrast, when the muscle is stimulated at 20 Hz the force remains nearly constant for 60 s or longer (Figure 1A, Jones, Bigland-Ritchie, & Edwards, 1979). The rapid fatigue at high frequencies is not due to the greater metabolic cost of these contractions since low frequency stimulation for prolonged periods results in more integrated force (the area under the force curve) and a greater total cost. After considerable force loss as a result of stimulating at high frequency, reducing the frequency leads to a rapid increase in force (Figure 2A). The force recovers more rapidly than metabolite resynthesis could occur. Examination of the action potential reveals that force loss may be due to failure of electrical propagation during high frequency stimulation (Bigland-Ritchie, Jones, & Woods, 1979). These potentials recover when the stimulation rate is reduced. When human muscles are stimulated in situ via the motor nerve, this sensitivity to high frequencies may, in part, be attributed to a failure of transmission at the neuromuscular junction. However, very similar behavior is seen when isolated, curarized muscle preparations are stimulated directly, so that no neuromuscular transmission is involved (Figure 2B).

This specific loss of force at high frequencies is often referred to as "high frequency" fatigue; it is accompanied by changes in the wave form of the muscle action potential, which becomes prolonged and loses amplitude as the muscle force declines (Figure 1B).

With isolated preparations, force can be increased by changing the stimulus characteristics (Jones, 1979). In fresh rat soleus muscle, stimulated

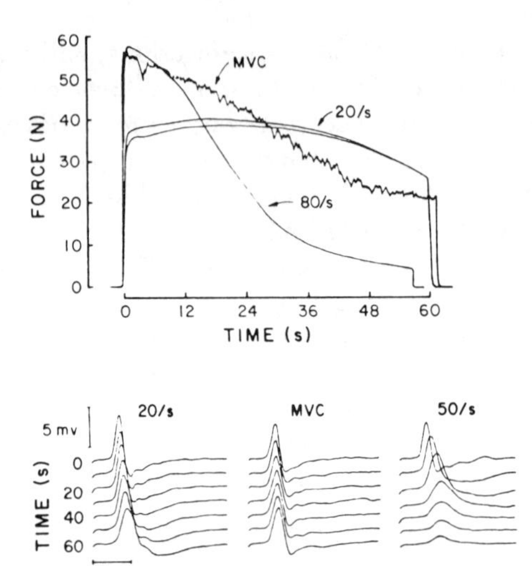

Figure 1(a) Voluntary and stimulated contractions of human skeletal muscle. Isometric force generated by the aductor pollicis; either during a sustained maximum voluntary (MVC) or stimulated contractions at 20 and 80 Hz.

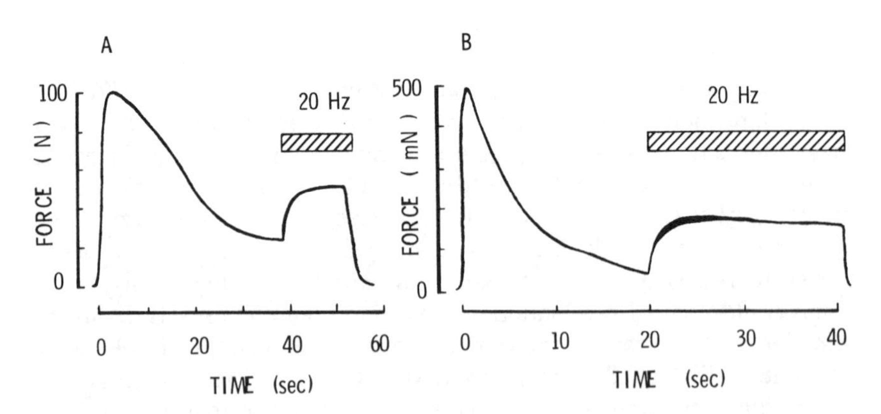

Figure 2(a)(b) Loss of force during high frequency stimulation. (a) Human adductor pollicis stimulated through the ulnar nerve at 100 Hz for 40 s when the frequency was reduced to 20 Hz. (b) Isolated and curarized preparation of human quadriceps muscle directly stimulated at 100 Hz for 20 s when the frequency was reduced to 20 Hz. In both cases, note the increase in force with reduction in frequency in the fatigued muscle. In fresh muscle, stimulation at 20 Hz gives about 60% of the force at 100 Hz.

directly via plate electrodes set approximately 1 cm apart, maximum tetanic force can be obtained with square wave pulses of 40 V and 20 μs duration. Alternatively, when a longer pulse of 200 μs is used, 12 V is sufficient. After a period of stimulation at high frequency, the force can be restored by either increasing the pulse duration or the voltage (Figure 3). These

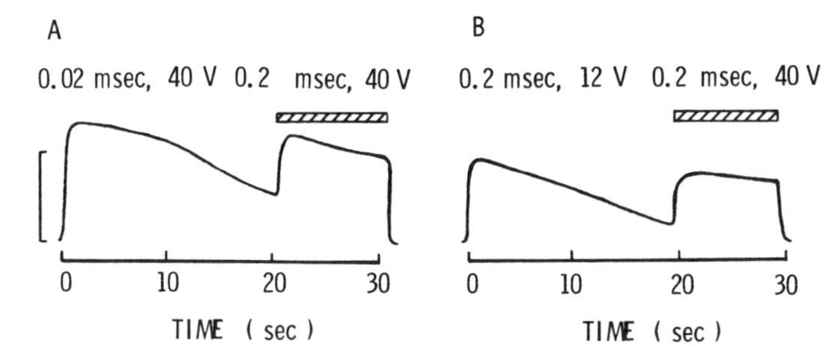

Figure 3(a)(b) Isolated rat soleus muscles directly stimulated at 200 Hz with pulses of different duration and voltage. During the periods shown by the shaded bar, pulse duration or voltage was altered as shown. Note that in the fresh muscle stimulating at either 0.02 ms, 40 V, or 0.2 ms, 12 V was maximal; (a) and (b) are two muscles, the var to the left indicates a force of 1N.

results show that in the fatigued muscle there is a change of excitability with a larger flow of current being required before an action potential can be initiated. The reduced membrane excitability is most likely an expression of the same change in membrane properties that causes slowing of action potential propagation and broadening of the wave form.

During a sustained maximum voluntary contraction, the change in the wave form of superimposed action potentials is slight compared with that seen during high frequency stimulation. The well maintained M waves might suggest that there are no changes in electrical transmission. If, however, the muscle is tested by brief bursts of high frequency stimulation at intervals during a maximal voluntary contraction, after about the first 12 s the muscle begins to show a rapid loss of force during the electrical stimulation, which becomes more pronounced as the contraction continues (Figure 4). It seems, therefore, that voluntary activity reduces the normal safety factor in the muscle and makes it progressively more vulnerable to failure.

The relationship between changes in conduction velocity and duration of the action potential can be directly demonstrated by recording from two points along a strip of mouse diaphragm (Figure 5A). The results of stimulating at 50 Hz for 20 s are shown in Figure 5B. Immediately at the end of the tetanic stimulation the action potential amplitude was much reduced and the wave form prolonged. From the relative shifts in the position of the action potential peaks the conduction velocity in the fatigued muscle can be calculated to have slowed by a factor of about 1.8. Single shocks were then recorded at intervals during recovery. There was a rapid recovery of action potential amplitude and velocity during the first 15 s followed by a much slower phase over the next 2 to 3 min.

It has been proposed that changes in the interfiber cation concentrations (increased K^+ and/or decreased Na^+) may occur during high frequency

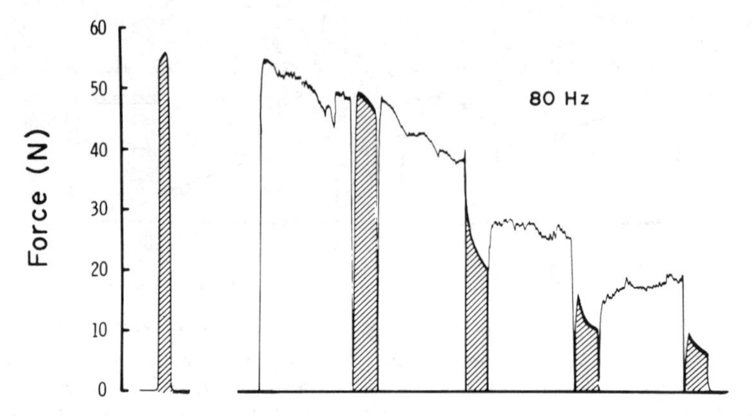

Figure 4 Electrical stimulation superimposed on a sustained voluntary contraction. An MVC of the adductor pollicis interrupted at intervals by brief periods of stimulation at 80 Hz (shaded areas). Contraction to the left is fresh muscle stimulated at 80 Hz, showing a close match of force with that of the MVC.

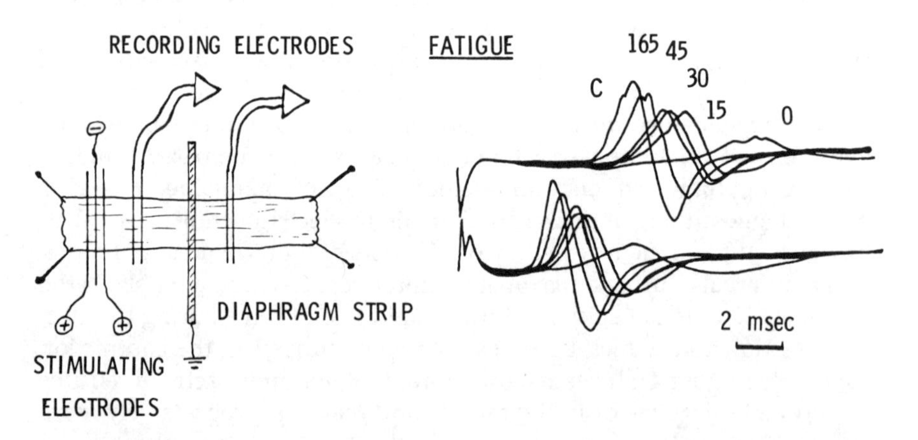

Figure 5(a)(b) Action potentials recorded from diaphragm strips. (a) Experimental arrangement for recording from a strip of mouse diaphragm. The muscle was stimulated at one end, and action potentials were recorded from two pairs of electrodes arranged along the length of the strip. (b) Action potentials recorded in the fresh control muscle (C), at the end of 20 s stimulation at 50 Hz (0), and after 15, 30, 45, and 165 s of recovery. Upper trace from the distal recording electrodes, lower trace from the proximal electrodes.

stimulation and be responsible for the loss of force (Bezanilla, Caputo, Gonzales-Serratos, & Venos, 1972; Bigland-Ritchie et al., 1979). Experimental reduction of the Na^+ concentration hastens the onset of high frequency fatigue in isolated mouse muscle preparations (Figure 6A, Jones et al., 1979). Increasing the K^+ concentration in the extracellular medium

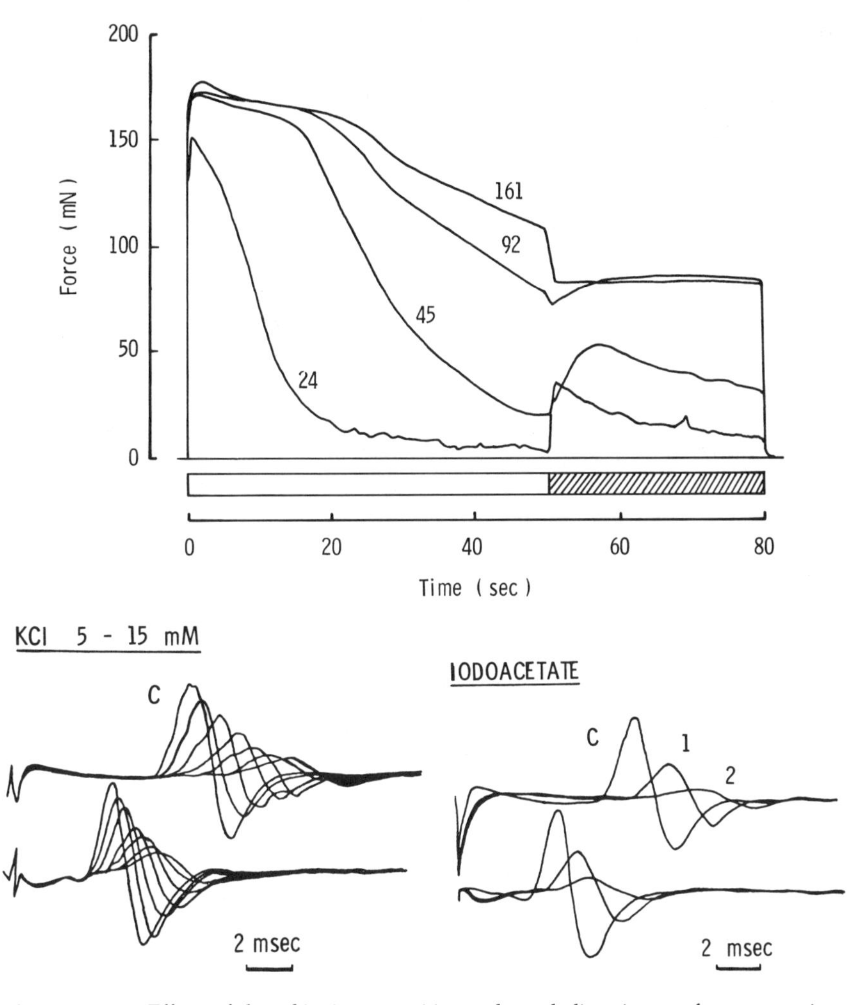

Figure 6(a)-(c) Effects of altered ionic composition and metabolic poison on force generation and action potential waveform. (a) Mouse soleus muscle, stimulated at 50 Hz in medium of differing Na content as indicated on the figure. After 50 s, the frequency was reduced to 20 Hz. (b) Action potentials recorded from mouse diaphragm (see Figure 5) in control medium contraining 5 mM K (C) and from single shocks recorded at one min intervals after increasing the K to 15 mM. (c) Action potentials recorded in control medium (C) and in response to single shocks 1 and 2 min after adding iodoacetic acid to the medium.

causes a similar rapid loss of force and slowing of action potential conduction velocity (Figure 6b). Adrian and Peachey (1973) estimated that for every muscle action potential the Na^+ concentration in the T tubes may fall by 0.5 mM and the K^+ concentration increase by 0.23 mM. Since the normal external K^+ is relatively low, the efflux of K^+ at this rate could lead rapidly to a significant increase in concentration. There have been several observations of K loss from active muscle and it has been reported that a 20 s tetanus at 50 Hz causes extracellular K to increase to 8 to 9 mM (Hník et al., 1976). Such an increase would be expected to reduce the resting potential of human muscle fibers by 10 to 15 mV (Kwiecinski, Lehmann-Horn, & Rudel, 1984). If the extracellular potassium, measured with intramuscular electrodes, rises to 8 to 9 mM then the potassium concentration within the depths of the T tubes will almost certainly be considerably higher than this since the surface-to-volume ratio is high and diffusion is restricted.

The changes in conduction velocity and excitability in fatigued muscle are consistent with an increase in membrane conductance. Fink and Luttgau (1976) reported large increases in potassium conductance in metabolically exhausted fibers, and our observations show that poisoning diaphragm strips with iodoacetic acid also causes a change in conduction velocity and action potential wave form (Figure 6C).

There is a report of calcium sensitive potassium channels in skeletal muscle membrane (Pallotta, 1985), which might be activated by the calcium released in contracting fibers. Another type of potassium channel has been described in cardiac muscle that is activated by decreased levels of ATP (Kakei, Noma, & Shibasaki, 1985; Noma, 1983). Similar channels have now been found in skeletal muscle (Spruce, Standen, & Stanfield, 1985), which may well contribute to reduced muscle membrane excitability with metabolic depletion during fatigue.

It is not clear whether the failure is due to depolarization of the membrane to a point where propagation is no longer possible or to a large increase in the K conductance, possibly linked to metabolite changes in the fiber. Measurements of membrane potential could resolve this question, but there are practical problems in maintaining an electrode in a contracting fiber.

It may be objected that in many forms of fatigue there is loss of force but no change in the surface-recorded electrical activity. In these cases it should be remembered that the action potential recorded from the surface of a single fiber, let alone a whole muscle, largely reflects the activity of the fiber surface membrane, the contribution of the T-tubular membranes being relatively small. It is possible, therefore, that there could be major changes occurring in the T-tubular system, without this being evident in the surface recorded action potential. Accumulations of potassium will be greatest in the depths of the T-tubular system, and this could lead to a situation where action potentials are conducted only a limited way into the interior of the muscle fiber, leaving a central core of inactive contractile material as described by Bezanilla et al. (1972).

Slowing of Relaxation

It has long been recognized that slowing of relaxation is a characteristic of fatigued muscle (Feng, 1931; Mosso, 1951). The half-time of the exponential phase typically increases 2- to 3-fold as the result of fatiguing voluntary contractions (Edwards, Hill, & Jones, 1972) and similar changes occur as the result of stimulated contractions of isolated muscle preparations (Edwards, Hill, & Jones, 1975). Under anaerobic conditions, there is little or no recovery of the slowing. When circulation is restored to the human muscle, the recovery has a half-time of about 60 s (Wiles & Edwards, 1982), which resembles the time course of phosphorylcreatine resynthesis (Harris, Edwards, Hultman, Nordesjo, & Sahlin, 1976).

Contractile slowing leads to a reduction in the tetanic fusion frequency with a shift to the left of the force/frequency relationship. In most forms of human exercise the muscles are seldom excited at their maximum tetanic frequencies, so muscles are working in the steep portion of the curve. Figure 7 shows how the force produced by fatigued muscle can actually increase with low frequency stimulation when compared to the unfatigued control, even though the maximum tetanic force was reduced.

Motor Unit Firing Frequency

In an MVC of the adductor pollicis muscle individual motor neurones discharge at different rates, generally ranging from 15 to 50 Hz (mean 30 ± 9). However, the mean frequency declines progressively if the contraction is maintained (Bigland-Ritchie, Johansson, Lippold, Smith, &

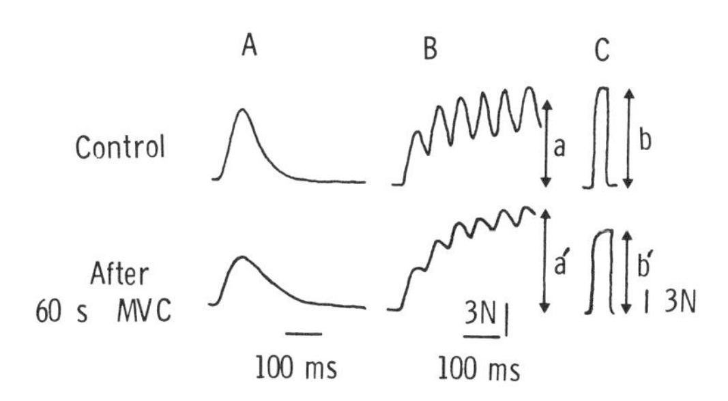

Figure 7 Effects of contractile slowing on force generation at low frequency. (A) Twitches, (B) unfused tetanus at 7 Hz, and (C) 50 Hz tetanic responses from adductor pollicis before and after fatigue. note that in the fatigued muscle, the unfused tetanus gives more force (a′) than the control (a), although the force at 50 Hz is lower (b′ compared to b).

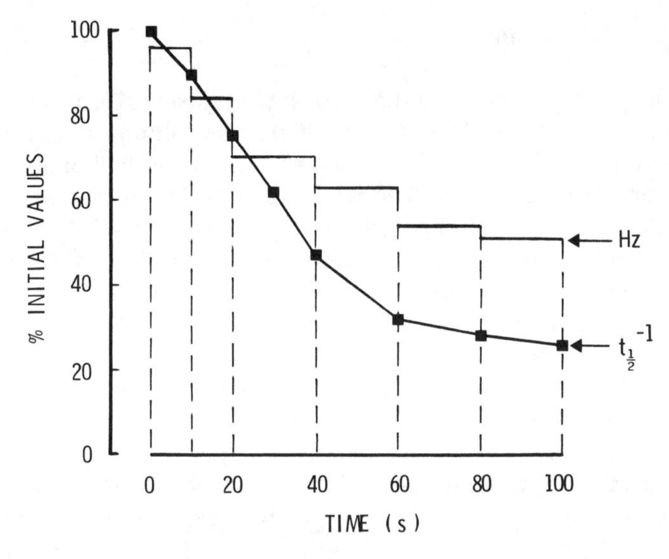

Figure 8 Changesin mean motor neurone firing rate (Hz) superimposed on changes in relaxation rate ($t_{1/2}^{-1}$). Values for frequency are the mean rates occurring in 10 or 20 s bins.

Woods, 1983). This decline is accompanied by a corresponding reduction in the muscle relaxation rate, which lowers the tetanic fusion frequency (Figure 8). The slowing is sufficient to allow the muscle to remain fully activated by the CNS despite the reduced excitation rates; for throughout the contraction the voluntary force continues to match that from tetanic stimulation of the motor nerve (Bigland-Ritchie, Johansson, Lippold, & Woods, 1983). Similar reductions in firing rates have been seen in sustained MVCs of tibialis anterior (Grimby, Hannerz, & Hedman, 1981), soleus (Kukulka, Russell, & Moore, 1984) and quadriceps (Bigland-Ritchie, Furbush, & Woods, in press).

These results suggest that during fatigue, the upper limit of motoneurone firing rates in response to maximum voluntary effort may be regulated to match changes in muscle contractile speed (Bigland-Ritchie & Woods, 1984).

Reflex Control of Motoneurone Firing Rates

If a mechanism exists to adapt MVC firing rates to changes in tetanic fusion frequency, it is of great interest to know if the regulation resides solely within the central nervous system, or whether the central discharge rates are modulated by a reflex originating from the fatigued muscle.

When a muscle is kept ischemic following fatigue, there is little or no recovery of force or relaxation rate. Using tungsten microelectrodes, we measured the decline in firing rates of human biceps brachii motor units during a 20 s MVC, and then during subsequent brief (10 s) MVCs repeated after various intervals of rest (Bigland-Ritchie, Dawson, & Lipold, 1986). During the first MVC these rates declined by 20% to 25%. Recovery of discharge rates was slow but complete after a 3 min rest period. However, when the blood supply to the muscle was occluded by a cuff during this period, no recovery of force occurred, and recovery of discharge rates was also prevented. After a 3 min rest following release of the cuff, both force and discharge rates recovered to normal values (Figure 9). This suggests that a peripheral reflex mechanism regulates the maximum motor neurone firing rates during voluntary contractions, the afferent limb probably originating from the fatigued muscle.

These experiments suggest that some reflex control of motor unit firing rates matches the frequency of activation with the contractile properties of the muscle. The receptors responsible for such a reflex might respond either to changes in the muscle contractile properties or to the accumulation of metabolites. There are many receptors that might play a part in this, but Mense and Stahake (1983) have shown that the Group III and Group IV free nerve endings respond vigorously to most of the muscle metabolites that accumulate with fatigue and to changes in the muscle contractile properties. They are implicated in the cardiovascular responses to exercise and have a powerful input to inhibitory motor interneurones (Cleland, Rymer, & Edwards, 1982). In addition, they reduce the discharge rates of gamma motor neurones (Ellaway, Murphy, & Tripathi, 1982). Therefore, they seem ideally suited to mediate a reflex that modulates

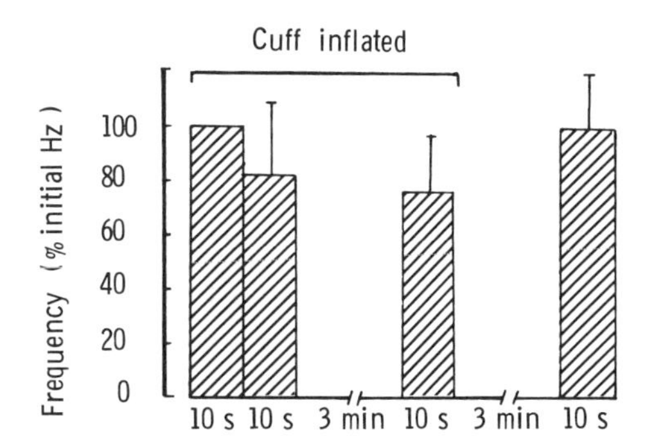

Figure 9 Changes in motor neurone firing rate during activity and with circulatory occlusion. Motor neurone firing rates in the biceps brachii during 20 s MVC and during a 10 s MVC after a 3 min rest with the circulation occluded. Frequency was again determined in 10 s MVC 3 min after the cuff was released.

motoneurone firing rates during fatigue. Such a reflex might serve to optimize force production during fatigue by protecting peripheral sites from potential failure due to excitation at high frequencies.

SUMMARY OF ACUTE CHANGES OCCURRING DURING HIGH FORCE CONTRACTIONS

When muscles are stimulated at frequencies in excess of about 20 Hz, there are large changes in electrical properties of the fibers leading to failure of action potential propagation in the surface membranes. During voluntary activity smaller changes are seen, but these may be indicative of larger changes occurring in the membranes of the T tubular system, which could result in action potentials of reduced amplitude and/or failure of propagation along the T tubes. Either of these will result in reduced activation of the center of the muscle fiber and loss of force.

The electrical changes are probably due to an increase in membrane K conductance, although which channels are activated and by what mechanism remains to be discovered. Depolarization as a result of accumulation of K^+ or activation of channels by a change in some muscle metabolite are two possibilities.

During sustained contractions there is a reduction in motor unit firing frequency that minimizes the changes in membrane properties, most likely by reducing the accumulation of extracellular K^+. The slowing of contractile characteristics helps to maintain the force despite the reduction in firing frequency. There may be reflex pathways by which metabolic or other changes in the muscle regulate the motor neurone firing rate.

These conclusions are based on findings for high force isometric contractions lasting around 1 min. In real life muscles are not often used in this manner, and we will now briefly consider how fatigue may affect contractions where there is movement.

FUNCTIONAL IMPLICATIONS

If the objective of the animal is to maintain isometric force (e.g., a sloth hanging upside-down or a man carrying a suitcase), the slowing of firing frequency and the change in contractile properties will combine to facilitate this. If the requirement is for the muscle to move and generate power, then the situation may not be so simple. Power output is determined both by force and velocity. The changes described above may help to maintain force, but the slowed contractile properties could be detrimental. The crucial question is, how is the slow relaxation reflected in the velocity that can be maintained for a given force?

Much depends on the nature and cause of the slowed relaxation. There are two main hypotheses to account for the slowing. These are, (a) that the slowing is due to a reduced rate of crossbridge cycling, or (b) that it is due to a reduction in the rate of calcium reaccumulation in the sarcoplasmic reticulum (see Jones, 1981). If the first is true, then changes in crossbridge cycling would be expected to be reflected in the force/velocity curve of the muscle, such that less power could be generated. If the second is true, then the prolongation of the active state is due to the continued presence of calcium and there is no obvious reason why force/velocity characteristics and power output should be affected. The present debate concerning these two theories is mainly concerned with the energetic costs of maintaining fatiguing contractions and is complicated by the use of different preparations (mouse, human, frog), different techniques (chemical, heat, and NMR), and different contraction protocols. More direct and relevant information could be obtained by measurement of the force/velocity characteristics of fatigued muscle. If an unequivocal answer can be obtained for this, we will then know whether the adaptive changes seen in the experimental situations are also of value in maintaining performance in competitive and everyday life.

Acknowledgments

The experiments with mouse diaphragm, illustrated in Figures 5 and 6B and C were carried out by Dr. Louise Gay. This work was supported by USPHS Grant NS-14756 and the Muscular Dystrophy Group of Great Britain.

REFERENCES

Adrian, R.H., & Peachey, L.D. (1973). Reconstruction of the action potential of frog sartorius muscle. *Journal of Physiology* (London), **235**, 103-131.

Belanger, A.Y., & McComas, A.J. (1981). Extent of motor unit activation during effort. *Journal of Applied Physiology*, **51**, 1131-1135.

Bezanilla, F., Caputo, C., Gonzales-Serratos, H., & Venosa, R.A. (1972). Sodium dependence of the inward spread of activation in isolated twitch muscle fibres of the frog. *Journal of Physiology* (London), **223**, 507-523.

Bigland-Ritchie, B., Dawson, N.J., & Lippold, O.C.J. (in press). Reflex origin for the slowing of motoneurone firing rates in fatigue of human voluntary contractions. *Journal of Physiology*.

Bigland-Ritchie, B., Furbush, F., & Woods, J.J. (in press). Central and peripheral fatigue in intermittent submaximal voluntary contractions. *Journal of Applied Physiology*.

Bigland-Ritchie, B., Johansson, R.S., Lippold, O.C.J., Smith, S., & Woods, J.J. (1983). Changes in motoneurone firing rates during sustained maximal efforts. *Journal of Physiology* (London), **340**, 335-346.

Bigland-Ritchie, B., Johansson, R.S., Lippold, O.C.J., & Woods, J.J. (1983). Contractile speed and EMG changes during fatigue of sustained maximal voluntary contractions. *Journal of Neurophysiology*, **50**(1), 313-324.

Bigland-Ritchie, B., Jones, D.A., Hosking, G.P., & Edwards, R.H.T. (1978). Central and peripheral fatigue in sustained maximum voluntary contractions of human quadriceps muscle. *Clinical Science and Molecular Medicine*, **54**(6), 609-614.

Bigland-Ritchie, B., Jones, D.A., & Woods, J.J. (1979). Excitation frequency and muscle fatigue electrical responses during human voluntary and stimulated contractions. *Experimental Neurology*, **64**, 414-427.

Bigland-Ritchie, B., & Woods, J.J. (1984). Changes in muscle contractile properties and neural control during human muscle fatigue. *Muscle and Nerve*, **7**, 691-699.

Cleland, C., Rymer, W., & Edwards, F. (1982). Force-sensitive interneurons in the spinal cord of the cat. *Science*, **217**, 652-655.

Edwards, R.H.T., Hill, D.K., & Jones, D.A. (1972). Effect of fatigue on the time course of relaxation from isometric contractions of skeletal muscle in man. *Journal of Physiology* (London), **227**, 260-278.

Edwards, R.H.T., Hill, D.K., & Jones, D.A. (1975). Metabolic changes associated with the slowing of relaxation in fatigued mouse muscle. *Journal of Physiology*, **251**, 287-301.

Ellaway, P.H., Murphy, P.R., & Tripathi, A. (1982). Closely coupled excitation rates of gamma motor neurones by group III muscle afferents with low mechanical threshold in the cat. *Journal of Physiology* (London), **331**, 481-498.

Fabiato, A., & Fabiato, F. (1978). Effects of pH on the myofillaments and sarcoplasmic reticulum of skinned cells from cardiac and skeletal muscles. *Journal of Physiology*, **276**, 233-255.

Feng, T.P. (1931). The heat-tension ratio in prolonged tetanic contractions. *Proceedings of the Royal Society*. (London. B. Biological Sciences), **108**, 522-537.

Ferenczi, M.A., Goldman, Y.E., & Summers, R.M. (1984). The dependence of force and shortening velocity on substrate concentration in skinned muscle fibres from Rana Temporaria. *Journal of Physiology*, **350**, 519-543.

Fink, R., & Luttgau, H.C. (1976). An evaluation of the membrane constants and the potassium conductance in metabolically exhausted muscle fibres. *Journal of Physiology*, **263**, 215-238.

Grimby, L., Hannerz, J., & Hedman, B. (1981). The fatigue and voluntary discharge properties of single motor units in man. *Journal of Physiology* (London), **316**, 545-554.

Harris, R., Edwards, R.H.T., Hultman, E., Nordesjo, L.-O., & Sahlin, K. (1976). The time course of phosphyl creatine resynthesis during recovery of the quadriceps muscle in man. *Pflügers Archiv*, **367**, 137-142.

Hník, P., Holas, M., Krekule, I., Kriz, N., Mejsnar, J., Smiesko, V., Ujec, E., & Vyskočil, F. (1976). Work induced potassium changes in skeletal muscle and effluent venous blood assessed by liquid ion exchange microelectrodes. *Pflügers Archiv*, **362**, 85-94.

Jones, D.A. (1979). Change in excitation threshold as a cause of muscular fatigue. *Journal of Physiology*, **295**, 90P-91P.

Jones, D.A. (1981). Muscle fatigue due to changes beyond the neuromuscular junction. Ciba Foundation Symposium 82. In R. Porter & J. Whelan (Eds.), *Human muscle fatigue: Physiological mechanisms* (pp. 178-196). London: Pitman Medical.

Jones, D.A., Bigland-Ritchie, B., & Edwards, R.H.T. (1979). Excitation frequency and muscle fatigue: Mechanical responses during voluntary and stimulated contractions. *Experimental Neurology*, **64**, 401-413.

Kakei, M., Noma, A., & Shibasaki, T. (1985). Properties of adenosine triphosphate regulated potassium channels in guinea pig ventricular cells. *Journal of Physiology*, **363**, 441-462.

Kukulka, C.G., Russell, A.G., & Moore, M.A. (1984). Changes in activation of human soleus muscle during sustained maximal isometric contractions. *Muscle & Nerve*, **7**, 74-79.

Kwiecinski, H., Lehmann-Horn, F., & Rudel, R. (1984). The resting membrane parameters of human intercostal muscle at low, normal, and high extracellular potassium. *Muscle & Nerve*, **7**, 60-65.

Mense, S., & Stahake. (1983). Responses in muscle afferent fibres of slow conduction velocity to contractions and ischaemia in the cat. *Journal of Physiology* (London), **342**, 383-397.

Merton, P.A. (1954). Voluntary strength and fatigue. *Journal of Physiology* (London), **128**, 553-564.

Mosso, A. (1951). *Fatigue*. (3rd ed.). (D.M. Drummond, Trans.). (pp. 78-80). London: Allen & Unwin.

Noma, A. (1983). ATP-regulated K^+ channels in cardiac muscle. *Nature*, **305**, 147-148.

Pallotta, B.S. (1985). Calcium activated potassium channels in rat muscle inactivated from a short duration open state. *Journal of Physiology*, **363**, 501-506.

Spruce, A.E., Standen, N.B., & Stanfield, P.R. (1985). Voltage-dependent, ATP sensitive potassium channels of skeletal muscle membrane. *Nature*, **316**, 736-738.

Stephens, J.A., & Taylor, A. (1972). Fatigue of maintained voluntary muscle contraction in man. *Journal of Physiology* (London), **220**, 1-18.
Wiles, C.M., & Edwards, R.H.T. (1982). The effect of temperature, ischaemia and contractile activity on the relaxation rate of human muscle. *Clinical Physiology*, **2**, 485-497.

Discussion from the Session

Muscular Fatigue

Jan Henriksson
Karolinska Institutet
Stockholm, Sweden

Albert W. Taylor
University of Western Ontario
London, Ontario, Canada

In the panel discussion, which is summarized below, selected speakers discussed recent data from some areas of muscle research, which might have importance for understanding the physiological mechanisms of muscle fatigue. Because the magnitude of the membrane potential has been shown to be important for Ca^{2+} release and for tension development, it is evident that changes in electrolyte composition over the sarcolemma will have effects on contraction. These aspects were discussed by Carsten Juel (Copenhagen, Denmark), and George Heigenhauser (Hamilton, Canada). Electrolyte changes are most likely, to some extent, caused by an impairment in the energy supply, which evidently will also influence several other processes leading to muscle fatigue. The effect of an impaired energy supply as well as pH changes caused by intense activity were discussed by Eric Hultman and Abram Katz (Stockholm, Sweden). Angelo Belcastro (Edmonton, Canada) presented data on changed Ca^{2+} pumping properties of the sarcoplasmic reticulum ATPase in exhausted rats, and Gunnar Nyberg (Gothenburg, Sweden) discussed the mechanism behind the abnormal muscle fatigue that is experienced in 10% to 20% of patients treated with β-adrenoceptor blocking drugs.

INTRACELLULAR pH RECOVERY AFTER MUSCULAR ACTIVITY—C. Juel

Summary of Juel Paper

Carsten Juel reported data from Sjøgaard, Adams, and Saltin (1985) showing that during 6 min of dynamic knee extension in humans (at an intensity corresponding to 100% of $\dot{V}O_2max$), the intracellular K-concentration was reduced from 165 at rest to 129 mM at exhaustion, corresponding to a 22% decrease in intracellular K. Part of this decrease was due to a net efflux of K^+, and part to an intracellular water increase. The extracellular K^+ concentration, as estimated from the venous K^+ level was increased from 5.4 mM to above 6 mM. With the electrode technique, a similar or slightly higher increase in the interstitial K^+ concentration in human muscle has been reported by Hník and associates. Juel pointed out that even higher changes could take place in T-tubules. Net K^+ loss is dependent on two factors: the activity induced K^+ efflux and the reuptake mediated by the Na^+-K^+ pump. It is possible to calculate from the membrane constants and the action potential parameters, that only approximately one third of the K^+ ions leave the cells through the classical action potential channels; the additional loss must have used other channels. These channels could be the Ca^{2+} activated K^+ channels, which are active a short period after the action potential. These channels have been demonstrated in rat skeletal muscles based on voltage clamp experiments. The K^+ loss, which is higher than necessary to generate the action potential, opens the possibility that the high K efflux is part of a mechanism controlling muscle function.

The other factor that determines the net ion changes during muscle activity is K^+ repumping, through the activity of the Na^+-K^+ pump. Using mouse muscle in vitro, Juel has shown that fatigue is increased if the pump is inhibited by ouabain. On the contrary, if the pump is stimulated by the beta-agonist terbutaline, the muscle is more resistant to repetitive stimulation (see Figure 1).

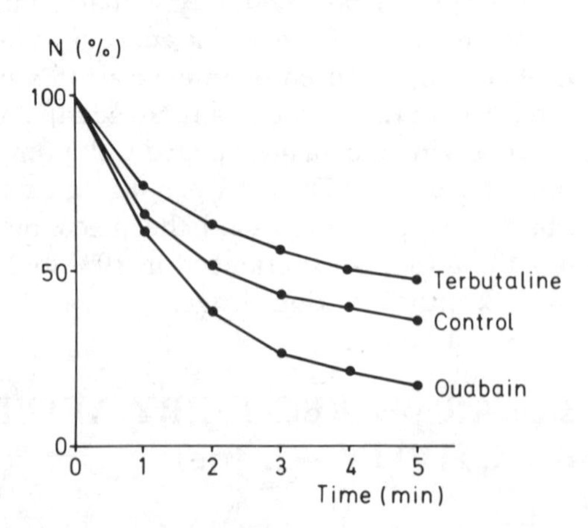

Figure 1 The effect of Na^+-K^+ pump activity manipulation on fatigue during stimulation of mouse muscles in vitro. Stimulation: 40 Hz in 400 ms trains repeated with 3 s intervals for 5 min. Abscissa: time after onset of stimulation. Ordinate: muscle force in % of the initial value. Ouabain (lo^{-4}M) or terbutaline (lo^{-5}M) were added 15 min before onset of stimulation. 25 °C.

The decrease in internal K^+, the increase in interstitial K^+, and the increase in internal Na^+ influence the membrane potential, as calculated from the Goldman equation. The depolarization of exhausted human muscles can be 15 to 20 mV, dependent on fiber type.

In the classical work with barnacle muscle fibers, Ashley and Ridgway (1970) showed that over a wide range, there exists a nearly linear relation between the membrane potential, the Ca^{2+} transient during activation, and the muscle force. Juel therefore concluded that the Ca^{2+} release is decreased due to the depolarization seen during exhaustive exercise. A combination of this effect with the reported increase of the amount of Ca^{2+} required to obtain submaximal force when pH is lowered, could be one of the mechanisms behind the force decline during sustained muscle activity.

Discussion of Juel Paper

Jones (London, England) questioned whether in fact the Ca-activated K-channels are important in skeletal muscle or whether other channels, for example, the ATP-dependent channels, are of more interest here. It was concluded that the nature of the channels mediating the "extra" K^+ loss can at present not be stated. Hník (Prague, Czechoslovakia), based on his own studies, reported that exercise may increase extracellular K^+ and from 5 mM at rest to 8 to 9 mM, sometimes even up to 10 mM. At 10 mM, there appears to be some kind of ceiling. Likewise, in the spinal cord, stimulation at 100 Hz increases extracellular K^+ rapidly, but when it has reached approximately 10 mM, no further increase occurs. The reason for this ceiling is at present not known. Bigland-Ritchie (New Haven, CT, U.S.A.), on the other hand, stated that the CNS sees higher extracellular K^+ concentrations than muscle. In the CNS there are K^+ channels in several cells, such as in glia cells and astrocytes (and in peripheral nerves: Schwann cells), which appear to function as K buffers. The same extent of buffering seems not to be present in skeletal muscle. But, as mentioned, although this buffering machinery is present in the CNS, the CNS still gets much higher extracellular K^+ levels than muscle can cope with. Juel reopened the possibility that the high K^+ efflux may be part of a mechanism controlling muscle function. That K^+ efflux may be a regulated variable was supported by Sjøgaard (Copenhagen, Denmark). She reported data from her laboratory that showed plasma K^+ is strongly correlated to the work load, and further, that there is a close relationship between the exercise heart rate and plasma K^+. This was true both in dynamic and isometric exercise (30 beats per min per 1 mM change in plasma K). K^+ efflux as a regulated variable was, however, doubted by Vøllestad (Oslo, Norway). Sjøgaard reaffirmed that the strong correlation between plasma K^+ and work load could be explained by a higher K^+ efflux with a higher number of active muscle fibers.

LACTATE, PROTON AND ION FLUXES IN THE STIMULATED PERFUSED RAT HINDLIMB—G. Heigenhauser, M. Lindinger, and L. Spriet

Summary of Heigenhauser et al. Paper

George Heigenhauser discussed the role of movements of strong ions and weak electrolytes across the muscle membrane and how this role relates to muscle pH and muscular fatigue. Many of the factors held to be important in muscle fatigue, such as inhibition of rate-limiting enzymes, changes in membrane K^+ conductance, and abnormalities in uptake and release of Ca^{++} from the sarcoplasmic reticulum, have in common an association with intramuscular hydrogen ion concentration ([H^+]). Traditionally, studies have investigated the regulation of intramuscular [H^+] by relating changes in PCO_2, pH, and [HCO_3^-] between arterial and venous blood, to changes in intramuscular [H^+] by assuming that arterial-venous changes in PCO_2, pH, and [HCO_3^-] reflect transmembrane fluxes of H^+. However, physicochemical principles state that three fundamental laws govern the [H^+] in aqueous salt solutions: the conservation of mass, the maintentance of electrical neutrality, and the dissociation equilibrium of weak electrolytes and water. Strong electrolytes, including lactic acid, which are completely or almost completely dissociated in solution, influence [H^+] through the strong ion difference (SID), and CO_2; weak electrolytes also contribute to the acid-base status. In solutions such as in muscle cytosol and blood, [H^+] is a dependent variable, its concentration being determined by the independent variables of PCO_2, the total weak acid concentration (primarily proteins and metabolites) and the SID (the difference between the sum of all strong base cations and strong acid anions). Since weak electrolytes, generated intramuscularly by glycolytic metabolism, are generally impermeable to the muscle membrane, the regulation of intramuscular [H^+] can only occur through the exchange of strong ions between the muscle and extracellular fluid and the regulation of intramuscular PCO_2 by the movement of CO_2 down its diffusion gradient.

Therefore, any changes that occur in intramuscular non-CO_2 [H^+] and changes in the blood arterialvenous non-CO_2 [H^+] are predominantly associated with a change in the SID in each of the fluid compartments. The regulation of intramuscular [H^+] is thus the result of the translocation of strong base cations or strong acid anions and not necessarily the translocation of H^+ per se. In skeletal muscle, there is some evidence that a ''regulatory'' process may translocate H^+ across the muscle membrane; however, this is always associated with appropriate movement of strong ions (Na^+, Cl^-) in the appropriate direction and the strong ion difference determines the (H^+) in the blood or muscle.

In contrast to the classical concept of the undissociated lactic acid diffusing into the extracellular fluid from muscle, recent studies suggest that La^- and H^+ may leave the muscle in the dissociated form and not in stoichiometrically equivalent amounts. Several investigations have shown that H^+ may apparently leave the muscle at higher rates than La^-. From these studies, it appears that La^- cannot account totally for the H^+ efflux, H^+ and La^- apparently translocate through the muscle membrane at independent rates, and the exchange of other strong acid anions and strong base cations between muscle and the extracellular fluid may account for this discrepancy.

Using the isolated perfused rat hindlimb preparation, they tested the hypothesis that H^+ efflux from muscle is not a simple function of La^- release from muscle. Instead, the efflux of H^+ from muscle is held to be dependent not only on La^- efflux from muscle, but also on the exchange of strong basic cations and strong acid ions between muscle and blood.

In the study, the force generated by the gastrocnemius-plantaris-soleus (G-P-S) muscle group declined by 43% during the 5 min of stimulation. The apparent efflux of H^+ across the G-P-S muscle group exceeded the La^- efflux by a factor of 4.5. The intramuscular ion contents before and at the end of stimulation were used to calculate the efflux or influx of cations and anions during exercise. During the 5 min electrical stimulation, there was an influx of Na^+ and a net efflux of K^+, Mg^{++}, and Ca^{++} from the soleus (Sol), plantaris (Pl), red gastrocnemius (RG), and white gastrocnemius (WG) (Figure 2). No significant differences were observed among the muscles in the influx of Na^+ or the efflux of Mg^{++} and Ca^{++}; however, the efflux of K^+ was related to the degree of glycogenolysis and magnitude of La^- accumulation in the muscle; that is, the highest La^- accumulation and K^+ influx were found in the WG, and the lowest in the Sol (Figures 2 & 3).

The intramuscular SID was calculated from intramuscular contents of Na^+, Cl^-, K^+, La^-, and Mg^{++}, before and after exercise. Exclusion of La^- from the calculation still yields a substantial decrease in SID; therefore, the change in SID is not due solely to lactate accumulation. According to the laws of physical chemistry and the principles outlined above, a decrease in the SID will result in an increase in [H^+].

These data suggested that the accumulation of intramuscular [H^+] may be linked to the fatigability of muscle through an increased efflux of K^+ to the extracellular space. The increased efflux of K^+ may be related to

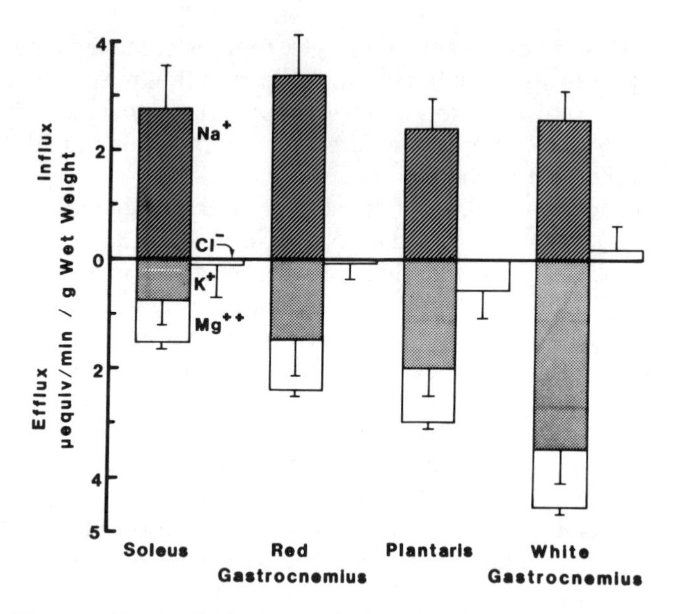

Figure 2 The mean flux (± SEM) of strong basic cations (Na^+, K^+, Mg^{++}) and strong acid anions ($C1^-$) in hindlimb muscles (n = 18) during 5 min tetanic stimulation.

changes in the conductance of the muscle membrane to K^+ and/or inhibition of the Na^+/K^+ pump. This efflux of K^+ was greatly in excess of that estimated to occur from the number of action potentials during the 5 min electrical stimulation. Increases in extracellular K^+ of this magnitude have been shown to decrease the resting membrane potential by 20 mV, which would decrease the amplitude of the action potential. The data suggest that the loci for fatigue may be at the level of the sarcolemmal membrane and may be related to the increased efflux of K^+ in relation to the elevated intramuscular (La^-) and (H^+). Additionally, the data are consistent with the increased fatigability of type II fibers (high glycolytic capacity) as compared to that of type I fibers (low glycolytic capacity).

Discussion of Heigenhauser Paper

Lewis (Dallas, TX, U.S.A.) pointed out that H^+ are not always implicated in fatigue from short-term exercise. In McArdle patients, there is excessive fatigue, but this, in fact, is accompanied by a slight increase in muscle pH. These patients also have an increased K^+ efflux during exercise, although the mechanism behind this is not known.

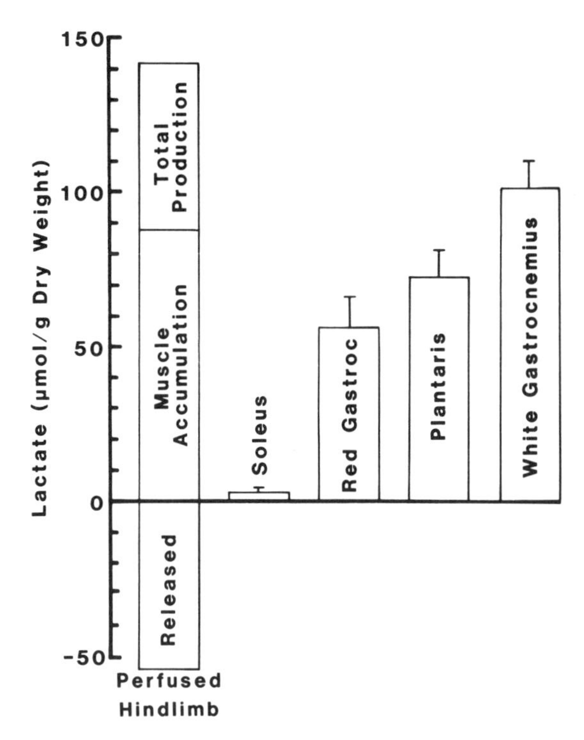

Figure 3 Lactate production, accumulation and release in the perfused hindlimb during 5 min electrical stimulation, and lactate accumulation in soleus, red gastrocnemius, plantaris, and white gastrocnemius ($n = 18$).

REGULATION OF METABOLISM DURING EXERCISE—E. Hultman and AMMONIA AND AMINO ACID METABOLISM IN HUMAN SKELETAL MUSCLE DURING ISOMETRIC CONTRACTION—A. Katz, J. Sahlin, and J. Henriksson

Summary of Hultman Paper

Eric Hultman started by referring to the lecture by Sahlin (1985) (Stockholm) earlier during the symposium, in which the latter proposed the following mechanism for the muscular fatigue limiting short-term intensive exercise:

> The protons released through lactate formation lead to a decreased PCr level through a displacement of the creatine kinase equilibrium. The decreased pH would also inhibit glycolysis at the PFK step if not counteracted by positive modulators, in particular, ADP and AMP. However, the increased ADP level leads to a further decline in PCr. The effect of acidosis on glycolysis and on the PCr level will result in a decreased rate of ADP rephosphorylation, and it was suggested that ADP increases transiently above the steady-state level in the contracting muscle fiber. Sahlin further suggested that the function of ATPases (mainly the Na-K-ATPase), is impaired by the increase of ADP, resulting in an impaired muscle function and fatigue.

Hultman's own experiments (electrical stimulation of the human thigh muscle, 1.6 s isometric contraction—1.6 s rest, continued until fatigue) showed a strong correlation between PCr decrease and force decline. Since it was supposed that when PCr declines, free ADP will rise, Hultman held it was quite probable that the ADP increase was the primary source of the decrease in force production.

Summary of Katz et al. Paper

Abram Katz described data on ammonia metabolism in human skeletal muscle during isometric contraction to fatigue (paper in preparation). At fatigue, after contraction of the thigh muscle at two thirds of maximal voluntary contraction force, muscle NH_3 had increased from 1.3 at rest to 3.6 mmoles per kg dry muscle. Concomitantly, muscle total adenine nucleotide (TAN) concentration had decreased by an average of 3.6 mmoles per kg dry muscle. It was further found that muscle NH_3 started to rise when the lactate concentration was approximately 60 mmoles per kg dry weight, but Katz presented evidence that the decreased pH is not the major cause of the increased AMP deamination. Instead, it was suggested that AMP deamination to IMP and NH_3 is a consequence of the increased muscle levels of AMP during intense exercise (caused by a high ATP turnover and a decreased capacity of ADP rephosphorylation). AMP deamination can thus be considered as a price to pay in order to maintain a high glycolytic rate at a low pH. Katz dismissed the theory that NH_3 produced by the AMP deamination is important in maintaining a high rate of glycolysis. It was further found that the TAN decrease was negatively correlated with the percentage of fast-twitch fibers in the post-exercise biopsy. This was explained partly by the higher levels of AMP deaminase and partly by the higher ATP turnover in these fibers. Katz finally pointed out that fatigue during the sustained isometric exercise is more related to a low PCr level than to a low pH. The evidence for this is that following contraction, force recovery paralleled the PCr recovery, whereas pH recovery was considerably slower.

Discussion of Hultman and Katz et al. Papers

Because of the similarities between the Hultman and Katz papers, the discussion was held after presentation of the two papers. It was intensely debated at which site the suggested ADP-induced fatigue might be located. Sahlin argued that an impaired activity of the myosin ATPase and the Ca^{2+} transport ATPase would only affect relaxation (detachment of crossbridges) and could thus not cause a decline in force during sustained isometric exercise (but may be important during dynamic exercise). On the other hand, an impairment of the Na-K-ATPase will, as discussed in Juel's presentation above, impair force production via a depolarization of the muscle cell. Hultman, on the other hand, wanted to leave open whether an impaired ion transport or an impaired crossbridge cycling was responsible for the fatigue occurring in his own experiments with repeated 1.6 s isometric exercise.

Jones was skeptical as to whether ADP was involved at all in the fatigue process and wanted more quantitative data on increases in free ADP levels at fatigue. Hultman pointed out that, due to protein binding, it is difficult to obtain a correct estimate of free muscle ADP concentration.

Williams (Loughborough, England) asked if there is biochemical evidence regarding K_m:s and concentrations of regulators for the different ATPases that are consistent with Sahlin's view that the Na-K-ATPase is primarily affected during isometric exercise. Sahlin replied that the other ATPases might be affected as well (which in fact might be the reason for the slowing of relaxation at fatigue), but that the point was that only impairment of the Na-K-ATPase would result in a decline in force during isometric exercise. It was further pointed out by Bigland-Ritchie that the time course of force changes during fatigue; this could be interpreted to indicate that the different ATPases may have different sensitivities.

KINETICS OF SARCOPLASMIC RETICULUM ATPase FOLLOWING EXHAUSTIVE TREADMILL EXERCISE IN MALE AND FEMALE RATS—I. MacLean, J. Gilchrist, R. Turcotte, and A. Belcastro

Summary of MacLean et al. Paper

Angelo Belcastro presented data on the altered kinetics of the sarcoplasmic reticulum (SR) ATPase, following an exhaustive run. Muscle relaxation is initiated by repolarization of the surface membranes and T-tubules, with closing of Ca^{2+} channels that permits accumulation of Ca^{2+} in the lumen of the SR. The active transport of Ca^{2+} from the cytoplasm into the SR occurs at the expense of ATP hydrolysis by the Ca^{2+} ATPase protein pump. The Ca^{2+} pump is capable of lowering the cytoplasmic free Ca^{2+} concentration to the 10^{-8}M and establishing a Ca^{2+} gradient of 1000-fold across the membrane. There are two sites, one with high affinity for Mg • ATP, involved in phosphoenzyme formation, and one with a low MG • ATP affinity (K_m in the mM range), the role of which is to modulate the ATPase activity of the catalytic sites.

When SR membranes were isolated from the gastrocnemius muscle of rats that had been exhausted by a prolonged run and incubated at low Mg • ATP concentrations (10 - 100 uM), to probe the high affinity sites, no changes from control in either the Km or the $\dot{V}$max of the ATPase reaction were found (Maclean, Gilchrist, Turcotte, & Belcastro, paper in preparation). However, when the SR membranes were incubated at higher Mg • ATP concentrations (0.2 to 5 mM), to study the role of the low affinity site, both a significantly lower Km and $\dot{V}$max of the Ca^{2+} ATPase were noted, when compared to results from resting rats. Thus, the regulatory role of ATP on the Ca^{2+} ATPase is altered under conditions of prolonged, repetitive contractions to exhaustion. Belcastro, however, pointed out that Ca^{2+} transport data were necessary in order to assess the physiological significance of these data.

The data on Ca^{2+} accumulation into SR vesicles at saturating Ca^{2+} levels, showed an increase in exhausted rats compared to control female rats. This greater Ca^{2+} accumulation was not due to enhanced Ca^{2+} influx, as oxalate supported (intravesicular Ca^{2+} is trapped) Ca^{2+} uptake values were unchanged by the prolonged exercise. This suggested that a decrease in Ca^{2+} efflux is responsible for the increased accumulations observed in exercised animals. It was concluded that together, the ATPase and Ca^{2+} transport data suggest an enhanced energy efficiency of Ca^{2+} transport in the exhausted female rats. However, further work is needed before a real biological meaning can be ascribed to these data.

Discussions of MacLean et al. Paper

Sjøgaard referred to electron probe data of Somlyo and coworkers, showing that at fatigue the Ca^{2+} concentration of the SR was actually higher than at rest. Belcastro pointed out that electron probe results are very difficult to interpret as regards actual ion concentrations and/or ion activities, since this technique simply measures elemental species.

MUSCULAR FATIGUE IN EXERCISE STUDIES INVOLVING β-ADRENOCEPTOR ANTAGONISTS—G. Nyberg

Summary of Nyberg Paper

Gunnar Nyberg discussed muscular fatigue in exercise studies involving β-adrenoceptor antagonists. He outlined that 10% to 20% of all patients who use β-blockers often experience a greater fatigue when performing physical work. Nyberg reviewed various exercise studies involving β-blockers that have been focused on quantitation of the subjective feeling of muscular fatigue and/or perceived exertion. The main aim was to review mechanisms as well as possible reasons for different responses. The studies presented had usually been directed to short-term (5 to 50 min) exercise, submaximal on constant or increasing load, and some near maximal short-term work. Subjects had been patients with coronary heart disease, hypertension, or normal young students. β-blockers used had different auxiliary properties (ISA, β_1-selectivity, α-blockade).

Several studies have pointed to a decrease in blood flow to the exercising muscle (resulting from a decreased cardiac output) as a factor common to all β-blockers. Nyberg proposed that this decreased blood flow is the most important factor behind the increased muscle fatigue often experienced with β-blockade. This factor is probably of minor importance when the heart rate reduction is below 10% to 15% at submaximal levels. This seems however, to be a threshold value, which, if exceeded, results in increased fatigue. In elderly patients, in particular those with impaired cardiac function and peripheral atherosclerosis, an inadequate blood pressure response during exercise will enhance the sense of muscular fatigue. An additional effect is probably caused by the inhibition of glycogenolysis mediated by β_2-receptors. β_1-blockers have been shown to cause less alteration of endurance time in long-term exercise than nonselective blockers. The inhibition of lipolysis, a β_1-mediated reaction, is, however, common to all blockers. Other factors that may contribute to the fatigue are increased levels of plasma potassium and lactate after both selective and nonselective blockers. The hyperkalemia is to some extent β_2-dependent (by β_2-mediated inhibition of Na-K-ATPase) but since it is quite substantial with selective β_1-blockade, other mechanisms must contribute. Intrinsic sympathetic activity (ISA) does not alternate the sense of muscular fatigue. Additional β-blockade (e.g., with labetalol) further enhances muscular fatigue, but the cause is not known. Finally a "central" factor may be important (particularly for "perceived exertion"). β-blockers may either directly, or perhaps by interacting with circulatory catecholamines in the brain, lead to a coloring of any perception of muscular exercise. It should also be pointed out that patients with impaired cardiac function bordering on failure may have either improved or decreased exercise capacity depending on the pathophysiological background.

Discussion of Nyberg Paper

Williams, in support of Nyberg, reported data from his laboratory that indicated that nonselective β-blockers, both during short-term and prolonged exercise, had a greater fatiguing effect than β_1-selective blockers. The comparison was based on doses giving similar heart rate reductions. Nyberg added that there is a lot of circumstantial evidence pointing to this difference between nonselective blockers and β_1-blockers, but also that he thought that final evidence had yet to be presented. Nyberg further suspected that not only the muscle but also the hepatic β_2-receptor could be of importance here.

One discussant (unidentified) questioned whether blood flow to exercising muscle in fact was reduced with β-blockade or whether this was overcome by locally released vasodilators. No conclusive evidence on this question was, however, presented in the discussion.

Katz presented evidence that during β-blockade (propranol), K^+ release from active muscles was not influenced (A-V difference, repeated bouts of maximal dynamic exercise). However, uptake of K^+ in inactive muscles is probably inhibited leading to an increased plasma K^+, which may then have a negative effect on the active muscles.

Similar data had been obtained by Sjøgaard, who in the one-leg human model (m. quadriceps femoris, dynamic exercise), found an unchanged A-V difference for K^+ after infusion of a β_{-2}-agonist (terbutaline), but decreased arterial and venous plasma K^+ concentrations. Sjøgaard added that the K^+ loss from active muscles, which did not appear to be changed by either β-stimulation or blockade, was a further indication that K loss is a regulated variable.

REFERENCES

Ashley, G.C., & Ridgway, E.B. (1970). On the relationship between membrane potential, calcium transient and tension in single barnach muscle fibres. *Journal of Physiology* (London), **209**, 105-130.

Hník, P., Holas, M., Krekule, I., Kříž, N., Mejsar, S., Smieško, V., Ujec, E., & Vyskočil, F. (1976). Work-induced potassium changes in skeletal muscle and efficient venous blood assessed by liquid ion exchange micro-electrodes. *Pflügers Archiv*, **362**, 85-94.

Sahlin, K. (1985). *Metabolic changes limiting muscle performance*. Lecture presented at the Sixth International Symposium on the Biochemistry of Exercise, Copenhagen, Denmark.

Sjøgaard, G., Adams, R.D., & Saltin, B. (1985). Water and ion shifts in skeletal muscle of humans with internal dynamic knee extension. *American Journal of Physiology*, **248**, R190-R186.

Part V
Comparative Physiology

Energetics of Locomotion: What Sets the Cost?

C. Richard Taylor
Harvard University
Bedford, Massachusetts, U.S.A.

The amount of energy required for humans and most terrestrial vertebrates to move some distance along the ground appears to be determined by how much they weigh, and to be independent of speed, gait (walk, run, trot, gallop), and mode of locomotion (bipedal, quadrupedal, saltatory, etc.).

The relationship between the energetic cost of locomotion and body mass can be expressed by a simple equation

$$E_{metab}/m \cdot M_b = 10.7 \text{ joules/m} \cdot M_b^{-0.316} \qquad (1)$$

where $E_{metab}/m \cdot M_b$ is the cost of locomotion expressed in joules required to move one kg mass one meter (Taylor, Heglund, & Maloiy, 1982). This equation is based on data from 62 avian and mammalian species, and differs little from an equation formulated from data on just four species of mammals 15 years ago by Taylor, Schmidt-Nielsen, and Raab (1970). Ninety percent of the values of cost calculated for a diverse assortment of avian and mammalian species using Equation 1 fall within 25% of the measured values, although the absolute value of cost differs by more than 1,400% from the smallest birds and mammals (a 15 g quail and a 10g pygmy mouse) to the largest (a 100 kg ostrich and a 212 kg eland).

Is there some fundamental physical mechanism that underlies this general relationship between an animal's mass and the energy cost of its locomotion? The most obvious place to look is the mechanical work that an animal's muscles must do to move its limbs and sustain a constant speed. Heglund, Fedak, Taylor, and Cavagna (1982) quantified the mechanical work required to move the limbs and sustain a constant speed and found it bore no relationship to the energy required, either as a function of speed or as a function of animal size.

The mechanical cost of locomotion (E_{tot}), which is defined as the total mechanical energy required to move one kg body mass one meter (joules/m) (this is the energy necessary to lift and reaccelerate the center of mass and swing the limbs), is given by the following equation

$$E_{tot}/m \cdot M_b = (0.478 \cdot vg^{1.53} + 0.685 \cdot vg + 0.072)/vg \qquad (2)$$

where vg is the ground speed in m/sec. This equation is independent of body mass, applying equally well to a 30 g chipmunk or a quail as to a 100 kg human, ostrich, or pony. In marked contrast, the metabolic energy cost of locomotion represented in Equation 1 is independent of the speed at which the distance is traveled, and varies dramatically with the body mass of the animal. The 30 g chipmunk or quail expends about 15 times the amount of energy to move each unit of body mass a unit distance as a 100 kg human, ostrich, or pony. It seems clear that one must look beyond a "mechanical work" explanation for the general relationship between energy cost of locomotion and body size.

WHAT DO ACTIVE MUSCLES DO DURING LOCOMOTION?

A good place to begin looking for an explanation seems to be to consider what the muscles do in order to sustain a constant speed. The classic studies of Cavagna, Saibene, and Margaria (1963, 1964) on the mechanics of human walking and running provide an important insight. Human walking involves a pendulum mechanism whereby most of the energy required to sustain the center of mass moving at a constant average speed is alternatively transferred between gravitational potential energy and kinetic energy within each stride (instead of being lost as heat and having to be supplied to the muscles). Cavagna, Heglund, and Taylor (1977) extended the human studies to birds and mammals and found the same "pendulum" mechanism applies generally. The main function of the muscles during walking appears to be to stabilize the joints and enable this pendulum system to operate effectively. Much of the muscular activity, therefore, does not involve muscles performing mechanical work, since work is equal to force times distance, and distance is zero because the muscle does not shorten. Instead, a great deal of the activity involves exerting an isometric force where the muscles consume energy (in order to generate the force) and perform no work.

Human running (Cavagna, Saibene, & Margaria, 1964) does not involve a pendulum-like kinetic-gravitational energy transfer. Instead, energy is conserved by another mechanism: alternate storage and recovery of energy as elastic strain energy. When humans and other animals (Cavagna, Heglund, & Taylor, 1977) run, trot, gallop, or hop at a constant speed, major muscle groups (e.g., the limb extensors) are alternately stretched and then shortened while they are active during each stride (Goslow, Seeherman, Taylor, McCutchin, & Heglund, 1981; Loeb, 1985). Work is performed on the active muscles as they are stretched and much of this energy is stored in elastic elements of the active muscle-tendon system.

Some of this elastic energy is recovered during the subsequent part of the stride as the active muscles and tendons shorten. Cavagna et al. (1964) found that when humans run at high speeds, up to half of the mechanical energy supplied by the muscles to lift and accelerate the center of mass during each stride is recovered from elastic energy stored as the center of mass fell and decelerated earlier in the stride. Cavagna et al. (1977) found similar amounts of elastic storage in ostriches and ponies running and galloping at high speeds.

MUSCLE STRESS AND CYCLE TIME: ARE THEY THE DETERMINANTS OF ENERGETIC COST AND LIMITS OF LOCOMOTORY PERFORMANCE?

Locomotion at a constant speed is a cyclic process with the muscles exerting force in a pattern that is repeated once during each stride. Studies in our laboratory have suggested that the peak stress (force/cross-sectional area) generated during each cycle by the major locomotory muscles is the same in all species under equivalent locomotory conditions (e.g., preferred speed within each gait, gait transitions, top speed, peak accelerations and decelerations, etc.). The metabolic cost of generating force, rather than the cost of performing mechanical work, therefore seems a good place to look for an explanation of the general relationships between energy cost of locomotion and body mass described in Equation 1.

What is the evidence that the peak muscle stress during each cycle of locomotion at a constant speed is the same in all species under equivalent conditions? The equivalent muscle-stress hypothesis would predict that animals adapted for running at high speeds would utilize greater cross-sectional areas of locomotory muscles in order to run faster at the same muscle stress and that they would switch from one gait to another at greater speeds. Peak force exerted by limb extensors increases within a gait, but decreases across gait transitions as animals increase their speed. Force platform and force ''shoe'' studies (Biewener, Thomason, Goodship, & Lanyon, 1982; Cavagna et al., 1977; Rubin & Lanyon, 1982) have shown that peak vertical force exerted on the force platform decreases dramatically as animals switch from a fast trot to a slow gallop, even though they are increasing their ground speed. For example, peak vertical in a dog increased from 1.3 times its body weight (1.3 G) at a slow trot to 2.5 G at a fast trot. Peak force then decreased from 2.56 to 1.5 G as the dog changed gaits from a fast trot to a slow gallop. Peak force at a fast gallop then increased to approximately the same level (2.5 to 2.76) as occurred during a fast trot. These results suggest that some peak force is reached as speed increases within a gait, which necessitates the redistribution of force over time in order for an animal to further increase its speed, and that this redistribution of force is accomplished by changing gaits. According to our equivalent muscle-stress hypothesis, animals adapted for running at high speed would have greater cross-sectional areas of active muscles than nonadapted animals, and the critical level of muscle stress necessitating gait changes would occur at higher speeds. Table 1 illustrates that the higher top speeds of the dog and horse when compared to the goat and cow are indeed accompanied by higher gait transition speeds.

The most convincing evidence for the equivalent muscle-stress hypothesis comes from recent studies in our laboratory carried out by Andrew Perry and Reinhard Blickhan. Their studies were designed to provide a direct test of the hypothesis by comparing muscle stresses in the ankle extensor group (gastrocnemius, plantaris, and soleus) of two mammals that utilize different modes of locomotion, the white rat (which is a quadrupedal walker, trotter, and galloper) and the kangaroo rat (which is a bipedal hopper). The studies compared peak muscle stress of ankle extensors when both species moved at their preferred galloping/hopping speed. The in vivo muscle forces were calculated from ground reaction forces measured with a force platform, and position of the joints determined using high speed films. Each animal's maximum isometric force was measured after the force platform-film analysis experiments using an in situ technique. Muscle stress was calculated from the calculated muscle force and the cross-sectional area determined using morphometric analysis

Table 1 Top speed[a] and speed at which animals change gaits from trot to gallop compared in animals adapted for high speed locomotion (dog and horse) and in animals of similar size that are not adapted for high speed locomotion (goats and cows)

Speed	Goat	Dog	Cow	Horse
M_b, kg	20	20	160	170
Top speed[a], m/s	4.25	8.98	6.43	10.4
Trot-gallop speed, m/s	2.75	4.17	3.78	4.97
Strides/s at T-G transition	2.51	2.52	2.04	2.48

[a]Top speed sustained for 2 min on treadmill.
Note. From "Force Development During Sustained Locomotion: A Determination of Gait, Speed, and Metabolic Power" by C.R. Taylor, 1985, *Journal of Experimental Biology*, **115**, pp. 253-262. Copyright 1985 by The Company of Biologists. Reprinted by permission.

of the extensor muscles. The values for peak stress at the animal's preferred speed, both absolute and as a percentage of maximum isometric stress measured in situ, were remarkably similar (Table 2). The mean value for the white rats of 57.8 kN/m^2 was not significantly different from values of 71.8 kN/m^2 for the kangaroo rats. These in vivo stress values at the animal's preferred speed amounted to 32 and 275 of the peak isometric stress of the ankle extensors measured in situ. The similarity of locomotory stress at the preferred speed of these two species is remarkable considering the large differences in how they move and the 2-1/2-fold difference in their body mass (Table 2). The kangaroo rats accelerate and decelerate their entire body with their hind limbs during each stride. In contrast, the white rats decelerate with their front limbs and accelerate with their hind limbs during each stride (Heglund, Cavagna, & Taylor, 1982). The fact that these two animals select a preferred speed that results in the same muscle stress supports the equivalent muscle-stress hypothesis.

The metabolic cost of generating force during locomotion has been found to exactly parallel the changes in metabolic cost of locomotion as a function of speed and body size (Taylor, Heglund, McMahon, & Looney, 1980). Thus, the energy cost for generating a Newton of force by a 30 g chipmunk, like the energy cost of locomotion, is 15 times as great as the cost of generating the same Newton of force in a 100 kg horse.

Differences in the time course of the cyclic event of locomotion, the stride, helps to explain the large differences both in metabolic cost of generating force and metabolic cost of locomotion between small and large animals. Although development of a Newton of force by the small 30 g

Table 2 Comparison of peak muscle stress of ankle extensors of white rats and kangaroo rats during steady-state locomotion at their preferred speed

	White Rats	Kangaroo Rats
Body Mass (grams)	237 ± 12	103 ± 3
Maximum Isometric Stress (in situ) (kN/m^2)	247 ± 31	267 ± 12.00
Preferred Speed (m/s)	1.68 ± 0.15	1.36 ± 0.10
Peak Stress in Ankle Extensors at Preferred Speed (kN/m^2)	57.8 ± 9.5	71 ± 9.1
Ratio: $\frac{\text{Peak stress at preferred speed}}{\text{Maximum isometric stress}}$	0.23	0.27

Table 3 Metabolic cost of locomotion (Taylor et al., 1982) and metabolic cost of generating force (Taylor et al., 1980) of large and small animals moving at a physiologically equivalent speed (trot-gallop transition)

Body mass (kg)	10 g	1.0 kg	100 kg
Metabolic cost of locomotion (ATP) Watts/kg	19.1	8.96	5.19
Metabolic cost of force generation (ATP) Watts/Newton	1.95	0.91	0.53
Ratio: locomotion/force	9.8	9.8	9.8

Note. From "Force Development During Sustained Locomotion: A Determination of Gait, Speed, and Metabolic Power" by C.R. Taylor, 1985, *Journal of Experimental Biology*, **115**, p. 260.

animal requires 15 times as much energy compared to the 100 kg animal, the force has to be developed at decay at 15 times the rate because the stride frequency is 15 times as great (Table 3). If one divides the metabolic cost of force generation/locomotion by stride frequency, one obtains a constant that is independent of an animal's size. Thus, it appears that two factors determine the energetics of steady-state locomotion: (a) the time course force generation and decay; and (b) the similarity of muscle stress from animal to animal under equivalent locomotory conditions.

Acknowledgments

The experiments from my laboratory reported in this paper and the preparation of the manuscript were supported by NIH Grant RO1 AM18140.

REFERENCES

Biewener, A.A., Thomason, J., Goodship, A.E., & Lanyon, L.E. (1982). Bone stress in horse forelimb during locomotion at different gaits: A comparison of two experimental methods. *Journal of Biochemistry*, **16**, 565-576.

Cavagna, G.A., Heglund, N.C., & Taylor, C.R. (1977). Mechanical work in terrestrial locomotion: Two basic mechanisms for minimizing energy expenditure. *American Journal of Physiology*, **233**(5), R243-R261.

Cavagna, G.A., Saibene, F.P., & Margaria, R. (1963). External work in walking. *Journal of Applied Physiology,* **18**, 1-9.
Cavagna, G.A., Saibene, F.P., & Margaria, R. (1964). Mechanical work in running. *Journal of Applied Physiology,* **19**, 249-256.
Goslow, G.E., Seeherman, H.J., Taylor, C.R., McCutchin, M.N., & Heglund, N.C. (1981). Electrical activity and relative length changes of dog limb muscles as a function of speed and gait. *Journal of Experimental Biology,* **94**, 15-42.
Heglund, N.C., Cavagna, G.A., & Taylor, C.R. (1982). Energetics and mechanics of terrestrial locomotion III; kinetic and potential energy changes of the center of mass as a function of speed and body size in birds and mammals. *Journal of Experimental Biology,* **97**, 41-56.
Heglund, N.C., Fedak, M.A., Taylor, C.R., & Cavagna, G.A. (1982). Energetics and mechanics of terrestrial locomotion: IV. Total mechanical energy changes as a function of speed and body size in birds and mammals. *Journal of Experimental Biology,* **97**, 57-66.
Loeb, G.E. (1985). Motorneuron task groups: Coping with kinematic heterogeneity. *Journal of Experimental Biology,* **115**, 137-146.
Rubin, C.T., & Lanyon, L.E. (1982). Limb mechanics as a function of speed and gait: A study of functional strains in the radius and tibia of horse and dog. *Journal of Experimental Biology,* **101**, 187-211.
Taylor, C.R. (1985). Force development during sustained locomotion: A determinant of gait, speed, and metabolic power. *Journal of Experimental Biology,* **115**, 253-262.
Taylor, C.R., Heglund, N.C., & Maloiy, G.M.O. (1982). Energetics and mechanics of terrestrial locomotion: I. Metabolic energy consumption as a function of speed and body size in birds and mammals. *Journal of Experimental Biology,* **97**, 1-21.
Taylor, C.R., Heglund, N.C., McMahon, T.Q., & Looney, T.R. (1980). Energetic cost of generating muscular force during running: A comparison of large and small animals. *Journal of Experimental Biology,* **86**, 9-18.
Taylor, C.R., Schmidt-Nielsen, K., & Raab, J. (1970). Scaling of energetic cost of running to body size in mammals. *American Journal of Physiology,* **219**, 1104-1107.

Muscle Aerobic Potential in the Animal Kingdom

Hans Hoppeler
University of Berne
Bern, Switzerland

Animals critically depend on the oxidative pathways to rephosphorylate ATP for their steady state energy requirements with only some invertebrates surviving anaerobically for prolonged periods of time (cf. Hammen & Ellington, 1984). The potential for oxidative phosphorylation of ATP is intimately related to the structure and molecular composition of mitochondria, in particular to the organization of their inner membrane, the site of the energy transducing system (Lehninger, 1978; Figure 1). To describe the potential for aerobic metabolism of whole animals, it is customary to measure their resting or basal oxygen consumption (Kleiber, 1932). However, more relevant with regard to muscle oxidative potential is an animal's maximal oxygen consumption ($\dot{V}O_2max$), as under limiting conditions of maximal oxygen transport more than 90% of the total oxygen flow is directed to the skeletal muscle tissue to fuel the contractile machinery (Weibel, 1979a).

ESTIMATING THE AEROBIC POTENTIAL OF MUSCLE TISSUE

It is presently not clear how oxygen consumption is distributed among mechanically active and nonactive muscle tissue. For the leg muscles of the rat, Armstrong and Laughlin (1983) have demonstrated that under conditions of maximal exertion, the largest blood flow (395 $ml \cdot min^{-1} \cdot 100g^{-1}$) occurs in the deep, fast-oxidative part of gastrocnemius, while the smallest blood flow was recorded in the superficial fast-glycolytic part of the same muscle (76 ml•min-1•100g-1). It is likely that the distribution pattern of oxygen consumption closely resembles the distribution pattern of blood flow among and within muscles.

The oxidative capacity of a single contracting muscle (skeletal muscle or heart) can ultimately be determined by directly measuring its maximal oxygen uptake capacity physiologically (Braunwald, 1971; Folkow & Halicka, 1968; Stainsby & Otis, 1964). However, the direct method of assessing a muscle's oxidative capacity is technically demanding and has

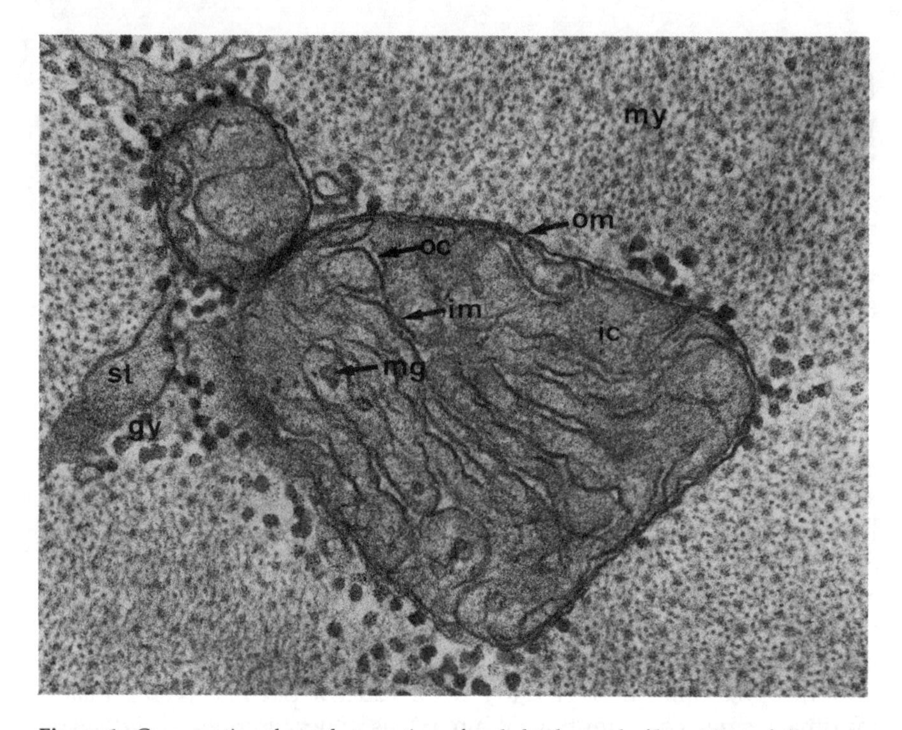

Figure 1 Cross-section through a portion of a skeletal muscle fiber. Most of the sarcoplasmatic space contains myofibrils (my). Parts of the sarcotubular system (st) and some glycogen granules (gy) can be seen in close proximity to mitochondria. Mitochondria are bound by an outer membrane (om). The inner membrane (im) is folded and separates the outer (oc) from the inner chamber (ic; matrix). The mitochondrial matrix contains mitochondrial granules (mg).

been standardized only for a handful of muscles that happen to lend themselves to a complete surgical isolation of their vascular bed.

Since mitochondria represent the cellular oxygen sink, muscle tissue oxidative capacity can also be assessed indirectly by estimating some characteristics of mitochondria. Ideally, these should quantitatively be linked to the rate at which mitochondria can utilize oxygen in vivo. Biochemical methods have been very useful in this respect, since they allow one to determine the activities of key enzymes of mitochondrial energy turnover, such as succinate dehydrogenase (citric acid cycle) or cytochrome oxidase (electron transfer system) efficiently, accurately, and if necessary, from muscle samples as small as a fraction of an individual muscle fiber (Essén, Jansson, Henriksson, Taylor, & Saltin, 1975; Reichmann & Pette, 1982).

Another less often used indirect method of estimating skeletal muscle oxidative capacity is to determine morphologically the fractional space occupied by mitochondria within a muscle fiber (Weibel, 1979b). Morphometry allows one to quantify the volume density of mitochondria (volume of mitochondria per unit volume of muscle fiber; units: $cm^3 \cdot cm^{-3}$) the surface density of mitochondrial inner and outer membranes (units: $m^2 \cdot cm^{-3}$) as well as the capillary network that delivers oxygen to the muscle cells (Ingjer, 1979; Mathieu, Cruz-Orive, Hoppeler, & Weibel, 1983). The biochemical approach has the advantage that it yields detailed information about the various metabolic pathways involved in aerobic (and anaerobic) energy production, including substrate metabolism. The morphometric approach allows one to define topological relationships between the different sites of energy turnover within a muscle cell (Mainwood & Rakusan, 1982).

There are relatively few studies that directly compare the biochemical to the morphometrical approach to muscle energy metabolism. It seems that both methods yield similar relative estimates of skeletal muscle oxidative capacity (Bylund et al., 1977; Morgan, Cobb, Short, Ross, & Gunn, 1971; Reichmann, Hoppeler, Mathieu-Costello, von Bergen, & Pette, 1985), although disparate changes in cytochrome oxidase activity and volume density of mitochondria have occasionally been reported (Kiessling, Pilström, Bylund, Saltin, & Piehl, 1974). Optimally, one would often like to combine biochemistry with morphometry as the two techniques together may give results not accessible with either technique alone (Schwerzmann & Hoppeler, 1985).

The major drawback of both indirect methods for determining muscle tissue oxidative capacity is that it is difficult to relate these data to in situ muscle oxygen consumption under limiting conditions. To our knowledge, there is no information that would allow one to calculate maximal in vivo oxygen consumption from muscle enzyme activity data. There is limited morphological evidence that indicates that 1 to 3 cm of mammalian skeletal muscle mitochondria consumes 2 to 5m102•min-1 during maximal sustained mechanical activity (Hoppeler & Lindstedt, 1985). The available data suggest that mitochondrial oxygen consumption is independent of species (mouse, cat, and man) and muscle type (oxidative and glycolytic). It may be noted that mitochondria isolated from cat soleus muscle likewise have been reported to use 0.8 to 4.4ml $O_2 \cdot min^{-1}\ cm^{-3}$ depending on substrate (Schwerzmann & Weibel, 1984).

The present overview will concentrate on morphometric data to describe the oxidative potential of muscle tissue in various animals and in some animals under various experimental conditions. The hypothesis will be that the volume density of mitochondria relates to the maximal aerobic power density of muscle tissue (Pennycuick & Rezende, 1984), while the absolute volume of mitochondria of a muscle relates to its maximal steady state power output (Hoppeler & Lindstedt, 1985). It is beyond the scope of this overview to address problems of the chemical to mechanical energy transduction in muscle (Kushmerick, 1983; Rall, 1985). However, this aspect of muscle energetics has an important bearing on skeletal muscle oxidative potential as illustrated by several examples in the subsequent discussion.

DISTRIBUTION OF SKELETAL MUSCLE MITOCHONDRIA IN ANIMALS

Before assessing the effects of various experimental procedures and body sizes on skeletal muscle oxidative potential, we might like to know how mitochondria are distributed within animals, within muscles, and among muscle fiber types. Using a statistical approach, we have sampled the entire skeletal musculature of the European woodmouse (Hoppeler et al., 1984) in such a way that we obtained representative morphological data not only from single muscles, but also from muscle groups and from the whole animal. Using a similar approach, Else and Hulbert (1985) found that at least 82% of the total mitochondria surface area of mammals resides in skeletal muscle tissue (liver 8%, kidney 5%, heart 3%, brain 1%, lung 1%). With regard to skeletal muscle mitochondria in the woodmouse we found that from the total amount of these mitochondria, 42% are found on the trunk, 36% in the limbs, and 22% in the head and neck region (Figure 2; Hoppeler et al., 1984). Muscles typically sampled for experimental purposes, such as gastrocnemius and tibialis anterior, contain less than 4% and 1% respectively of the total muscle mitochondrial volume. This points to some major limitations of many training experiments in which changes in whole-body $\dot{V}O_2max$ are related to changes in oxidative potential of one single skeletal muscle representing only a minute fraction of the total skeletal muscle mass.

This precarious sampling situation is further complicated by muscle oxidative potential not being uniformly distributed within muscles or within muscle groups. It has been well documented for mammals that muscles or portions of muscles located close to the bone (deep location) have a larger proportion of highly oxidative muscle fibers (Laughlin & Armstrong, 1982). Deep portions of semitendinosus in cats and cows and tibialis anterior in rabbits contain twice the volume density of mitochondria than the superficial portions of the very same muscles (Hoppeler et al., 1981; Reichmann et al., 1985). The inhomogeneity of the distribution of skeletal muscle oxidative capacity both within and among muscles has to be taken into account when extrapolations are made from structural or biochemical data obtained from any particular sampling location in a given muscle or muscle group.

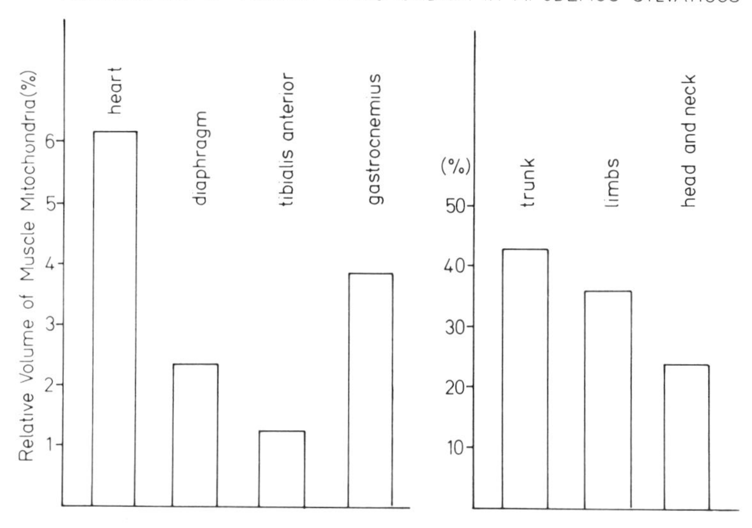

Figure 2 Distribution of mitochondria in individual muscles and in muscle groups in control woodmice given as percent of total skeletal muscle mitochondria. From "Oxygen Consumption and the Composition of Skeletal Muscle Tissue After Training and Inactivation in the European Woodmouse (*Apodemus sylvaticus*)," by H. Hoppeler, S.L. Lindstedt, E. Uhlmann, A. Nielsel, L.M. Cruz-Orive, and E.R. Weibel, 1984, *Journal of Comparative Physiology*, **B155**, pp. 51-61.

Analyzing the oxidative capacity of single muscle fibers by morphometry shows that there is a continuum of mitochondrial densities found in fibers belonging to the different fiber types (cf. Eisenberg, 1983). In human vastus lateralis, the largest volume fraction of total mitochondria was found in histochemical type I fibers (6.2%), followed by type IIa (4.5%), and finally type IIb fibers (2.3%; Howald, Hoppeler, Claassen, Mathieu, & Straub, 1985). Using a different approach for fiber typing similar results for interfibrillar mitochondria were obtained for the same muscle by Sjöström et al. (1982). Likewise, the distribution of oxidative capacity among fiber types may vary considerably between animal species (Essén-Gustavsson, 1986).

In mammalian muscles, fiber types are typically arranged in a mosaic-like pattern. This is not true for all classes of animals. In teleost fish, fiber types of different oxidative capacities are located in anatomically discrete zones (Figure 3; cf. Johnston, Davison, & Goldspink, 1977). Interestingly enough, in contrast to mammals, the most oxidative fibers are located most superficially on the axial musculature of fish. However, there is good evidence that both in fish and in mammals, the fibers with high oxida-

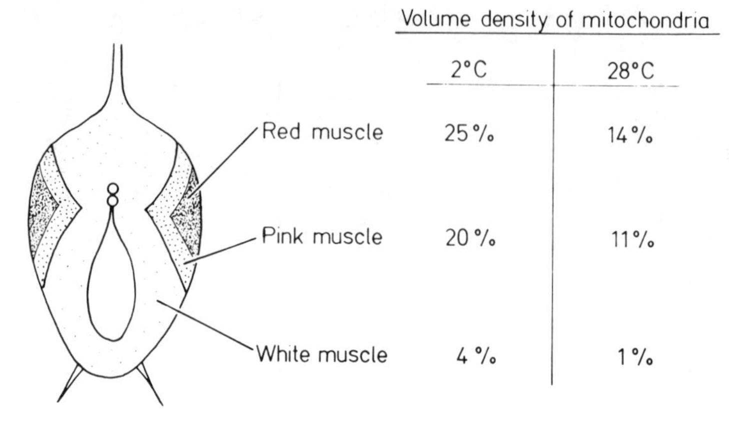

Figure 3 Volume density of mitochondria in the three muscle fiber types in cold- and warm-adapted carp (fiber areas not to scale). Redrawn after "Temperature Acclimation: Improved Sustained Swimming Performance in Carp at Low Temperatures" by L.C. Rome, P.T. Loughna, and G. Goldspink, 1985, *Science*, **228**, pp. 194-196. Copyright 1985 by The American Association for the Advancement of Science. Adapted by permission. Data from "Temperature Acclimation in Crucian Carp, *Carassius carassius L.*, Morphometric Analyses of Muscle Fiber Ultrastructure" by I.A. Johnston and B. Maitland, 1980, *Journal of Fish Biology*, **17**, pp. 113-125. Copyright 1980 by The Fisheries Society of the British Isles. Adapted by permission.

tive capacities are recruited first in graded locomotor activity (Armstrong, Marum, Saubert, Seeherman, & Taylor, 1977; Rome, Loughna, & Goldspink, 1985).

MITOCHONDRIA AND EXERCISE

The adaptation of skeletal muscle oxidative potential to endurance exercise has been well documented for men and laboratory rodents as competently reviewed by Saltin and Gollnick (1983) and Holloszy and Coyle (1984). In longitudinal studies, it is generally found that the oxidative capacity of muscles directly involved in endurance training increases considerably more than whole-body $\dot{V}O_2max$ (Davies, Packer, & Brooks, 1981; Henriksson & Reitmann, 1977). This has been taken as evidence against a causal link between muscle oxidative capacity and whole-body $\dot{V}O_2max$ (Blomqvist & Saltin, 1983). The relationship between local and general changes in aerobic capacity remains debated as both theoretical considerations (Di Prampero, in press) as well as experimental data (Hoppeler et al., 1985) indicate that large changes in oxidative potential in smaller muscle groups may well have only minor effects on whole-body $\dot{V}O_2max$.

Endurance exercise in mammals leads to increases in muscle oxidative capacity while leaving fiber size or muscle mass mostly unaffected (cf. Hoppeler et al., 1985; Saltin & Gollnick, 1983). In contrast, strength training induces a selective increase in myofibrillar volume in combination with a decrease in the volume density of mitochondria (MacDougall et al., 1979; MacDougall, Sale, Elder, & Sutton, 1982). Due to the increase in total muscle mass in strength training, the absolute volume of mitochondria in strength trained muscles remains unchanged (Lüthi et al., in press). Neither endurance nor strength training changes the ultrastructural composition of muscle mitochondria with regard to surface densities of inner and outer mitochondrial membranes or the relative size of the inner and outer chambers (Figure 1; Davies et al., 1981; Hoppeler, Lüthi, Claassen, Weibel, & Howald, 1973; Lüthi et al., in press).

Exercise training increases mitochondrial volume only in muscles directly activated during physical exercise. The untrained leg in one-legged training shows no change in oxidative capacity (Saltin et al., 1976). There is even some indication that during strenuous endurance training the volume fraction of mitochondria may actually decrease in nonactivated muscle groups such as the head and neck region in running woodmice (Figure 4; Hoppeler et al., 1984) or the deltoideus muscle in humans training on

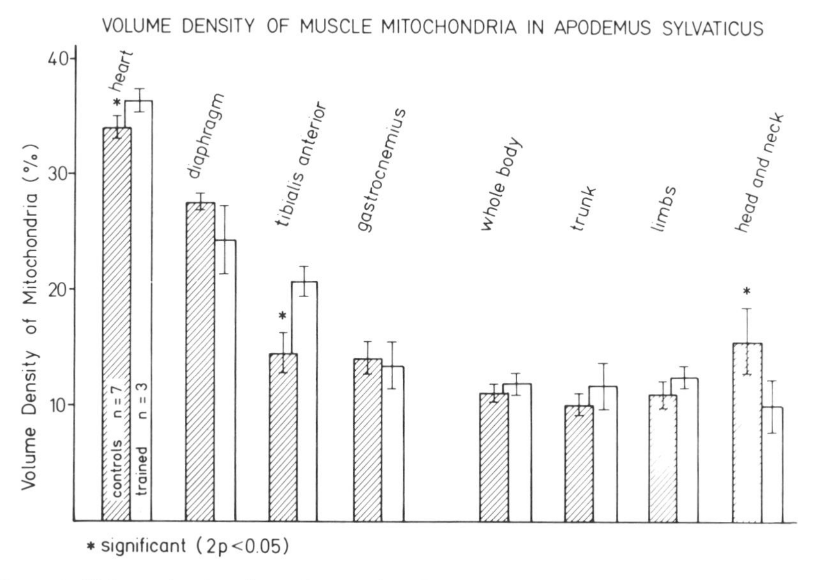

Figure 4 Volume density of muscle mitochondria in various muscles and muscle groups in control and trained woodmice. From "Oxygen Consumption and the Composition of Skeletal Muscle Tissue After Training and Inactivation in the European Woodmouse (*Apodemus sylvaticus*)," by H. Hoppeler, S.L. Lindstedt, E. Uhlmann, A. Nielsel, L.M. Cruz-Orive, and E.R. Weibel, 1984, *Journal of Comparative Physiology*, **B155**, pp. 51-61.

a bicycle ergometer (Rösler et al., 1985). The latter finding would indicate that subjects at a given (elevated) $\dot{V}O_2max$ might be able to differentially stimulate mitochondrial synthesis or degradation in muscles according to the specific needs for sustained mechanical energy production of various motor tasks.

Endurance training protocols have not only successfully been applied to many mammalian species but also to fish. Johnston & Moon (1980a, 1980b) succeeded in exercising trout (Salvelinus fontinalis) and coalfish (Pollachius virens) by swimming these fish at 2 to 3 body lengths per second for more than 23 hr per day during 3 weeks. Unlike endurance exercise in mammals, the oxidative potential of red and white muscle fibers remained essentially unchanged (volume density of mitochondria approximately 30% in red muscle fibers), while the cross-sectional area of the red fibers doubled (471 and 907 m^2 before and after training, respectively). The effect of endurance training on fish red skeletal muscle fibers can therefore be compared to the adaptation of mammalian heart muscle tissue, which has also been reported to adapt to strenuous endurance exercise by increasing its mass, rather than its oxidative enzyme activities (Schaible & Scheuer, 1985). It may be noted that in fish red muscle fibers, 30% of all mitochondria are located subsarcolemmally (human vastus lateralis only approximately 10%), while intracellular lipids account for 10% of the fiber volume (humans 1%; Hoppeler et al., 1985). Unlike in humans, mitochondrial distributions and intracellular lipid stores were unaffected by endurance exercise in fish (Johnston & Moon, 1980a).

ACTIVE AND INACTIVE ANIMALS

In analogy to training, it has been shown that the oxidative potential of muscles of wild individuals of a species is larger than that of the domesticated individuals of the same species (Bass, Gutmann, Melichna, & Syrovy, 1973; Schmalbruch, 1979). This has also been shown to be the case when comparing muscle tissue of the wild brown rat to that of the Wistar rat (Melichna, Gutmann, Havlickova, Stichova, & Herbrychova, 1978). The difference in muscle oxidative potential is believed to be related to the larger capacity of wild animals to do physical work, and hence, to their greater maximal oxygen uptake capacity (cf. Bennett, 1978). We have recently compared mammals of the same body mass (Mb), but of different natural activity levels, to see whether the pattern described above would also hold for mammalian species well characterized for their $\dot{V}O_2max$ as well as their skeletal muscle mitochondria. We found that active dogs have a weight specific $\dot{V}O_2max$, which is more than twice as high as that of inactive goats of the same body mass (2.34 and 0.95 ml $O_2 \cdot kg^{-1} \cdot sec^{-1}$, respectively). Likewise, the volume density of mitochondria in three skeletal muscles was also about 2 times larger in dogs than in goats (Figure 5). Comparing the relationship between whole-body $\dot{V}O_2max$ and muscle oxidative capacity in training to that found in active and inactive animals, one could speculate that training affects only the muscles directly involved in the particular endurance exercise protocol, while in active species, a large number of muscles (perhaps all muscles) might be geared towards higher aerobic work capacities.

REPTILES AND MAMMALS

If a fair comparison is made between reptiles and mammals, that is, if animals of the same body mass and at the same body temperature are compared, it is found that resting oxygen consumption in mammals is about 6 to 8 times higher than resting oxygen consumption in reptiles. At $\dot{V}O_2max$, this difference is believed to be maintained (Bennett, 1978), or it may be reduced to about 4-fold (Else & Hulbert, 1981). The difference in resting metabolism between mammals and reptiles can be accounted for by mammals having larger relative weights of their internal organs

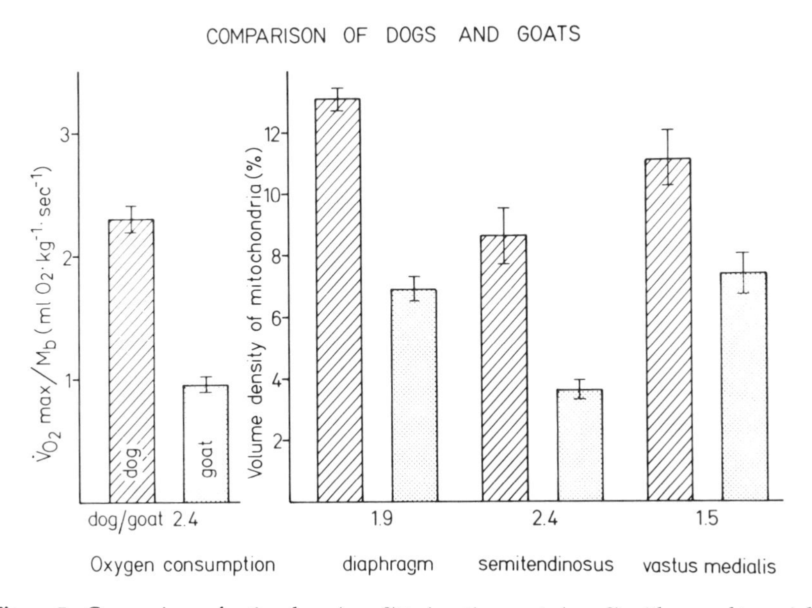

Figure 5 Comparison of active dogs (n = 3) to inactive goats (n = 3) with regard to weight specific $\dot{V}O_2max$ and volume density of mitochondria in three skeletal muscles.

(liver, kidney, heart, brain). All of these organs contain a larger volume fraction of mitochondria in mammals than in reptiles, and their mitochondria have a greater cristae surface density than mitochondria in reptile organs. It was thus reasoned that the greater oxidative enzyme activity found in organs of mammalian species is due to a greater quantity of enzymes and not by a greater enzyme specific activity (Else & Hulbert, 1981). This contention is supported by biochemical data indicating that isolated reptile mitochondria are capable of consuming the same amount of oxygen as mammalian mitochondria when compared on a per protein content basis (Cassuto, 1971; Mersmann & Privitera, 1964). There is a shortage of directly comparable data for a comparison between $\dot{V}O_2max$ and morphology of skeletal muscle mitochondria in reptiles and mammals. Available data on frog and rat (cf. Eisenberg, 1983) suggest the latter to have considerably larger volume fractions of mitochondria in their skeletal muscle fibers.

ADAPTATION TO COLD

Exposure of homeothermic animals to a cold environment represents a serious challenge to the respiratory system (Weiss, 1954). Keeping young rats at 10 °C instead of 24 °C increased 24 hr oxygen consumption of cold-exposed animals by as much as 64% (Buser, Kopp, Gehr, Weibel, & Hoppeler, 1982). Morphometry showed an increase in the volume density of mitochondria by nearly 30%, both in diaphragm and soleus muscle. Not only was there a significant increase in the volume fraction of mitochondria, but the surface density of the inner mitochondrial membranes was also significantly increased by up to 50% over control values. The changes in mitochondrial membrane areas are thought to be associated with hormonal changes induced in the cold-exposed animals (John-Alder, 1984; Page & McCallister, 1973). As there are no apparent changes in the locomotor activity levels of long-term cold-adapted rats, it was concluded that during cold adaptation, skeletal muscle mitochondria might significantly be involved in nonshivering thermogenesis (Greenway & Himms-Hagen, 1978).

Poikilothermic animals meet an altogether different challenge than homeothermic animals when suddenly exposed to a cold environment. In carp, it was observed that to swim at the same speed in cold as in warm water the fish had to recruit their rapidly fatiguing white muscle fibers earlier than when swimming in warm water (Rome, Loughna, & Goldspink, 1985). Some fish have been shown to be able to adapt to a cold environment by increasing the specific activity of their actomyosin ATPase, allowing them to maintain or even improve the mechanical power output of their cold adapted muscles (Johnston & Brill, 1984; Johnston

& Maitland, 1980; Rome, Loughna, & Goldspink, 1985). In order to produce ATP at the same rate as a fish adapted to a warm environment, cold-adapted fish have been shown to increase the volume fraction of mitochondria 2- to several-fold in all fiber types (Figure 3); Johnston & Maitland, 1980; Tyler & Sidell, 1984). It thus appears that cold-adapted fish can maintain their mechanical power output by a qualitative change in the myofibrillar ATPase and by a quantitative change in the muscle oxidative capacity.

SCALING OF OXIDATIVE CAPACITY IN SKELETAL MUSCLE

It is well known since Kleiber (1932) that the resting oxygen consumption of mammals is proportional to $Mb^{0.75}$. Likewise, it was found that the exponent of the allometric regression relating $\dot{V}O_2max$ to body mass is 0.809 for 22 species of wild and domestic mammals (Mb = 7 g to 263 kg; Taylor et al., 1981). This indicates that a mouse of 20 g must be able to transport and consume oxygen at 15 times the rate of a 500 kg steer. To achieve these high rates of oxygen consumption under conditions of maximal mechanical activity, skeletal muscle tissue of small animals must contain a larger volume fraction of mitochondria than the skeletal muscle tissue of larger animals. It was shown that there is a constant proportional relationship between $\dot{V}O_2max$ and the total volume of mitochondria in three skeletal muscles of animals ranging between 0.4 and 240 kg of body mass (Mathieu et al., 1981). These results have recently been expanded to include the cristae surface areas of skeletal muscle mitochondria, which are found to scale in proportion to $Mb^{0.78}$ (Else & Hulbert, 1985). Likewise, Emmett and Hockacka (1981) found that the scaling of citrate synthase, malate dehydrogenase and β-hydroxybutyryl CoA dehydrogenase activities in skeletal muscles of 10 mammalian species (4g-1000kg) was not significantly different from the scaling of the mass specific $\dot{V}O_2max$ estimated by Taylor et al. (1981).

What could be the reason for small animals needing a much larger aerobic capacity in their skeletal muscle tissue? It has been demonstrated that the ATPase activity of skeletal muscle myosin depends not only on muscle fiber type, but also on the body size of the animal (Syrovy & Gutmann, 1975), small animals having larger ATPase activities in their skeletal muscles than large ones. Since the ATPase activity has been shown to be strongly related to the intrinsic rate of muscle shortening (Barany, 1967), it has been hypothesized that the ATPase activity, and hence, the rate of cross bridge cycling between the actin and the myosin heads, ultimately sets the cost for muscular contraction (Goldspink, 1978; Heglund, Fedak,

Taylor, & Cavagna, 1982; Hoppeler, Lindstedt, & Mathieu, 1980). In order to achieve the high rates of muscle shortening occurring during locomotion in small animals, these animals need high myosin ATPase activities, which in turn result in a high energetic cost for locomotion (Lindstedt, Hoppeler, Bard, & Thronson, 1985; Taylor, 1986). The high energetic costs for operating the "fast" muscle tissue in small animals under maximal steady state aerobic conditions is matched by a proportionally larger size of the mitochondrial compartment. As in the previous example, we find that the contractile machinery of skeletal muscle tissue is adapted in terms of a qualitative change (specific ATPase activity) while the oxidative machinery is adapted by a quantitative change, namely by an adjustment of the volume fraction of mitochondria.

CONCLUSIONS

It is found that skeletal muscle oxidative capacity is extremely variable among species and within species among muscles and muscle fiber types. In adaptation experiments, it is found that a larger aerobic power output of muscle tissue can be achieved either by an increase in the volume density of mitochondria (exercise and cold-exposure in mammals) or by an increase in the size of oxidative muscle fibers (exercise in fish skeletal muscle and mammalian heart). In muscle tissue with a high actomyosin ATPase activity (fast muscles, small animals), a large volume density of mitochondria is needed to support continuous mechanical activity, making locomotion energetically expensive for small animals. Available data suggest that the rate at which ATP is broken down in muscle cells is regulated by some intrinsic properties of the myofibrillar ATPase, while the rate of aerobic ATP production is determined by the size of the mitochondrial compartment, mitochondria being similar in terms of their energy turnover characteristics among animal species.

Acknowledgments

The author thanks H. Claassen, E. Uhlmann, K. Babl, and R.M. Fankhauser for excellent technical assistance. This work was supported by Swiss National Science Foundation Grant 3.036.0.84.

REFERENCES

Armstrong, R.B., & Laughlin, H.M. (1983). Blood flows within and among rat muscles as a function of time during high speed treadmill exercise. *Journal of Physiology* (London), **344**, 189-208.

Armstrong, R.B., Marum, P., Saubert, C.W. IV, Seeherman, H.J., & Taylor, C.R. (1977). Muscle fiber activity as a function of speed and gait. *Journal of Applied Physiology*, **43**, 672-677.

Barany, M. (1967). ATPase activity of myosin correlated with speed of muscle shortening. *Journal of General Physiology*, **50**, 197-218.

Bass, A., Gutmann, E., Melichna, J., & Syrovy, I. (1973). Contractile and enzymatic properties of fast and slow muscles of rabbit and hare. *Physiologia Bohemoslovenica*, **22**, 477-486.

Bennett, A.F. (1978). Activity metabolism of the lower vertebrates. *Annual Review of Physiology*, **40**, 447-469.

Blomqvist, C.G., & Saltin, B. (1983). Cardiovascular adaptations to physical training. *Annual Review of Physiology*, **45**, 169-189.

Braunwald, E. (1971). Control of myocardial oxygen consumption: Physiologic and clinical considerations. *American Journal of Cardiology*, **27**, 416-432.

Buser, K.S., Kopp, B., Gehr, P. Weibel, E.R., & Hoppeler, H. (1982). Effect of cold environment on skeletal muscle mitochondria in growing rats. *Cell and Tissue Research*, **225**, 427-436.

Bylund, A.-C.H., Bjurö, T., Cederblad, G., Holm, J., Lundholm, K., Sjöström, M., Ängquist, K.A., & Scherstén, T. (1977). Physical training in man. Skeletal muscle metabolism in relation to muscle morphology and running ability. *European Journal of Applied Physiology*, **36**, 151-169.

Cassuto, Y. (1971). Oxidative activities of liver mitochondria from mammals, birds, reptiles, and amphibia as a function of temperature. *Comparative Biochemistry and Physiology*, **B39**, 919-923.

Davies, K.J.A., Packer, L., & Brooks, G.A. (1981). Biochemical adaptation of mitochondria, muscle, and whole-animal respiration to endurance training. *Archives of Biochemistry and Biophysics*, **209**, 539-554.

Di Prampero, P.E. (1985). Metabolic and circulatory limitations to $\dot{V}O_2max$ at the whole animal level. *Journal of Experimental Biology*, **115**, 319-331.

Eisenberg, B.R. (1983). Quantitative ultrastructure of mammalian skeletal muscle. In L.D. Peachy, R.H. Adrian, & S.R. Geiger (Eds.), *Handbook of Physiology*. Skeletal Muscle (pp. 73-112). Baltimore, MD: Williams & Wilkins.

Else, P.L., & Hulbert, A.J. (1981). Comparison of the "mammal machine" and the "reptile machine": Energy production. *American Journal of Physiology,* **240**, R3-R9.

Else, P.L., & Hulbert, A.J. (1985). Mammals: An allometric study of metabolism at tissue and mitochondrial level. *American Journal of Physiology,* **248**, R415-R421.

Emmett, B., & Hochachka, P.W. (1981). Scaling of oxidative and glycolytic enzymes in mammals. *Respiration Physiology,* **45**, 261-272.

Essén, B., Jansson, E., Henriksson, J., Taylor, A.W., & Saltin, B. (1975). Metabolic characteristics of fiber types in human skeletal muscle. *Acta Physiologica Scandinavica,* **95**, 153-165.

Essén-Gustavsson, B. (1986). Activity and inactivity related muscle adaptation in the animal kingdom. In B. Saltin (Ed.), *Proceedings of the 6th International Symposium of the Biochemistry of Exercise* (Vol. 14, pp. 435-444). Champaign, IL: Human Kinetics.

Folkow, B., & Halicka, H.D. (1968). A comparison between "red" and "white" muscle with respect to blood supply, capillary surface area, and oxygen uptake during rest and exercise. *Microvascular Research,* **1**, 1-14.

Goldspink, G. (1978). Energy turnover during contraction of different types of muscle. In E. Asmussen & K. Jørgensen (Eds.), *Biomechanics VI-A*. Baltimore, MD: University Park Press.

Greenway, D.C., & Himms-Hagen, J. (1978). Increased calcium uptake by muscle mitochondria of cold-acclimated rats. *American Journal of Physiology,* **234**, C7-C13.

Hammen, C.S., & Ellington, W.R. (1984). Anaerobic metabolism of invertebrates. *Federation Proceedings,* **43**, 220-225.

Heglund, N.C., Fedak, M.A., Taylor, C.R., & Cavagna, C.A. (1982). Energetics and mechanics of terrestrial locomotion. IV. Total mechanical energy changes as a function of speed and body size in birds and mammals. *Journal of Experimental Biology,* **97**, 57-66.

Henriksson, J., & Reitman, J.S. (1977). Time course of changes in human skeletal muscle succinate dehydrogenase and cytochrome oxidase activities and maximal oxygen uptake with physical activity and inactivity. *Acta Physiologica Scandinavica,* **99**, 91-97.

Holloszy, J.O., & Coyle, E.F. (1984). Adaptations of skeletal muscles to endurance exercise and their metabolic consequences. *Journal of Applied Physiology,* **56**, 831-838.

Hoppeler, H., Howald, H., Conley, K.E., Lindstedt, S.L., Claassen, H., Vock, P., & Weibel, E.R. (1985). Endurance training in humans: Aerobic capacity and structure of skeletal muscle. *Journal of Applied Physiology,* **59**.

Hoppeler, H., & Lindstedt, S.L. (1985). Malleability of skeletal muscle tissue in overcoming limitations: Structural elements. *Journal of Experimental Biology*, **115**, 355-364.

Hoppeler, H., Lindstedt, S.L., & Mathieu, O. (1980). Scaling structural parameters of oxygen consumption against $\dot{V}O_2$max and body mass. In P. Cerretelli & B.J. Whipp (Eds.), *Exercise bioenergetics and gas exchange* (pp. 129-135). Amsterdam: Elsevier.

Hoppeler, H., Lindstedt, S.L., Uhlmann, E., Niesel, A., Cruz-Orive, L.M., & Weibel, E.R. (1984). Oxygen consumption and the composition of skeletal muscle tissue after training and inactivation in the European woodmouse (*Apodemus sylvaticus*). *Journal of Comparative Physiology*, **B155**, 51-61.

Hoppeler, H., Lüthi, P., Claassen, H., Weibel, E.R., & Howald, H. (1973). The ultrastructure of the normal human skeletal muscle. A morphometric analysis on untrained men, women, and well trained orienteers. *Pflügers Archiv*, **344**, 217-232.

Hoppeler, H., Mathieu, O., Krauer, R., Claassen, H., Armstrong, R.B., & Weibel, E.R. (1981). Design of the mammalian respiratory system. VI. Distribution of mitochondria and capillaries in various muscles. *Respiration Physiology*, **44**, 87-111.

Howald, H., Hoppeler, H., Claassen, H., Mathieu, O., & Straub, R. (1985). Influence of endurance training on the ultrastructural composition of the different muscle fiber types in humans. *Pflügers Archiv*, **403**, 369-376.

Ingjer, F. (1979). Effects of endurance training on muscle fibre ATPase activity, capillary supply and mitochondrial content in man. *Journal of Physiology* (London), **294**, 419-432.

John-Alder, H.B. (1984). Season variations in activity, aerobic energetic capacities, and plasma thyroid hormones (T3 and T4) in an iguanid lizard. *Journal of Comparative Physiology*, **B154**, 409-419.

Johnston, I.A., & Brill, R. (1984). Thermal dependence of contractile properties of single skinned muscle fibres from antarctic and various warm water marine fishes including Skipjack tuna (Katsuwonus pelamis) and Kawakawa (Euthynnus affinis). *Journal of Comparative Physiology*, **B155**, 63-70.

Johnston, I.A., Davison, W., & Goldspink, G. (1977). Energy metabolism of carp swimming muscles. *Journal of Comparative Physiology*, **114**, 203-216.

Johnston, I.A., & Maitland, B. (1980). Temperature acclimation in crucian carp, Carassius carassius L., morphometric analyses of muscle fibre ultrastructure. *Journal of Fish Biology*, **17**, 113-125.

Johnston, I.A., & Moon, T.W. (1980a). Exercise training in skeletal muscle of brook trout (Salvelinus fontinalis). *Journal of Experimental Physiology*, **87**, 177-194.

Johnston, I.A., & Moon, T.W. (1980b). Endurance exercise training in the fast and slow muscles of a teleost fish (Pollachius virens). *Journal of Comparative Physiology*, **135**, 147-156.

Kiessling, K.-H., Pilström, L., Bylund, A.-Ch., Saltin, B., & Piehl, K. (1974). Enzyme activities and morphometry in skeletal muscle of middle-aged men after training. *Scandinavian Journal of Clinical and Laboratory Investigation*, **33**, 63-69.

Kleiber, M. (1932). Body size and metabolism. *Hilgardia*, **6**, 315-353.

Kushmerick, M.J. (1983). Energetics of muscle contraction. In L.D. Peachy, R.H. Adrian, and S.R. Geiger (Eds.), *Handbook of Physiology*. Skeletal Muscle (pp. 189-236). Baltimore, MD: Williams & Wilkins.

Laughlin, M.H., & Armstrong, R.B. (1982). Muscular blood flow distribution patterns as a function of running speed in rats. *American Journal of Physiology*, **243**, 296-306.

Lehninger, A.L. (1978). *Biochemistry* (pp. 509-542). New York: Worth Publisher.

Lindstedt, S.L., Hoppeler, H., Bard, K.M., & Thronson, H.A., Jr. (1985). An estimate of muscle shortening rate during locomotion. *American Journal of Physiology*, **249**, R699-R703.

Lüthi, J.M., Howald, H., Claassen, H., Rösler, K., Vock, P., & Hoppeler, H. (in press). *Structural changes in skeletal muscle tissue with heavy resistance exercise*.

MacDougall, J.D., Sale, D.G., Elder, G.C., & Sutton, J.R. (1982). Muscle ultrastructural characteristics of elite powerlifters and bodybuilders. *European Journal of Applied Physiology*, **48**, 117-126.

MacDougall, J.D., Sale, D.G., Moroz, J.R., Elder, G.C.B., Sutton, J.R., & Howald, H. (1979). Mitochondrial volume density in human muscle following heavy resistance training. *Medicine and Science in Sports and Exercise*, **11**, 164-166.

Mainwood, G.W., & Rakusan, K. (1982). A model for intracellular energy transport. *Canadian Journal of Physiology and Pharmacology*, **60**, 98-102.

Mathieu, O., Cruz-Orive, L.M., Hoppeler, H., & Weibel, E.R. (1983). Estimating length density and quantifying anisotropy in skeletal muscle capillaries. *Journal of Microscopy*, **131**, 131-146.

Mathieu, O., Krauer, R., Hoppeler, H., Gehr, P., Lindstedt, S.L., Alexander, R.McN., Taylor, C.R., & Weibel, E.R. (1981). Design of the mammalian respiratory system. VII. Scaling mitochondriaml volume in skeletal muscle to body mass. *Respiration Physiology*, **44**, 113-128.

Melichna, J., Gutmann, E., Havlickova, L., Stichova, J., & Herbrychova, A. (1978). Comparison of contractile, histo- and biochemical properties of different skeletal muscles of the brown rat (Rattus norvegicus) with those of the domesticated Wistar rat. *Journal of Comparative Physiology*, **126**, 263-268.

Mersmann, H.J., & Privitera, C.A. (1964). In vitro metabolism by turtle heart mitochondria. *American Journal of Physiology,* **206**, 980-984.

Morgan, T.E., Cobb, L.A., Short, F.A., Ross, R., & Gunn, D.R. (1971). Effects of long-term exercise on human muscle mitochondria. In B. Pernow & B. Saltin (Eds.), *Muscle metabolism during exercise* (pp. 87-95). New York: Plenum.

Page, E., & McCallister, L.P. (1973). Quantitative electron microscopic description of heart muscle cells. Application to normal, hypertrophied and thyroxin-stimulated hearts. *American Journal of Cardiology,* **31**, 172-181.

Pennycuick, C.J., & Rezende, M.A. (1984). The specific power output of aerobic muscle, related to the power density of mitochondria. *Journal of Experimental Biology,* **108**, 377-392.

Rall, J.A. (1985). Energetic aspects of skeletal muscle contraction: Implication of fiber types. *Exercise and Sports Sciences Reviews,* **13**, 33-74.

Reichmann, H., Hoppeler, H., Mathieu-Costello, O., von Bergen, F., & Pette, D. (1985). Biochemical and ultrastructural changes of skeletal muscle mitochondria after chronic electrical stimulation in rabbits. *Pflügers Archiv,* **404**, 1-9.

Reichmann, H., & Pette, D. (1982). A comparative microphotometric study of succinate dehydrogenase activity levels in type I, IIA and IIB fibres of mammalian and human muscles. *Histochemistry,* **74**, 27-41.

Rösler, K.M., Conley, K.E., Claassen, H., Howald, H., & Hoppeler, H. (1985). Transfer effects in endurance exercise: Adaptations in trained and untrained muscles. *European Journal of Applied Physiology,* **54**, 355-362.

Rome, L.C., Loughna, P.T., & Goldspink, G. (1985). Temperature acclimation: Improved sustained swimming performance in carp at low temperatures. *Science,* **228**, 194-196.

Saltin, B., & Gollnick, P.D. (1983). Skeletal muscle adaptability: Significance for metabolism and performance. In L.D. Peachy, R.H. Adrian, & S.R. Geiger (Eds.), *Handbook of physiology*. Skeletal Muscle (pp. 555-631). Baltimore, MD: Williams and Wilkins.

Saltin, B., Nazar, K., Costill, D.L., Stein, E., Jansson, E., Essén, B., & Gollnick, P.D. (1976). The nature of the training response; peripheral and central adaptations to one-legged exercise. *Acta Physiologica Scandinavica,* **96**, 289-305.

Schaible, T.F., & Scheuer, J. (1985). Cardiac adaptations to chronic exercise. *Progress in Cardiovascular Disease,* **27**, 297-324.

Schmalbruch, H. (1979). The membrane systems in different fibre types of the triceps surae muscle of cat. *Cell and Tissue Research,* **204**, 187-200.

Schwerzmann, K., & Hoppeler, H. (1985). Stereology: A working tool for cell biologists. *Trends in Biochemical Science,* **10**, 184-187.

Schwerzmann, K., & Weibel, E.R. (1984). A morphometric approach to the molecular architecture of mitochondria. (Abstract). *EBEC Report Vol. 3B* (pp. 731-732). Miami, FL: ICSU Press.

Sjöström, M., Ängquist, K.A., Bylund, A.-C.H., Fridén, J., Gustavsson, L., & Scherstén, T. (1982). Morphometric analyses of human muscle fiber types. *Muscle and Nerve,* **5**, 538-553.

Stainsby, W.N., & Otis, A.B. (1964). Blood flow, blood oxygen tension, oxygen uptake, and oxygen transport in skeletal muscle. *American Journal of Physiology,* **206**, 858-866.

Syrovy, I., & Gutmann, E. (1975). Myosin from fast and slow skeletal and cardiac muscles of mammals of different size. *Physiologia Bohemoslovenica,* **24**, 325-334.

Taylor, C.R. (1986). Energetics of locomotion: What sets the cost? In B. Saltin (Ed.), *Proceedings of the 6th International Congress of the Biochemistry of Exercise* (Vol. 14, pp. 409-415). Champaign, IL: Human Kinetics.

Taylor, C.R., Maloiy, G.M.O., Weibel, E.R., Langman, V.A., Kamau, J.M.Z., Seeherman, M.J., & Heglund, N.C. (1981). Design of the mammalian respiratory system. III. Scaling maximum aerobic capacity to body mass: Wild and domestic mammals. *Respiration Physiology,* **44**, 25-37.

Tyler, S., & Sidell, B.D. (1984). Changes in mitochondrial distribution and diffusion distances in goldfish upon acclimation to warm and cold temperatures. *Journal of Experimental Biology,* **232**, 1-9.

Weibel, E.R. (1979a). Oxygen demand and size of respiratory structures in mammals. In S.C. Wood & C. Lenfant (Eds.), *Evolution of respiratory processes* (pp. 289-346). New York: Dekker.

Weibel, E.R. (1979b). *Stereological methods. Vol. I: Practical methods for Biological morphometry*. (Chapters 4 and 6). London—New York—Toronto: Academic Press.

Weiss, K. (1954). Adaptations of rats to cold air and effects on tissue oxygen consumption. *American Journal of Physiology,* **177**, 201-207.

Activity- and Inactivity-Related Muscle Adaptation in the Animal Kingdom

Birgitta Essén-Gustavsson
Swedish University of Agricultural Sciences
Uppsala, Sweden

It is well-known, mainly from studies on rats, horses and humans, that muscular adaptation occurs in response to physical activity (see Saltin & Gollnick, 1983). Endurance activity has been shown to increase the oxidative capacity of muscle, thereby improving its capacity to oxidize both fats and carbohydrates. This higher oxidative capacity may spare glycogen and decrease lactate formation during exercise.

Wild animals are exposed daily to endurance activity in the search for feed, in contrast to domestic animals such as pigs and cattle that are confined and hand-fed, resulting in complete inactivity. Some of our domestic animals are, however, also exposed by man to a great amount of activity; for example, horses and greyhounds that are used in races. In the Scandinavian countries there are also the reindeer, semidomestic animals, which are extremely active during their migration. Thus, among our domesticated animals pigs and cattle must be considered to be extremely inactive in comparison to racehorses and greyhounds and the wild animals, which always are somewhat active, as they are moving about freely. It is therefore of interest to compare muscle characteristics in some domesticated and wild animals.

MATERIAL AND METHODS

Each group of animals presented in this study contained 6 to 20 individuals, except for the wild animals in which each group contained two to three animals. More details about some of the groups of animals have been presented earlier, for example, wild pigs (Essén-Gustavsson & Lindholm, 1984), trained pigs (Essén-Gustavsson & Lindholm, 1983), inactive and active horses (Essén-Gustavsson & Lindholm, 1985), trained horses (Thornton, Essén-Gustavsson, Lindholm, McMiken, & Persson, 1983), and reindeer (Essén-Gustavsson & Rehbinder, 1985). Most groups of animals consisted of adults, except for the foals and some of the wild animals, which were 1 to 2 years of age. When animals were pastured they were kept outside and allowed to move freely for 12 to 24 hours. Otherwise animals were kept most of the time inside stalls.

Muscle samples were taken in some animals from both the gluteus and longissimus muscles, and in others from either the gluteus or the longissimus. Most of the samples were obtained with the needle biopsy technique described by Lindholm and Piehl (1974). Surgical samples were taken from those wild animals that were shot in the wild and from pigs and bulls that were slaughtered. Two muscle samples were always obtained. One piece of muscle was immediately frozen in liquid nitrogen and then stored at -80 °C until analyzed for enzyme activities. The second piece of muscle was gently rolled in talcum powder before it was frozen in liquid nitrogen. This piece was also stored at -80 °C until histochemical analyses were performed. Fluorimetric techniques were used in the analyses of enzymes using methods earlier described (Essén-Gustavsson, Karlström, & Lindholm, 1984; Essén, Lindholm, & Thornton, 1980). Citrate-synthase (CS) was analyzed as a marker for the citric acid cycle capacity, 3-OH acyl CoA dehydrogenase (HAD) as a marker for lipid oxidation and lactate dehydrogenase (LDH) as a marker for glycolytic capacity.

Histochemical analyses to identify fiber types were performed using the myofibrillar ATPase stains as described by Brooke and Kaiser (1970). Capillaries were visualized by staining sections using the Amylase-PAS method (Andersen, 1975). The stained sections were photographed and a large area containing a minimum of 225 fibers was framed. Within that area, the capillary density (cap/mm^2) and the mean number of capillaries in contact with fibers of each type, relative to fiber area, were analyzed according to Andersen and Henriksson (1977). The total area and the individual fiber areas were analyzed with a MOP digiplan analyzer. When fiber areas are described on different animals, these have been measured on the ATPase stain after acid preincubation (pH 4.6) also using the MOP digiplan analyzer.

RESULTS AND DISCUSSION

Fiber Types, Fiber Areas and CS Activities

The mean fiber composition and the CS activities are shown in Figure 1 for m. gluteus and in Figure 2 for m. longissimus. Fiber areas are shown in Figure 3. The mean percentage of type II fibers was high in the muscles of all the animals (> 65%). A somewhat higher percentage of type II fibers was seen in longissimus compared to gluteus.

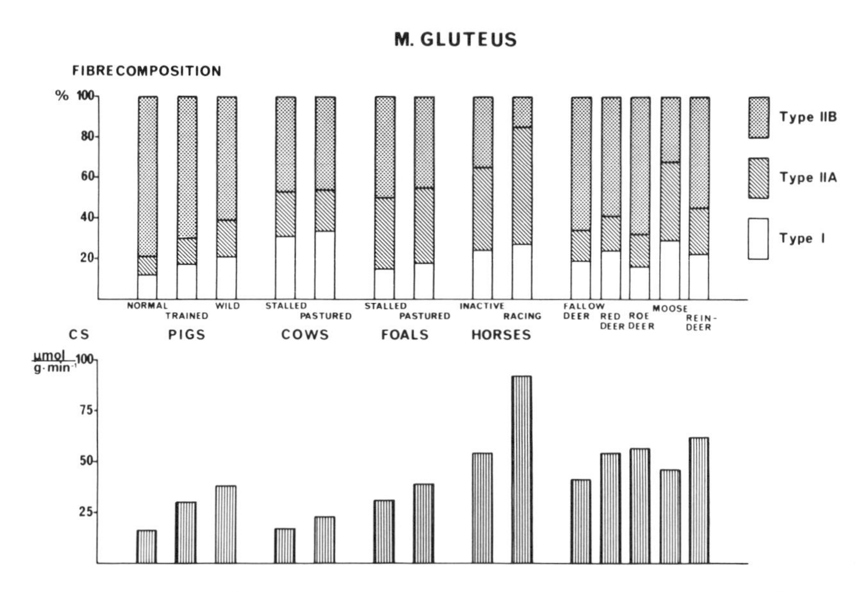

Figure 1 Fiber composition and citrate synthase (CS) activities in m. gluteus of different animals.

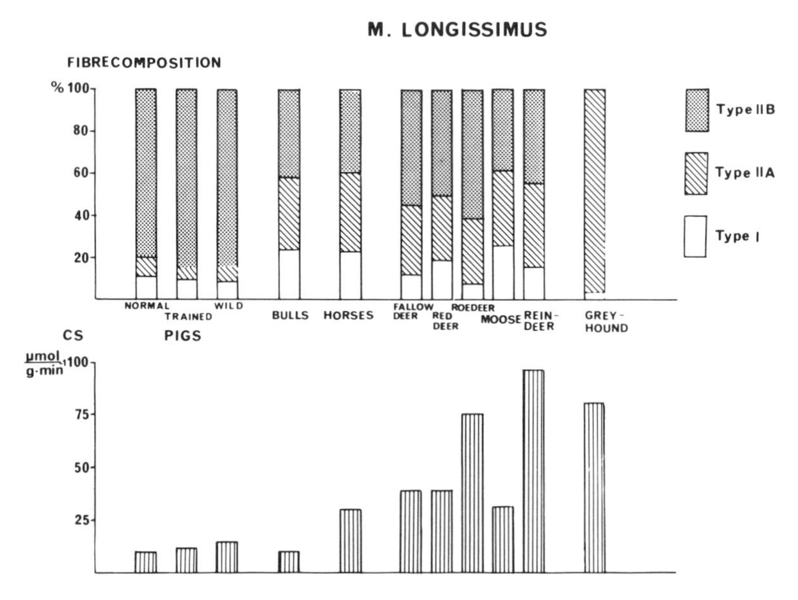

Figure 2 Fiber composition and citrate synthase (CS) activities in m. longissimus of different animals.

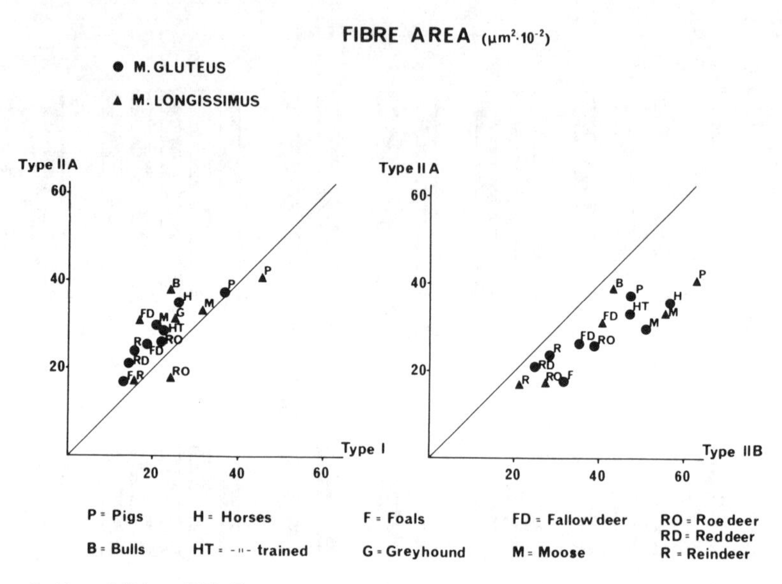

Figure 3 Type I, IIA and IIB fiber areas in m. gluteus and m. longissimus of different animals.

Type II fibers can be further subgrouped into type IIA and IIB fibers (Brooke & Kaiser, 1970). It has been shown that the percentage of these subgroups and the oxidative capacity within these fibers can vary markedly between muscles and animals (Brooke & Kaiser, 1970; Essén et al., 1980; Reichman & Pette, 1982; Sher & Cardasis, 1976). A high type IIA/IIB ratio and a high oxidative capacity are usually found in trained athletes (Jansson & Kaiser, 1977) and in racehorses (Essén-Gustavsson & Lindholm, 1985). Training has also been shown to increase the type IIA/IIB ratio and the oxidative capacity both in man (Henriksson & Reitman, 1975) and in horses (Lindholm, Essén-Gustavsson, McMiken, Persson, & Thornton, 1983). Not only genetic factors but also environmental factors such as an increased or decreased activity level may be of importance for the adaptive response in oxidative potential and fiber composition within a given muscle.

As seen in Figures 1 and 2, the lowest CS activity was found in the domestic pigs, animals that are almost totally inactive because their management systems restrict free movement. These pigs had as much as 80% to 90% type II fibers, of which most are type IIB fibers. Only 5% to 10% IIA fibers are found in pig muscle. The largest fiber areas were also found in domestic pigs and a remarkably large relative area thus consists of type IIB fibers. The histochemical stain for oxidative capacity (NADH) shows that it is the few type I and IIA fibers that are oxidative. Some type IIB fibers that lie close to type I and IIA are also sometimes oxidative (Essén-Gustavsson & Lindholm, 1984), but most of them are unstained for NADH. By contrast, the CS activity levels were higher in pigs that had been trained (10 min at 2 to 3 m/s, 5 days/week for 10 weeks) and in wild pigs. Fiber composition was not changed except for the gluteus of the wild pigs, which had a higher type IIA/IIB ratio than the other pigs. In pigs, the gluteus is probably more involved in locomotion than the longissimus, which may explain its larger increase in CS and in type IIA/IIB ratio. However, in an animal such as the greyhound, the longissimus is utilized extensively during locomotion, which may explain its very high CS activity in these animals and its composition of almost 100% type IIA fibers. These data agree with earlier findings (Guy & Snow, 1981). Gluteus is known to be an active locomotory muscle of the horse, and racehorses had higher CS activities and a higher type IIA/IIB ratio than inactive horses. In muscles of cows and bulls, CS activities were as low as those in pigs. However, the muscles contained a rather high percentage of type I and type IIA fibers. The oxidative capacity was mostly found in these fibers as seen from NADH stains. Despite having a very high CS activity level, the wild animals also showed a high percentage of type IIB fibers in both gluteus and longissimus, both of which are likely to be involved in locomotion. Histochemical stains showed that the oxidative capacity was located in all the fiber types, but to the greatest extent in type I and IIA fibers. Type IIB fibers in reindeer may stain as darkly as type I and IIA fibers (Essén-Gustavsson & Rehbinder, 1985). Because wild animals not only roam about freely but, in flight situations from predators, must have bursts of speed, it may be favorable for them to have oxidative type IIB fibers to provide both high speed and endurance. In cats, type I and IIA fibers are said to be fatigue-resistant and recruited during steady and continuous activity, whereas type IIB fibers, which are glycolytic, are said to be fast-fatigable and involved in maximal efforts (Burke, Levine, Tsairis, & Zajac, (1973).

The data in Figures 1 and 2 clearly show that CS activity does not have to be related to fiber composition of a muscle, but seems to be strongly influenced by the activity level of the muscle and animal. It is notable that the slightly higher activity imposed on the muscles when animals are pastured will significantly increase the CS activities, as seen in foals and cows in Figure 1.

Growth is also an important factor that may influence fiber composition and fiber areas. Horses biopsied from 6 months to 2 years of age seemed to show an increase in type IIA/IIB ratio due to growth rather than activity (Essén-Gustavsson, Lindholm, McMiken, Persson, & Thornton, 1983). The areas of the fibers also increased with age as larger areas are seen in adult horses compared to foals. In rats a good correlation has been shown between body weight and muscle fiber area (Sillau & Banchero, 1977). The area of a fiber seems to be related to body size as smaller animals had smaller fiber areas than in bulls, horses and moose. In all animals, however, type I fibers were always smallest in size, whereas type IIB fibers were the largest (Figure 3). The unusually large areas found in domestic pigs are most likely related to the many years of artificial selection for rapid muscle growth in this species, as domestic pigs increase their body weight from 1 to 100 kg within a year.

Enzyme Activities and Capillaries

The HAD activities were similar to the CS activities, being highest in the more active animals, whereas pigs, cows and bulls had very low activities (Figure 4). A high correlation was found between CS and HAD activities. LDH activities, on the other hand, showed a negative correlation to CS activities, but this relationship was not as clear as it appears that racehorses, greyhounds, trained pigs and wild pigs still keep their high glycolytic capacity even when their oxidative capacities are very high (Figure 5). From Figure 6 it can also be seen that there is a very high correlation between the capillarization of the muscle and its oxidative capacity. The wild animals had 3 to 4 times more capillaries/mm² than pigs and bulls. The fiber sizes seem to play an important role in determining the capillarization in muscle as capillaries per fiber did not markedly differ among the animals but fiber areas did. The number of capillaries in contact with

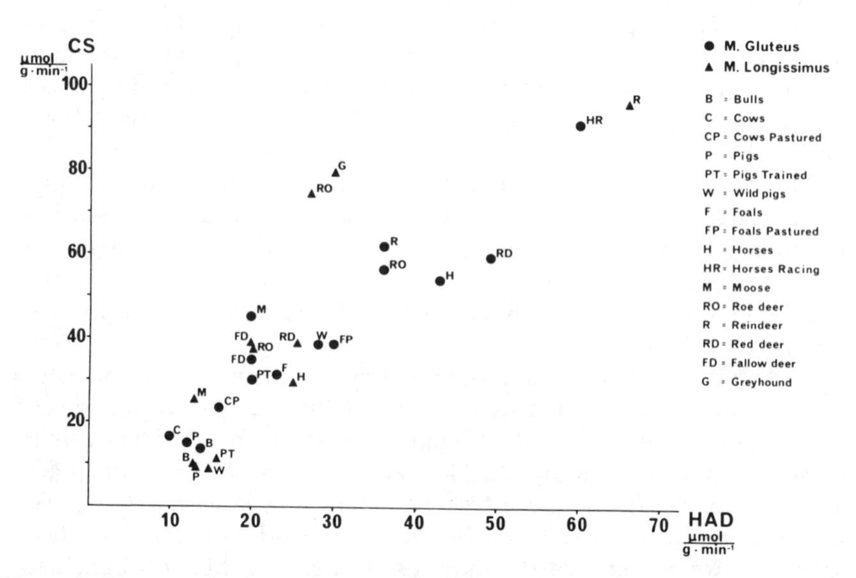

Figure 4 Citrate synthase activities (CS) in m. gluteus and m. longissimus of different animals in relation to the activities of 3 OH- acyl CoA dehydrogenase (HAD).

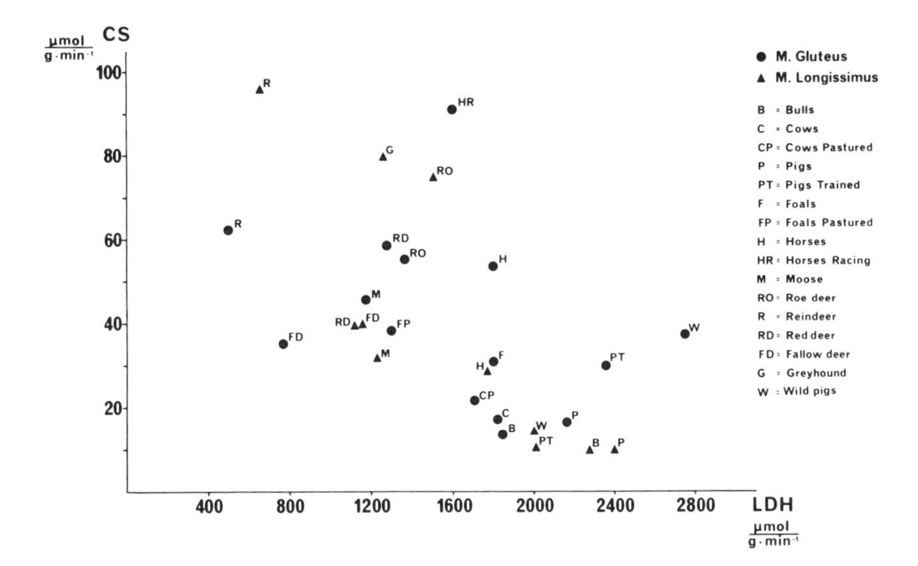

Figure 5 Citrate synthase activities (CS) in m. gluteus and m. longissimus of different animals in relation to the activities of lactate dehydrogenase (LDH).

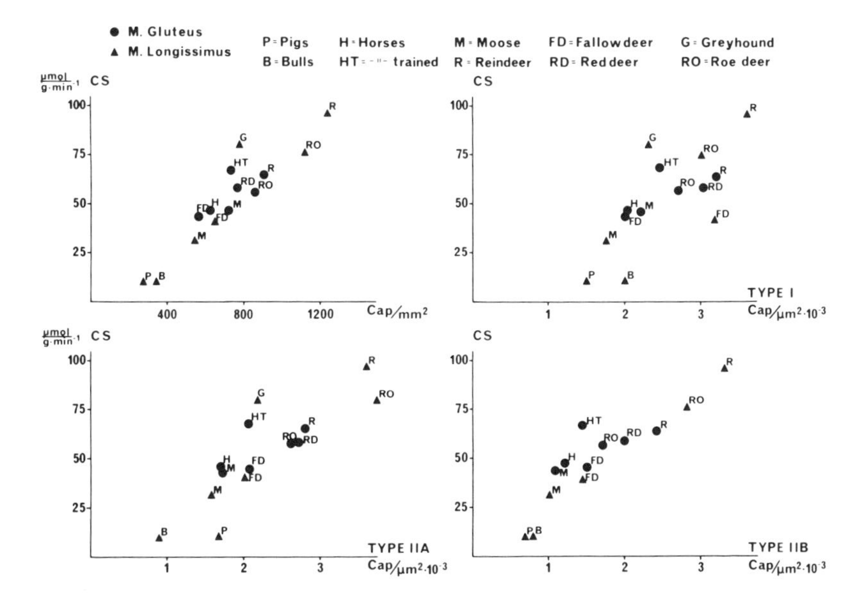

Figure 6 Citrate synthase activities in m. gluteus and m. longissimus of different animals in relation to capillaries/mm² and in relation to the number of capillaries in contact with a given area of each fiber type.

a given area of each fiber type is 3 to 4 times higher in muscles of wild animals compared with those of pigs and bulls, which have much larger fiber sizes. The smallest fiber sizes were found in reindeer and roe deer muscles which were most capillarized and had the highest oxidative capacity. The smaller fiber sizes and many capillaries in a muscle may not only facilitate the uptake of oxygen and blood-borne substrates like glucose and free fatty acids, but may also facilitate the removal of wasteproducts like lactate. Of note is that type II fibers of racehorses are usually smaller in size than the same fibers in inactive horses (Figure 3). When horses were trained each day for 5 weeks, capillarization increased in their muscles (Figure 6), in part due to a decrease in type I and II fiber areas (Figure 3). The trained horses also showed their lower blood lactate accumulation at similar workloads compared to their untrained state (Thornton et al., 1983). It is notable that this lowered blood lactate accumulation and higher oxidative capacity was still maintained after the trained horses had been exposed to 5 weeks of relative inactivity. In humans, the oxidative capacity has been shown to decrease within 2 weeks of detraining (Henriksson & Reitman, 1977). Time courses for muscular adaptations may thus vary among different species.

The enzyme analyses indicate that domestic pigs have a very low capacity for energy release by oxidative metabolism. Glycogen utilization with lactate formation is probably the main metabolic pathway when the low-oxidative fibers are activated. In trained pigs, however, the higher CS activity indicates an enhancement of oxidative pathways. After treadmill exercise, blood lactate response is also lower in trained pigs (Essén-Gustavsson & Lindholm, 1983). In wild animals and in racehorses it seems as if oxidation of lipids and carbohydrates are both important metabolic pathways. In greyhounds, the low LDH and high CS activities relative to HAD activity indicate that oxidation of carbohyrates and pyruvate, rather than fatty acids, may be more important for energy release. Enzyme activities are often analyzed on whole muscle in which the metabolic profile of the fiber types can vary markedly. In reindeer, for example, all fiber types are highly oxidative and contain glycogen, but type IIB fibers show only minor lipid storage. In contrast, large lipid stores are seen in type I and IIA fibers with histochemical stains (Essén-Gustavsson & Rehbinder, 1985). This suggests that the amount of carbohydrates and lipids that is oxidized within the different fiber types may vary. In the future, more knowledge is needed about muscular adaptations within the different fiber types from muscles of various animals.

In conclusion, the data presented here show that fiber composition, fiber areas, oxidative and glycolytic capacity and capillarization can vary markedly among the same muscles of different mammalian species and within muscles of the same species.

Acknowledgments

The presented studies were made possible by grants from the Swedish Council for Forestry and Agricultural Research, the Swedish Racing Board (ATG), and the Swedish University of Agricultural Sciences.

REFERENCES

Andersen, P. (1975). Capillary density in skeletal muscle of man. *Acta Physiologica Scandinavica,* **95**, 203-205.

Andersen, P., & Henriksson, J. (1977). Training induced changes in the subgroups of human Type II skeletal muscle fibers. *Acta Physiologica Scandinavica,* **99**, 123-125.

Brooke, M.H., & Kaiser, K. (1970). Muscle fiber types: How many and what kind? *Archives of Neurology,* **23**, 369-379.

Burke, R.E., Levine, D.N., Tsairis, P., & Zajak, F.E. (1973). Physiological types and histochemical profiles in motor units of the cat gastrocnemius. *Journal of Physiology,* **234**, 723-748.

Essén, B., Lindholm, A., & Thornton, J. (1980). Histochemical properties of muscle fiber types and enzyme activities in skeletal muscles of Standardbred trotters of different ages. *Equine Veterinary Journal,* **12**, 175-180.

Essén-Gustavsson, B., Karlström, K., & Lindholm, A. (1984). Fibre types, enzyme activities and substrate utilization in skeletal muscles of horses competing in endurance rides. *Equine Veterinary Journal,* **16**(3), 197.

Essén-Gustavsson, B., & Lindholm, A. (1983). Influence of exercise on muscle metabolic characteristics in pigs and on backfat thickness at slaughter. *Proceedings of the Fifth International Conference on Production Disease in Farm Animals* (pp. 356-362). Uppsala.

Essén-Gustavsson, B., & Lindholm, A. (1984). Fibre types and metabolic characteristics in muscle of wild boars, normal and halothane sensitive Swedish Landrace pigs. *Comparative Biochemistry and Physiology,* **78A**, 67-71.

Essén-Gustavsson, B., & Lindholm, A. (1985). Muscle fibre characteristics of active and inactive standardbred horses. *Equine Veterinary Journal,* **17**(6), 434-439.

Essén-Gustavsson, B., Lindholm, A., McMiken, D., Persson, S.G.B., & Thornton, J. (1983). Skeletal muscle characteristics of young Standardbreds in relation to growth and early training. In D.H. Snow, S.G.B. Persson, & R.J. Rose (Eds.), *Equine Exercise Physiology. Proceedings of the First International Conference* (pp. 200-210). Oxford.

Essén-Gustavsson, B., & Rehbinder, C. (1985). Skeletal muscle characteristics of reindeer (*Rangifer Tarandus L.*) *Comparative Biochemistry and Physiology*, **82A**(3), 675-679.

Guy, P.S., & Snow, D.H. (1981). Skeletal muscle fibre composition in the dog and its relationship to athletic ability. *Research in Veterinary Science*, **31**, 244-248.

Henriksson, J., & Reitman, J.S. (1975). Quantitative measures of enzyme activities in type I and II muscle fibers of man after training. *Acta Physiologica Scandinavica*, **97**, 392-397.

Henriksson, J., & Reitman, J.S. (1977). Time course of changes in human skeletal muscle succinate dehydrogenase and cytochrome oxidase activities and maximal oxygen uptake with physical activity and inactivity. *Acta Physiologica Scandinavica*, **99**, 91-97.

Jansson, E., & Kaiser, L. (1977). Muscle adaptation for extreme endurance training in man. *Acta Physiologica Scandinavica*, **100**, 315-324.

Lindholm, A., Essén-Gustavsson, B., McMiken, D., Persson, S., & Thornton, J.R. (1983). Muscle histochemistry and biochemistry of Thoroughbred horses during growth and training. In D.H. Snow, S.G.B. Persson, & R.J. Rose (Eds.), *Equine Exercise Physiology. Proceedings of the First International Conference* (pp. 211-217). Oxford.

Lindholm, A., & Piehl, K. (1974). Fibre composition, enzyme activity and concentration of metabolites and electrolytes in muscles of Standardbred horses. *Acta Veterinaria Scandinavia*, **15**, 287-309.

Reichmann, H., & Pette, D. (1982). A comparative microphotometric study of succinate dehydrogenase activity levels in the type I, IIA and IIB fibres of mammalian and human muscles. *Histochemistry*, **74**, 27-41.

Saltin, B., & Gollnick, P.D. (1983). Skeletal muscle adaptability: Significance for metabolism and performance. In L.D. Peachy, R. Adrian, & S.R. Geiger (Eds.), *Handbook of physiology: Sec. 10. Skeletal Muscle* (pp. 555-631). Baltimore, MD: Williams & Wilkins.

Sher, J., & Cardasis, C. (1976). Skeletal muscle fiber types in the adult mouse. *Acta Neurologica Scandinavica*, **54**, 45-56.

Sillau, A.H., & Banchero, N. (1977). Effect of maturation on capillary density, fiber size and composition in rat skeletal muscle. *Proceedings of the Society for Experimental Biology and Medicine*, **154**, 461-466.

Thornton, J., Essén-Gustavsson, B., Lindholm, A., McMiken, D., & Persson, S. (1983). Effects of training and detraining on oxygen uptake, cardiac output, blood gas tensions, pH and lactate concentrations during and after exercise in the horse. In D.H. Snow, S.G.B. Persson, & R.J. Rose (Eds.), *Equine exercise physiology*. Proccedings of the First International conference (pp. 470-486). Oxford.

Part VI
Metabolic Capacity and Response of the Performing Horse

Limitations to Maximal Performance in the Racing Thoroughbred

David H. Snow
Roger C. Harris
The Animal Health Trust
Newmarket, England

The equine species has a much greater capacity for energy production via aerobic and anaerobic metabolism than might otherwise be predicted from normal body-scaling (Snow & Harris, 1985). The enhanced capacity is consistent with the athletic ability of the horse, and in particular of selected breeds developed for racing; for example, the Thoroughbred. Over the past 3 years we have been concentrating on defining the metabolic stress, as indicated by changes in both muscle and blood metabolite concentrations, to which horses are exposed when exercising maximally. Initial studies have been conducted in the field as a prelude to more standardized studies to be undertaken using a newly installed high speed treadmill.

The purpose of this paper is to highlight some of the changes found in three studies undertaken, which may have some bearing on the cause of fatigue, and which are of interest when compared to metabolic alterations seen following exercise of similar intensities in man. We have observed some very dramatic alterations in blood and muscle biochemistry on a scale rarely observed in human studies.

Except where otherwise indicated values given are mean (SD). Results will be taken from the following three investigations:

- Four × 620 m gallops with a 5 min interval between each gallop (four horses). Full details have recently been reported (Snow, Harris, & Gash, 1985).
- A single 800 m gallop (five horses, mean time 56.1 [2.4] s).
- A single 2000 m gallop (four horses, mean time 149 [7.3] s).

Unfortunately exercise was carried out on different tracks and therefore conditions are not exactly comparable.

In addition to determining alterations in muscle and blood with the exercise bout, recovery was also monitored. In Study 1, however, the animals were kept still during the recovery period, while in Studies 2 and 3 they maintained a slow walk.

GLYCOGEN UTILIZATION AND LACTATE PRODUCTION

As in man, during maximal exercise muscle glycogen is quantitatively the major fuel for ATP production. In the middle gluteal, one of the major propulsive muscles in the horse, the glycogen content varies from 400 to 700 mmol glycosyl units/kg dry muscle (d.m.) ($\bar{x}$ 575.9, SD 92.4, $n = 8$). In the 800 and 2000 m single gallops glycogen utilization amounted to 162 (57) and 177 (35) mmol glycosyl units/kg d.m. with average rates of utilization of 2.85 (0.87) and 1.20 (0.29) mmol glycosyl units/kg d.m./s. The falloff in rate between the two gallops, despite similar average running speeds of 14.3 (0.6) and 13.4 (0.7) m/s, can probably be explained on the basis of an increase in the utilization of blood-borne glucose as time of exercise progresses. In the horse maximal exercise can result in blood glucose concentrations of the order of 10 mmol/1. Total glycogen utilization after 4 × 620 m amounted to 225 (41) mmol glycosyl units/kg d.m. Following the 800 and 2000 m gallops, less than 20% of the muscle glycogen utilized had been restored by the end of 60 min recovery.

Not all the glycogen utilized during exercise reaches pyruvate, as at the time of biopsying about 15% to 20% was found in both single gallops in the form of hexose monophosphate (HMP). Concentrations of HMP of the order of 30 mmol/kg d.m. were not uncommon. During the 40 to 60 min recovery most of the HMP disappeared, sufficient to account for most of the glycogen resynthesized in this period. Between 12 (800 m) and 20 (2000 m) mmol/kg d.m. of glycerol 3-P was found in the middle gluteal immediately postexercise. The accumulation of glycerol 3-P was correlated to that for lactate. As in humans (Harris, 1981) about 1 mol of glycerol 3-P was accumulated for every 11 mol of lactate.

Following maximal exercise mean muscle lactate contents of 109 (12.6), 124 (50), and 167 (21) were observed at the end of 1 × 620 m, 800m, and 2000 m gallops, respectively. Corresponding concentrations in blood immediately after exercise were 13.7 (1.70), 17.8 (3.9), and 26.5 (1.6) mmol/l. In Study 1, subsequent gallops of 620 m resulted in further increases in muscle lactate. Despite the very high levels of lactate attained the buffering capacity in horse muscle is on a par with that in man (Harris, Katz, Sahlin, & Snow, 1984) and by comparison, therefore, very low muscle pH values are reached. In the case of one horse participating in the 4 × 620 m study, it began and completed the final gallop with muscle lactate contents of 149 and 204 mmol/kg d.m., respectively, corresponding to muscle pH values of 6.51 and 6.27. However, it could still maintain a speed of 10.1 m/s (comparable to that of a 100 m sprinter fresh from the starting blocks), a reduction of 26% from the 13.6 m/s seen in the first 620 m gallop. The pH of the middle gluteal at rest is approximately 7.11. In the one study completed to date on the changes in muscle pH in man with sprint exercise, a decrease from 7.04 to 6.63 was recorded in the gastrocnemius following an exhaustive 400 m run (Costill, Barnett, Sharp, Fink, & Katz, 1983); a 54 to 105 s treadmill sprint to fatigue at 125% VO_2max resulted in a decrease of pH to 6.88.

Termination of the 800 and 2000 m gallops resulted in an immediate decline in muscle lactate content with half times of 22.9 and 18.9 min respectively. These half times are much slower than reported in man following isometric (Harris, Sahlin, & Hultman, 1981) and dynamic (Sahlin, Harris, Nylind, & Hultman, 1976) exercise. This may have been due to the much higher immediate postexercise blood lactates in the horses. Muscle-to-blood lactate gradients averaging 1.5 to 1.7 immediately postexercise fell to just below unity within 5 to 10 min of recovery, and thereafter further change in the intramuscle cell concentration paralleled that in blood. We estimate that at most only 10% of the lactate disappearance from muscle could have been used in the resynthesis of local muscle glycogen or oxidized locally to CO_2 and water.

Interestingly in the 4 × 620 m study, no recovery in the muscle lactate content was seen during 30 min. In this case the muscle-to-blood lactate gradient was near to unity by the time of the first postexercise sample. The absence of recovery in muscle seems in this case to have been due to the almost complete lack of clearance of lactate from blood, the mean concentration decreasing from 31.4 (1.0) to just 28.3 (4.3) mmol/l over 40 min.

The higher muscle lactate contents attained in horse than in man may reflect the greater proportion (i.e., 80%) of type II fibers found in the middle gluteal of the horse (Snow & Guy, 1980). Whether a higher lactate content is reached within individual fibers awaits further investigation.

PHOSPHOCREATINE AND ATP DEPLETION

One of the most consistent findings has been of a pronounced reduction in muscle ATP and phosphocreatine following maximal galloping (Table 1). As can be seen there is a clear trend towards lower muscle ATP contents with increasing racing distance. In the case of Study 1 the three subsequent gallops resulted in further decreases in ATP that occurred in parallel to an increase in running time. In Study 1, one of the four animals did not follow this pattern of ATP decrease and increase in running time, and in fact showed a decrease in performance time. We believe that this may have been related to a lower energy demand imposed on this horse during the first gallop as indicated by a lower muscle lactate content (32.8 compared to a mean of 109.2 [12.6] mmol/kg d.m. in the

Table 1 Muscle ATP and Phosphocreatine (PCr) Following Maximal Exercise of Different Durations [Values are Means (SD)]

Distance	0 m	620 m	800 m	2000 m
Time (s)	—	48.3 (3.4)	56.1 (2.4)	14.90 (7.3)
ATP (mmol/kd d.m.)	21.80 (1.84)	19.39 (3.53)	15.33 (4.02)	11.29 (2.56)
PCR (mmol/kg d.m.)	55.86 (6.21)	31.11 (13.13)	31.10 (6.55)	18.48 (8.60)
n	8	4	5	4

other three). Lactate, however, did increase in subsequent gallops eventually reaching a level at the end of the fourth equal to that seen in the others at the end of the first gallop. The results suggest that decrease in the muscle ATP content occurs only after the lactate content reaches a critical value and the running speed (or rate of energy demand) is sufficiently high. This may explain why decreases in ATP comparable to those shown in Table 1 have only rarely been described in man (Boobis, Williams, & Wootton, 1983; Hultman, Bergström, & McLennan-Anderson, 1967), the increase in muscle lactate generally being too low. In man, after sprinting events of 400 to 800 m, blood lactate concentrations of the order of 15 mmol/l are generally attained whereas in the thoroughbred concentrations of 25 mmol/l occur over flat racing distances (Snow, Mason, Ricketts, & Douglas, 1983) and national hunt events (Snow, unpublished data). It is probable that most horses exhibit a marked drop in muscle ATP content during the course of a race.

From the 4 × 620 m study and also a study in man (Hultman & Sjöholm, in press) it would appear that there is a breakpoint at an ATP content of about 18 mmol/kg d.m. below which muscle performance is compromised and increasing fatigue occurs.

In the single gallop studies much of the ATP lost during exercise was restored during 30 to 60 min recovery. In contrast, in the 4 × 620 m study, no resynthesis of ATP was observed.

We have recently commenced studies to determine whether the reduction in ATP content occurs uniformly throughout the muscle, or is confined to just type I or type II muscle fibers, or fibers within the same motor unit (indicated by nonuniformity within the same fiber type). It is known that type II fibers have a higher activity of AMP-deaminase than type I. Preliminary measurements of ATP in fragments of single fibers from one horse obtained after two consecutive 800 m gallops, which resulted in a 40% drop in the total muscle ATP content, have so far shown that the decrease occurs fairly uniformly throughout the muscle.

The fall in ATP represents a loss of adenine nucleotide, since there was no equivalent increase in either ADP or AMP. Instead the decrease in ATP was matched by an approximately equal rise in IMP (Snow et al., 1985), which is formed from the deamination of AMP by AMP-deaminase. Further degradation to inosine and eventually uric acid is indicated by a progressive rise in the plasma concentration of the latter. Following the single 800 and 2000 m gallop studies, peak uric acid concentrations in plasma were obtained after 40 and 60 min and averaged 175 (62) and 193 (53) μmol/l, respectively (rest 23 [10]).

The importance of the AMP-deaminase catalyzed reaction to metabolism during maximal exercise appears to be in the removal of AMP so that the myokinase reaction can proceed in the forward direction. The equilibrium of the reaction is normally in favor of ADP formation. Removal of ADP will prevent its accumulation when ATP breakdown by myofibrillar ATPase exceeds its resynthesis from phosphocreatine or aerobic and anaerobic metabolism. Raised ADP and a lowered ATP/ADP ratio has been implicated in the development of force fatigue in muscle (Dawson, Gadian, & Wilkie, 1978; Hultman & Sjöholm, in press).

From studies of rat muscle, Wheeler and Lowenstein (1979) have concluded that the major regulators of AMP deaminase are ATP, AMP, H^+, and inorganic phosphate (Pi). At rest the activity of the enzyme is probably inhibited by Pi, and in any case the concentration of substrate is very low compared to the apparent affinity constant. During maximal exercise, rising AMP concentrations and increasing acidosis will effect an increase in activity despite increased concentrations of Pi. The enzyme exhibits a pH optimum of around 6.2 (Setlow & Lowenstein, 1967), which compares closely to an estimated muscle pH at the end of the 800 and 2000 m gallops of 6.62 and 6.43 respectively. Recently, Harris and Hultman (1985) in human muscle, and Dudley and Terjung (1985) in rat muscle, have shown that deamination of AMP occurs only after depletion of the PCr store and accumulation of 40 and 60 mmol lactate/kg d.m. respectively, with an estimated fall in muscle pH to 6.8 or less.

GLYCEROL ACCUMULATION IN MUSCLE

It has previously been shown that in addition to plasma glycerol increasing with submaximal exercise, even more dramatic increases are seen after maximal exercise. Plasma concentrations peak approximately 30 min postexercise, with concentrations as high as 1.5 mmol/l being found (Snow & Mackenzie, 1977). In an attempt to account for the rise in glycerol, Snow, Fixter, Kerr, and Cutmore (1983) investigated the contribution from lipolysis. A decrease in plasma FFA content and change in composition from preexercise values were observed, indicating that FFA were being used as substrate for exercise. However, these changes did not explain either the extent or profile of the rise in plasma glycerol content.

Recent studies, however, may explain this accumulation of glycerol in the blood. A further finding in all our field studies has been of a small increase during exercise of glycerol content within muscle from an initial content of 0.4-0.5 mmol/kg d.m. to 2.28 (1.57) (800 m) and 2.70 (1.15) (2000 m), with a further increase during recovery peaking 20 min postexercise. Peak 20 min muscle contents were 9.83 (5.24) and 11.73 (2.74) mmol/kg d.m. after the 800 and 2000 m respectively. Blood glycerol concentrations in these studies peaked at 40 min postexercise and were 1.26 (0.68) and 1.64 (0.59) mmol/l. Throughout the studies, the kinetics of glycerol appearance in blood lagged behind those in muscle. From glycerol infusion studies we have concluded that the glycerol in muscle represents a local production.

Measurements of triglyceride at rest indicate mean content of 28.3 (18.7) mmol/kg d.m., a value similar to that of Essén-Gustavsson, Karlström, and Lindholm (1984). Measurements during exercise and recovery, however, have proved ambiguous because of pronounced within-subject variability, but generally indicate no decrease during recovery that could explain the rise in glycerol. The postexercise rise in glycerol is so great in any case that if this were from triglyceride breakdown, the resultant intracellular concentration of FFAs would be so high (about 9 to 12 mmol/l intracellular water) as to be almost certainly toxic to the cells.

As noted earlier, maximal exercise resulted in large accumulations of glycerol 3-P within muscle, for example, 13.55 (1.73) and 19.41 (2.41) mmol/kg d.m. at the end of the 800 and 2000 m gallops respectively. It is currently believed that glycerol 3-P is reoxidized to dehydroxyacetone phosphate by mitochondrial-membrane-located glycerol 3-phosphate dehydrogenase. However, in our study we observed that the decay in glycerol 3-P was exactly matched by the rise in muscle glycerol concentration (Harris & Snow, 1985). The implication is that glycerol 3-P, derived from glycogen breakdown, is the source of the rise in muscle and blood glycerol under these conditions. This intriguing possibility would also explain a further finding that the increase in blood glycerol after maximal exercise correlates closely to the increase in blood lactate. As explained earlier, during maximal exercise glycerol 3-P and lactate, the two major end products of anaerobic glycolysis accumulated in the muscle increase in a ratio of 1 to 11.

Explaining the conversion of glycerol 3-P to glycerol, however, is not easy. Glycerol kinase does occur in muscle, but under normal conditions the thermodynamic equilibrium greatly favors glycerol 3-P formation. Conceivably, the reaction could be reversed if a sufficient decrease in the muscle ATP content occurred. In many of these studies a 50% decrease in the ATP content was observed after exercise and this could have been much greater in the cytoplasm. However, in two further studies in which little or no decrease in muscle ATP occurred, the same stoichiometry between muscle glycerol 3-P decrease and glycerol increase during recovery was found. The alternative to glycerol kinase is that horse muscle possesses a dephosphatase to glycerol 3-P, but no such enzyme has been described for mammalian muscle.

REFERENCES

Boobis, L.H., Williams, C., & Wootton, S.A. (1983). Influence of sprint training on muscle metabolism during brief maximal exercise in man. *Journal of Physiology* (London), **342**, 36-37P.

Costill, D.L., Barnett, A., Sharp, R., Fink, W.J., & Katz, A. (1983). Leg muscle pH following sprint running. *Medicine and Science in Sports and Exercise,* **15**, 325-329.

Dawson, M., Gadian, D.G., & Wilkie, D.R. (1978). Muscular fatigue investigated by phosphorous nuclear magnetic resonance. *Nature* (London), **274**, 861-866.

Dudley, G.A., & Terjung, R.L. (1985). Influence of aerobic metabolism on IMP accumulation in fast-twitch muscle. *American Journal of Physiology,* **248**, C37-C42.

Essén-Gustavsson, B., Karlström, K., & Lindholm, A. (1984). Fibre types, enzyme activities and substrate utilisation in skeletal muscles of horses competing in endurance rides. *Equine Veterinary Journal,* **16**, 197-202.

Harris, R.C. (1981). *Muscle energy metabolism in man in response to isometric contraction. A biopsy study*. Unpublished master's thesis, University College of Wales, Aberystwyth.

Harris, R.C., & Hultman, E. (1985). Adenine nucleotide depletion in human muscle in response to intermittent stimulation in situ. *Journal of Physiology* (London), **365**, 73.

Harris, R.C., Katz, A., Sahlin, D., & Snow, D.H. (1984). Measurement of muscle pH in horse muscle and its relation to lactate content. *Journal of Physiology* (London), **357**, 119P.

Harris, R.C., Sahlin, K., & Hultman, E. (1981). Metabolic recovery in human muscle following isometric contraction to fatigue. *Pflügers Archiv,* **389**, 277-282.

Harris, R.C., & Snow, D.H. (1985). Glycerol 3-phosphate in muscle as a source of blood glycerol in the horse following maximal short-term exercise. *Journal of Physiology* (London), **361**, 84P.

Hultman, E., Bergström, J., & McLennan-Anderson, N. (1967). Breakdown and resynthesis of phosphorylcreatine and adenosine triphosphate in connection with muscular work in man. *Scandinavian Journal of Clinical and Laboratory Investigation*, **19**, 56-66.

Hultman, E., & Sjöholm, H. (in press). Biochemical causes of fatigue. In N.L. Jones, N. McCartney, & A.J. McComas (Eds.), *Human Muscle Power*. Champaign, IL: Human Kinetics.

Sahlin, K., Harris, R.C., Nylind, B., & Hultman, E. (1976). Lactate content and pH in muscle samples obtained after dynamic exercise. *Pflügers Archiv*, **367**, 143-149.

Setlow, B., & Lowenstein, J.M. (1967). Adenylate deaminase. II. Purification and some regulatory properties of the enzyme from calf brain. *Journal of Biological Chemistry*, **242**, 607-615.

Snow, D.H. (1984). [Biochemical changes in blood following National Hunt Racing]. Unpublished raw data.

Snow, D.H., Fixter, L.M., Kerr, M.G., & Cutmore, D.M. (1983). Alterations in composition of venous plasma FFA pool during prolonged and sprint exercises in the horse. In E.G. Knuttgen, J.A. Vogel, & J. Poortmans (Eds.), *Biochemistry of exercise* (Vol. 13, pp. 336-350). Champaign, IL: Human Kinetics.

Snow, D.H., & Guy, P.S. (1980). Fibre composition of a number of limb muscles in different breeds of horse. *Research in Veterinary Science*, **28**, 137-144.

Snow, D.H., & Harris, R.C. (1985). Thoroughbreds and greyhounds: Biochemical adaptations in creatures of nature and man. In R. Gilles (Ed.), *Proceedings of the 1st International Comparative Physiology and Biochemistry Congress, Vol. 1* (pp. 336-350). Amsterdam: Springer Verlag.

Snow, D.H., Harris, R.C., & Gash, S. (1985). Metabolic response of equine muscle to intermittent maximal exercise. *Journal of Applied Physiology*, **58**, 1689-1697.

Snow, D.H., & Mackenzie, G. (1977). Some metabolic effects of maximal exercise in the horse and adaptations with training. *Equine Veterinary Journal*, **9**, 134-140.

Snow, D.H., Mason, D.K., Ricketts, S.W., & Douglas, T.A. (1983). Post-race blood biochemistry in thoroughbreds. In D.H. Snow, S.G.B. Persson, & R.J. Rose (Eds.), *Equine exercise physiology* (pp. 389-399). Cambridge: Granta Editions.

Wheeler, T.J., & Lowenstein, J.M. (1979). Adenylate deaminase from rat muscle. Regulation by purine metabolites and orthophosphate in the presence of 150 mM KCl. *Journal of Biological Chemistry*, **254**, 8994-8999.

Limitations to Maximal Performance in the Standardbred Horse: Some Muscle Morphological and Biochemical Aspects

Arne Lindholm
Swedish University of Agricultural Sciences
Uppsala, Sweden

The physiological mechanisms related to performance capacity are incompletely understood in the standardbred horse (Persson, Essén-Gustavsson, Lindholm, McMiken, & Thornton, 1982; Thornton, Essén-Gustavsson, Lindholm, McMiken, & Persson, 1982). Biochemical and morphological investigations of skeletal muscle have demonstrated that growth and training cause adaptive changes of oxidative and glycolytic capacity, as well as alterations in the proportions of different fiber types (Essén-Gustavsson, Lindholm, McMiken, Persson, & Thornton, 1982; Lindholm & Piehl, 1974).

The object of this paper is to discuss these adaptations and especially focus upon the influence of age and training.

RESULTS

Muscle Fiber Composition

In most studies the middle gluteal muscle has been the muscle of choice for studies of muscle metabolism as this muscle is easily accessible and known to be active during trotting (Lindholm & Piehl, 1974).

Muscle fiber composition in this muscle changes with age and training (Lindholm & Piehl, 1974; Essén, Lindholm, & Thornton, 1980). In these studies the type IIA/IIB ratio increased but there was a rather large SD within the different fiber-type populations in the different age groups. No difference was found in the type I/II ratio.

In order to separate the effects on muscle fiber composition of age from those of training, two groups of horses were studied. Ten horses were trained from 18 months of age whereas six horses in a second group were trained from the age of 3 years. For their first 3 years, the horses in the second group were kept in stables during nights and were kept on pasture during the days. Muscle biopsies from all horses were obtained once a year from 1 year of age to 4 to 5 years of age. The results showed that horses that were trained from 18 months of life showed a significant increase in the type IIA/IIB fiber ratio, whereas those whose training started at 3 years showed no change; the type I/II fibers were unaffected in both groups (Figure 1).

The fiber composition was also found to be different in horses with different racing abilities (Essén-Gustavsson & Lindholm, 1985). Three groups of horses were studied. The best group of horses had a mean racing time of 1.16/min × km^{-1}, the second group raced had a mean of 1.21/min × km^{-1}, and the third group were inactive standardbreds. The results showed no difference in the type I fiber percentage between the three groups. The highest percentage of type IIA fibers (mean 58 ± 11%) and the lowest percentage of type IIB fibers (mean 15 ± 9%) was seen in group 1, that is, the best trained horses. The inactive horses of group 3 revealed the highest percentage of type IIB fibers (mean 35 ± 8%) and the lowest percentage of type IIA fibers (mean 41 ± 5%). The second group of horses had fiber percentages between groups 1 and 3.

Fiber Area

In the same study (Essén-Gustavsson & Lindholm, 1985) it was shown that the superior race horses had small fiber areas of type I, IIA, and IIB fibers. These horses also had the smalles type IIB fiber areas whereas the inactive horses had significantly larger type IIB fiber areas.

Enzymes

With age and training there was a change in both oxidative enzymes (citric synthase [CS] and 3-OH-acyl-CoA-dehydrogenase [HAD]) and

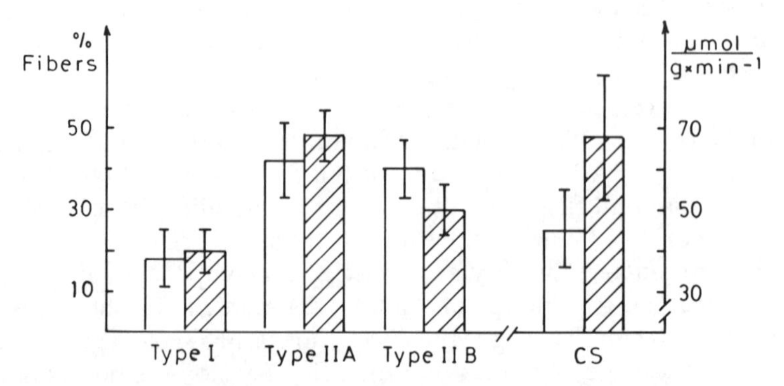

Figure 1 A comparison of muscle fiber composition between horses trained from 18 months of age to horses trained from the age of three years.

glycolytic enzymes (lactate dehydrogenase [LDH] and triose-phosphate-dehydrogenase [TPDH]) (Essén et al., 1980). Training from 18 months of age resulted in an increased CS activity, which was apparent at 2 years of age. These horses had higher CS activities in the middle gluteal muscle, compared to horses that commenced training at 3 years of age.

Lactate

In order to study the glycolytic capacity of horses and the muscles' ability to produce lactate at different speeds, 36 horses of different ages were studied. The horses were allowed to trot 1000 m at four to five speeds and blood samples for lactate measurements were collected. The exponential curves relating lactate values to the speed were analyzed and the speed at which the horses passed 4 mM of blood lactate were recorded. The results showed that horses with the same capacity to race often had quite different blood lactate curves. Two-year-old horses passed the 4 mM level at a speed of 1.37 min $\times$ km^{-1} and the slope of the lactate curve was quite steep.

Three-year-olds passed the 4 mM levels at about 1.35 min $\times$ km^{-1}. In this group the slope of the curve varied widely. The best horses passed the 4 mM level at a speed of 1.26 min $\times$ km^{-1}. Additionally, muscle biopsies from 17 horses after a race were taken for evaluation of peak muscle lactate. High intramuscular lactate values after the race (110-130 mmol $\times$ kg^{-1} d.w.) were correlated with low ATP concentrations in the muscle (12-13 mmol $\times$ kg^{-1} d.w.). Furthermore, a low concentration of ATP in the muscle was also correlated with a high percentage of type IIB fibers (Valberg, 1985).

DISCUSSION

It is obvious that skeletal muscle of well trained, elite standardbred trotters possesses a high oxidative potential. This appears related to the relatively small cross-sectional area of all the fiber types and a high capillary density (Essén-Gustavsson & Lindholm, 1985).

Because a high proportion of type IIB fibers is positively correlated with high muscle lactate values and low ATP concentrations, the proportion of oxidative type IIB fibers may play an important role for limitation to maximal performance. Well trained horses have oxidative type IIB fibers and small fiber areas (Essén et al., 1980). Large fiber areas could limit diffusion of oxygen and/or removal of lactate becomes delayed. As the fast-twitch glycolytic fibers are recruited only at high speeds (Lindholm & Piehl, 1974), speed training seems necessary in order to adapt these fibers to sustain strenuous exercise.

Any training program has to be adapted to the individual horse. However, interval training can be recommended (700 to 1000 m per interval) as this form of training activates all fiber types and is not as strenuous on tendons and joints as longer work bouts (1600 to 2100 m).

Excessive training may in some horses give an overtraining effect and these horses show very low blood lactate values after maximal exercise, in spite of the fact that they possess a high oxidative capacity in their muscles. The limitation to performance may be caused by poor breeding selection and by training. These factors appear to most influence the type IIA/IIB ratio, fiber areas, and oxidative enzyme capacities. A late start to training in life seems to slow the onset of adaptational changes of these variables.

REFERENCES

Essén-Gustavsson, B., & Lindholm, A. (1985). Fibre types and areas and enzyme activities in muscles of active and inactive standardbred horses. *Equine Veterinary Journal*, **17**(6), 432-438.

Essén-Gustavsson, B., Lindholm, A., McMiken, D., Persson, S.G.B., & Thornton, J. (1982). Skeletal muscle characteristics of young standardbreds in relation to growth and early training. In D.H. Snow, S.G.B. Persson, & R.J. Rose (Eds.), *Equine exercise physiology* (pp. 200-210). Cambridge: Granta Editions.

Essén, B., Lindholm, A., & Thornton, J. (1980). Histochemical properties of muscle fibre types and enzyme activities in skeletal muscles of standardbred trotters of different ages. *Equine Veterinary Journal*, **12**(4), 175-180.

Lindholm, A., & Piehl, K. (1974). Fibre composition, enzyme activity and concentrations of metabolites and electrolytes in muscles of standardbred horses. *Acta Veterinaria Scandinavica*, **15**, 73-79.

Persson, S.G.B., Essén-Gustavsson, B., Lindholm, A., McMiken, D., & Thornton, J. (1982). Cardiorespiratory and metabolic effects of training of standardbred horses. In D.H. Snow, S.G.B. Persson, & R.J. Rose (Eds.), *Equine exercise physiology* (pp. 458-469). Cambridge: Granta Editions.

Thornton, J., Essén-Gustavsson, B., Lindholm, A., McMiken, D., & Persson, S.G.B. (1982). Effects of training and detraining on oxygen uptake, cardiac output, blood gas tensions, pH and lactate concentrations during and after exercise in a horse. In D.H. Snow, S.G.B. Persson, & R.J. Rose (Eds.), *Equine exercise physiology* (pp. 470-486). Cambridge: Granta Editions.

Metabolic and Respiratory Responses to Prolonged Submaximal Exercise in the Horse

Reuben J. Rose
D.L. Evans
University of Sydney
Sydney, Australia

Competitive endurance exercise in horses usually involves exercise over distances of 80 to 160 km at speeds varying from 150 to 300 m/min, depending upon the terrain and environmental temperature. A number of studies have been carried out investigating the hematological (Carlson, Ocen, & Harrold, 1976; Rose, 1982), biochemical (Carlson & Mansmann, 1974; Grosskopf, Van Rensburg, & Bertschinger, 1983; Lucke & Hall, 1980a, 1980b; Rose, Purdue, & Hensley, 1977) and metabolic (Rose & Sampson, 1982; Snow, Baxter, & Rose, 1981; Snow & Rose, 1981) effects of endurance exercise. These studies were all performed at competitive endurance rides that restricted the measurements that could be performed. More controlled conditions permitted a wide range of investigations in the study of Snow, Kerr, Nimmo, and Abbott (1982).

In many of these studies, the major changes were evident by the midpoint of the endurance rides. This suggested that some of the biochemical and metabolic disturbances may occur quite early in the exercise period. Additionally, most of the measurements were undertaken after the horses had ceased exercise and so may have reflected the recovery period, rather than the effects of exercise.

The study was therefore designed so that measurements could be made while the horses were exercising, throughout a 90 min period of submaximal treadmill work.

METHODS

Five Standardbred horses, aged between 4 and 7 years and with weights ranging from 390 to 531 kg were used. At least 3 months prior to the experiment, the left common carotid arteries were raised to a subcutaneous position using a modification of the technique described by Tavenor (1969). The horses were trained to exercise on an adjustable incline treadmill (Equitred, Australia), wearing a face mask for expired gas collection. The face mask was designed using two inspiratory and two expiratory valves all 10 cm in diameter.

Immediately prior to the experiment, each of the horses was weighed and its left common artery catheterized with an 18 gauge catheter, 5 cm long. This catheter was connected to extension tubing, the deadspace of which was filled with heparinized saline (2 IU/ml). Electrodes were placed as previously described (Rose et al., 1983) for recording of the electrocardiogram by telemetry, so that the heart rate could be calculated. The horse was then placed on the treadmill and a muscle biopsy taken from the left middle gluteal muscle, using a 5 mm diameter biopsy needle (Stille, Sweden). The muscle sample obtained was immediately placed in liquid nitrogen. Later, following freeze drying and weighing, muscle glycogen concentrations were measured using the technique described by Hodgson, Rose, Allen, and DiMauro (1984).

The face mask was placed on to permit the respiratory measurements to be taken. The gas from the expiratory valves was channelled into a 10 cm diameter flexible tube and from there into a perspex mixing chamber which had a volume of 39 L and internal baffles to ensure mixing of expired air. The mixing chamber was connected to a GD 101 Flowmeter (Fluid Inventor, Sweden) for measurement of minute respiratory volume ($\dot{V}_E$). Sample tubes were placed downstream from the flowmeter for connection to a Servomex oxygen analyzer (Sybron-Taylor, U.K.) and a carbon dioxide analyzer (Datex, Finland). A thermometer projecting into the airstream permitted the measurement of expired air temperature, and respiratory rate (f) was measured by observation. Arterial blood samples (2 ml) were collected into heparinized syringes for measurement of PaO_2, $PaCO_2$, pH and standard bicarbonate as described by Rose et al. (1983), and 10 ml arterial blood samples were collected into tubes containing ammonium heparin, for later plasma removal. Both samples were placed immediately into an ice bath and then either analyzed (blood-gas samples) or had the plasma removed within 30 min of collection. The plasma sodium, potassium, chloride, glucose, total protein, and creatinine were measured with an SMAC Autoanalyzer (Technicon, New Jersey, U.S.A.), using standard techniques.

All respiratory measurements were corrected to STPD except the tidal volume (V_T) and alveolar ventilation ($\dot{V}_A$), which were corrected to BTPS. From the respiratory measurements the following were calculated: V_T, $\dot{V}_A$, oxygen consumption ($\dot{V}O_2$), ventilatory equivalent for oxygen (VE_{O2}), oxygen pulse, respiratory exchange ratio (R) and physiological deadspace (V_D/V_T). All the respiratory calculations were made using standard formulas. Respiratory, blood gas, acid base, plasma biochemical and heart rate measurements were made at rest and then after 5, 15, 30, 45, 60, 75 and 90 min of treadmill exercise. The treadmill was set at a slope of 2%

and a speed of 180 m/min. Rectal temperature was taken at rest and after 30, 60 and 90 min of exercise. At the conclusion of the exercise period a muscle biopsy for muscle glycogen determination was collected from the middle gluteal muscle. The postexercise body weight of each horse was then measured.

Statistical analysis of the results was undertaken using a paired Student's t test comparing the 5 min exercise results with the other exercise values. All results are expressed as mean ± sem.

RESULTS

The results of the respiratory measurements are presented in Table 1, while the results of heart rate, acid base and plasma biochemical values are shown in Table 2. Muscle glycogen decreased from 666 ± 31 μmol/g to 564 ± 54 μmol/g as a result of the exercise. The work performed was 1570 ± 87 Kpm/min, while the body weight loss during exercise was 17.0 ± 3.3 kg (3.7 ± 0.7% body weight). The environmental temperature during the experiments ranged from 16.6 to 19.6 °C. Rectal temperatures (°C) were 37.7 ± 0.2 (rest), 38.6 ± 0.2 (30 min), 38.8 ± 0.2 (60 min) and 39.1 ± 0.1 (90 min).

DISCUSSION

Although all the horses used in the experiment had been exercised previously on the treadmill, they had received no training. A pilot study indicated that after 90 min of exercise at a speed of 3 m/s, unfit horses were likely to show fatigue. Lowered muscle glycogen stores have been thought to be one of the most important factors producing fatigue during prolonged submaximal exercise (Saltin & Karlsson, 1971; Snow et al., 1981). However, most of the horses in the study were reluctant to exercise beyond the 90 min exercise period and yet had five sixths of their muscle glycogen remaining. It is obvious that fatigue is a complex process and that substrate depletion is only one factor. The rate of glycogen utilization in this study (1.1 mmol/kg/min) was similar to rates during endurance exercise (Hodgson, 1984), so there was unlikely to have been a greatly increased energy demand over that of competitive endurance exercise. From the $\dot{V}O_2$ values during exercise, it can be calculated that the metabolic rate was approximately 4300 Kcal/hr. This represents a 15-fold increase over the calculated metabolic rate at rest (Carlson, 1983). Although there was no significant change in R during the course of the

Table 1 **Changes in Various Respiratory Values (Mean ± SEM) Associated With Prolonged Submaximal Exercise**

Value	Rest	5 min	15 min	30 min	45 min	60 min	75 min	90 min
$\dot{V}_E$ (l/min)	68.6 ± 24.2	491.8 ± 60.2	547.8 ± 60.6	633.4 ± 45.7	598.9 ± 72.9[a]	619.5 ± 73.6	625.8 ± 63.2[a]	628.3 ± 51.6[a]
f (breaths/min)	23.2 ± 5.6	86.4 ± 3.2	88.6 ± 1.5	90.4 ± 3.2	96.4 ± 7.6	100.8 ± 11.0	99.2 ± 11.3	100.8 ± 10.1
V_T (l)	3.1 ± 0.8	6.7 ± 0.8	7.1 ± 0.6	8.1 ± 0.3	7.1 ± 0.6	7.1 ± 0.5	7.3 ± 0.5	7.2 ± 0.2
V_D/V_T	0.54 ± 0.09	0.51 ± 0.06	0.55 ± 0.04	0.61 ± 0.02	0.60 ± 0.04	0.65 ± 0.02[a]	0.66 ± 0.02[a]	0.69 ± 0.02[a]
$\dot{V}_A$ (l/min)	28.6 ± 11.6	190.6 ± 15.4	192.0 ± 13.1	198.3 ± 15.8	186.2 ± 10.7	168.5 ± 10.7	167.1 ± 8.4	156.6 ± 8.3[a]
$\dot{V}O_2$ (ml/kg/min)	4.9 ± 1.6	30.5 ± 2.0	31.2 ± 2.5	33.7 ± 3.2	30.6 ± 2.6	29.6 ± 2.6	31.4 ± 3.4	27.9 ± 2.2[a]
VE_{O2}	38.1 ± 6.5	41.9 ± 5.0	46.4 ± 6.5	49.8 ± 5.6	51.2 ± 6.6	53.6 ± 4.1	51.6 ± 3.2	58.3 ± 4.1[a]
O_2 pulse (ml/beat)	44.8 ± 13.8	113.5 ± 5.9	116.9 ± 10.4	128.3 ± 13.0	114.1 ± 9.3	109.1 ± 7.6	116.2 ± 9.6	102.0 ± 6.7
P_aO_2 (mmHg)	105.9 ± 3.2	105.1 ± 1.1	104.6 ± 3.0	106.0 ± 4.8	106.3 ± 2.7	102.7 ± 1.4	101.9 ± 3.9	101.8 ± 2.4
P_aCO_2 (mmHg)	41.5 ± 0.5	39.2 ± 0.7	40.7 ± 0.8	38.8 ± 0.9	39.3 ± 0.8	39.5 ± 1.5	41.6 ± 1.9	41.0 ± 1.5
R	0.82 ± 0.05	0.87 ± 0.01	0.90 ± 0.03	0.83 ± 0.06	0.88 ± 0.06	0.81 ± 0.03	0.81 ± 0.03	0.84 ± 0.05

Number of horses = 5.

[a] $p < 0.05$.

Significant differences from 5 min values.

Table 2 Changes in Heart Rate, Acid Base and Plasma Biochemical Values (Mean ± SEM) Associated With Prolonged Submaximal Exercise

Value	Rest	5 min	15 min	30 min	45 min	60 min	75 min	90 min
HR (beats/min)	45.2 ±4.3	121.6 ±5.9	121.6 ±6.3	119.2 ±3.9	121.6 ±5.3	121.6 ±3.0	120.0 ±3.8	123.2 ±4.6
pH (units)	7.420±0.008	7.452±0.006	7.445±0.013	7.466±0.005[b]	7.467±0.009	7.472±0.012	7.471±0.012	7.485±0.009[b]
Std HCO_3 (mmol/l)	26.2 ±0.5	27.3 ±0.2	27.6 ±0.6	28.1 ±0.6	28.5 ±0.6	28.8 ±0.2[a]	29.8 ±0.4[b]	30.1 ±0.2[b]
Na (mmol/l)	134.0 ±0.7	134.4 ±0.9	134.8 ±1.2	134.4 ±0.7	133.2 ±0.9	134.5 ±0.8	—	134.6 ±1.0
K (mmol/l)	3.9 ±0.1	4.6 ±0.3	4.5 ±0.2	4.3 ±0.1[a]	4.1 ±0.1[a]	4.0 ±0.3[a]	—	3.9 ±0.1[b]
Cl (mmol/l)	100.2 ±1.0	102.0 ±0.8	101.8 ±1.4	100.4 ±0.8[b]	98.8 ±1.1[b]	98.0 ±0.6[a]	—	95.8 ±2.6[c]
Total protein (g/l)	68.0 ±2.3	71.4 ±2.0	70.8 ±2.4	71.4 ±3.2	74.5 ±2.9	75.5 ±3.5	—	79.2 ±3.2[a]
Creatinine (μmol/l)	120.6 ±3.9	120.2 ±3.6	125.6 ±6.7	133.0 ±5.4[b]	137.2 ±3.5[b]	140.6 ±3.3[b]	—	164.4 ±5.1[c]
Glucose (mmol/l)	5.3 ±0.1	5.4 ±0.1	5.1 ±0.2	5.4 ±0.2	5.1 ±0.1	5.2 ±0.1	—	5.8 ±0.1

Number of horses = 5.
[a] $p < 0.05$.
[b] $p < 0.01$.
[c] $p < 0.001$.
Significant differences from 5 min values.

exercise, four of the five horses showed a mean decrease of 0.1 in the RER after 90 min of exercise, indicating a greater proportion of fat contribution to aerobic energy production. Blood glucose values remained constant during the 90 min of exercise, indicating a balance between peripheral glucose utilization and hepatic glycogenolysis. It is unlikely that any significant amounts of lactate were generated during exercise, as the blood pH did not decrease during exercise. Previous work has shown that the onset of blood lactate accumulation (OBLA) occurs in unfit horses at speeds varying from 240 to 300 m/s during treadmill exercise at a 10% slope (Lovell & Rose, unpublished data). A progressive metabolic alkalosis occurred during the exercise period, there being a mean base accumulation of 4 mmol/L over resting values. This was probably due to the hypochloremia resulting from sweat electrolyte loss, as reported by Carlson (1975). The average weight loss was approximately 17 L (11 L/hr) in relatively cool conditions. This fluid deficit resulted in an increase in total protein and probably contributed to a rise in plasma creatinine, together with increased creatinine production from creatine phosphate utilization in exercising muscle. The major source of the fluid loss would have been from the sweat, although small losses would have occurred from the respiratory and gastrointestinal tracts. Despite the fluid and electrolyte losses in the sweat, there was no change in plasma sodium values. This would seem to indicate that equine sweat is isotonic rather than hypertonic as suggested by Kerr and Snow (1983).

There were few changes in the respiratory measurements or heart rate during the 90 min exercise. This indicated that the horses were in a steady state and that they reached this quite quickly, as all values during exercise were compared with those at 5 min. This confirms the findings of Bayly, Gabel, and Barr (1983).

Despite a progressive increase in V_D/V_T and corresponding decrease in $\dot{V}_A$ towards the end of exercise, arterial blood gas values showed little change during the exercise period. This contrasts with the findings of Bayly, Grant, Breeze, and Kramer (1983) and Thornton, Essén-Gustavsson, Lindholm, McMiken, and Persson (1983), where a decrease in PaO_2 and increase in $PaCO_2$ were found during higher intensity exercise. The increase in V_D/V_T associated with exercise duration suggests that there was a shift in $\dot{V}/\dot{Q}$ towards higher $\dot{V}/\dot{Q}$ ratios. It is unclear why this should have occurred.

From this study it can be seen that steady state values are maintained during submaximal exercise, probably until fluid and electrolyte losses in the sweat produce thermoregulatory and circulatory problems. Further studies during exercise of several hours duration may help in the identification of factors limiting endurance performance.

REFERENCES

Bayly, W.M., Grant, B.D., Breeze, R.G., & Kramer, J.W. (1983). The effects of maximal exercise on acid-base balance and arterial blood gas tension in Thoroughbred horses. In D.H. Snow, S.G.B. Persson, & R.J. Rose (Eds.), *Equine exercise physiology* (pp. 400-407). Cambridge: Granta.

Carlson, G.P. (1975). Fluid and electrolyte alterations in endurance trained horses. *Proceedings of the First International Symposium on Equine Hematology* (pp. 473-480). CO: American Association of Equine Practitioners.

Carlson, G.P. (1983). Thermoregulation and fluid balance in the exercising horse. In D.H. Snow, S.G.B. Persson, & R.J. Rose (Eds.), *Equine exercise physiology* (pp. 291-309). Cambridge: Granta.

Carlson, G.P., & Mansmann, R.A. (1974). Serum electrolyte and plasma protein alterations in horses used in endurance rides. *Journal of the American Veterinary Association,* **165**, 262-264.

Carlson, G.P., Ocen, P.O., & Harrold, D. (1976). Clincopathologic alterations in normal and exhausted endurance horses. *Theriogenology,* **6**, 93-104.

Grosskopf, J.F.W., Van Rensburg, J.J., & Bertschinger, H.J. (1983). Hematology and blood biochemistry of horses during a 210 km endurance ride. In D.H. Snow, S.G.B. Persson, & R.J. Rose (Eds.), *Equine exercise physiology* (pp. 416-424). Cambridge: Granta.

Hodgson, D.R. (1984). *Studies on exercise in horses*. Unpublished doctoral dissertation, Univeristy of Sydney, Australia.

Hodgson, D.R., Rose, R.J., Allen, J.R., & DiMauro, J. (1984). Muscle glycogen depletion patterns in Thoroughbred horses performing maximal exercise. *Research in Veterinary Science,* **36**, 169-173.

Kerr, M.G., & Snow, D.H. (1983). Composition of sweat of the horse during prolonged epinephrine (adrenaline) infusion, heat exposure, and exercise. *American Journal of Veterinary Research,* **44**, 1571-1577.

Lucke, J.N., & Hall, G.M. (1980a). Further studies on the metabolic effects of long distance riding: Golden Horseshoe Ride 1979. *Equine Veterinary Journal,* **12**, 189-192.

Lucke, J.N., & Hall, G.M. (1980b). Long distance exercise in the horse: Golden Horseshoe Ride 1978. *Veterinary Record,* **106**, 405-407.

Rose, R.J. (1982). Haematological changes associated with long distance exercise. *Veterinary Record,* **110**, 175-177.

Rose, R.J., Allen, J.R., Brock, K.A., Clark, C.R., Hodgson, D.R., & Stewart, J.H. (1983). Effects of clenbuterol hydrochloride on certain respiratory and cardiovascular parameters in horses performing treadmill exercise. *Research in Veterinary Science,* **31**, 301-303.

Rose, R.J., Purdue, R.A., & Hensley, W. (1977). Plasma biochemistry alterations in horses during an endurance ride. *Equine Veterinary Journal,* **9**, 122-126.

Rose, R.J., & Sampson, D. (1982). Metabolic changes associated with food deprivation and long distance exercise. *Research in Veterinary Science,* **32**, 198-202.

Saltin, B., & Karlsson, J. (1971). Muscle glycogen utilization during work of different intensities. In B. Pernow & B. Saltin (Eds.), *Muscle metabolism during exercise* (pp. 289-299). New York: Plenum Press.

Snow, D.H., Baxter, P., & Rose, R.J. (1981). Muscle fibre composition and glycogen depletion in horses competing in an endurance ride. *Veterinary Record,* **108**, 374-378.

Snow, D.H., Kerr, M.G., Nimmo, M.A., & Abbot, E.M. (1982). Alterations in blood, sweat, urine and muscle composition during prolonged exercise in the horse. *Veterinary Record,* **110**, 377-384.

Snow, D.H., & Rose, R.J. (1981). Hormonal changes associated with endurance exercise. *Equine Veterinary Journal,* **13**, 195-197.

Tavenor, W.D. (1969). Technique for the subcutaneous relocation of the common carotid artery in the horse. *American Journal of Veterinary Research,* **30**, 1881-1883.

Thornton, J., Essén-Gustavsson, B., Lindholm, A., McMiken, D., & Persson, S. (1983). Effects of training and detraining on oxygen uptake, cardiac output, blood gas tensions, pH and lactate concentrations during and after exercise in the horse. In D.H. Snow, S.G.B. Persson, & R.J. Rose (Eds.), *Equine exercise physiology* (pp. 470-486). Cambridge: Granta.

The Possible Role of the Ventilatory System in Limiting Maximal Equine Performance

Warwick M. Bayly
Barrie D. Grant
Washington State University
Pullman, Washington, U.S.A.

Normal alveolar ventilation and diffusion of oxygen and carbon dioxide across the alveolar-pulmonary capillary interface have long been considered integral components of optimal performance. It has long been accepted that in healthy subjects, the ability to perform under maximal or near maximal conditions is not limited by respiratory considerations (Dempsey, Vidruk, & Mastenbrook, 1980). Although respiratory studies in exercising horses have been few, reports from plethysmographic investigations with horses and treadmill studies with ponies (Gillespie, 1974; Leith & Gillespie, 1971) suggest that equidae and human beings may be similar in the response of their respiratory systems to exercise (Bisgard et al., 1978; Parks & Manohar, 1983; Parks & Manohar, 1984).

The results from studies involving a limited number of highly trained human athletes indicated that the supposition that the respiratory system does not limit performance may not always hold (Dempsey, Hanson, & Henderson, 1984; Holmgren & Linderholm, 1958; Rowell, Taylor, Wang, & Carlson, 1964). In one of these studies (Dempsey et al., 1984), the majority of runners exercising maximally experienced some degree of arterial hypoxemia and an associated oxygen desaturation of hemoglobin in arterial blood. Observations on small numbers of strenuously exercising horses found that they consistently experienced arterial oxygen desaturation (Bayly, Grant, Breeze, & Kramer, 1983; Thornton, Essén-Gustavsson, Lindholm, McMiken, & Persson, 1983), and some also became hypercapnic, a change not previously noted in humans. In this report, we present further documentation of the arterial blood gas changes that accompany maximal exercise in the Thoroughbred horse.

METHODS

Eleven healthy Thoroughbred horses ranging in age from 4 to 16 years were used. Samples (5 ml each) for blood gas analysis were collected in heparinized 10 ml syringes with the horse in its normal resting state, while galloping and 5 min after stopping. Rectal temperature and blood lactate concentrations were measured at rest and 5 min postexercise. The exercise load consisted of galloping 1600 m as fast as possible on a 800 m track.

The rider withdrew blood after 800 m, 1600 m and immediately after stopping the horse (an extra 100 to 250 m). During the gallop each sample was collected over approximately 5 s and then dropped on to the track. An assistant picked it up, expressed all air bubbles, capped it with an airtight seal and placed it on ice. After stopping, the horse was walked until the 5 min postexercise sample was taken.

On three occasions, respiratory frequency (f) and HR were simultaneously determined. The former was recorded using a microphone taped to the horse's halter, which was worn under the bridle for this purpose. The head of the microphone was positioned on the right side of the head about 8 cm caudad to the right nostril. The sounds associated with the respiratory cycle were recorded on magnetic tape carried in a pack on the rider's back.

Heart rate was measured using a commercially available cardiotachometer as previously described by Foreman and Rabin (1984). The rider noted the HR immediately before drawing the blood sample. Resting and 5 min postexercise HR was recorded by an assistant.

RESULTS

Means, standard deviations and ranges for PaO_2, $PaCO_2$, percent saturation of hemoglobin with oxygen (% O_2 sat), pH, bicarbonate concentration, base excess and plasma lactate concentrations are presented in Table 1. Although there was considerable individual variation, the changes observed were consistent for all 11 horses. After 1600 m all horses were very fatigued and displayed a profound hypoxemia and acidemia. All but two were hypercapnic ($PaCO_2 > 48.0$ Torr), the exceptions having values of 39.9 and 43.0 Torr respectively. In the time (8 to 20 s) that it took to pull each horse up, marked changes occurred. The acidemia generally became more severe but was metabolic in origin. All horses were either isocapnic or hypocapnic, although the three that stopped most quickly remained markedly hypoxemic. The others had a PaO_2 greater than 80 Torr.

Respiratory frequencies and HR had reached their apparent maximum values after 800 m (Table 1), and were not markedly changed at 1600 m. There was a decrease in both (particularly HR) in the brief interim between completing the 1600 m, and pulling up. This reduction continued during the 5 min post exercise period.

Table 1 Blood gas and acid-base data (mean ± SD) from 11 horses, and respiratory frequency (f) and heart rate (HR) from three of them, during and after a 1600 m maximal gallop. The ranges of values are shown in parentheses. (ND = not done)

Measurement	At rest	800 m	1600 m	On stopping	5 min Postexercise
pH	7.39 ± 0.04 (7.31 – 7.44)	7.24 ± 0.10 (7.02 – 7.34)	7.11 ± 0.09 (6.96 – 7.25)	7.05 ± 0.15 (6.84 – 7.20)	7.00 ± 0.06 (6.86 – 7.10)
P_aO_2 Torr	92.3 ± 5.0 (86.1 – 101.0)	62.2 ± 6.5 (52.0 – 72.7)	62.2 ± 8.0 (49.1 – 73.4)	81.8 ± 18.7 (50.1 – 102.1)	108.3 ± 4.2 (103.1 – 114.4)
P_aCO_2 Torr	43.7 ± 1.8 (41.2 – 45.9)	49.2 ± 3.9 (43.1 – 56.4)	52.3 ± 5.5 (39.9 – 58.0)	39.7 ± 9.6 (25.3 – 53.7)	24.3 ± 9.2 22.0 – 30.5)
HCO_3 mmol/l	26.3 ± 3.1 (20.0 – 28.6)	20.8 ± 5.1 (11.9 – 24.6)	15.9 ± 3.3 (10.6 – 21.2)	11.8 ± 3.1 (8.1 – 16.4)	6.9 ± 1.6 (4.5 – 8.7)
Base excess	1.3 ± 3.5 (−4.9 – 4.9)	−7.5 ± 7.4 (−21.9 – −0.7)	−14.9 ± 6.1 (−27.4 – −7.0)	−18.6 ± 4.3 (24.9 – −10.90)	−24.5 ± 4.2 (−30.3 – −20.1)
% O_2 sat	95.7 ± 0.6 (94.2 – 96.8)	83.2 ± 5.0 (74.6 – 87.9)	76.8 ± 5.2 (74.6 – 84.1)	85.7 ± 9.5 (69.8 – 97.1)	92.3 ± 1.6 (90.8 – 94.5)
Lactate mmol/l	0.87 ± 0.07 (0.7 – 1.0)	ND	ND	ND	18.5 ± 5.5 (16.3 – 26.1)
f	18 ± 6	140 ± 4	128 ± 7	114 ± 1	103 ± 9
HR	46 ± 3	228 ± 4	232 ± 5	176 ± 10	128 ± 12

DISCUSSION

The results of this study and those reported by others (Thornton et al., 1983) strongly suggest that all horses undergoing short-term, maximal exercise similar to that experienced when racing, became hypoxemic. The majority also retain CO_2 to some extent. These findings are very different to those observed under comparable conditions in men (Whipp & Wasserman, 1969) or ponies (Bisgard et al., 1978; Parks & Manohar, 1984). Some trained, human athletes of a high competitive caliber have been shown to develop an arterial hypoxemia and O_2 desaturation when worked strenuously (Dempsey et al., 1984; Rowell et al., 1964), but never hypercapnia.

The reason(s) for the development of these blood gas changes during maximal exercise can only be surmised. By definition, the development of hypercapnia indicates the existence of some degree of alveolar hypoventilation (West, 1979). Alveolar ventilation has not been reported in maximally exercising horses, although Bisgard et al. (1978) reported that it increased at high levels of exercise in five ponies that were hypocapnic, rather than hypercapnic at near maximal exercise.

The high f values observed in these horses may have contributed to the retention of CO_2 in that they may have a similar effect to panting during exercise. There is a 1:1 coupling of f and stride frequency in galloping horses (Attenburrow, 1982), with the result that f max is often 130 or greater, which is much higher than that normally seen in man.

Not all hypoxemic, exercising horses are hypercapnic, suggesting that alveolar hypoventilation is not the sole cause of the observed blood gas changes. Piiper, Meyer, Marconi, and Scheid (1980) suggested that under conditions of heavy exercise, the exchange of CO_2 may be diffusion or equilibration limited by the $CO_2/HCO_3/H^+$ system in blood. The end result of this would be that a sizable arterial-alveolar PCO_2 difference would eventuate. Further studies are needed to determine whether such a differential exists during supramaximal equine exercise.

The finding that horses become hypoxemic when exercising maximally, and with high respiratory rates, could be construed as support for the concept of "stratified inhomogeneity" and its purported limiting effects on diffusion (Piiper, 1979; Weibel et al., 1981). The size of the pulmonary acinus in equine lung may provide greater opportunity for the development of serial inhomogeneities in alveolar PO_2 and PCO_2. The extent to which stratification might influence the rate of gas exchange under conditions of increased respiratory frequency and greater alveolar-pulmonary capillary O_2 diffusion gradient remains to be determined.

When pondering the mechanisms underlying the development of exercise-induced hypoxemia, consideration must be given to the pulmonary capillary transit time of erythrocytes. Maximally exercising horses increase their cardiac output 6- to 8-fold from resting values (Bayly, Gabel, & Barr, 1983; Thomas & Fregin, 1981; Thornton et al., 1983), most of this rise being facilitated by an increased HR. Despite the fact that circulating blood volume increases greatly due to splenic contraction (Persson, Eckman, Lydin, & Tufvesson, 1973), stroke volume at maximal exercise is not significantly different from that at rest (Bayly et al., 1983; Thornton et al., 1983). To accommodate such changes, blood flow must increase greatly. Mixed venous PO_2 was not recorded from the horses used in the current study. However, a study of Standardbred horses working maximally on a treadmill found P_vO_2 values of consistently less than 15 Torr (Thornton et al., 1983). Given these figures plus, the $HR_{max} > 230$ beats/min recorded in the three horses in this study, it is conceivable that at these intensities of exercise, pulmonary capillary transit times may be insufficient to allow complete alveolar-blood gas exchange.

It is difficult to believe that the observed changes in arterial blood gas tensions are due to vascular shunting or ventilation perfusion inequities. Mild hyperoxia ($F_IO_2 = 0.24$) during heavy exercise normalized PaO_2 in hypoxemic individuals (Dempsey et al., 1984). If pulmonary capillary percent saturation is assumed to be 100%, mixed venous percent saturation 5% and hemoglobin concentration 200 gm/L, it can be calculated that 20% to 25% of the cardiac output would be needed for the observed hypoxemia to be due entirely to venoarterial shunting. While the assumed percent saturation values are extreme, such calculations serve to underline how unlikely it is that shunting plays a major role in the genesis of exercise-induced hypoxemia. Conversely, if a 5% shunt is assumed, it would require 82% saturation of end pulmonary capillary blood to produce the overall arterial saturation of 77% observed in our horses. This seems conceivable in light of the above discussion regarding stratification, rapid respiratory rates, and brief pulmonary capillary transit times.

Ventilation-perfusion (V/Q) ratios have not been investigated in exercising horses. At rest, horses exhibit much milder V/Q imbalances than do human beings (Amis, Pascoe, & Hornof, 1984) the vertical gradient of ventilation being matched by a similar perfusion gradient. If alveolar ventilation is conservatively estimated to be 900 L/min based on a minute ventilation of 1500 L (Hörnicke, Meixner, & Pollman, 1983), an overall V/Q ratio of approximately 4 would occur during exercise. Under these circumstances, it would take extreme regional V/Q inequities to produce the observed changes in PaO_2.

A question of whether the changes in PaO_2 and $PaCO_2$ seen in this study represent limitations to high speed, short-term equine performance remains to be answered. It seems likely that all horses exercising under these conditions become hypoxemic. However, because of the sizable splenic reserve of erythrocytes in horses, the O_2 content of arterial blood is still greater during exercise than at rest. Increases in temperature and $PaCO_2$ and reduction in pH serve to push the hemoglobin dissociation curve to the right. This increases the likelihood that sizable reductions in percent saturation and arterial O_2 carrying capacity would occur with relatively small decrements in PaO_2. It is not known to what extent such variations can occur between individual horses, or whether such differences bear any direct relationship to their performance capacity.

Acknowledgments

This work was supported in part by the Washington State Equine Research Program, Grants #10S-3925-0011 and 10S-3925-0041. We gratefully acknowledge the technical assistance of Carlene Emerson and Patty Sheridan, and the assistance of Mary Estes and Dee Madison in preparing the manuscript.

REFERENCES

Amis, T.C., Pascoe, J.R., & Hornof, W. (1984). Topographic distribution of pulmonary ventilation and perfusion in the horse. *American Journal of Veterinary Research,* **45**, 1597-1601.

Attenburrow, D.P. (1982). Time relationship between the respiratory cycle and limb cycle in the horse. *Equine Veterinary Journal,* **14**, 69-72.

Bayly, W.M., Gabel, A.A., & Barr, S.A. (1983). Cardiovascular effects of submaximal, aerobic training in Standardbred horses using a standardized exercise test. *American Journal of Veterinary Research,* **44**, 544-553.

Bayly, W.M., Grant, B.D., Breeze, R.G., & Kramer, J.W. (1983). The effects of maximal exercise on acid-base balance and arterial blood gas tension in Thoroughbred horses. In D.H. Snow, S.G.B. Persson, & R.J. Rose (Eds.), *Equine exercise physiology* (pp. 400-407). Cambridge: Burlington Press.

Bisgard, G.E., Forster, H.V., Byrnes, B., Stanek, K., Klein, J., & Manohar, M. (1978). Cerebrospinal fluid acid-base balance during muscular exercise. *Journal of Applied Physiology,* **45**, 94-101.

Dempsey, J.A., Hanson, P.G., & Henderson K.S. (1984). Exercise-induced hypoxaemia in healthy human subjects at sea level. *Journal of Physiology* (London), **355**, 161-175.

Dempsey, J.A., Vidruk, E.H., & Mastenbrook, S.M. (1980). Pulmonary control mechanisms in exercise. *Federation Proceedings,* **39**, 1498-1505.

Foreman, J.H., & Rabin, D. (1984). Determination of accuracy of a digitally displaying equine heart rate meter. *Journal of Equine Veterinary Science,* **4**, 161-163.

Gillespie, J.R. (1974). The role of the respiratory system during exertion. *Journal of the South African Veterinary Association,* **45**, 305-309.

Holmgren, A., & Linderholm, H. (1958). Oxygen and carbon dioxide tensions of arterial blood during heavy and exhaustive exercise. *Acta Physiologica Scandinavica,* **44**, 203-215.

Hörnicke, H., Meixner, R., & Pollman, U. (1983). Respiration in exercising horses. In D.H. Snow, S.G.B. Persson, & R.J. Rose (Eds.), *Equine exercise physiology* (pp. 7-16). Cambridge: Burlington Press.

Leith, D.E., & Gillespie, J.R. (1971). Respiratory mechanics of normal horses and one with chronic obstructive lung disease. *Federation Proceedings,* **30**, 556. (Abstract)

Parks, C.M., & Manohar, M. (1983). Distribution of blood flow during moderate and strenuous exercise in ponies *(Equus caballus). American Journal of Veterinary Research,* **44**, 1861-1866.

Parks, C.M., & Manohar, M. (1984). Blood-gas tensions and acid-base status in ponies during treadmill exercise. *American Journal of Veterinary Research,* **45**, 15-19.

Persson, S.G.B., Ekman, L., Lydin, G., & Tufvesson, G. (1973). Circulatory effects of splenectomy in the horse. 1. Effect on red-cell distribution and variability of the haematocrit in the peripheral blood. *Zentralblatt für Veterinärmedizin Reihe A,* **203**, 441-455.

Piiper, J. (1979). Series ventilation, diffusion in airways, and stratified inhomogeneity. *Federation Proceedings,* **38**, 17-21.

Piiper, J., Meyer, M., Marconi C., & Scheid, P. (1980). Alveolar-capillary equilibration kinetics of $^{13}CO_2$ in human lungs studied by rebreathing. *Respiration Physiology,* **42**, 29-41.

Rowell, L.B., Taylor, H.L., Wang, Y., & Carlson, W.S. (1964). Saturation of arterial blood with oxygen during maximal exercise. *Journal of Applied Physiology,* **19**, 284-286.

Thomas, D.P., & Fregin, G.F. (1981). Cardiorespiratory and metabolic responses to treadmill exercise in the horse. *Journal of Applied Physiology,* **50**, 864-868.

Thornton, J., Essén-Gustavsson, B., Lindholm, A., McMiken, D., & Persson, S. (1983). Effects of training and detraining on oxygen uptake, cardiac output, blood gas tensions, pH and lactate concentrations during and after exercise in the horses. In D.H. Snow, S.G.B. Persson, & R.J. Rose (Eds.), *Equine exercise physiology* (pp. 470-486). Cambridge: Burlington Press.

Weibel, E.R., Taylor, C.R., Gehr, P., Hoppeler, H., Mathieu, O., & Maloiy, G.M.O. (1981). Design of the mammalian respiratory system. IX. Functional and structural limits for oxygen flow. *Respiration Physiology,* **44**, 151-164.

West, J.B. (1979). *Respiratory Physiology—the Essentials* (2nd ed.). (pp. 152-153). Baltimore: Williams and Wilkins.

Whipp, B.J., & Wasserman, K. (1969). Alveolar-arterial gas tension differences during graded exercise. *Journal of Applied Physiology,* **27**, 361-365.

Discussion from the Session

Metabolic Capacity and Response of the Performing Horse

David R. Hodgson
Washington State University
Pullman, Washington, U.S.A.

Poul Henckel
August Krogh Institute
University of Copenhagen
Copenhagen, Denmark

MAXIMAL PERFORMANCE IN THE RACING THOROUGHBRED

Hodgson. What relationship do you think the decrease in intracellular ATP values has with the production of fatigue, based on the studies of Donaldson and Hermansen using isolated muscle preparations? They demonstrated that decreases in intracellular ATP did not relate closely to reductions in the contractility of the muscle.

Snow. I am not aware of that study, and I do not know what lactate levels and other changes, such as muscle pH, these workers demonstrated. I do not know if it is the ATP that is directly related to fatigue, or just the decrease in muscle pH, which we clearly showed in our studies. We don't know which is the cart and which is the horse. I think it is probably all related. Everybody is asking, "How important is the decrease in muscle pH?" I think decreases in pH affect all these metabolic systems and regulations. At rest, muscle pH lies around pH 7.0, and we found them to be around 6.3 following strenuous exercise. Obviously, this will cause activation of certain enzymes, inhibition of others, and upsets in glycolytic regulation.

Rose. David, do you have any values for glycerol in the horses after the four 600 m gallops?

Snow. Yes, they are in a *Journal of Applied Physiology* paper and they follow exactly the same pattern.

Rose. What do you think of the inhibitory effect of lactate? What effect will high lactate levels have on triglycerides?

Snow. Lipolysis, that is it! Well, we don't know if lactate inhibits intramuscular lipolysis, but it inhibits general fat in adipose tissue lipolysis.

Rose. What do you think are the basic applications of those findings, in terms of the physiological importance to the animal?

Snow. Of the glycerol formation? I don't know whether it has any physiological importance, but it is just an intriguing thing if this is an event of metabolic significance, or at least for us to explain why we are getting these large increases in glycerol. What the importance is, I don't know, but I think that the other thing is that we do find a relationship, a correlation between glycerol and lactate. I think that the glycerol is a reflection of glycolysis, and that this is just coming from glycerol-3-phosphate, and we know that there is a relationship of glycerol-3-phosphate to lactate in the order of 11 moles of lactate to 1 mole of glycerol-3-phosphate, as I have just shown.

Essén-Gustavsson. If glycerol comes from glycerol-3-phosphate where does the phosphate go?

Snow. That's a good point. Well, where does it go? It goes back to dihydroxyacetone and back through the glycerol-3-phosphate shuttle. It builds up again!

Essén-Gustavsson. You have a lot of 3-phosphate floating around and ATP is still very low.

Snow. But then we also know that during recovery from exercise, you get an increase in the circulation—some of it may go out of the cell. Well, I think that Roger Harris has considered these implications of this increase in phosphate due to this in our paper in the *Journal of Applied Physiology*.

Bayly. You glossed over the fact that for 30 min following the fourth interval gallop there was only a minor decrease in blood lactate, I think it was from 32 to 28 mmoles per liter. Could you elaborate on why you think that may have occurred?

Snow. The distribution has gone as far as it can. There has been some work that shows that there is saturation as far as the liver is concerned. In other words, there is a maximal amount that can be removed.

Bayly. You are implying that given the fact that if all the tissue is saturated with lactate, and for instance even if the liver is saturated, it isn't doing anything with the lactate.

Snow. It is probably very slow with some slowly seeping out of the muscle. I don't know, but it is intriguing, and I can't give a full explanation for this. We are still looking into it.

Bayly. Given that the tissues are saturated—if we can accept that explanation—that to me still doesn't excuse the liver's function in not metabolizing or utilizing the lactate. So I would expect that you could still see a progressive decrease. You showed a decrease following the 2000 m exercise. I can't see why the interval experiment should be any different to the 2000 m experiment.

Snow. I agree with you. We can't fully understand it. What other explanations are there? It's just that the lactate levels were so abnormally high, one of the animals' blood lactate went over 40 mmoles per liter. It's just an extreme case and we have no real explanation, just suggestions. So if anybody has any other ideas as to why this occurs, I would like to hear them.

Bayly. Are there any clinical impressions or quantitative objective information regarding, say, the level of dehydration following the intervals?

Snow. I do not think they were dehydrated, if we look at the values for total plasma protein.

Bayly. I was just wondering, was there any reason for reduced hepatic blood flow in that experiment compared to the others?

Snow. No, except that we are finding very high blood glucose levels in that experiment, which indicates that hepatic blood flow is still occurring to a certain degree. I do not know what the explanations would be, but these horses seemed fairly normal. They were very tired immediately following the exercise, but the next day they were normal.

MAXIMAL PERFORMANCE IN STANDARDBRED HORSES

Rose. What predictive value may be obtained from a muscle biopsy in relation to performance at a given age?

Lindholm. It also depends on many factors. For example, in the United States where you have 2-year-olds racing, they are competing very early. With these horses, you might be able to predict it 1 year earlier. It depends on the training or when the speed training starts.

Rose. This change you showed in the horse with rhabdomyolysis on the NADH stain; would this be a severe case? Because, we have biopsied some horses with rhabdomyolysis that don't show those sorts of gross changes. Do you find that it is a common feature?

Lindholm. Yes, it is a common feature. If you have not such a high magnification, you find many fibers like that one shown on the field. I think that you can still find it even if you don't have high ASAT values.

Rose. The ones that have CPK values of around 800 to 1000?

Lindholm. You see more.

Snow. You don't think you can have high CPK values like that and have no changes? We often find high CPK changes and don't see anything clinically.

Lindholm. Well, the CPK changes come very quickly, and these pathological changes in the muscle fibers are delayed 1 or 2 days before you see them clearly. As long as you have a CPK increase, you also have myolysis going on, and that's why after 7 days you see more of these abnormal fiber structures than you see on the first day.

Ghesquiere. When you talk about training very hard: If you see what kind of training this is, compared to training of human athletes, it is hardly warming up! Horses are trained very little compared to training programs of human beings. Is this really training so hard?

Lindholm. Well, it is hard for a horse, because it weighs 400 to 500 kg. When it lands, there are tons of weight on the legs and there is a great risk of injury. But you are right, they do not train that much by comparison. They train maybe twice a week and the rest of the training is very bad.

I mean, it is not training, and my ideas are quite different. I want them to train more, but in smaller amounts over several days. I have been testing these sorts of programs and they work well!

Krusic. I just want to add a comment on the appearance of this syndrome that results in changes in muscle structure of racehorses, Thoroughbreds and Standardbreds. There are a lot of studs and racetracks that have these problems. I've seen them a lot myself, where there are no changes in CPK at all. These horses have no obvious abnormalities in their muscles, but if you measure the electrical potential of the muscles in these horses, there are obvious differences. This technique provides a very good and practical method for practitioners to assess muscle function in horses.

Snow. What was the measurement you said again?

Krusic. The electrical potential measurement.

Rose. Where do you measure it?

Krusic. Just in the muscle, at two separate points. The two parts of the muscle have a potential difference. Very simple!

Rose. With two electrodes in the muscle?

Krusic. Right.

Lindholm. Is that the EMG?

Krusic. It can take up the EMG.

Bayly. With respect to the enzyme concentrations in the horses that began training at 1-1/2 years of age as opposed to 3, looking at your graphs, I couldn't be sure that there really was what I would call a significant difference in the citrate synthase concentrations between the two groups at 3 years of age. I seem to recall that your group has done some work on the enzyme changes occurring in animals just as a result of age. As I recall, the enzymes increased with age, regardless of training. Was there in fact a difference between the groups at 3 years of age?

Lindholm. Yes, there was. It was not a good significance, with a p value of less than 0.05.

Bayly. Another thing regarding training. I think we have to be very careful concluding that horses are not being trained as hard as human athletes by comparison. When we look at training studies involving human subjects, we can just train them and look at the end result by means of a maximal exercise test. I am not aware of data that relates to metabolic changes in humans following a specific bout of training, and I think we should actually look at some of the metabolic changes in horses following training. You just showed some effects of interval training. The fact that some people are giving horses, say, four intervals twice a week, may in itself represent fairly intense training. The other thing from studies on humans showed that the actual frequency of training bouts per week, that is, the number of times they train per week, may not have as great an effect on overall performance as does the duration of the bouts and/or their intensity, particularly when you look at the value of training more than three times per week. So I feel that until we have a little more information regarding the specific changes occurring on those training days, we have to be very careful in making the statement that just because people train seven times per week means that they are training harder or deriving a greater training effect than horses, who may be trained on fewer occasions per week.

Lindholm. Now that is a good point. I didn't go into a detailed discussion on the different kinds of training. It is very important that we also realize that training for every age is specific. I mean, up until the horses are 2 years of age, there is one way to train, and after 3 years of age they have to be trained differently. An older horse does not need as much training as a younger horse, for example, and this is also a very important point for a trainer. As you say, we should know more about the daily training requirements of the different age groups.

DISCUSSION ON "RESPONSE OF EQUINE MUSCLE TO HIGH INTENSITY AND ENDURANCE EXERCISE"—R. Rose

Snow. Did you have any problems with the liver biopsy technique?

Rose. We have just started to do this and we have run into some slight problems such as hemorrhage, and I must come to Uppsala to refine my technique. It concerned me a little bit, as in a couple of cases we had performed liver biopsies and later on we did abdominal paracentesis and found a very large amount of blood in the abdominal fluid. So I was a little concerned about doing it on these horses. If you have some comments about liver glycogen, I would like to hear them, because you have done some studies in this area.

Lindholm. The last time we did it after the horses had exercised submaximally for 1 hr at a high work load, liver glycogen levels were almost zero, and after 4 hr at about the same speed as you had it was down to 30% of initial levels.

Hodgson. May I just make a comment? We have performed studies where the speeds of exercise were very similar to Dr. Rose's, and we found a decrease in lever glycogen of approximately 35% after 90 min, or in this case, after 15 miles of exercise.

Rose. A 35% decrease after 15 miles; these horses' blood glucose did not change throughout the period of exercise?

Hodgson. No, they did not.

Bayly. How many horses were trotting?

Rose. They were all trotting.

Bayly. With reference to the respiratory parameters, did you notice if any of them tended to display some uncoupling in this one-to-one gait? Because when it does occur, and we most frequently note it in a trotting animal, I was wondering if this in any way contributed or became evident late in exercise when the respiratory frequency increased?

Rose. There was a certain relationship between gait and respiration, and in two horses it became less reliable as the distance increased. There was a breath every second stride, so that was the general relationship, but as you can see, there are big standard errors, the result of the two horses.

Valberg. A question on the role of type I fibers in endurance events in relation to glycogen depletion of the fiber types: Where you showed the complete depletion of type I fibers based on their PAS staining, do you think they contributed to the exercise, or were not functioning?

Rose. I do not know. It is interesting in the view of what Birgitta Essén and Arne Lindholm and their coworkers demonstrated earlier with respect to intramuscular triglycerides. In the discussion of that paper, it was suggested that perhaps glycogen depletion was not so important if one still had triglycerides present to contribute to the energetic demands of the exercise.

Essén-Gustavsson. You showed the RQ values and there was no change. That is very surprising to me, with this type of exercise, because

I think from Arne's earlier studies we know that fatty acid values increased at least.

Rose. Four horses showed a decrease in RQ and one did not. I do not know why it was so.

Hodgson. There is some relationship to training?

Rose. Obviously it was; people have shown a decrease in RQ. It tends to parallel training.

ALVEOLAR OXYGEN TENSION IN HORSES

Taylor. How high can alveolar oxygen tension go?

Bayly. I think that maximal alveolar oxygen tension is about 115 mm Hg. There are studies with people showing that PO_2 will increase slightly with exercise.

Taylor. What about the exercise level you have used?

Bayly. In the galloping horse, it is possible that values are well below that. Other investigators have not discussed problems related to the one-to-one coupling of respiratory rate to stride. It has been shown in dogs working at a given workload, that when they start to pant and increase their respiratory frequency, arterial PO_2 falls. I feel that although the horses are not consciously panting, the high respiratory frequency that we observe (i.e., 130 to 140) could be equated with the effects of panting, and certainly would result in a marked increase in dead space ventilation. Thus, I think that in fact alveolar oxygen tensions are probably well below 100. Some of the problems and confounding attempts to try and measure ventilatory parameter relate to the fact that in the horse, the only way you can make these determinations requires wearing a facemask. At these levels of exercise, unless you have a facemask that is extremely sophisticated, the dead space rebreathing automatically increases simply because of the CO_2 of the dead space of the mask.

Taylor. Human studies have shown that the wearing of a mask during heavy exercise decreases respiratory frequency. Does this happen in horses?

Bayly. I don't know that it occurs in horses. You may decrease the frequency, but as I say, our indications are that because of this very strong one-to-one coupling, frequency is going to equal the stride rate.

Bayly. As far as I know from what little work we have done on the treadmill, and we have just started to do that, the wearing of the mask does not really have any effect on frequencies of breathing, so strong is this one-to-one coupling.

Lindholm. Have you studied whether obstruction of the airways has any effect on the $\dot{V}O_2$ under submaximal or maximal exercise?

Bayly. The only work we have done where we have tried to induce pharyngitis and measure arterial blood gasses under maximal situation is on the race track. In the cases of layngeal hemiplegia, the severity of the hypoxemia is more marked, and its point of onset is sooner than in normal animals.

Part VII

Muscle Mechanics and Adaptation with Use and Disuse

Specific Tension of Human Elbow Flexor Muscles

V. Reggie Edgerton
Roland R. Roy
University of California
Los Angeles, CA, U.S.A.

Peter Apor
Research Institute of the Hungarian University
of Physical Education
Budapest, Hungary

It has become increasingly apparent that almost every aspect of muscle function is directly or indirectly related to the design of that muscle. We have referred to this design over the last several years as the architecture of the muscle (Bodine, 1982; Powell, Roy, Kanim, Bello, & Edgerton, 1984; Spector, Gardiner, Zernicke, Roy, & Edgerton, 1980; Wickiewicz, Roy, Powell, & Edgerton, 1983). More specifically, the variables of primary relevance are muscle mass, fiber length, fiber angle and tendon length. The density of muscle is also important but its variance seems to be so small as to be a negligible factor in the variations of properties from muscle to muscle (Mendez & Keys, 1960).

Each of these variables, that is, muscle mass, fiber lengths, fiber angle, and tendon length are difficult to estimate in vivo with the desired, and usually the necessary, accuracy. Finding the mass, at least, of muscle groups is possible at this time using imaging techniques, and this will become more commonplace in the near future. However, fiber length and angle as well as tendon length measurements in living subjects are virtually impossible to determine now and no immediate technical breakthroughs to fill this void are apparent.

The purpose of this presentation is to illustrate those variables related to muscle design that influence its functional properties. A further objective is to present what we think is the best estimate possible at this time of the specific tension capability of human skeletal muscle.

METHODS

Isokinetic Measurements

Isokinetic torques exerted by the elbow flexors were measured in 14 normal adult subjects using an isokinetic device (Cybex II) used previously in this laboratory (Apor, Edgerton, Roy, & Tihanyi, 1985; Gregor, Edgerton, Perrine, Campion, & DeBus, 1979; Perrine & Edgerton, 1978; Wickiewicz, Roy, Powell, Perrine, & Edgerton, 1984). To measure torques, the upper arm was placed horizontally on a bench with the chest held against the edge of the bench to minimize a shift of the elbow axis from the rotational axis of the apparatus. The maximum isometric torque of the elbow flexors was measured at full extension, and at 20°, 40°, 60°, 80°, 90°, 100°, 110°, and 120° of flexion. One minute of rest was given between each contraction. The testing procedure was repeated in an inverse order on a subsequent day. When the angle specific torques of all subjects were averaged and plotted in reference to elbow angle, the highest mean torque occurred at 80° from full extension. This highest mean torque, regardless of the velocity at which it occurred, was used to calculate specific tension (force per cross-sectional area of muscle).

Architectural Determinations of Cadavers

The flexor muscle group included the biceps brachii (Bic Br), short and long heads, the brachioradialis (Brachiorad), the brachialis (Brach), the pronator teres (PT), and the extensor carpi radialis longus (ECRL). The extensors included the three heads of the triceps brachii.

Muscles of formalin-fixed upper extremities from four cadavers were dissected. After the fat was removed, the weights and lengths of the elbow flexor and extensor muscles were measured. The muscles then were placed in 15% to 20% sulfuric acid to digest the connective tissue and to facilitate muscle architectural determinations (Sacks & Roy, 1982; Wickiewicz et al., 1983). The lengths of small fiber bundles (approximately 5 to 15 fibers per bundle) were determined as described by Sacks and Roy (1982). Ten to 20 measurements of fiber bundle lengths were made from several regions of each muscle. The overall average bundle length was used as the average fiber length.

The physiological CSA was calculated using the following equations:

$$\text{CSA} = \frac{\text{muscle weight}}{(\text{fiber length})\ (\text{muscle density})}$$

where muscle density was assumed to be 1.056 (Mendez & Keys, 1960).

RESULTS

Isokinetic Torques

The mean isokinetic torque at the optimal elbow position for all subjects was 48 ± 10 N•m. The peak torques were similar in magnitude and occurred approximately at the same angle as in other studies (Ikai & Fukunaga, 1968).

Morphometric and Architectural Measurements from Cadavers

The muscle wet weights and lengths, fiber lengths, and physiological CSA of the elbow flexors and triceps brachii from four cadavers are shown in Table 1. Particular points of interest are shown in the comparison of individual values among cadavers and among muscles. Fiber length variations among cadavers were particularly noticeable in the Brachiorad and PT. The Bic Br and Brach muscles had similar relative physiological CSAs and together accounted for 57% of the flexor CSA. Also note the consistently larger values for cadaver III (Table 1; and Figure 1). Its total flexor muscle CSA was almost twice that of the average of the four cadavers. In all cadavers, the elbow extensors had a physiological CSA that was considerably larger than the total for the flexors (Figure 1).

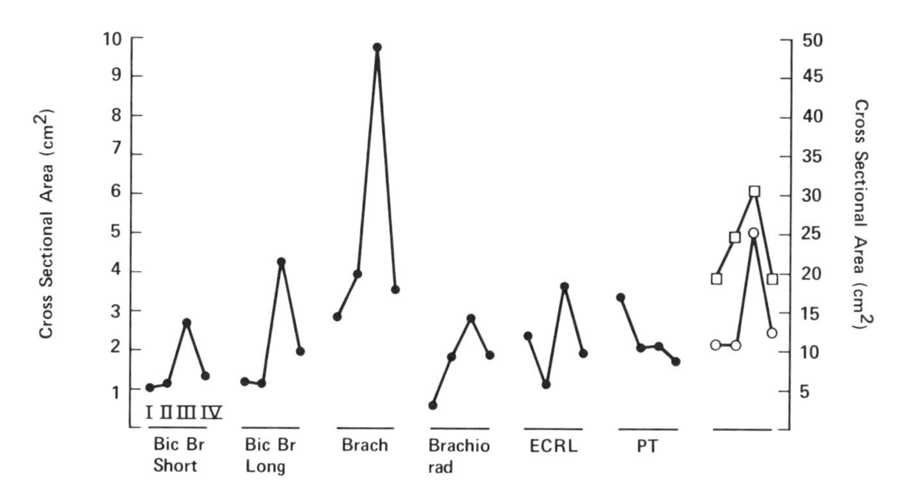

Figure 1 The physiological cross-sectional areas (CSA) for the individual elbow flexors (•) of the four cadavers (I, II, III and IV) used in the study are plotted. Also, the total CSA for all elbow flexor (°) and extensor (□) muscles for each cadaver are shown on the far right. Note that the values for cadaver III are much larger than for the other cadavers.

Table 1 Basic Architectural Data of Elbow Flexors and Extensors

Muscle[a]	Cadaver	Muscle Length (cm)	Muscle Weight (g)	Fiber[b] Length (cm)	Physiol.[c] CSA (cm^2)
Bic Br, short head	I	19.5	19	17.0	1.06
	II	21.0	27	19.0	1.20
	III	21.5	39	13.0	2.84
	IV	23.0	21	16.5	1.36
Bic Br, long head	I	23.0	23	18.0	1.21
	II	27.0	32	24.2	1.12
	III	23.0	64	16.0	4.38
	IV	25.0	40	19.0	1.99
Brach	I	19.7	35	11.5	2.86
	II	19.4	57	13.7	3.93
	III	19.9	120	11.5	9.89
	IV	21.5	46	21.0	2.07
Brachiorad	I	26.0	14	20.0	0.66
	II	25.6	17	9.0	1.84
	III	22.0	46	15.0	2.93
	IV	21.0	-	-	1.89
PT	I	15.2	15	4.1	3.43
	II	16.1	14	6.2	2.07
	III	16.5	34	15.0	2.13
	IV	16.0	18	10.0	1.72
ECRL	I	17.1	17	6.7	2.44
	II	15.0	7	6.4	1.04
	III	11.5	27	6.6	3.73
	IV	14.0	11	5.5	1.90
Triceps Brachii	I	22.3	165	8.2	18.88
	II	22.3	177	6.7	24.79
	III	24.3	310	8.9	31.72
	IV	25.8	140	6.5	20.00

[a]Muscle abbreviations are explained in Methods.
[b]Based on average fiber bundle lengths as described in Methods.
[c]Physiological cross-sectional area calculated as described in Methods.

Moment arm lengths, the physiological CSA, the predicted torque and forces and the percent contribution of each muscle to the flexor torque of the elbow are shown in Table 2. Data from the present study are compared with that taken from Amis, Dowson, and Wright (1979), An, Hui, Morrey, Linscheid, and Chao (1981), and Pauwels (1980). In general, there seems to be agreement on the moment arm lengths and the relative contributions of individual muscles to the flexor CSA (Table 2; Figure 2). How-

Table 2 Comparison of Estimated Moment Arms, Cross-sectional Areas and Torques of Human Elbow Flexors

Flexors	Pauwels			Amis			An			Present Study			Overall Mean		
	Moment Arm	CSA	Torque[b]	Moment Arm	CSA	Torque	Moment Arm	CSA	Torque	Moment Arm[d]	CSA	Torque	Moment Arm	CSA	Torque
	(cm)	(cm^2)	(N•m)	(cm)	(cm^2)	(N•m)	(cm)	(cm^2)	(N•m)	(cm)	(cm^2)	(N•m)	(cm)	(cm^2)	(N•m)
Bic Br	4.5	9.0	9.14	3.8	5.7	4.86	3.2	4.6	3.33	3.8	3.8	3.27	3.8	5.8	4.96
		(203)[a]	(31)[c]		(128)	(37)		(104)	(29)		(86)	(29)		(131)	(31)
Brach	3.6	12.4	10.4	3.0	5.6	3.78	2.0	7.0	3.16	2.9	4.7	3.07	2.9	7.4	4.83
		(279)	(34)		(126)	(29)		(158)	(27)		(106)	(27)		(167)	(30)
Brachiorad	8.0	3.0	5.44	5.0	1.7	1.90	5.2	1.5	1.77	6.1	1.8	2.50	6.1	2.0	2.75
		(68)	(19)		(38)	(14)		(34)	(15)		(41)	(22)		(45)	(17)
PT	1.3	4.2	1.24	1.2	4.6	1.25	2.0	3.4	1.54	1.5	2.3	0.78	1.5	3.6	1.23
		(95)	(4)		(104)	(9)		(77)	(13)		(52)	(7)		(82)	(8)
ECRL	3.1	4.8	3.35	2.4	2.7	1.46	3.4	2.4	1.84	3.0	2.3	1.56	3.0	3.1	2.07
		(108)	(11)		(61)	(11)		(54)	(16)		(52)	(14)		(69)	(13)

[a]Predicted maximum force = (CSA) (22.5 N•cm^2) (Based on Spector et al., 1980; Powell et al., 1984).
[b]Predicted torque = (predicted maximum force) (moment arm) (10^{-2}).
[c]Percent of total flexor torque contributed by each muscle.
[d]Mean moment arm of Pauwels (1980); Amis et al. (1979) and An et al. (1981).

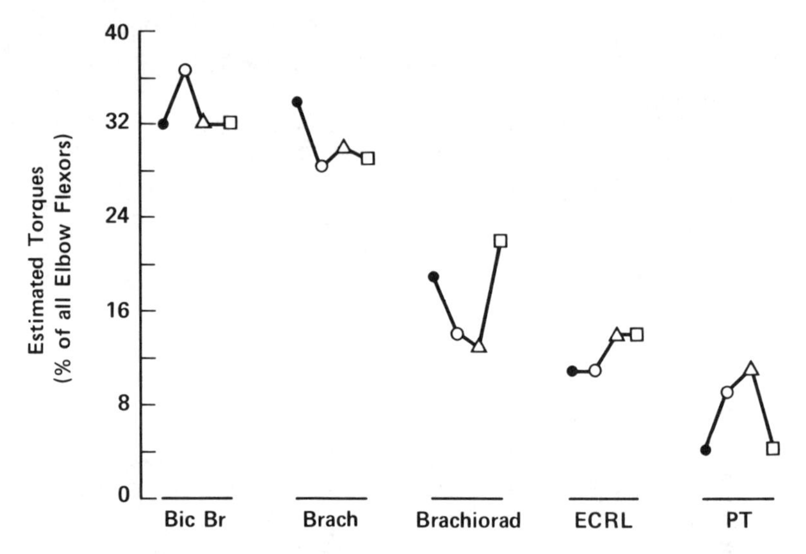

Figure 2 The estimated individual flexor muscle torques are represented as a percent of the estimated total flexor torque based on the data of Pauwels (1980) (•), Amis et al. (1979) (°), An et al. (1981) (△), and the present study (□).

ever, there is considerable variation among studies on the total physiological CSA and consequently, the predicted torques. To avoid variations between studies and among cadavers, the weighted values (the product of moment arm and the proportion that the CSA of each muscle is relative to all flexors) were used to estimate the total "effective" moment arm for all muscles combined. This value was 3.7 cm (Pauwels, 1980), 2.9 cm (Amis et al., 1979), 3.3 cm (An et al., 1981) and 3.3 cm (present study) based on the data in Table 2. This weighted moment arm divided into the total flexor CSA provides a means of estimating the force potential of the elbow flexor group.

Specific Tension

By combining the maximal isokinetic torque measurements of healthy subjects, the moment arm of the elbow flexors in cadavers and the morphologic and architectural data from cadaver muscles, it is possible to estimate the maximal force per physiological CSA, that is, specific tension. Based on a maximal torque of 48 N•m, a weighted moment arm of 3.3 cm and a mean physiological CSA of 34.7 cm^2 (Table 3), the resulting specific tension estimate is 42 N•cm^2.

Table 3 Comparison of Basic Data Used to Derive Specific Tension of Human Elbow Flexors

Data Source	CSA[e] (cm²)	Torque (N•m)	Force (N)	Specific (N•cm⁻²)
Present Paper[a]	34.7	48.0	1297	37
Ikai and Fukunaga (1968)	43.0[b]	47.8	1294	30
Nygaard et al. (1983)	10.2[c]	48.1	337	33
Ralston et al. (1949)	9.2	—	214[d]	23
Pauwels (1980)	44.8			
Amis et al. (1979)	27.2			
An et al. (1981)	25.3			

[a]Based on data from the largest cadaver shown in Table 1.
[b]Based on ultrasonic measurements of subjects tested for maximum torque.
[c]Based on the assumption that the CSA measured by computerized tomography produced 34% of the total elbow flexor torque.
[d]Voluntary contraction from isolated tendon of amputee.
[e]All CSA values listed have been corrected by 34%, which is the estimated increase in CSA when the arm is flexed from a fully extended position to a 90° elbow angle (see Methods).

Relationship of Muscle Design to Moment Arm

If a muscle is to function effectively, the design of the muscle must be matched with the mechanics associated with its attachments. For example, the displacement and velocity potential of a muscle is a function of muscle fiber length. Also, the actual displacement and velocity of movement that the muscle produces depends on its moment arm. This muscle-moment arm interdependence is illustrated in Figure 3. Those muscles with the longer moment arms tend to have longer muscle fibers relative to the tension capability of the muscle. That is, if a muscle is designed with a relative bias for displacement at the expense of tension, it will also have a longer moment arm.

DISCUSSION

Factors Affecting Specific Tension

The tension produced by a muscle is limited by the number of cross bridge attachments that exist in parallel per half of a sarcomere (Close,

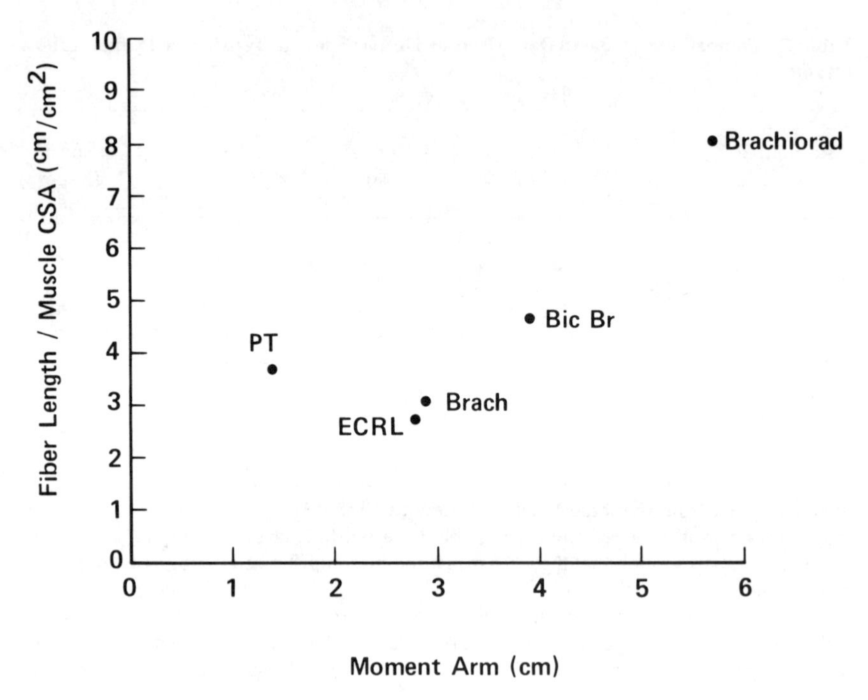

Figure 3 Moment arms plotted versus fiber length/muscle CSA ratios for individual elbow flexors. The moment arms are based on the mean of the four cadavers shown in Table 2. The fiber lengths and muscle CSA are based on the data from the four cadavers shown in Table 1. A high ratio indicates that the muscle is designed to emphasize displacement and/or velocity as opposed to force. This graph suggests that those muscles that have a "bias" for long fibers also have long moment arms.

1972; Kushmerick & Krasner, 1982). Theoretically, the number of in parallel attachments that exist at any point in time is a function of the cycle rate per cross bridge and the duration of attachment per cycle relative to the duration of detachment. Although the number of cross bridges, the cycle rate and the duration of attachment cannot be determined easily, a relative approximation of a muscle's potential to produce tension can be made by measuring the physiological CSA. This measure seems to be possible to make because of the consistency in the density of the myofibrils relative to the cytoplasm in practically all muscles (Eisenberg, 1983). Thus, one only needs to use a common point of reference in measuring the physiological CSA to compare the maximal forces between muscles even though they may vary widely in their architectural design. For a variety of mammalian muscles that have been studied with reasonable thoroughness, the specific tension (tension per CSA) has been rather consistent ranging from about 20 to 28 N•cm^{-2} (Close, 1972; Powell et al., 1984; Spector et al., 1980; Witzmann, Kim, & Fitts, 1983).

However, there may be a difference in the specific tension of muscle fibers that consist of predominantly fast versus slow type myosin. Data on rats (Witzmann et al., 1983) and guinea pigs (Powell et al., 1984) suggest that slow muscles have a specific tension of about 17 N•cm^{-2} compared to 23 N cm^{-2} for fast muscle. However, further consideration should be given to the possibility that slow muscle fibers may have a lower specific tension when they are located in a predominantly fast muscle but not when it is in a predominantly slow muscle. This appears to be the case in the cat (Bodine, Roy, Eldred, & Edgerton; Burke, 1981; Spector et al., 1980).

Because of this rather remarkable consistency in the specific tension of skeletal muscle among mammals, the same could be expected for humans. However, there have been some extremely large variations in specific tension reported for human muscle. This large variation is probably due to some fundamental experimental errors in either the technique or in the assumptions underlying the technique. Some of the potential sources of error are discussed below.

Torque Measurements

The maximal torques of the elbow flexors in humans reported in several studies are of the same order of magnitude (Table 3). Therefore, it appears unlikely that errors in the measurement of torques account for the wide variations observed in specific tension. However, confusion has resulted from studies that have referred to strength and force measurements interchangeably with torque measurements. In addition, when torques have been measured, often the force arm and resistance arm lengths have not been noted clearly. Barring these difficulties, one is left with the general impression that the differences in elbow flexor torques largely reflect the differences in the size of the subjects tested.

Moment Arm Measurements

As is true for the torque measurements, the moment arms are reasonably consistent across studies. The weighted moment arms based on the data of Pauwels (1980), Amis et al. (1979) and An et al. (1981) as well as our data, were 3.7 cm, 2.9 cm, 3.3 cm and 3.3 cm, respectively. These measurements also seem to be consistent with the apparent estimates of Ikai and Fukunaga (1968) and those of Wilkie (1950). Thus, it appears the estimates of the moment arms are not the major cause for the wide variations in estimating specific tension of human muscles.

Cross-Sectional Areas

An et al. (1981) have suggested that the apparent discrepancies in specific tension can be attributed largely to errors in the estimates of CSA. For the reasons described in this paper, it is fundamentally incorrect to use anatomical CSA as a reference for tension or force potential of a muscle. The anatomical CSA does not take into account the variety of anatomical arrangements that exist among muscles. For example, the proximodistal point at which the arm circumference is measured affects the CSA estimate of the flexors for several reasons. One of the more obvious considerations is the difference in location of individual muscles of the muscle group along the proximodistal axis. As shown in Figure 4, a cross-sectional plane through the approximate midlength of the humerus would sample only the Bic Br and a portion of the Brach. Another potentially serious error is in assuming that the anatomical CSA and physiological CSA are the same. This is not the case as has been demonstrated quite clearly by Powell et al. (1984), Sacks and Roy (1982), and Spector et al. (1980). Based on the fiber lengths and muscle lengths shown in Table 1 and assuming a simple muscle design, it is evident from Figure 4 that the proximo-distal points at which a cross-section is taken will have a marked effect on the estimated anatomical and/or physiological CSA values.

Current technology in noninvasive imaging permits one to measure accurately the anatomical CSA of a muscle group and in some cases even of individual muscles. Because of variations in muscle positions, shapes, designs and the different fiber to muscle length ratios, these imaging approaches have the same potential errors in estimating physiological CSA as do anthropometric approaches (see Figure 4). However, it is technically feasible to avoid most of these problems with a more thorough imaging approach such as using multiple scans to reconstruct muscle volumes.

In judging the validity of the cadaver data obtained in the present study and earlier studies, there are two major points that need consideration. First, most cadaver material is obtained from older, and often debilitated, individuals in which muscle atrophy is common. The muscles may also be reduced in volume during the fixation procedures. Therefore, it is likely that the specific tension will be overestimated when torque measurements are taken from young healthy subjects and the physiological CSA is based on cadaver material. The potential effect of variations of CSA on the specific tension is evident when comparing the data from cadaver III with that of the other three cadavers (Table 1; Figure 1). If we assume that the largest cadaver best approximated the CSA of our pool of subjects, then the specific tension of the elbow flexors would be 42 $N \cdot cm^{-2}$.

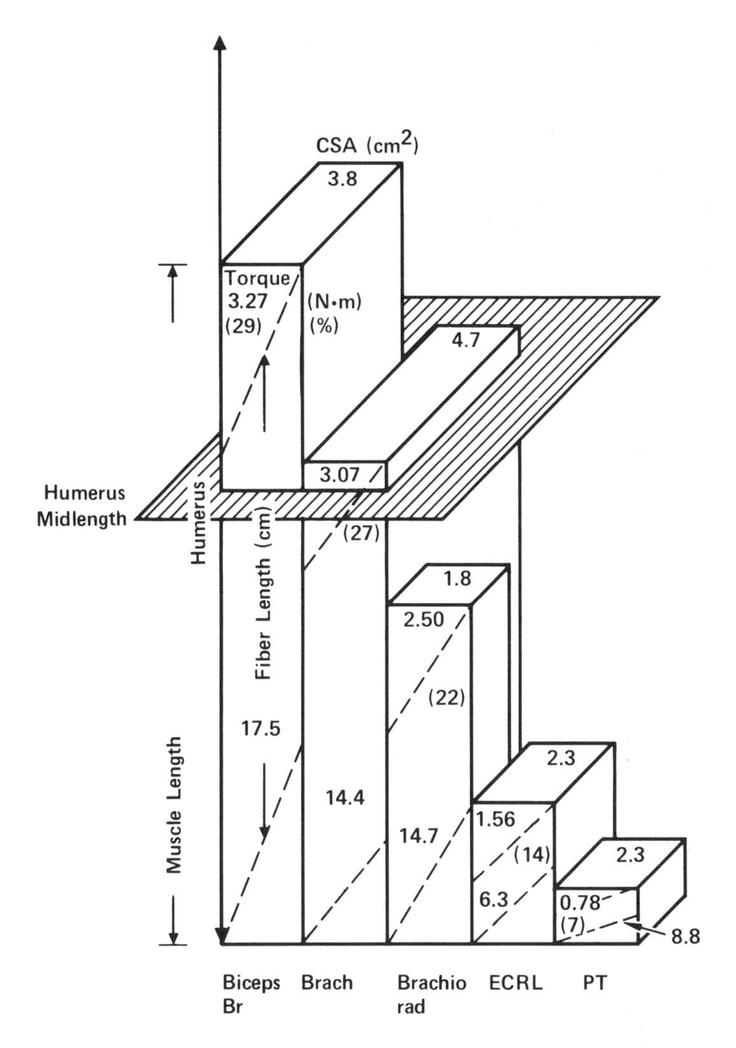

Figure 4 This figure illustrates several features regarding each of the elbow flexors. The vertical line labelled humerus represents the distance between the midlevel of the head of the humerus and the middle of the condyle. The five columns represent the distance that each muscle extends along the length of the humerus. The more distal portions (beyond the elbow) of the muscles are not included. The distance between the dashed, diagonal lines represent the distance that the fibers of a muscle span relative to the whole muscle length. The bottom number in each column is the mean fiber length of each muscle from four cadavers. The top surface of each column is scaled to be proportional to the physiological cross-sectional area of that muscle. The actual mean CSA values also are shown. At the top front surface of each column, the torque that can be produced by each muscle is shown as well as the percentage of the torque that can be produced by each muscle relative to all of the flexor muscles combined. The hatched horizontal plane illustrates why a cross-section of the upper arm at the midlength of the humerus would sample all of the fibers of the biceps brachii and some of the fibers of the brachialis, but none of the other flexor muscles.

Comparison of Specific Tension Data on Humans

There have been many studies in which tension per CSA has been reported. Unfortunately, the information reported is not comparable in many cases because all of the appropriate considerations discussed above have not been addressed. Some studies that do provide comparative data are shown in Table 3. Note that the CSAs are reasonably consistent with the exception of Nygaard, Houston, Suzuki, Jorgensen, and Saltin 1983 and Ralston, Polissar, Inman, Close, and Feinstein (1949). The inconsistency in the data of Nygaard et al. (1983) can be explained by the fact that only a small portion of the CSA was measured in a single scan. However, they accounted for this when estimating the amount of tension resulting from the CSA measured. The CSA reported by Ralston et al. (1949) may have been smaller because the data were based on amputee subjects. The specific tensions range from 23 to 42 $N \cdot cm^{-2}$ in the studies cited. These data are similar in range and absolute values to those reported for other mammals.

To summarize, it appears that human muscle has a specific tension that is similar to that of other mammalian skeletal muscle. Further, it appears that with the appropriate application of present imaging capabilities, the specific tension of human muscle can be defined more precisely.

REFERENCES

Amis, A.A., Dowson, D., & Wright, V. (1979). Muscle strengths and musculo-skeletal geometry of the upper limb. *Engineering Medicine,* **8**, 41-48.

An, K.N., Hui, F.C., Morrey, B.F., Linscheid, R.L., & Chao, E.Y. (1981). Muscles across the elbow joint: a biomechanical analysis. *Journal of Biomechanics,* **14**, 659-669.

Apor, P., Edgerton, V.R., Roy, R.R., & Tihanyi, J. (1985). A karhajlito izmok izokinetikus ero-schesseg jellemzoi. [In Hungarian]. *Kiserletes Orvostudomany,* **37**, 56-68.

Bodine, S.C., Roy, R.R., Eldred, E., & Edgerton, V.R. (1985). Innervation ratio, fiber size and specific tension of type-identified motor units in the cat tibialis anterior. *Society of Neuroscience Abstracts* **11**, 211.

Bodine, S.C., Roy, R.R., Meadows, D.A., Zernicke, R.F., Sacks, R.D., Fournier, M., Edgerton, V.R. (1982). Architectural, histochemical, and contractile characteristics of a unique biarticular muscle: The cat semitendinosus. *Journal of Neurophysiology.* **48**, 192-201.

Burke, R.E. (1981). Motor units: Anatomy, physiology, and functional organization. In J.M. Brookhart, V.B. Mountcastle, V.B. Brooks, & S.R. Geiger (Eds.), *Handbook of physiology. Sec. 1. The Nervous System* (pp. 315-422). Bethesda, MD: American Physiological Society.

Close, R.I. (1972). Dynamic properties of mammalian skeletal muscle. *Physiological Reviews*, **52**, 129-197.

Eisenberg, B.R. (1983). Quantitative ultrastructure of mammalian skeletal muscle. In L.D. Peachey (Ed.), *Handbook of physiology. Sec. 10. Skeletal muscle* (pp. 73-112). Bethesda, MD: American Physiological Society.

Gregor, R.J., Edgerton, V.R., Perrine, J.J., Campion, D.S., & DeBus, C. (1979). Torque-velocity relationships and muscle fiber composition in elite female athletes. *Journal of Applied Physiology: Respiratory, Environmental and Exercise Physiology*, **47**, 388-392.

Ikai, M., & Fukunaga, T. (1968). Calculation of muscle strength per unit cross-sectional area of human muscle by means of ultrasonic measurement. *Internacionale zeitschrift für angewandte physiologie einschliesslich arbeitsphysiologie* (Berlin), **26**, 26-32.

Kushmerick, M.J., & Krasner, B. (1982). Force and ATPase rate in skinned skeletal muscle fibers. *Federation Proceedings*, **41**, 2232-2237.

Mendez, R.A., & Keys, A. (1960). Density and composition of mammalian muscle. *Metabolism, Clinical and Experimental*, **9**, 184-188.

Nygaard, E., Houston, M., Suzuki, Y., Jorgensen, K., & Saltin, B. (1983). Morphology of the brachial biceps muscle and elbow flexion in man. *Acta Physiologica Scandinavica*, **117**, 287-292.

Pauwels, F. (1980). *Biomechanics of the locomotor apparatus*. Berlin: Springer-Verlag.

Perrine, J.J., & Edgerton, V.R. (1978). Muscle force-velocity and power-velocity relationships under isokinetic loading. *Medicine and Science in Sports*, **10**, 159-166.

Powell, P.L., Roy, R.R., Kanim, P., Bello, M.A., & Edgerton, V.R. (1984). Predictability of skeletal muscle tension from architectural determinations in guinea pig hindlimbs. *Journal of Applied Physiology: Respiratory, Environmental and Exercise Physiology*, **57**, 1715-1721.

Ralston, H.J., Polissar, M.J., Inman, V.T., Close, J.R., & Feinstein, B. (1949). Dynamic features of human isolated voluntary muscle in isometric and free contractions. *Journal of Applied Physiology*, **1**, 526-533.

Sacks, R.D., & Roy, R.R. (1982). Architecture of the hindlimb muscles of the cat: Functional significance. *Journal of Morphology*, **173**, 185-195.

Spector, S.A., Gardiner, P.F., Zernicke, R.F., Roy, R.R., & Edgerton, V.R. (1980). Muscle architecture and force-velocity characteristics of cat soleus and medial gastrocnemius: Implications for motor control. *Journal of Neurophysiology*, **44**, 951-960.

Wickiewicz, T.L., Roy, R.R., Powell, P.L., & Edgerton, V.R. (1983). Muscle architecture of the human lower limb. *Clinical Orthopedics and Related Research*, **179**, 317-325.

Wickiewicz, T.L., Roy, R.R., Powell, P.L., Perrine, J., & Edgerton, V.R. (1984). Muscle architecture and force-velocity relationships in humans. *Journal of Applied Physiology: Respiratory, Environmental and Exercise Physiology*, **57**, 435-443.

Wilkie, D.R. (1950). The relationship between force and velocity in human muscle. *Journal of Physiology*, **110**, 249-280.
Witmann, F.A., Kim, D.H., & Fitts, R.H. (1983). Effect of hindlimb immobilization of the fatigability of skeletal muscle. *Journal of Applied Physiology: Respiratory, Environmental and Exercise Physiology*, **54**, 1242-1248.

Adaptability of Muscle to Strength Training—A Cellular Approach

J. Duncan MacDougall
McMaster University
Hamilton, Ontario, Canada

The adaptations in skeletal muscle at the cellular level that occur in response to strength training are discussed here. *Cellular level* has been interpreted to include those changes that could be detected by the light microscope, whereas the *subcellular* adaptations would be those that could only be detected by the electron microscope. Changes at the cell level are obviously the result of changes at the subcellular level.

Individuals perform strength and power training for a number of reasons: Weight lifters and power lifters train in order to increase their strength and skill so that they can lift more weight; bodybuilders train in order to increase their muscle size and to attain muscle symmetry; athletes in other sports use muscle specific strength and power training in order to improve performance in their sport; and individuals train for rehabilitative purposes following injury or surgery. It is well accepted that such training results in an increase in maximal voluntary strength and usually an increase in muscle size.

METHODS

Much of the data that are presented in this section was collected by applying the needle biopsy procedure to a series of studies with human volunteers. These studies were of two types: (a) a series of training studies in which groups of untrained subjects trained either their elbow extensor or their elbow flexor muscles for periods ranging from 4 to 24 months, and (b) a series of studies where tissue from previously trained subjects such as bodybuilders and powerlifters was compared with that of untrained or short-term trained subjects.

Biopsy samples were used for either histochemical, biochemical or ultrastructural analysis as previously described (MacDougall et al., 1979; MacDougall, Elder, Sale, Moroz, & Sutton, 1980; MacDougall, Sale, Alway,

& Sutton, 1984; MacDougall, Sale, Elder, & Sutton, 1982; MacDougall, Ward, Sale, & Sutton, 1977).

RESULTS AND DISCUSSION

Changes in Fiber Area

Cross-sectional areas of both type I and type II fibers increase with heavy resistance training; however, the magnitude of this increase varies considerably between individuals. The greatest increase in fiber areas that we have noted in a longitudinal training study was a mean increase of 33% in type II fibers and a mean increase of 27% in type I fibers in a group of previously untrained subjects who trained their triceps for 6 months (MacDougall et al., 1979). Within the group, individual increases in fiber area were as little as 3% and as great as 49% despite the fact that all subjects followed the same training program.

Whether or not there is a limit to which muscle fibers can increase in size with training is not known. In a comparison study, fiber areas have been found in biceps brachii in a group of bodybuilders who had trained for 6 to 8 years to be approximately 58% (type II fibers) and 39% (type I fibers) larger than those of untrained age-matched controls (MacDougall et al., 1984).

Although both fiber types increase in cross-sectional area with strength training, a greater relative hypertrophy occurs in the type II units (MacDougall et al., 1979; MacDougall et al., 1980; Tesch, Häkkinen, & Komi, 1985; Thorstensson, 1976). Moreover, when healthy subjects have their limbs immobilized for several weeks in elbow casts there is also a greater relative atrophy of the type II fibers (MacDougall et al., 1980).

Conversion of Fiber Types with Training

Although recent evidence from Pette's laboratory indicates that it may be possible to increase the proportion of type I fibers by endurance training (Green et al., 1984), conventional strength training does not appear to have the opposite effect, that is, to increase the proportion of type II fibers. This conclusion is based on our finding of no change in the percentage of type I and type II fibers following 6 months of training (MacDougall et al., 1980) as well as our finding of the same percentage fiber type in triceps and biceps of elite bodybuilders as that of untrained subjects despite 6 to 8 years of intensive training by the bodybuilders (MacDougall et al., 1982, 1984) (see Figure 1).

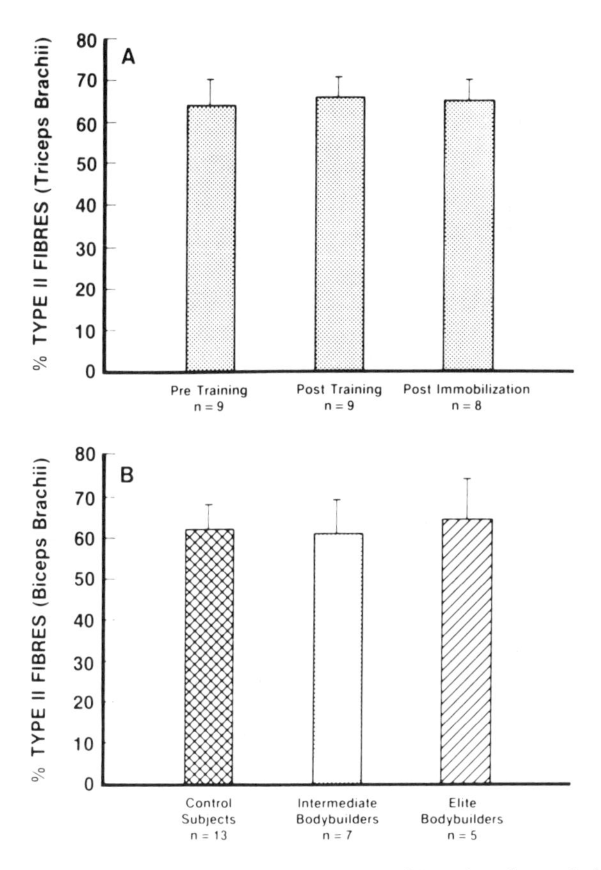

Figure 1. A. Percent type II fibers in triceps brachii of 9 male subjects before and after 6 months of heavy resistance training and after 6 weeks of immobilization of the elbow joint. B. Percent type II fibers in biceps brachii in a group of untrained controls, a group of intermediate bodybuilders and a group of elite bodybuilders. Values are means ± 1 SD.

Hyperplasia of Fibers with Training

Although it has been demonstrated that heavy resistance training may result in an increase in fiber number in certain animal species (Gonyea, 1980; Gonyea, Erickson, & Bonde-Petersen, 1977), we do not believe that such a process occurs to any significant extent in humans. We recently calculated fiber numbers in biceps brachii in a group of elite bodybuilders, a group of novice bodybuilders and a group of untrained controls of the same age (MacDougall et al., 1984). This was done by correlating muscle cross-sectional areas from CT scans with fiber areas obtained from needle biopsies. Although we found wide ranges in fiber numbers between different individuals, the average number of fibers was the same for each

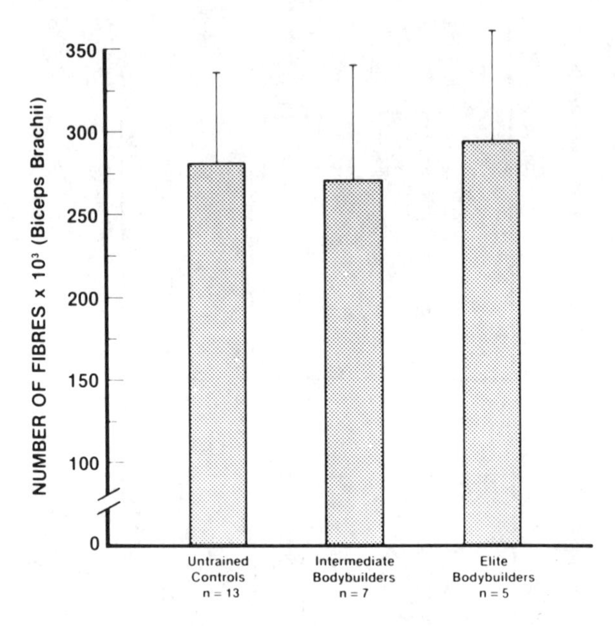

Figure 2 Estimated fiber number in biceps brachii for a group of untrained controls, a group of intermediate bodybuilders and a group of elite bodybuilders. Values are means ± 1 SD. From "Muscle Fiber Number in Biceps Brachii in Bodybuilders and Control Subjects." by J.D. MacDougall, D.G. Sale, S.E. Alway, and J.R. Sutton, 1984, *Journal of Applied Physiology: Respiratory, Environmental and Exercise Physiology*, **57**, p. 1401. Copyright 1984 by the American Physiology Society. Adapted by permission.

group (Figure 2). Since both groups of bodybuilders had trained their biceps intensively for 6 to 8 years, our results are interpreted as indicating that such training does not cause an increase in muscle fiber number.

It should be pointed out, however, that within each group, we found a tendency for the individuals with the largest muscle to also have a higher than average number of fibers. Thus, although it is the size of the individual fibers that is the main determinant of muscle size, the bodybuilder who inherits a greater than average number of fibers would have a greater potential for increasing his muscle size than would the bodybuilder with an average number of fibers.

Biochemical Adaptations to Strength Training

Although alterations in muscle enzyme activities have been widely investigated with endurance training, there have been very few similar studies with strength training (Table 1). Earlier literature reports increases in myokinase activity (Thorstensson et al., 1976) and possibly creatine phosphokinase (Thorstensson, Sjödin, & Karlsson, 1975) with strength training, but the training in these studies was not sufficient to cause significant muscle hypertrophy. When training is of sufficient intensity or duration to elicit pronounced hypertrophy of the type II fibers, it has been recently shown that the activity of these two enzymes decreases (Tesch et al., 1985). Likewise, the activity of PFK and other glycolytic enzymes is either unaffected by strength training (Gollnick, Armstrong, Saubert, Piehl, & Saltin, 1972; Thorstensson, Hultén, Von Döbeln, & Karlsson, 1976) or decreases when significant hypertrophy occurs (Tesch et al., 1985). The activity of mitochondrial enzymes such as succinic dehydrogenase has been shown to be 30% lower in muscles of weight lifters compared to untrained subjects (Gollnick et al., 1972), as well as to decrease following 6 months of heavy resistance training (Tesch et al., 1985).

The lower oxidative enzyme activity in the muscles of weight lifters is probably the result of a reduced mitochondrial volume density (mitochondrial/myofibrillar volume ratio) that has been found to occur with heavy resistance training (MacDougall et al., 1979). Apparently the increase in contractile protein dilutes the mitochondrial portion of the fiber since the decrements in mitochondrial volume density show a high correlation with the increase in fiber area that occurs with this form of training.

Strength training can also result in an increase in the resting concentration of high-energy phosphates and muscle glycogen. In an investigation of nine previously untrained subjects who trained their triceps for 5 to 6 months, significant increases in glycogen, creatine, CP and ATP were found (MacDougall et al., 1977). When these same subjects underwent immobilization of their arms for 5 weeks these changes were reversed.

Table 1 Biochemical Adaptations with Strength Training

Enzymes	Data Sources
Myokinase ↑	(Thorstensson et al., 1976)
↓	(Tesch et al., 1985)
CPK ↑	(Thorstensson et al., 1975)
→	(Thorstensson et al., 1976)
↓	(Tesch et al., 1985)
PFK →	(Gollnick et al., 1972; Thorstensson et al., 1976)
↓	(Tesch et al., 1985)
SDH ↓	(Gollnick et al., 1972; Tesch et al., 1985)
(mitochondrial volume density ↓)	(MacDougall et al., 1979)
glycogen ↑, CP ↑, C ↑, ATP ↑	(MacDougall et al., 1977)

Presumably the increase in high-energy phosphates in the muscle homogenates can be attributed to the greater relative hypertrophy of the type II fibers, which are considered to have higher phosphagen stores than type I fibers. The increase in muscle glycogen suggests that this form of training places considerable demands on glycolytic energy supply in addition to the high-energy phosphate systems. This is consistent with recent findings by Tesch and Kaiser (1984) of reduced muscle glycogen and high muscle lactates immediately following strength training.

Ultrastructural Adaptations to Strength Training

The increase in cross-sectional fiber area that occurs with strength training is the result of increased myofibrillar area with little or no change in the myofibrillar packing density. The increased myofibrillar area is caused by the addition of actin and myosin filaments to the periphery of the myofibrils.

In a study where muscle ultrastructure in 6 subjects was examined before and after 6 months of strength training, it was found that fiber area increased to a greater extent than did myofibrillar area (MacDougall, in press). Since the volume density for myofibrils remained unaltered, this indicates that there was also an increase in myofibrillar number as well as an increase in myofibrillar size. Presumably the increase in myofibrillar number was the result of a longitudinal splitting process as has been shown to occur in normal postnatal growth in animals (Goldspink, 1970, 1974).

The decrease in fiber area that occurs when healthy muscle is immobilized involves the reversal of the above process; that is, there is a loss of contractile protein from the periphery of the myofibril and a corresponding shrinkage in myofibrillar and fiber size (MacDougall, in press). Changes in ultrastructural dimensions with training-induced hypertrophy and immobilization-induced atrophy are summarized in Figure 3.

Other Changes

Although it is generally accepted that endurance training may result in an increase in capillary supply (Anderson, 1975; Ingjer, 1979), strength training appears to have no effect on the capillary-to-fiber ratio. Moreover, the increased contractile protein caused by strength training appears to dilute capillary density (expressed as capillaries per mm^2) so that post-training values are lower than pretraining (MacDougall, in press) and capillary densities in weight and power lifters may be as much as 35% lower than in untrained subjects (Tesch, Thorsson, & Kaiser, 1984).

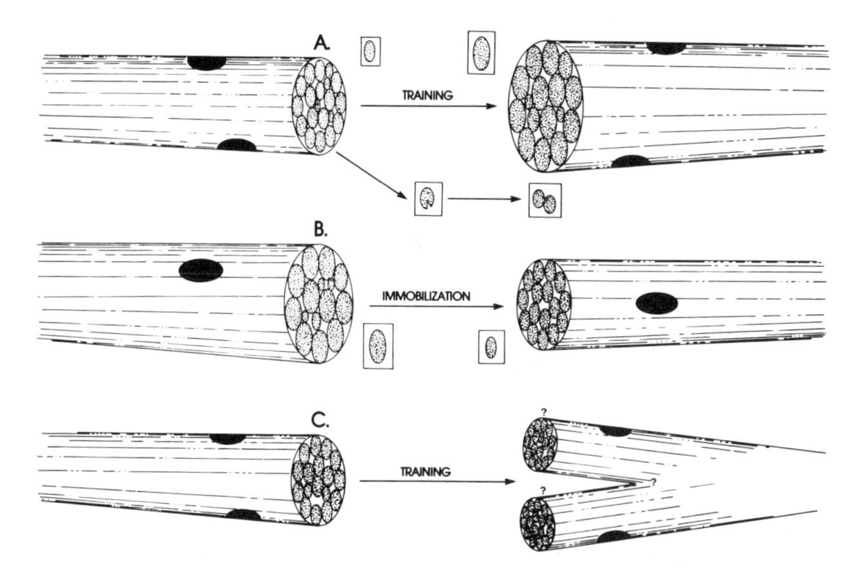

Figure 3 A possible model for changes in muscle size that occur in response to strength training and immobilization. (A) With training, cross-sectional fiber area increases in direct portion to the increases in myofibrillar size and number. (B). With immobilization, fiber area decreases in proportion to the decrease in myofibrillar size. (C). The possibility of training-induced fiber splitting has been discussed previously in this chapter. From "Morphological Changes in Human Skeletal Muscle Following Strength Training and Immobilization" by J.D. MacDougall, in press, in N.L. Jones, N. McCartney, and A.J. McComas (Eds.), *Human Muscle Power*, Champaign, IL: Human Kinetics. Reprinted with permission.

Although the relative amount of connective tissue remains the same there is an increase in absolute amount with strength training. We have estimated the volume density for collagen and other noncontractile tissue in biceps of elite bodybuilders, novice bodybuilders and untrained controls (MacDougall et al., 1984). This proportion was found to be similar for each group, comprising approximately 13% of the total tissue sample with approximately 6% identified as collagen and 7% as other tissue.

Although there is a correlation between maximal voluntary strength and muscle cross-sectional area (Sale, MacDougall, Alway, & Sutton, 1983) we have not found this correlation to be as high as previously reported (Ikai & Fukunaga, 1968). We have also found the correlation between changes in maximal voluntary strength and the changes in fiber areas with either training or detraining to be low and nonsignificant (MacDougall et al., 1980). Thus, maximal voluntary strength is only partially determined by the quantity of contractile tissue, and changes within the central nervous system may be equally as important as fiber size (Sale, in press) in its expression (see Figure 4).

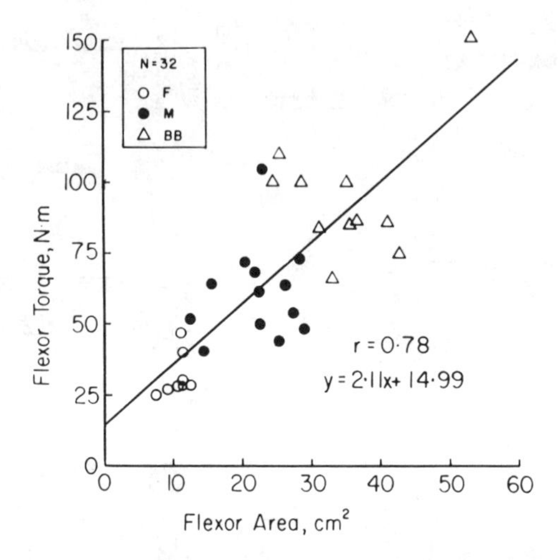

Figure 4 The correlation between maximal voluntary strength (elbow flexion at 30° • sec^{-1} on a Cybex Dynamometer) and total cross sectional area of the elbow flexors (biceps brachii plus brachialis). The subjects were 8 females, 13 untrained males and 11 trained bodybuilders. Muscle areas were calculated from CT scans.

THE STIMULUS FOR HYPERTROPHY

It is well accepted that a training program that utilizes maximal or near maximal contractions will result in an increase in muscle size and that this increase in size is largely the result of increased contractile protein. The mechanism(s), however, by which these mechanical events stimulate an increase in RNA synthesis and subsequent protein synthesis are not known.

Although it has been shown that passive stretch of a skeletal muscle will result in an increase in amino acid uptake and protein synthesis (Sola, Christensen, & Martin, 1973; Vandenburgh & Kaufman, 1979), it appears that this requires a more chronic stimulus (18 hr or more) than the brief stimulus (less than 1 min per day) provided by lifting heavy weights. Moreover, it has been demonstrated that the magnitude of the amino acid uptake response with passive stretch does not relate directly to the magnitude of the stretch (Vandenburgh & Kaufman, 1979), whereas the magnitude of training-induced hypertrophy is closely linked with the magnitude of the loading. It is thus unlikely that the mechanism that results in muscle hypertrophy with strength training is the same mechanism that occurs with passive stretch.

It may be that a portion of the hypertrophy process in response to training may be due to a simple repair process. Forceful muscular contractions are well known to result in delayed muscle soreness and have been shown to yield microscopic evidence of tissue damage (Giddings, Neaves, & Gonyea, 1985). Such damage, particularly evident following eccentric contractions, is greatest in the type II units and persists for 2 to 3 days before strength returns to normal (Fridén, Sjöstrom, & Ekblom, 1983). Lifting (and lowering) of heavy weights during a training session may thus result in damage to contractile elements and connective tissue, which is repaired over the several days that normally elapse between training sessions. This repeated process of damage and repair may result in an overshoot of protein synthesis, somewhat similar to the overcompensation of muscle glycogen that occurs in response to endurance training.

Whatever the mechanism is for stimulating protein synthesis, it is known that the intensity of the loading on the muscle is the main determinant of the degree of size and strength gain. Traditionally, athletes perform strength and power training at loads ranging between 60% and 100% of their maximal voluntary strength (Figure 5). It has become conventional to express the intensity of the loading as a function of maximal repetitions (RM). For example, 1 RM would be the maximal amount of weight that could be lifted for a single repetition, 2 RM would be the maximal amount that could be lifted for 2 repetitions, and so on.

The relationship between various RMs and their percentage of a single maximal voluntary contraction is presented in Figure 5. It can be seen, for example, that the maximal weight that would permit an athlete to complete 10 repetitions of a given exercise would be approximately 75% of what he could lift for a single repetition (1 RM). Bodybuilders have learned, through trial and error, that unless they train at high percentages of their maximum strength, little or no hypertrophy will occur. The optimal combination of loading and number of repetitions, however, has long been a subject of debate among strength athletes.

Traditionally it has been thought that the greatest gains in strength would result from training with sets of 1 to 3 RM while the greatest gains in muscle size would result from training with sets of 5 to 6 RM. Recently, a training study showed that subjects who trained one arm with 6 sets of 10 to 12 RM showed greater gains in both strength and size (muscle and fiber area) than in that arm they trained with 6 sets of 2 to 3 RM (Sale, 1985). It is thus evident that although the loading of the muscle must be very high in order to result in hypertrophy, the total duration during which the muscle develops tension also affects the magnitude of the hypertrophy response.

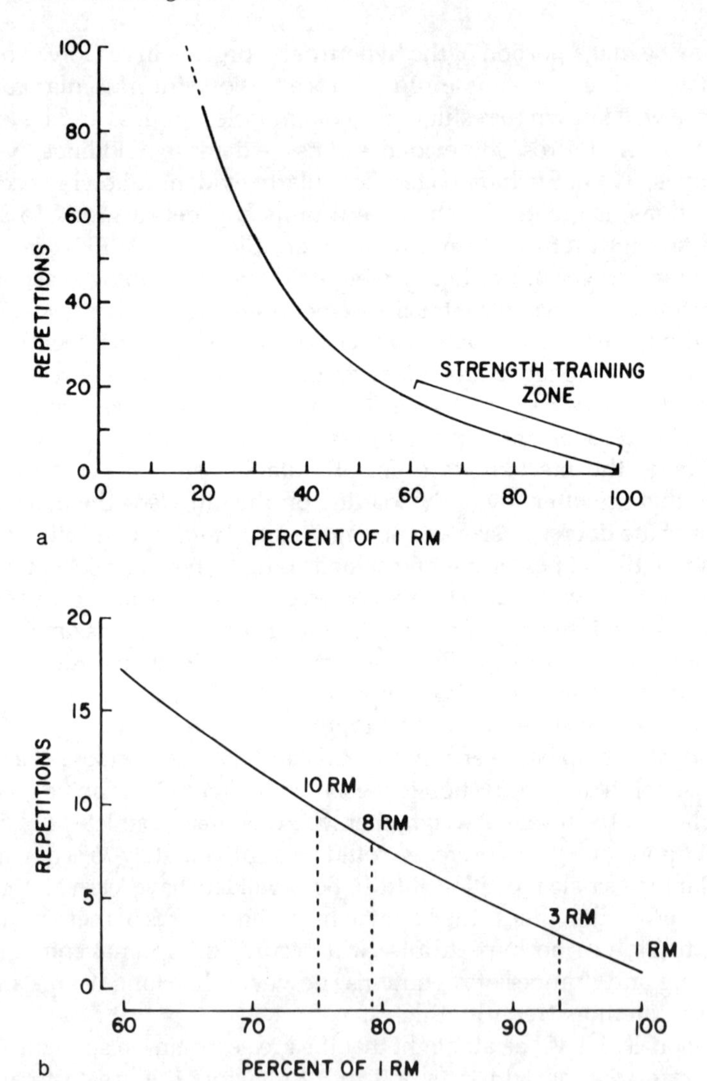

Figure 5 (a) Relationship between percent of 1 RM and the number of repetitions that can be performed. Also indicated is the normal strength training zone between 60 and 100% of 1 RM. (b) Bottom: The training zone has been expanded to illustrate the percentages of 1 RM and the number of maximal repetitions that could be performed. From "Specificity in Strength Training. A Review for the Coach and Athlete" by D.G. Sale and J.D. MacDougall, 1981, *Canadian Journal of Applied Sport Sciences*, **6**, p. 89. Copyright 1981 by Canadian Association of Sport Sciences. Reprinted with permission.

REFERENCES

Anderson, P. (1975). Capillary density in skeletal muscle of man. *Acta Physiologica Scandinavica,* **95**, 203-205.

Fridén, J., Sjöstrom, M., & Ekblom, B. (1983). Myofibrillar damage following intense eccentric exercise in man. *The International Journal of Sports Medicine,* **3**, 170-176.

Giddings, C.J., Neaves, W.B., & Gonyea, W.J. (1985). Muscle fiber necrosis and regeneration induced by prolonged weight-lifting exercise in the cat. *The Anatomical Record,* **211**, 133-141.

Goldspink, G. (1970). The proliferation of myofibrils during muscle fibre growth. *Journal of Cell Science,* **6**, 593-603.

Goldspink, G. (Ed.). (1974). *Differentiation and growth of cells in vertebrate tissue.* London: Chapman and Hall.

Gollnick, P.D., Armstrong, R.B., Saubert, C.W., Piehl, K. & Saltin, B. (1972). Enzyme activity and fiber composition in skeletal muscle of untrained and trained men. *Journal of Applied Physiology,* **33**, 312-319.

Gonyea, W.J. (1980). Role of exercise in inducing increases in skeletal muscle fiber number. *Journal of Applied Physiology: Respiratory, Environmental and Exercise Physiology,* **48**, 421-426.

Gonyea, W.J., Erickson, G.C., & Bonde-Peterson, F. (1977). Skeletal muscle fiber splitting induced by weight-lifting exercise in cats. *Acta Physiologica Scandinavica,* **99**, 105-109.

Green, H.J., Klug, G.A., Reichmann, H., Seedorf, U., Wiehrer, W., & Pette, D. (1984). Exercise-induced fibre transitions with regard to myosin, parvalbimin and sarcoplasmic reticulum in muscles of the rat. *Pflügers Archiv,* **400**, 432-438.

Ikai, M., & Fukunaga, T. (1968). Calculation of muscle strength per unit cross-sectional area of human muscle by means of ultrasonic measurements. *International Zeitschrift für Anglewandte Physiologie,* **26**, 26-32.

Ingjer, F. (1979). Capillary supply and mitochondrial content of different skeletal muscle fiber types in untrained and endurance trained men. A histochemical and ultrastructural study. *European Journal of Applied Physiology and Occupational Physiology,* **40**, 197-209.

MacDougall, J.D. (in press). Morphological changes in human skeletal muscle following strength training and immobilization. In N.L. Jones, N. McCartney, & A.J. McComas (Eds.), *Human Muscle Power.* Champaign, IL: Human Kinetics.

MacDougall, J.D., Elder, G.C.B., Sale, D.G., Moroz, J.R., & Sutton, J.R. (1980). Effects of strength training and immobilization on human muscle fibers. *European Journal of Applied Physiology*, **43**, 25-34.

MacDougall, J.D., Sale, D.G., Alway, S.E., & Sutton, J.R. (1984). Muscle fiber number in biceps brachii in bodybuilders and control subjects. *Journal of Applied Physiology: Respiratory, Environmental and Exercise Physiology*, **57**, 1399-1403.

MacDougall, J.D., Sale, D.G., Elder, G.C.B., & Sutton, J.R. (1982). Muscle ultrastructural characteristics of elite powerlifters and bodybuilders. *European Journal of Applied Physiology*, **48**, 117-126.

MacDougall, J.D., Sale, D.G., Moroz, J.R., Elder, G.C.B, Sutton, J.R., & Howald, H. (1979). Mitochondrial volume density in human skeletal muscle following heavy resistance training. *Medicine and Science in Sports*, **11**, 164-166.

MacDougall, J.D., Ward, G.R., Sale, D.G., & Sutton, J.R. (1977). Biochemical adaptation of human skeletal muscle to heavy resistance training and immobilization. *Journal of Applied Physiology: Respiratory, Environmental and Exercise Physiology*, **43**, 700-703.

Sale, D.G., (in press). Neural adaptation in strength and power training. In N.L. Jones, N. McCartney, & A.J. McComas (Eds.), *Human Muscle Power*. Champaign, IL: Human Kinetics.

Sale, D.G., & MacDougall, J.D. (1981). Specificity in strength training. A review for the coach and athlete. *Canadian Journal of Applied Sport Sciences*, **6**, 87-92.

Sale, D.G., MacDougall, J.D., Alway, S.E., & Sutton, J.R. (1983). Muscle cross-sectional area, fibre type distribution and voluntary strength in humans. *Canadian Journal of Applied Sport Sciences*, **8**, 221.

Sola, O.M., Christensen, D.L., & Martin, A.W. (1973). Hypertrophy and hyperplasia of adult chicken latissimus dorsi muscles following stretch with and without denervation. *Experimental Neurology*, **41**, 76-100.

Tesch, P.A., Häkkinen, K., & Komi, P.V. (1985). The effect of strength training and detraining on various enzyme activities. *Medicine and Science in Sports and Exercise*, **2**, 245.

Tesch, P.A., & Kaiser, P. (1984). Substrate utilization during exhaustive heavy resistance exercise. *Medicine and Science in Sports and Exercise*, **16**, 174.

Tesch, P.A., Thorsson, A., & Kaiser, P. (1984). Muscle capillary supply and fibre type characteristics in weight and power lifters. *Journal of Applied Physiology: Respiratory, Environmental and Exercise Physiology*, **56**, 35-38.

Thorstensson, A. (1976). Muscle strength, fibre types and enzyme activities in man. *Acta Physiologica Scandinavica*, **433**(Suppl.), 1-44.

Thorstensson, A., Hultén, B., Von Döbeln, W., & Karlsson, J. (1976). Effect of strength training on enzyme activities and fibre characteristics in human skeletal muscle. *Acta Physiologica Scandinavica,* **96**, 392-398.

Thorstensson, A., Sjödin, B., & Karlsson, J. (1975). Enzyme activities and muscle strength after "sprint training" in man. *Acta Physiologica Scandinavica,* **94**, 313-318.

Vandenburgh, H.H., & Kaufman, S. (1979). In vitro model for stretch-induced hypertropy of skeletal muscle. *Science,* **203**, 265-268.

How Important Is Neural Drive for Strength and Power Development in Human Skeletal Muscle?

Paavo V. Komi
University of Jyväskylä
Jyväskylä, Finland

Detailed molecular changes or an altered organismic mechanism underlying the improvement of the functional capacity of the skeletal muscle are still more or less unknown. This is despite the fact that it has been known for almost a century that a major stimulus for an increase in the force of the voluntary contraction is the production of tension above the levels used in normal daily activities (Roux, 1895). Human skeletal muscle seems therefore to follow a general rule of adaptation for a living organism so that the muscle enhances its functional capacity by working against a greater functional load. This overload principle would, if followed strictly, imply that the type of contractions that produce the highest tensions could cause the greatest force increase. Some indications to this effect have been observed in training where high tension eccentric contractions have been utilized (Figure 1). However, some caution must be exercised in order to avoid too simple generalizations. Repeated eccentric contractions can cause muscle soreness (Komi & Rusko, 1974; Komi & Viitasalo, 1977), which often leads to subcellular damage (Fridén, Sjöström & Ekblom, 1983), although the muscle can quite quickly regain its adaptation to high intensity eccentric training (Komi & Buskirk, 1972). A common observation is, however, that almost any strength training method results in an increase in muscle strength. This happens naturally only if the frequency of exercises and loading intensities are progressively increased.

However, despite the strong practical experience that training per se may be the primary contributor for the increase in muscle strength or power, some more mechanismic possibilities to explain the increased performance can be suggested: (a) neural activation as an important determinant of the type and growth of myofibrils; (b) chemotrophic effect on muscle fibers, and (c) hormonal influence on the myofibrils. Although all of these factors have been discussed in connection with muscle hypertrophy or atrophy, muscle strength and especially power must not necessarily be synonymous with the growth of individual fibers. In fact, many of the recent studies imply that the degree of hypertrophy is not only dependent

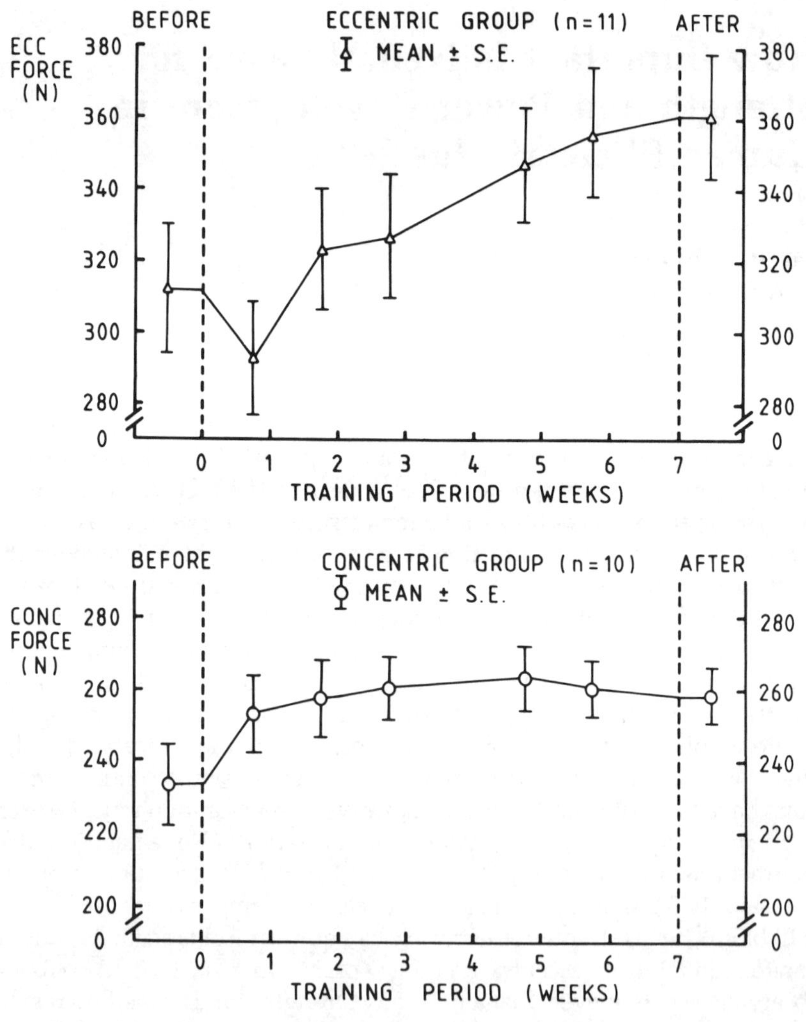

Figure 1 (a) Mean maximal eccentric tension for a group that trained the formearm flexors using maximal eccentric contractions four times a week. (b) Mean maximal concentric tension for a group that trained the forearm flexors using maximal concentric contractions four times a week. From "Effect of Eccentric and Concentric Muscle Conditioning on Tension and Electrical Activity of Human Muscle" by P.V. Komi and E. Buskirk, 1972, *Ergonomics*, **15**, pp. 417-434.

on the type of strength/power training used, but that its occurrence may follow the effects of the motor input, and that the preceding influence of the motor unit activation could be the necessary condition for the hypertrophic myofibrillar changes. The major focus of this paper lies in the examination of the time courses of the neural and hypertrophic factors during strength/power training.

CHANGES IN NEUROMOTORIC ACTIVATION DURING STRENGTH TRAINING

In addition to the improvement in timing and coordination between muscles (Person, 1960), muscular training results in improvement in economy of work production. In strength training this means that a set submaximal force can be produced with less motor unit activation and the regression line representing the relationship between integrated EMG (IEMG) is shifted to the right (Figure 2; Häkkinen & Komi, 1983; Komi & Buskirk, 1972; Komi, Viitasulo, Rauramaa, & Vihko, 1978). This observation seems quite natural, because increase of the force production capacity of individual muscle fibers should mean that for a given unit of tension a smaller number of muscle fibers and consequently motor units need to be activated.

Electromyographic changes measured under submaximal contractions are apparently easy to demonstrate and also to understand. A more difficult task is, however, to observe uniform patterns of changes in maximal EMG activation during the course of strength or power training. The results of the various investigations are also slightly conflicting.

Friedebolt, Nüssgen, and Stoboy (1957) were among the first ones to follow the adaptation of maximum EMG activity during the course of strength training. Their observation was that the early part of strength

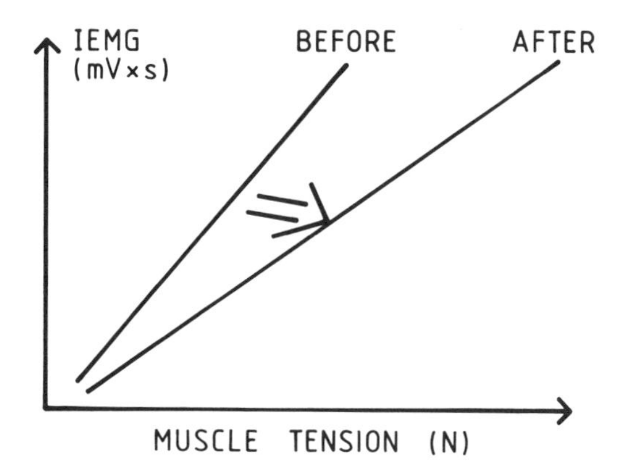

Figure 2 Schematic presentation to demonstrate the influence of strength training on the relationship between integrated electromyographic activity (IEMG) and muscle tension.

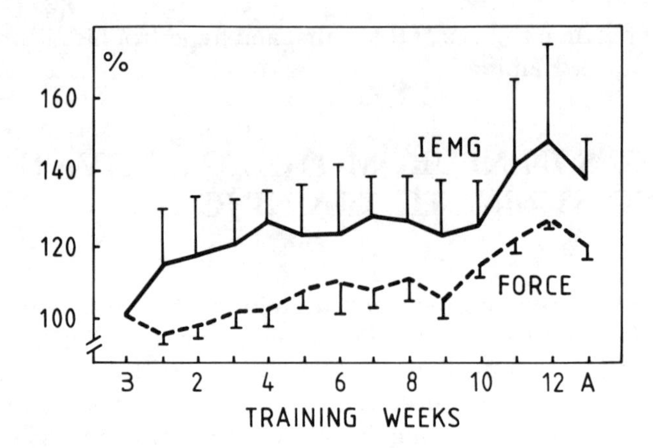

Figure 3 Increase in strength can often take place with parallel increase in neuromotoric activation of the muscle. Young subjects (age range 13 to 15 years) trained four times a week with maximal isometric contractions of the knee extensor muscles. From "Effect of Isometric Strength Training on Mechanical, Electrical and Metabolic Aspects of Muscle Function" by P.V. Komi, J. Viitasalo, r. Rauramaa, and V. Vihko, 1978, *European Journal of Applied Physiology*, **40**, pp. 45-55.

increase was associated with increase in maximum EMG with subsequent lowering of the activation so that the value of the IEMG was slightly lower at the end as compared to the beginning of the strength training period. In the study reported by Komi and Buskirk (1972) the results were slightly different: the training group that trained with maximal eccentric contraction had a larger increase in IEMG as compared to the group that trained with maximal concentric contractions. This report was followed later by a study in which training was performed with maximal isometric contractions (Figure 3; Komi, et al., 1978), and the result was that changes in IEMG and force took place almost in parallel during the course of 12 weeks' training. These findings were later confirmed utilizing a combination of high intensity concentric and eccentric exercises (Häkkinen & Komi, 1983). Figure 4 presents results of this study and suggests that (a) during the plateau phase of the strength development IEMG begins to decrease, and (b) this decrease continues at a very high rate during the first weeks after termination of the training program. When these observations are complemented with those of Düntsch and Stoboy (1966) and Moritani and DeVries (1979), it could be summarized that strong evidence exists to support the concept that in strength training maximum IEMG increases rapidly during early conditioning and then decreases or increases at a diminished rate during later training.

An important question is as follows: What is the cause of the possible increase in neural activation during strength training? Integrated EMG

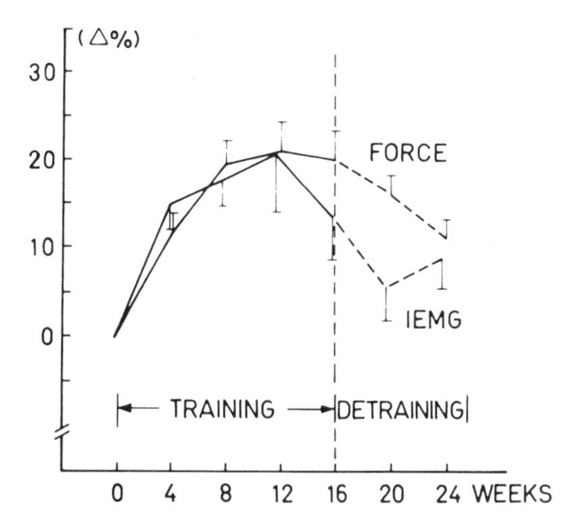

Figure 4 Influence of training and detraining on force and integrated electromyographic (IEMG) activity. The adult male subjects trained with progressive high intensity training of combined concentric and eccentric contractions three times per week. During detraining, strength training was terminated totally, but the subjects maintained their normal daily activities. From "Electromyographic Changes During Strength Training and Detraining" by K. Häkkinen and P.V. Komi, 1983, *Medicine and Science in Sports and Exercise*, **15**, pp. 455-460.

does not reveal anything else except that the magnitude of EMG activity has increased and that this increase may result from the increased number of active motor units and/or increase of their firing frequency. IEMG does not also reveal whether this increased motor unit activity comes from the cortical or reflex (or both) sources. Friedebolt et al., (1957) and Düntsch and Stoboy (1966) were the first ones to suggest that especially the early part of strength training is associated with increased synchronization of motor units. In a healthy muscle, motor unit synchronization can be regarded as a normal phenomenon, but reduction of synchronization as has been reported, for example, in neuropathy (Milner-Brown, Stein, & Lee, 1975), may be a secondary consequence of the disuse of muscle. Milner-Brown, Stein, and Lee (1974) were also able to demonstrate that not only the weight lifters had elevated levels of MU synchronization ratios but that increased synchronization resulted from a specific strength training program. There are at least two possibilities to explain the increased motor unit synchronization: (a) The dendrites of α-motor neurons receive increased inputs from the sensory fibers, and (b) the higher motor centers increase their descending activity. It is probable that both of these mechanisms operate, although the latter one has received more conclusive support (Milner-Brown et al., 1974).

The above discussion suggests that an increase of maximum IEMG during the course of strength training is a desirable phenomenon. It must, however, be wondered why IEMG would increase during training at a diminished rate or even begin to decrease after an initial rapid increase. In order to test the possible influence of the relative training load a study was designed where the weekly load intensities were varied between 70% and 120% (Häkkinen, Komi, & Alén, in press-a). The training exercises were comprised of dynamic squat lifts with barbells on the shoulders. The results indicated that changes in IEMG were related to the load intensity. With training loads of 70% to 80% IEMG decreased but increased when the training loads were 80% to 90% or more. These increases that took place in IEMG during the various training months were usually related significantly to the increases in muscle strength. The subjects in this study were well trained and the results suggest that in order to maintain increases in maximal neural activation the training intensities must be periodically varied and/or kept at progressively increasing levels.

Increased neural input to the muscle is functionally more important in situations where the movement or contraction is performed very rapidly.

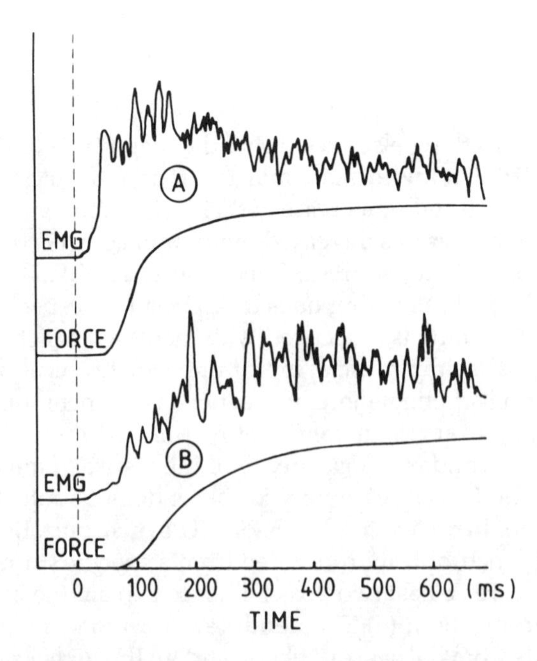

Figure 5 "Parallelism" of rates of EMG and force developments during maximum rapid isometric elbow extensors. The subject in (A) had high rate of EMG increase that was associated with rapid force increase. The subject in (B) had in both curves much slower rates of increase. (Unpublished observation from the Department of Biology of Physical Activity, University of Jyväskylä)

Figure 5 is an example, in which two subjects differed both in the rate of force and EMG development. With regard to training, explosive-type strength exercises should cause the force time curve to be displaced to the left. Similar changes should be expected to take place in the EMG/time curve as well. Figure 6 confirms the close correspondence between the changes in neural activation and force production when the two parameters were analyzed during the early part of the respective curves. Thus the changes in EMG and force at least during early training are expected to take place in parallel when measurements are taken from the short time but maximal contractions.

These findings can be interpreted so that training has resulted in an increase in activation power because during a short period of time the amount of neural input (energy) to the muscle was increased. The type of training can be expected to influence in which specific point in the EMG/time curve the changes take place. With high intensity but low load training the increases in IEMG are expected to take place more in the very early part of the contractions but in training with higher loads the point of increase in IEMG/time curve may be slightly delayed and/or it may persist longer. The early part of the force development must be emphasized for the following reasons: (a) It is advantageous in terms of synchronization; and (b) it is relevant for practical purposes, because the effective time for muscles to conntract in normal movements and in athletic activities is very short.

Additional support for the concept of parallelism comes from a very recent observation of Häkkinen and Komi (1985) on specificity of strength/power training: (a) The high load strength training caused changes primarily in the force-end of the force-velocity curve. The increases in EMG were observed during movements of low velocity and high load; and (b) specif-

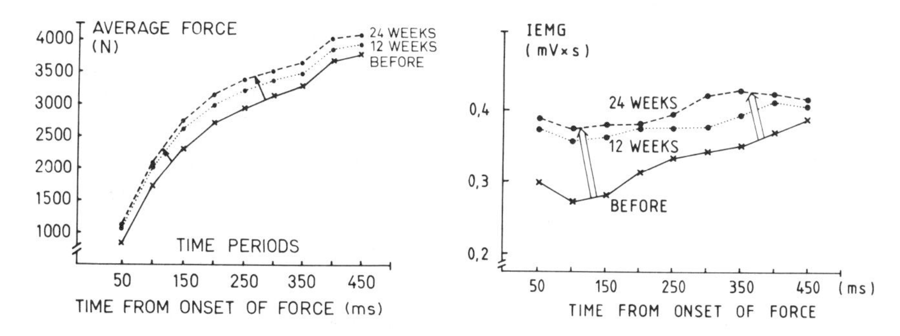

Figure 6 Changes in force-time (left) and IEMG-time (right) curves in the course of 24 weeks explosive type strength and power training. From "Effect of Explosive Type Strength Training on Isometric Force- and Relaxation-Time, Electromyographic and Muscle Fiber Characteristics of Leg Extensor Muscles" by K. Häkkinen, P.V. Komi, and M. Allén, in press, *Acta Physiologica Scandinavica*.

ic jumping exercises resulted in changes in the velocity end of the force-velocity curve and the EMG changes also took place in movements of low load but high velocity.

The influences of strength training on motor unit activation are very much opposite to those observed in limb immobilization. Sale, McComas, MacDougall, and Upton (1982) found that while strength training resulted in an increase in voluntary strength and in reflex potentiation, the limb immobilization caused decreases in both muscle strength and reflex potentiation. Increased reflex potentiation as measured with electrical stimulation during maximal isometric contraction (Sale, MacDougall, Upton, & McComas, 1983) may imply that the trained subjects can recruit more readily additional motor units and/or discharge the active ones with higher frequency. It can therefore be suggested that the increased α-motoneuron activation with concomitant motor unit synchronization does not only cause muscle force to increase, but may serve as an important stimulus for the hypertrophic factors that are expected to result after a period of progressively increasing strength/power training.

INTERACTION BETWEEN NEURAL ACTIVATION AND MUSCLE HYPERTROPHY

The training-induced hypertrophy in skeletal muscle is usually associated with an increase in myofibrillar material of the individual fibers (Goldspink, 1964; Helander, 1961). This is characterized by an increase in the number of myofibrils (Goldspink & Howells, 1974), which has physiological implications by making the contractile force of the fibers (and the muscle) greater. Recent studies (Gonyea, 1980; Gonyea, Erickson, & Bonde-Petersen, 1977; Hall-Craggs, 1972) have suggested that the training-induced hypertrophy can also be characterized by an increase in the number of muscle fibers. These conclusions have, however, been criticized by some authors (e.g., Gollnick, Timson, Moore, & Riedy, 1981) and the suggestion has been made that methodological errors may have been involved in estimating the fiber number. The recent study of MacDougall, Sale, Alway, Sutton (1984) on bodybuilders gives good evidence that even in bodybuilders who possess large muscles the fiber number per muscle (m. biceps brachii) is not different from normal control persons. The same study also suggested that the increase in size of the individual fiber is associated with parallel increases in connective tissue between the fibers. Thus, evidence seems to be present to contradict the fiber splitting and associated hyperplasia as a result of strength training.

The following important question is relevant for the discussion of strength training: What is the necessary duration of strength/power training or

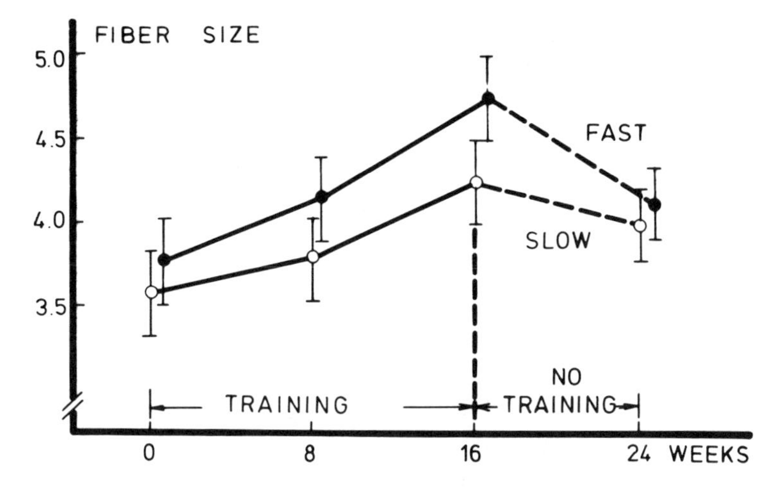

Figure 7 Influence of 16-week strength training (the same as in Figure 2) and 8-week detraining on the mean (± S.D.) size of fast-twitch and slow-twitch fibers of m. vastus lateralis. Note the greater rate of hypertrophy during the latter half of training and fast atrophy during detraining. From "Effect of Combined Concentric and Eccentric Strength Training and Detraining on Force-time, Muscle Fibre and Metabolic Characteristics of Leg Extensor Muscles" by K. Häkkinen, P.V. Komi, & P. Tesch, 1981, *Scandinavian Journal of Sports Sciences*, **3**, pp. 50-58.

the nervous stimulus before any hypertrophic measures can be observed in the muscle? Figure 7 is from a recent study (Häkkinen, Komi, & Tesch, 1981) where fourteen subjects trained with high intensity loads of combined concentric and eccentric contractions. During detraining the subjects maintained normal daily activities, excluding strength training. Despite an accelerated increase in force during the first 8 weeks of training (see Figure 4, which is from the same study), the fiber hypertrophy was only minor during the corresponding period. Greater muscle hypertrophy of both fiber types could be observed during the last 8-week strength training. This may also explain the increased strength because no increases or some decreases in maximum IEMG (Figure 4) were noted during that period. These results are therefore in line with the finding of Moritani and DeVries (1979) and specify also that hypertrophic changes may take place in both fiber types, although it may be greater in FT muscle fibers. Thus early changes in strength training may be accounted for largely by the neural factors with a gradually increasing contribution of the hypertrophic factors. The right side of Figures 4 and 7 represent the detraining period, during which the subjects maintained their normal daily activities, but were not engaged in strength training. The curves suggest that the similar mechanisms occur also during detraining: The initial decrease in strength

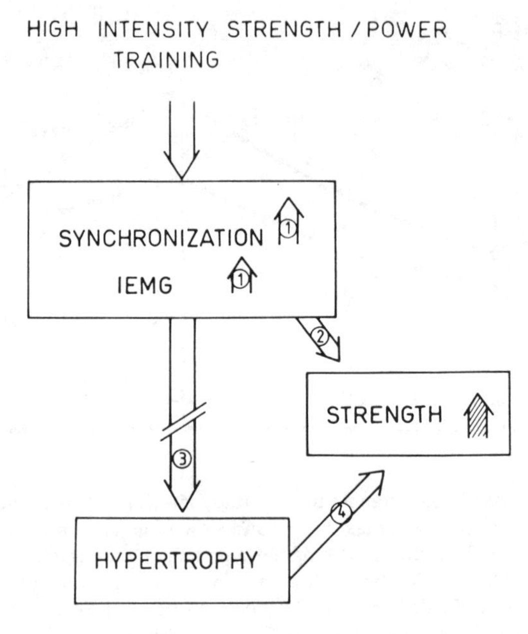

Figure 8 Schematic presentation of the sequence of events leading to increase in muscle strength (or power) during the course of high intensity training. Increases in synchornized firing of active motor units and increase in overall motor unit activity are assumed to take place simultaneously. Hypertrophy is a delayed process, but brings its important contribution to the strength development.

may be due to a reduction in the maximal neural activity with a gradually increasing contribution of muscle atrophy.

Figure 8 is an attempt to describe schematically the interaction between neural activation and hypertrophic factors for causing the muscle to increase its strength. In immobilization and detraining neural input decreases, and consequently the force declines and the muscle atrophies.

NEURAL ACTIVATION AND MUSCLE STIFFNESS IN STRENGTH AND POWER TRAINING

In many practical sport activities the fast rate of force development usually implies that the muscle must have the ability to become stiff in a short period of time. Data are available to demonstrate in human subjects that, for example in running at moderate speeds, the directly measured Achilles tendon forces exceed by four to five times the maximum vertical ground reaction forces measured during the contact phase (Komi, Salo-

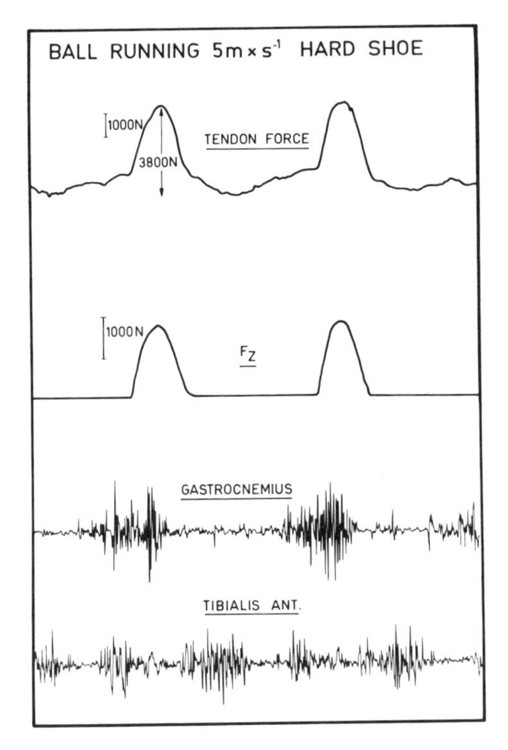

Figure 9 Direct in vivo measurements of tendon forces demonstrate that under normal movement conditions the muscle develops force very rapidly over a short change in muscle length. In the example the Achilles tendon force was recorded while the subject was running at a speed of 5 m x s^{-1} over the long force-plate floor. EMG activity of the recorded muscles takes place primarily during the impact phase, which corresponds to the rising phase of the Achilles tendon force. From "Measurement of In-Vivo Achilles Tendon Forces in Man and Their Calibration" by P.V. Komi, M. Salonen, and M. Järvinen, in press, *Medicine and Science in Sports and Exercise.*

nen, & Järvinen, 1984; Komi, Salonen & Järvinen, in press). And more importantly the rate of force development is very fast with concomitant high stiffness values (Figure 9).

Hypotheses have been given to illustrate how strength and power training can be used to improve muscular stiffness (Komi, 1985). The whole concept of stiffness regulation of muscle is, however, very complex (Houk & Rymer, 1983), and it is difficult to separate the chemomechanical components from those of nervous control. As has been presented earlier in this paper, the nervous input to the muscle is under considerable influence of training and detraining and subsequently can impose corresponding adaptations in the overall stiffness as well. Explosive jumping exercises can be effectively used for improvement of muscle stiffness (Häkkinen &

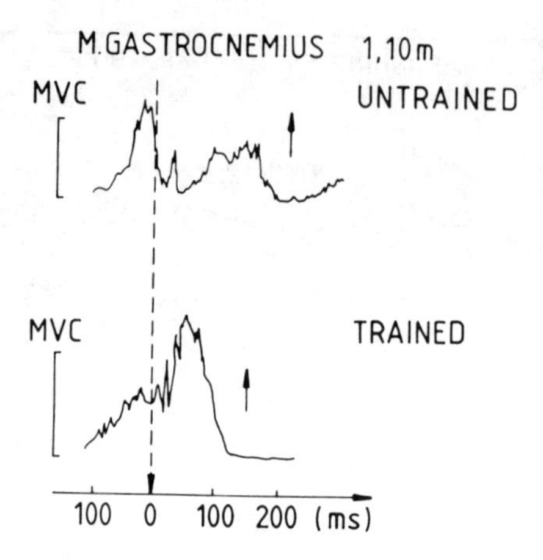

Figure 10 Training has considerable influence on the activation pattern of the gastrocnemius muscle measured during the drop jumps from the height of 1.10 m. The trained subject (high jumper) demonstrates facilitated reflex potentiation during early impact, whereas in the untrained subject EMG activity is inhibited during the same instant. MVC denotes the values of the maximum isometric leg extension strength of the subjects. From "Neuromuskuläre Untersuchungen zur Bestimmung individueller Belastungsgrössen für ein Tiefsprungtraining" by D. Schmidtbleicher and A. Gollhofer, 1982, *Leistungssport*, **12**, pp. 298-307.

Komi, 1985). And, as Schmidtbleicher and Gollhofer (1982) have demonstrated, the high muscle activation immediately before and during early impact phase (Figure 10) are necessary preconditions for the muscle to sustain high impact loads and subsequently maintain good recoil characteristics in the stretch-shortening cycle exercises.

CONCLUSIONS

Enough evidence seems to be available to emphasize the importance of the nervous system to activate the human skeletal muscle for improved performance. In this regard the voluntarily controlled human neuromuscular system responds to enhanced functional loads in many ways similarly to those used in animal exercise models. In training of muscular strength and power the maximum nervous input to the muscle can be increased, especially during the first weeks of intensive training. This causes concomitant increase in muscle strength or power. The form of performance increase (strength, power, or velocity) depends also on the load the strongly activated muscle must move or resist under concentric or eccentric contractions. In addition to the increased performance per se the high nervous activation to the muscle may be the necessary condition for the hypertrophic changes to take place in the myofibrils and connective tissue. Hypertrophy is therefore a delayed process and duration and intensity of neuronal activation to the muscle determines the time course and magnitude of the hypertrophy. The role of the nervous system is especially important in stretch-shortening cycle exercises in which the purpose of training is to improve muscular stiffness so that the muscle can tolerate higher stretch loads and utilize the elastic recoil characteristics optimally.

REFERENCES

Düntsch, G., & Stoboy, H. (1966). Das Verhalten von Kraft und Ausdauer während eines isometrischen Trainings in Abhängigkeit von der Muskelmasse. *Sportarzt und Sportmedizin,* **17**, 499-541.

Fridén, J., Sjöström, M., & Ekblom, B. (1983). Myofibrillar damage following intense eccentric exercise in man. *International Journal of Sports Medicine,* **4**, 170-176.

Friedebolt, G., Nüssgen, W., & Stoboy, H. (1957). Die Veränderung der elektrischen Aktivität der Skeletmuskulatur unter den Bedingungen eines isometrischen Trainings. *Zeirtschrift ges. exp. Med.,* **129**, 401-411.

Goldspink, G. (1964). The combined effects of exercise and reduced food intake of skeletal muscle fibers. *Journal of Cell Comp. Physiol.,* **63**, 209-261.

Goldspink, G., & Howells, K. (1974). Work-induced hypertrophy in exercised normal muscles of different ages and the reversibility of hypertrophy after cessation of exercise. *Journal of Physiology* (London), **239**, 179-193.

Gollnick, P.D., Timson, B.F., Moore, R.L., & Riedy, M. (1981). Muscular enlargement and number of fibers in skeletal muscles of rats. *Journal of Applied Physiology: Respiratory, Environmental and Exercise Physiology,* **50**, 936-943.

Gonyea, W.J. (1980). Role of exercise in inducing increases in skeletal muscle fiber number. *Journal of Applied Physiology: Respiratory, Environmental and Exercise Physiology,* **48**, 421-426.

Gonyea, W., Erickson, G.C., & Bonde-Petersen, F. (1977). Skeletal muscle fiber splitting induced by weight-lifting exercise in cats. *Acta Physiologica Scandinavica,* **99**, 105-109.

Häkkinen, K., & Komi, P.V. (1983). Electromyographic changes during strength training and detraining. *Medicine and Science in Sports and Exercise,* **15**(6), 455-460.

Häkkinen, K., & Komi, P.V. (1985). *Effect of explosive type strength training on electromyographic and force production characteristics of leg extensor muscles during concentric and various stretch-shortening cycle exercises.* Manuscript submitted for publication.

Häkkinen, K., Komi, P.V., & Alén, M. (in press-a). Changes in isometric force- and relaxation-time, electromyographic and muscle fibre characteristics of human skeletal muscle during strength training and detraining. *Acta Physiologica Scandinavica.*

Häkkinen, K., Komi, P.V., & Alén, M. (in press-b). Effect of explosive type strength training on isometric force- and relaxation-time, electromyographic and muscle fiber characteristics of leg extensor muscles. *Acta Physiologica Scandinavica.*

Häkkinen, K., Komi, P.V., & Tesch, P. (1981). Effect of combined concentric and eccentric strength training and detraining on force-time, muscle fibre and metabolic characteristics of leg extensor muscles. *Scandinavian Journal of Sports Science,* **3**, 50-58.

Hall-Craggs, E.C.B. (1972). The significance of longitudinal fibre division in skeletal muscle. *Journal of Neurological Sciences,* **15**, 27-33.

Helander, E.A.S. (1961). Influence of exercise and restricted activity on the protein composition of skeletal muscle. *Biochemical Journal,* **78**, 478-482.

Houk, J.C., & Rymer, W.Z. (1983). Neural control of muscle length and tension. *Journal of Physiology,* **314**, 118-127.

Komi, P.V. (1985). *Training of muscle strength and power: Interaction of neuromotoric, hypertrophic and mechanical factors.* Manuscript submitted for publication.

Komi, P.V., & Buskirk, E. (1972). Effect of eccentric and concentric muscle conditioning on tension and electrical activity of human muscle. *Ergonomics,* **15**, 417-434.

Komi, P.V., & Rusko, H. (1974). Quantitative evaluation of mechanical and electrical changes during fatigue loading of eccentric and concentric work. *Scandinavian Journal of Rehabilitation Medicine,* **3**(Suppl. 3), 121-126.

Komi, P.V., Salonen, M., & Järvinen, M. (1984). In vivo-measurements of Achilles tendon forces in man. *Medicine and Science in Sports and Exercise,* **16**, **2**, 165.

Komi, P.V. Salonen, M., & Järvinen, M. (in press). Measurement of in-vivo Achilles tendon forces in man and their calibration. *Medicine and Science in Sports and Exercise.*

Komi, P.V., & Viitasalo, J.T. (1977). Changes in motor unit activity and metabolism in human skeletal muscle during and after repeated eccentric and concentric contractions. *Acta Physiologica Scandinavica,* **100**, 246-254.

Komi, P.V., Viitasalo, J., Rauramaa, R., & Vihko, V. (1978). Effect of isometric strength training on mechanical, electrical and metabolic aspects of muscle function. *European Journal of Applied Physiology,* **40**, 45-55.

MacDougall, J.D., Sale, D.G., Alway, S.E., & Sutton, J.R. (1984). Muscle fiber number in biceps brachii in body builders and control subjects. *Journal of Applied Physiology: Respiratory, Environmental and Exercise Physiology,* **57**(5), 1399-1403.

Milner-Brown, H.S., Stein, R.B., & Lee, R.G. (1974). The contractile and electrical properties of human motor units in neuropathies and motor neurone disease. *Journal of Neurology, Neurosurgery and Psychiatry,* **37**, 670-676.

Milner-Brown, H.S., Stein, R.B., & Lee, R.G. (1975). Synchronization of human motor units: Possible roles of exercise and supraspinal reflexes. *Electroencephalography and Clinical Neurophysiology,* **38**, 245-254.

Moritani, T., & DeVries, H. (1979). Neural factors versus hypertrophy in the course of muscle strength gain. *American Journal of Physical Medicine,* **58**(3), 115-130.

Person, R.S. (1960). *Studies of human movements when elaborating motor habits.* 3rd International Conference on Medical Electronics, London.

Roux, W. (1895). *Gesammelte Abhandlungen über Entwicklungsmechanik der Organismen.* Band I: Funktionelle Anpassung. Leipzig.

Sale, D.G., McComas, A.J., MacDougall, J.D., & Upton, A.R.M. (1982). Neuromuscular adaptation in human thenar muscles following strength training and immobilization. *Journal of Applied Physiology: Respiratory, Environmental and Exercise Physiology,* **53**(2), 419-424.

Sale, D.G., MacDougall, J.D., Upton, A.R.M., & McComas, A.J. (1983). Effect of strength training upon motor neuron excitability in man. *Medicine and Science in Sports and Exercise,* **15**(1), 57-62.

Schmidtbleicher, D., & Gollhofer, A. (1982). Neuromuskuläre Untersuchungen zur Bestimmung individueller Belastungsgrössen für ein Tiefsprungtraining. *Leistungssport,* **12**, 298-307.

Reflex Inhibition of Muscle Activity and the Morphological Consequences of Inactivity

Archie Young
Maria Stokes
Royal Free Hospital School of Medicine
London, England

This paper will examine the macroscopic and microscopic changes induced in human skeletal muscle by the inactivity that results from joint injury and/or immobilization. In particular, it will discuss the wasting of the quadriceps muscle group that follows knee injury and/or immobilization. The paper will deal with the overall severity of atrophy, will go on to examine the histochemical characteristics of the wasted muscle, and will finish by offering reflexly mediated inhibition of muscle activity as an explanation for the severity of wasting that occurs and for the selective atrophy of different muscle fiber types (see Figure 1).

SEVERITY OF ATROPHY

It is common experience that there may be considerable wasting of the thigh musculature following knee injury and/or immobilization. This occurrence can be examined in more detail by techniques that provide an image of a transverse section through the thigh; this makes it possible to measure

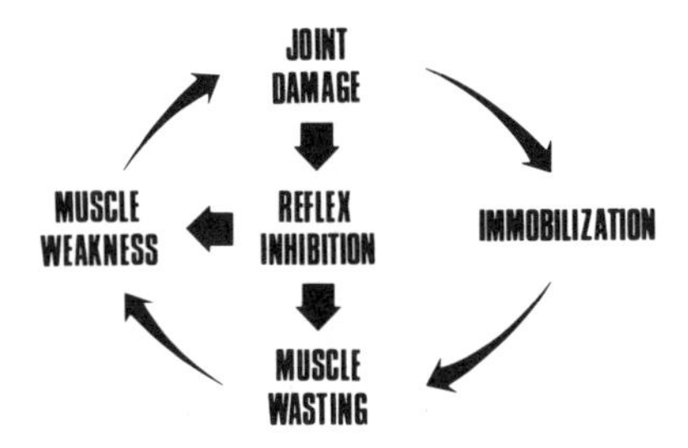

Figure 1 "Vicious circles" of arthrogenous muscle weakness. From "The Contribution of Reflex Inhibition to Arthrogenous Muscle Weakness" by M. Stokes and A. Young, 1984, *Clinical Science*, **67**, p. 7. Copyright 1984 by The Biochemical Society, London. Reprinted by permission.

changes in the size of the quadriceps muscle group itself, irrespective of whatever changes may be occurring in the other muscles of the thigh and in the thickness of the subcutaneous fat. We have used the technique of compound ultrasound B-scanning (Young, Hughes, Russell, Parker, & Nichols, 1980). Others have used computerized axial tomography (CAT) (Häggmark, Jansson, & Svane, 1978; Ingemann-Hansen & Halkjaer-Kristensen, 1980; Lo Presti et al., 1984). Although CAT is faster, ultrasonography has the advantages that it uses much cheaper equipment and does not involve exposure to ionizing radiation.

It is apparent from such measurements that it is not unusual for the quadriceps to atrophy by 30% to 50% (Young et al., 1980). The severity of the atrophy is not accurately reflected by the reduction in thigh circumference, as measured with a tape measure, and is much more severe than might be suspected from circumference measurements (Ingemann-Hansen & Halkjaer-Kristensen, 1980; Lo Presti et al., 1984; Young et al., 1980). The tape measure is also inadequate for following quadriceps growth in response to strength-training (Young, Stokes, Round, & Edwards, 1983).

Can this severity of muscle wasting be explained solely on the basis of muscle fiber shrinkage, or is there also a loss of fibers? Microscopic examination of bilateral needle biopsy specimens taken from the quadriceps muscles of otherwise healthy patients with unilateral thigh muscle wasting secondary to knee injury shows no evidence of macrophage infiltration (Young, Hughes, Round, & Edwards, 1982). Nor is there any histochemically demonstrable increase in acid phosphatase activity. The biopsy from the wasted muscle shows a considerable reduction in the size in the muscle fibers but no morphological evidence of fiber destruction.

Within an individual patient, the ratio of the quadriceps' cross-sectional area (CSA) to the mean cross-sectional area of the muscle fibers in its biopsy (MFA) is a constant function of the number of fibers in the muscle. In a series of 14 young adults with unilateral thigh muscle wasting following knee injury, there was some variation from person to person in the value for the ratio CSA/MFA but there was close similarity between the two limbs of each individual. There is therefore no need to invoke destruction of muscle fibers to explain the muscle wasting, severe though it may be (Young et al., 1982).

FIBER TYPES

Our first study in this area concerned seven young servicemen undergoing rehabilitation following plaster-cast immobilization of one knee as treatment of tibial fracture (Sargeant, Davies, Edwards, Maunder, & Young, 1977). One or two biopsies were taken from the lateral mass of each quadriceps of each subject, at about midthigh. The mean fiber area of type I fibers (MFA I) and the mean fiber area of type II fibers (MFA II) were calculated for each biopsy, from measurments of 100 fibers of each type (distinguished by their histochemical reaction for alkali-stable myosin adenosine triphosphatase). All seven patients showed atrophy of both fiber types, but in six of them the injured/uninjured limb ratio was nearer to 100% for the type II fibers than for the type I fibers (Figure 2a). In other words, type I atrophy was more marked than type II atrophy. In the seventh patient, type II atrophy was more severe than type I atrophy. At the time, we thought this might reflect the fact that, unlike the other six, he was still nonweight-bearing.

Unfortunately, this explanation did not hold up when a similar analysis was applied to the next 21 patients on whom we had bilateral data (Figure 2b). In some, type I atrophy was more pronounced, in others type II atrophy, and in others the two fiber types were equally affected. It is not at all clear what clinical features determine whether an individual patient's muscle shows type I atrophy, type II atrophy or equal atrophy of both fiber types. All three patterns of atrophy have been observed (Table 1). Irrespective of which fiber type is more atrophic, it seems that a type I to type II conversion may occur (Eriksson, 1982; Ingemann-Hansen & Halkjaer-Kristensen, 1983; Young et al., 1982), the predictable result of a sufficiently continuous inactivity stimulus (Salmons & Henriksson, 1981).

Selective type II fiber atrophy is not unusual in muscle histopathology, occurring in muscle wasting due to corticosteroid excess, osteomalacia and other nonmuscular conditions. Since the type II fibers are those in the high-threshold motor units, it is no surprise to find them selectively atrophied in someone who has suffered joint injury. One would not expect such a patient to make many contractions strong enough to recruit the high-threshold motor units. It is harder to explain the fact that type I atrophy is at least as common as type II atrophy in such patients. It may be that the explanation lies in the duration of immobilization, the completeness of immobilization, joint position during immobilization, the duration of postimmobilization rehabilitation, the nature of the rehabilitation activity, or clinical characteristics such as the presence or absence of pain or effusion. We suspect that the explanation for some of the fiber type selective changes may be related to the central connections of afferents from in and around the knee joint. For example, the selective inhibition of motor units may hold the key to understanding selective fiber-type atrophy.

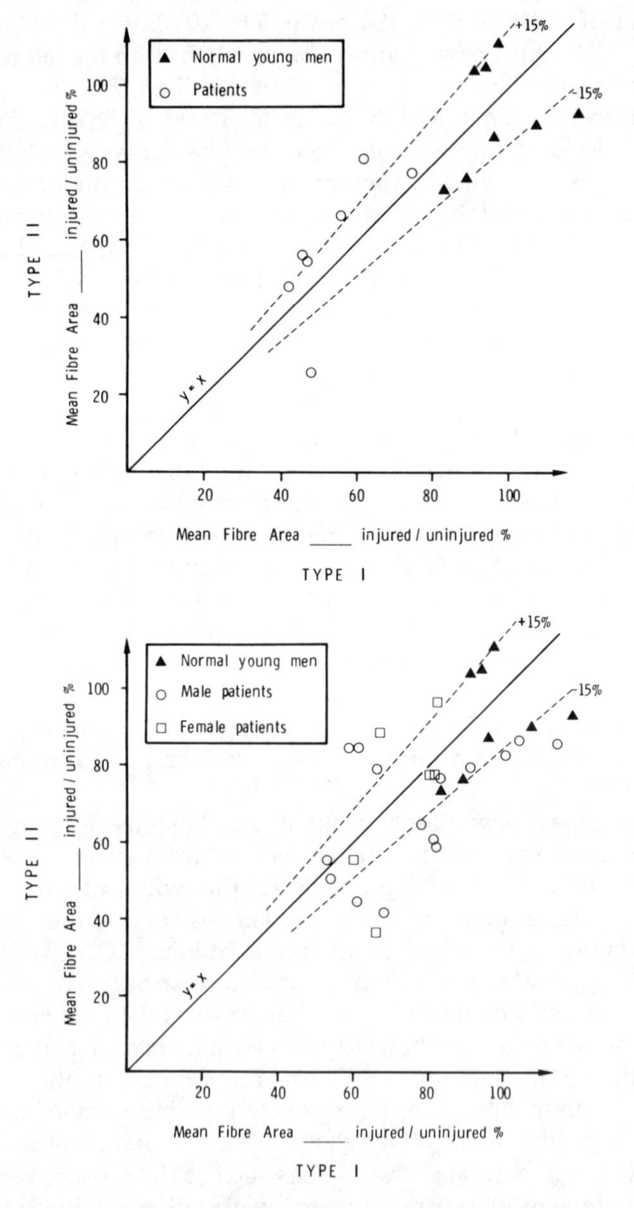

Figure 2. Comparison of the between-limb differences in the size of type I and type II fibers from the quadriceps of patients and normal young men. (Weaker quadriceps/stronger quadriceps ratios have been plotted for normal young men.) (a) The 7 tibial fracture patients described by Sargeant et al. (1977). (b) Another 15 men and 6 women, who had suffered unilateral knee injury, including those described by Young et al. (1982).

Table 1 Patterns of Fiber-Type Atrophy Associated With Joint Damage and/or Immobilization in Patients. (Present Authors' Interpretation of Data Presented in Various Published Papers)

Patients	Biopsy	Muscle	n	Predominant atrophy I	II	I≒II	Reference
TA repair, 6 week postoperation	O + N	S	7	✓			Häggmark & Eriksson, 1979b
tibial fracture, postimmobilization	N	LQ					Sargeant et al., 1977
nonweight-bearing			1		1		
weight-bearing			6	4		2	
tibial fracture	N	LQ	3		✓		
knee injury/surgery			17		✓		
knee injury/surgery	N	LQ	14	3	8	3	Young et al., 1982
meniscectomy, 4 week postoperation	N	VM	16			✓	Karumo et al., 1977
old ACL injury repair, 5 week postoperation	N	LQ					Häggmark & Eriksson, 1979a
cylinder cast			8	7		1	
hinged cast			8	2	3		
chronic ACL dysfunction	O	VM	10	8			Edström, 1970
chronic ACL dysfunction	O	VM	8			✓	Baugher et al., 1984
acute ACL injury, 4 to 11 days postoperation			8	✓			

(Cont.)

N needle biopsy
O open biopsy
OA osteoarthritis
RA rheumatoid arthritis
ACL anterior cruciate ligament
TA tendo achilles
LQ lateral quadriceps (i.e., vastus lateralis and/or intermedius
VL vastus lateralis
VM vastus medialis
GMX gluteus maximus
GMD gluteus medialis
TFL tensor fascia lata
S soleus
BB biceps brachialis

Table 1 (Cont.)

Patients	Biopsy	Muscle	n	Predominant atrophy I	Predominant atrophy II	Predominant atrophy I≒II	Reference
acute knee-joint lesions 3 days immobilization	O	VM	10	1	4	2	Lindboe & Platou, 1984
chronic hip arthritis, moderate	O	GMX	10	2	3	1	Suchenwirth et al., 1972
chronic hip arthritis, severe			10	2	5	2	
OA hip, aged >65	O	GMX	8	✓			Širca & Sušec-Michieli, 1980
		GMD	17			✓	
		TFL	10		✓		
Frequent, sudden knee pain	O	VM or VL	3	✓			Staudte & Brussatis, 1977
chronic, serious disability (most OA)			9		✓		
very serious disability (most RA)			6			✓	
RA, active inflammation	O	BB	9		7		Brooke & Kaplan, 1972
RA, joint damage/-deformity			7	4	1	2	
RA, very severe disability			2			2	
RA	N	LQ	13	1	9		Edström & Nordemar, 1974

N needle biopsy
O open biopsy
OA osteoarthritis
RA rheumatoid arthritis
ACL anterior cruciate ligament
TA tendo achilles
LQ lateral quadriceps (i.e., vastus lateralis and/or intermedius
VL vastus lateralis
VM vastus medialis
GMX gluteus maximus
GMD gluteus medialis
TFL tensor fascia lata
S soleus
BB biceps brachialis

REFLEX INHIBITION OF MUSCLE ACTIVITY

Pain in a joint results in voluntary inhibition of activity in muscles acting across that joint (Basmajian, 1970) (''immobilization,'' Figure 1). Pain is not necessary, however, for inhibition of activity in muscles acting across a damaged joint. Activity in other afferents from the joint may reflexly inhibit anterior horn cells innervating the muscle. This ''reflex inhibition'' (Figure 1) was the subject of a number of investigative efforts in French neurology schools in the latter half of the last century. Early this century, Beryl Harding (1929) demonstrated, in animals, that dorsal root section prevented the muscle wasting due to experimental arthritis but had no effect on that produced by plaster cast immobilization. She also observed that muscle wasting across control arthritic joints did not appear to be due to pain.

Further animal evidence for this phenomenon came from the demonstration, in the decerebrate cat, that filling the knee with fluid reduced the reflex response of the quadriceps' anterior horn cells to stimulation of the proximal end of the cut quadriceps nerve (Ekholm, Eklund, & Skoglund, 1960). Similarly, again in the decerebrate cat, squeezing the anterior part of the knee capsule inhibited the quadriceps' reflex response to pinching the contralateral heel (Ekholm et al., 1960). In man, experimental infusion into the knee impairs the ability to make a voluntary quadriceps contraction before the volume of the infused fluid is sufficient to cause pain (de Andrade, Grant, & Dixon, 1965; Jayson & Dixon, 1970).

For most of our studies of quadriceps inhibition in man, we used young men undergoing arthrotomy and meniscectomy as our experimental model. Advantages of this model were that our subjects were basically healthy, the knee injury (i.e., the surgery) was relatively standardized, the injury was unilateral, and preoperative measurements were possible.

Measurement of Voluntary Activation

Surface electrodes were placed at a reproducible site over rectus femoris at midthigh. The precise position of the electrodes was marked on the skin and, as an additional precaution, was recorded on a sheet of transparent plastic along with a ''map'' of any small scars, nevi or other skin blemishes (Dons, Bollerup, Bonde-Petersen, & Hancke, 1979). The electromyographic (EMG) signal was recorded during a maximal, voluntary, isometric contraction of the quadriceps with the knee in extension. The

EMG signal was rectified and integrated, and the greatest 0.9 s integral (maximal voluntary activation, MVA) was noted from at least two contractions each lasting approximately 4 or 5 s. The process was then repeated for the opposite quadriceps. In 14 patients studied on five occasions over a 3-week period, the day-to-day variability of repeated measurements of MVA in the absence of inhibition (i.e., in the unoperated limb) gave a coefficient of variation of 6% (Stokes, 1984).

Results

In the early postoperative period, there is a drastic reduction in the extent to which the quadriceps can be activated by a maximal, voluntary effort (Figure 3). This is not simply a result of general anesthesia, since there is no reduction in the maximal voluntary activation that can be achieved with the quadriceps of the unoperated limb. In the operated limb, a 70% to 90% inhibition of MVA persists for at least the first 3 days postoperatively and substantial inhibition is still commonplace 10 to 15 days postoperatively (Shakespeare, Stokes, Sherman, & Young, 1985; Stokes & Young, 1984).

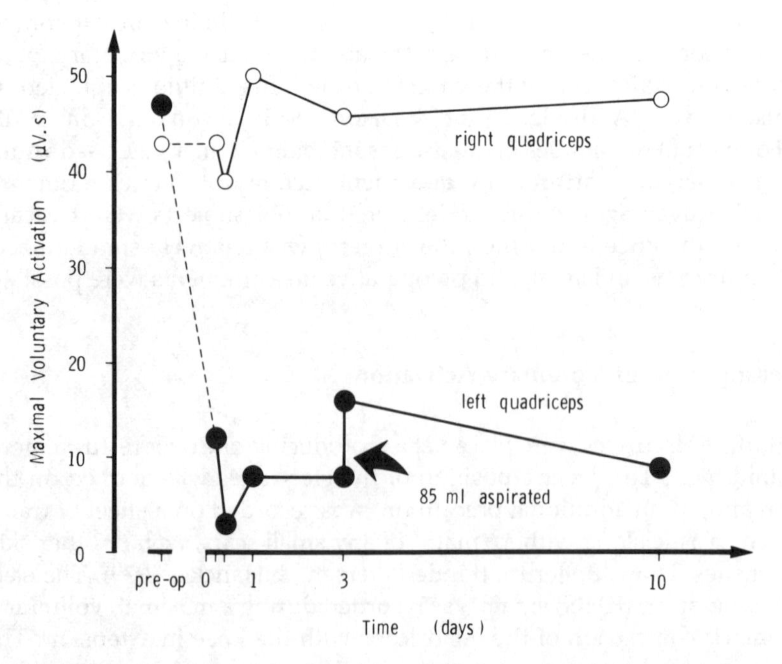

Figure 3. Bilateral measurements of quadriceps MVA before and after left arthrotomy and medial meniscectomy in a 33-year-old man. On the third postoperative day, MVA was recorded before and after aspiration of 85 ml of effusion fluid from the left knee. None of the other measurements was associated with a clinically apparent effusion.

Maximal contractions of the quadriceps of the operated limb during the first 24 hours postoperatively were often painful. Peroperative infiltration of bupivacaine into the capsular incision and into the meniscal bed prevented much of the pain during contraction and allowed a much greater degree of quadriceps activation (Shakespeare et al., 1985). A smaller does of bupivacaine, however, produced equivalent pain-relief during contractions without influencing the profound inhibition observed in the absence of local anesthesia. This demonstrates that the inhibition of voluntary quadriceps activation is not due to perceived pain; it seems likely that the inhibitory afferent stimuli are carried by sensory fibers that are more resistant to bupivacaine than are nociceptive fibers (implying that they are of larger diameter than the nociceptive fibers).

Further evidence of the dissociation between inhibition and perceived pain is observed at 3 days postoperatively, when inhibition remains just as severe as at 24 hours but contractions are virtually (and in many cases completely) pain-free (Shakespeare et al., 1985). This is true irrespective of whether patients have had their initial levels of inhibition and/or pain modified by the infiltration of local anaesthetic. Contractions at 10 to 15 days postoperatively are almost always pain-free.

The origin of the inhibitory afferent stimuli is not clear. Inhibition after arthroscopy, with or without meniscectomy, is approximately half that seen after arthrotomy, with or without meniscectomy (Sherman, Young, Stokes, & Shakespeare, 1984). This suggests that tension in the capsular suture line may be relevant. It seems clear, moreover, that inhibitory stimuli need not arise from within a joint but may have a periarticular source (Raymond, 1890; Stokes & Young, 1984).

We have already referred to the inhibition of anterior horn cells by the presence of an intra-articular infusion (de Andrade et al., 1965; Ekholm et al., 1960; Jayson & Dixon, 1970). None of the postmeniscectomy data in our studies, however, was recorded in the presence of a clinically apparent effusion. Nevertheless, some patients did develop a clinically apparent effusion. When this happened, MVA was measured before and after aspiration of the effusion (e.g., Figure 3). This always resulted in an increase in the level of activation that could be attained, although it was unusual for it to be possible for patients to achieve the preoperative level of activation merely as a result of aspiration of the effusion (Stokes & Young, 1984).

Inhibition of Quadriceps H-Reflex

Having confirmed that excess intra-articular fluid reduces voluntary activation, we next examined whether an intra-articular infusion (Jayson & Dixon, 1970) would reduce the reflex excitability of anterior horn cells, as distinct from their excitability in response to voluntary effort. A similar study was conducted elsewhere (Spencer, Hayes, & Alexander, 1984). The results of the two studies confirm that the infusion of sterile saline into the normal knee substantially reduces the quadriceps H-reflex both under resting conditions (Iles, Stokes, & Young, 1985; Spencer, Hayes, & Alexander, 1984; Stokes, Iles, & Young, in press) and during submaximal (15% to 20%) voluntary effort (Iles et al., 1985; Stokes, Iles & Young, in press). Suppression of the H-response was apparent with even the first 10 ml of saline infused, a volume which was not clinically apparent (Stokes et al., in press). Infusion of another 10 ml (still clinically undetectable) further reduced the H-response/M-response ratio. Similarly, when, in the course of these experiments, two of our experimental subjects were asked to perform maximal isometric quadriceps contractions, there was a 60% reduction in MVA after only 20 to 30 ml had been infused (Stokes, 1984). These findings have important implications for the understanding of inhibition, and perhaps therefore of selective fiber type atrophy, in patients with knee pathology but without a detectable effusion. There may be many patients with quadriceps inhibition and quadriceps wasting due in large part to the presence of a knee effusion so small that it is clinically undetectable.

Central Connections

Spatial facilitation between the H-reflex inhibition produced by knee joint infusion and that produced by electrical stimulation of Ib afferents in the tibial nerve (from Golgi tendon organs in gastrocnemius/soleus) implies that the two inhibitory afferent pathways have a common interneurone (Iles, Stokes, & Young, 1985; Stokes, Iles & Young, in press). Some preliminary data also suggest the possibility of convergence with a cutaneous flexor reflex afferent pathway. There is as yet no evidence of facilitation of reciprocal inhibition of the quadriceps H-reflex by knee joint infusion.

CONCLUSIONS

It is not unusual for 30% to 50% quadriceps atrophy to occur after knee injury and/or immobilization. Accurate quantification requires an appropriate imaging technique, such as CAT or compound ultrasound B-scanning. Despite its severity, the wasting should be completely reversible since it is due only to atrophy; there is no loss of muscle fibers. It is not yet clear what clinical features determine whether the atrophy is selectively localized to type I or type II muscle fibers, or whether it affects both equally.

Very substantial suppression of both voluntary and reflex excitability of quadriceps anterior horn cells may be caused by afferent stimuli arising in and/or around the knee. Such inhibitory afferent stimuli may be provoked by joint effusions so small as to seem of little clinical importance or, indeed, to be clinically undetectable. Clearly, these findings have major, practical implications for clinical practice, particularly in orthopedics, rheumatology, geriatric medicine, and rehabilitation.

In addition, we suggest that they may provide a key to understanding the specificity of fiber-type atrophy seen in some patients. Elucidation of this possibility requires further investigations of the central connections of the inhibitory afferents and the extent to which their effects are concentrated on high-threshold or low-threshold motor units.

In the meantime, it is clear that very great care must be taken in the interpretation of data obtained from animal models of joint immobilization. In these models, joints may be immoblized with techniques such as the insertion of a metal pin between the bones of the joint. Clearly, this creates a potential source of inhibitory afferent stimuli, even when the initial clinical evidence of inflammatory reaction and effusion has apparently settled. Perhaps even external joint fixation may provoke inhibitory afferent stimuli from skin receptors. Data obtained from such experiments need not necessarily reflect the effects of immobilization alone but may, in fact, reflect the effects of a combination of immobilization and reflex inhibition of the motoneurones supplying the wasted muscle.

Acknowledgments

This chapter is based on work conducted while the authors were associated with the Nuffield Departments of Orthopaedic Surgery and Clinical Medicine, University of Oxford. (Dr. Stokes is now in the Department of Medicine, University of Liverpool). We are pleased to acknowledge the collaboration of numerous co-authors in the work on which this paper is based. We also thank the Office of the Chief Scientist, Department of Health and Social Security, for financial support.

REFERENCES

Basmajian, J.V. (1970). Re-education of vastus medialis: A misconception. *Archives of Physical Medicine and Rehabilitation*, **51**, 245-247.

Baugher, W.H., Warren, R.F., Marshall, J.L., & Joseph, A. (1984). Quadriceps atrophy in the anterior cruciate insufficient knee. *American Journal of Sports Medicine*, **12**, 192-195.

Brooke, M.H., & Kaplan, H. (1972). Muscle pathology in rheumatoid arthritis, polymyalgia rheumatica, and polymyositis: A histochemical study. *Archives of Pathology,* **94**, 101-118.

de Andrade, J.R., Grant, C., & Dixon, A. St. J. (1965). Joint distension and reflex muscle inhibition in the knee. *Journal of Bone and Joint Surgery,* **47-A**, 313-322.

Dons, B., Bollerup, K., Bonde-Petersen, F., & Hancke, S. (1979). The effect of weight-lifting exercise related to muscle fiber cross-sectional area in humans. *European Journal of Applied Physiology and Occupational Physiology,* **40**, 95-106.

Edström, L. (1970). Selective atrophy of red muscle fibres in the quadriceps in long-standing knee-joint dysfunction: Injuries to the anterior cruciate ligament. *Journal of the Neurological Sciences,* **11**, 551-558.

Edström, L., & Nordemar, R. (1974). Differential changes in type I and type II muscle fibres in rheumatoid arthritis: A biopsy study. *Scandinavian Journal of Rheumatology,* **3**, 155-160.

Ekholm, J., Eklund, G., & Skoglund, S. (1960). On the reflex effects from the knee joint of the cat. *Acta Physiologica Scandinavica,* **50**, 167-174.

Eriksson, E. (1982). Role of sports medicine today and in the future. *International Journal of Sports Medicine,* **3**, 2-3.

Häggmark, T., & Eriksson, E. (1979a). Cylinder or mobile cast brace after knee ligament surgery. A clinical analysis and morphologic and enzymatic studies of changes in the quadriceps muscle. *American Journal of Sports Medicine,* **7**, 48-56.

Häggmark, T., & Eriksson, E. (1979b). Hypotrophy of the soleus muscle in man after Achilles tendon rupture. Discussion of findings obtained by computed tomography and morphologic studies. *American Journal of Sports Medicine,* **7**, 48-56.

Häggmark, T., Jansson, E., & Svane, B. (1978). Cross-sectional area of the thigh muscle in man measured by computed tomography. *Scandinavian Journal of Clinical and Laboratory Investigation,* **38**, 355-360.

Harding, B. (1929). An investigation into the cause of arthritic muscular atrophy. *Lancet,* **i**, 433-434.

Hultén, B., Renström, P., & Grimby, G. (1981). Glycogen-depletion patterns with isometric and isokinetic exercise in patients after leg injury. *Clinical Science,* **61**, 35-42.

Iles, J.F., Stokes, M., & Young, A. (1985). Reflex actions of knee-joint receptors on quadriceps in man. *Journal of Physiology,* **360**, 48P.

Ingemann-Hansen, T., & Halkjaer-Kristensen, J. (1980). Computerized tomographic determination of human thigh components. The effects of immobilization in plaster and subsequent physical training. *Scandinavian Journal of Rehabilitation Medicine,* **12**, 27-31.

Ingemann-Hansen, T., & Halkjaer-Kristensen, J. (1983). Progressive resistance exercise training of the hypotrophic quadriceps muscle in man. *Scandinavian Journal of Rehabilitation Medicine*, **15**, 29-35.

Jayson, M.I.V., & Dixon, A. St.J. (1970). Intra-articular pressure in rheumatoid arthritis of the knee. III. Pressure changes during joint use. *Annals of the Rheumatic Diseases*, **29**, 401-408.

Karumo, I., Rehunen, S., Näveri, H., & Alho, A. (1977). Red and white muscle fibres in meniscectomy patients. Effects of postoperative physiotherapy. *Annales Chirurgiae et Gynaecologiae*, **66**, 164-169.

Lindboe, C.F., & Platou, C.S. (1984). Effect of immobilization of short duration on the muscle fiber size. *Clinical Physiology*, **4**, 183-188.

LoPresti, C., Kirkendall, D., Street, G., Lombardo, J., Weiker, G., Bergfeld, J., & Andrish, J. (1984). Degree of quadriceps atrophy at 1 year post anterior cruciate repair. *Medicine and Science in Sports and Exercise*, **16**, (2), 204.

Raymond. (1890). Recherches expérimentales sur la pathogénie des atrophies musculaires consécutives aux arthrites traumatiques. *Révue de Médécine*, **10**, 374-392.

Salmons, S., & Henriksson, J. (1981). The adaptive response of skeletal muscle to increased use. *Muscle & Nerve*, **4**, 94-105.

Sargeant, A.J., Davies, C.T.M., Edwards, R.H.T., Maunder, C., & Young, A. (1977). Functional and structural changes after disuse of human muscle. *Clinical Science and Molecular Medicine*, **52**, 337-342.

Shakespeare, D.T., Stokes, M., Sherman, K.P., & Young, A. (1985). Reflex inhibition of the quadriceps after meniscectomy: Lack of association with pain. *Clinical Physiology*, **5**, 137-144.

Sherman, K.P., Young, A., Stokes, M., & Shakespeare, D.T. (1984). Joint injury and muscle weakness. *Lancet*, **ii**, 646.

Širca, A., & Sušec-Michieli, M. (1980). Selective type II fibre muscular atrophy in patients with osteoarthritis of the hip. *Journal of the Neurological Sciences*, **44**, 149-159.

Spencer, J.D., Hayes, K.C., Alexander, I.J. (1984). Knee joint effusion and quadriceps reflex inhibition in man. *Archives of Physical Medicine and Rehabilitation*, **65**, 171-177.

Staudte, H.W., & Brussatis, F. (1977). Selective changes in size and distribution of fibre types in vastus muscle from cases of different knee joint affections. *Zeitschrift für Rheumatologie*, **36**, 143-160.

Stokes, M. (1984). *Reflex inhibition of the human quadriceps in the presence of knee joint damage.* Unpublished doctoral dissertation, The Polytechnic of North London, London, England.

Stokes, M., Iles, J.F., & Young, A. (in press). *Actions of knee joint afferents during contraction of the human quadriceps.* Manuscript submitted for publication.

Stokes, M., & Young, A. (1984). The contribution of reflex inhibition to arthrogenous muscle weakness. *Clinical Science,* **67**, 7-14.

Suchenwirth, R., d'Avis, W., & Bundschu, H.D. (1972). Enzymhistologische Befunde an der Skeletmuskulatur des Menschen. IV. Inaktivitätsatrophie. *Klinische Wochenschrift,* **50**, 199-204.

Young, A., Hughes, I., Round, J.M., & Edwards, R.H.T. (1982). The effect of knee injury on the number of muscle fibres in the human quadriceps femoris. *Clinical Science,* **62**, 227-234.

Young, A., Hughes, I., Russell, P., Parker, M.J., & Nichols, P.J.R. (1980). Measurement of quadriceps muscle wasting by ultrasonography. *Rheumatology and Rehabilitation,* **19**, 141-148.

Young, A., Stokes, M., Round, J.M., & Edwards, R.H.T. (1983). The effect of high-resistance training on the strength and cross-sectional area of the human quadriceps. *European Journal of Clinical Investigation,* **13**, 411-417.

Adaptability of Connective Tissue

Andrus Viidik
University of Aarhus
Aarhus, Denmark

"If by some magic solution one could dissolve all the connective tissue of the body, all that would remain would be a mass of slimy epithelium, quivering muscle and frustrated nerve cells" (Arcadi, 1952, quoted by Hansen, 1979).

This admittedly humoristic and from a biological point, unrealistic statement, emphasizes the role of connective tissues in the body. They supply mechanical protection towards external violence by forming the toughest part of the skin, that is, the dermis, and maintain the integrity of soft organs by supplying them with capsules and with "skeletons" constituted of trabeculae. The same is true for muscles, in which fasciae, perimysia, epimysia and endomysia are formed by connective tissue elements. Further, the tendons transmitting forces from muscles to bones, and ligaments limiting joint motion are constituted solely of connective tissue. Blood vessel walls derive their resistance against blood pressure and the elastic recoil following a pulse wave from their connective tissue elements; the smooth muscle cells have mainly a regulatory or "fine-tuning" function. In a bone a specific connective tissue component, collagen type I microfibrils, provides sites for the origin of the mineralization process. Only the central nervous system is normally void of connective tissues; they constitute, however, the surrounding meninges.

The main components of connective tissues are fibers of the proteins collagen and elastin, embedded in a ground substance, in which the important macromolecules are proteglycans (controlling hydration and providing "lubrication") and glycoproteins. Collagen is the connective tissue protein mainly responsible for resistance against and transmission of tensile forces. Collagen is the single most abundant protein in the mammalian body being about 30% of all proteins. It is also the strongest protein: The Achilles tendon of a horse breaks when loaded with 4000 kg (Yamada, 1970) and that of a human at 400 kg (Stucke, 1950). This means, translated to physical material properties, that the ultimate tensile strength of a tendon is in the range of 50 to 100 $N \cdot mm^{-2}$: a 5 to 10 kg weight can be suspended from a fixed point by a tendon with a cross-sectional area of 1 mm^2.

Collagen in tendons and ligaments is by no means a static tissue, an impression too easily acquired from classical anatomical atlases. The strength of tendons and ligaments can increase in response to exercise (Viidik, 1967; Woo, Gomez, Woo, & Akeson, 1982) while it can deteriorate following immobilization (Woo et al., 1982). That the influence of exercise on connective tissues is systemic, is suggested by the observation that elasticity of skin is improved after physical training (Suominen, Heikkinen, & Parkatti, 1977).

COLLAGEN: MOLECULAR STRUCTURE AND AGGREGATION

Collagen is not a single entity; there are a number of distinct species with varying tissue distributions (for review, see Nimni, 1983).

- Type I, the "original collagen": skin, tendon, bone, aorta and most organ capsules and trabecular networks.
- Type II: hyaline cartilage.
- Type III: same as Type I, except bone; in tendons and ligaments only in sheaths.
- Type IV: basement membranes, lens capsule.
- Type V: muscle (skeletal and smooth), fetal membranes, corneal stroma; it might contribute to the formation of an exocytoskeleton and interconnections with other connective tissue components.
- "Minor collagens": a number of collagen species now being characterized by molecular biologists; their physiological functions are not clear.

The collagen species responsible for the mechanical properties of tendons and ligaments is Type I. This molecule is assembled from three polypeptide chains (alpha chains), each consisting of about 1000 amino acid residues. Each chain is a left-handed helix with a pitch of 0.89 nm and with three residues in each turn. The three helices are wound together into a right-handed superhelix with a pitch of 8.7 nm. The whole molecule is about 3000 nm long. The entity on the next hierarchical level is the microfibril, which consists of five rows of molecules, wound together into a left-handed "super-superhelix" with a pitch of probably about 120 nm and a diameter of 4 nm. The fibril constitutes the next level: It is a right-handed "super-super-superhelix" with a pitch of about 1000 nm and a diameter of 500 to 2000 nm. This alternation between right- and left-handed helicality from alpha chains to fibrils is comparable to rope-building technique and tightens, when subjected to tensile forces, these units to increase the structural stability. The fibrils are packed into fibers (diameter 1 to 10 microns), fiber bundles, fascicles and finally whole tendons (and ligaments). There is no evidence for helical structure of any of these hierarchical levels, with the "exception" of certain ligaments with twisted courses. (For review, see Viidik, 1980b.)

The helical part of the collagen molecule is 1011 residues long with every third of them being glycine. This sequence can be written as 337 x (Gly-X-Y), where X and Y are various amino acids. The sequence Gly-Pro-Hyp (Pro = proline, Hyp = hydroxyproline) has the highest physicochemical stability, followed by Gly-Pro-Pro, Gly-Pro-Y, Gly-X-Pro and Gly-X-Y (Segal, 1969). These imino acid residues are thus important for the stability of the collagen molecule. While the incorporation of proline into the polypeptide chain is determined by the genome, the conversion of some proline residues to hydroxyproline by prolyl hydroxylase is possibly subject to environmental influence. There is a correlation between tissue in vivo temperature and the physical stability of its collagen (measured as shrinkage temperature) (Viidik, 1971) as there is between imino acid, especially hydroxyproline, content and shrinkage as well as denaturation temperatures (for review see Viidik, 1982). The skrinkage temperature is, however, also dependent on the characteristics of collagen cross-linking (see below); whether the changes in shrinkage temperature of tendon collagen induced by physical training (discussed below) are caused by changes in proline hydroxylation or cross-linking patterns is not clear.

The collagen molecules in the five helical rows in a microfibril are not attached end-to-end; their helical regions are separated from each other by 44 nm. There are in this space nonhelical telopeptides on both ends of the molecule, leaving gaps of 40 nm in the rows. The molecules in adjacent rows are "quarter-staggered," that is, the "beginning" of molecules in the five rows is successively displaced by 67 nm, resulting in overlaps of 27 nm. This gap and overlap pattern is seen on the electron micrograph as the typical 67 nm cross-striation of the collagen fibril. The aggregation of the microfibril is guided by electrostatic forces of hydrophobic interaction; clusters of hydrophobic residues along the molecule are repeated with the quarter-stagger pattern (for example, see Kühn & Glanville, 1980, and Miller, 1980).

STABILIZATION OF COLLAGEN

The gradual increase of stability, which occurs with maturation and aging of the tissue, is achieved by the formation of cross-links between the telopeptide of one molecule and the helical region of a molecule in an adjacent row (for example, see Light & Bailey, 1980).

The first step in cross-link formation is the oxidative deamination of a telopeptidal hydroxylysine to hydroxyallysine:

$$\begin{array}{c} | \\ C-(CH_2)_2-CHOH-CH_2-NH_2 \\ | \qquad\qquad \downarrow \\ | \\ C-(CH_2)_2-CHOH-CHO \\ | \end{array}$$

(In the conversion of lysine to allysine the side chain contains $-CH_2-$ instead of $-CHOH-$.) (Hydroxy)allysines in adjacent chain telopeptides can form an aldol condensation, which has been shown to exist as an *intra*-molecular cross-link. The fibrillar assembly, however, attains its stability from *inter*molecular cross-links formed between a telopeptidal (hydroxy) allysine and a "helical" (hydroxy)lysine:

$$\begin{array}{c} -CHOH-CHO + NH_2-CH_2-CHOH- \\ \downarrow \\ -CHOH-CH=N-CH_2-CHOH- \end{array}$$

Provided a hyroxyallysine and not an allysine participates in this cross-link formation, the aldimine formed (dehydro – dihyroxylysinonorleucine) is stabilized by an Amadori rearrangement to a ketoimine (hydroxylysino – 5 – keto – norleucine):

$$-CO-CH_2-NH-CH_2-CHOH-$$

The main differences between the aldimine and ketoimine cross-links are that the aldimines can be split by heat (utilized when measuring shrinkage temperature, T_s, and shrinkage characteristics at a constant temperature above T_s) and D-penicillamine. There is, on the other hand, no evidence available to suggest that there are any differences between the mechanical properties of these two types of cross-links.

These cross-links "disappear" later in the maturation process; they are probably modified so that the "ultimate" cross-link involves three or more collagen molecules. A number of different configurations, including histidino-hydroxymerodesmosine (hydroxylysine + allysine – aldol + histidine), pyridinoline (hydroxylysine + hydroxyallysine + allysine) and gem diamines (/hydroxy/lysinonorleucine + /hydroxy/lysine) have been suggested. A probable mechanism is, however, a lateral aggregation of several ketoimines or aldimines into a poly-cross-link. The aldimine and ketoimine cross-links are formed between parts of the collagen molecule, which after cyanobromide digestion are found in the alpha – 1(I) CB5 and alpha – 1(I) CB6 fragments. They disappear with maturation and, if the cross-link is tritiated (by ^3H – borohydride reduction), the isotope is found in a high molecular weight component after SDS-polyacrylamide gel electrophoresis (Light & Bailey, 1980).

The mechanisms for the stabilization of collagen at fibrillar level are not known. The proteoglycans probably play a role, though the removal of most of them enzymatically with hyaluronidase and chondroitinase ABC does not affect the mechanical properties of tendon fibers (Viidik, Danielsen, & Oxlund, 1982). The sheaths surrounding fibrils and fibers probably play a role. They exhibit considerable mechanical strength and/or extensibility: When single fibrils have failed in tensile tests, the sheaths still hold (for review, see Viidik, 1980c). The composition of these sheaths is not known in detail.

MORPHOLOGICAL AND BIOCHEMICAL RESPONSE TO TRAINING

The morphological changes induced by physical exercise seem to be most pronounced during growth of the organism. The number of nuclei (i.e., mostly fibrocytes) and the weight of tendons increase in young mice (Ingelmark, 1948), while in older mice and rabbits tendon weight is not changed (Ingelmark, 1945; Viidik, 1967). Ligament weight increases in young male rats but not in females (Tipton, Martin, Matthes, & Carey, 1975). For adult dogs a decrease in fiber bundle diameter is reported (Tipton, James, Mergner, & Tcheng, 1970).

Biochemical changes have also been reported. Training induces increase of aerobic enzyme activity (Heikkinen, Suominen, Vihersaari, Vuori, & Kiiskinen, 1975; Tipton et al., 1975) as well as of collagen synthesis (Heikkinen & Vuori, 1972) in tendons. There are, on the other hand, no data available on collagen turnover. An indirect measure is to quantitate the amount of collagen by measuring hydroxyproline, an animo acid virtually unique for collagen and present in a constant fraction of the amino acid residues (there are small amounts present in elastin and complement proteins not present in tendons and ligaments). Hydroxyproline concentration is not increased by training in tendons from young mice (Kiiskinen & Heikkinen, 1976a) nor in ligaments from young rats (Tipton et al., 1975) but is in ligaments from adult dogs (Tipton et al., 1970).

The systemic response to physical training is also seen in biochemical data. Hydroxyproline concentration in skin is increased in immature mice (Kiiskinen & Heikkinen, 1976b) as well as adult and old males (Suominen, Heikkinen, Moisio, & Viljama, 1978).

The hydroxyproline concentration data must be interpreted with caution. While a change in this parameter indicates that something has influenced the tissue, it does not establish the nature of the event. A decrease, for example, can be the result of loss of collagen from the tissue as well as an increase of other tissue components (in an extreme case an increase of collagen could be masked).

PHYSICOCHEMICAL STABILITY OF COLLAGEN

Methods that measure the physicochemical stability of collagen split aldimine cross-links and assess some property that depends on the amount of remaining, stable cross-links. After heating samples to a temperature well above T_s the amount of collagen solubilized can be measured: It (a) increases when the amount of ketoimines falls and that of aldimines increases and (b) decreases with the increase of the calculated amount of the "ultimate" cross-links (see Viidik, 1979b). This method, however, yields no information about the structural integrity of the part of the sample that is not solubilized and is rather insensitive, when only a minor part of collagen is solubilized. Human skin thus has only an insignificant soluble fraction after the age of 15 years (Viidik, 1979b), while other methods record increase in stability up to the age of 90 years (Allain, Le Lous, Bazin, Bailey, & Delaunay, 1978; Rasmussen, Wakim, & Winkelmann, 1964).

Some of these methods are based on the old observation that collagen shrinks and becomes rubbery when exposed to heat (Gotschlich, 1893). Verzär (1955) was the first to use this phenomenon to study the stability of collagen. Others have used chemical means to induce similar changes in collagen: immersion in 40% potassium iodide (Banga, Balo, & Szabo, 1954) and 8 M urea (Elden & Webb, 1961) solutions. The parallel-fibered collagenous tissue shrinks rapidly under isotonic conditions and later relaxes somewhat, provided the isotonic tension is of sufficient magnitude. Under isometric conditions a tension develops (as shrinkage is prevented) followed by a relaxation as the fibrillar structure disintegrates. One method (Boros-Farkas & Everitt, 1967) uses time to specimen rupture as the parameter for stability.

Verzär (1955) was the first to demonstrate that with maturation and subsequent aging there is a continuous increase of the physicochemical stability of collagen. Since then a large number of reports have been published on this topic (for review see Verzär, 1964; Viidik, 1969, 1982).

This physiological process can be altered by a number of "interventions." Repeated pregnancies increase the maximum isometric tension recorded for tail tendons from old rats (Rundgren, 1974). Diabetes mellitus induced in rats by streptozotozin causes a pronounced increase (Andreassen, Seyer-Hansen, & Bailey, 1981). Corticosteroid treatment has a similar, although somewhat less pronounced effect (Oxlund, Sims, & Light, 1982; Vogel,

1969) as has an increased level of thyroxin (Everitt, Giles, & Gal, 1969). Hypothysectomy (Everitt, 1976), thyroidectomy (Andreassen, 1976; Giles & Everitt, 1967) and long-term (Everitt, 1971) but not short-term (Andreassen, 1976) food restriction, on the other hand, retard the development of increased physicochemical stability in rat tail tendons. A transient decrease of this stability is seen during healing of incisional dorsal skin wounds (Viidik, Holm-Pedersen, & Rundgren, 1972).

A number of changes in the normal physiological balance can thus accelerate or retard the normal temporal development of physicochemical stability of collagen. Whether physical activity can produce any change has been investigated in the laboratory of this author (previously unpublished data).

TRAINING DECREASES THE PHYSICOCHEMICAL STABILITY OF TENDON COLLAGEN

Methodological Study

Distal tendons of the extensor digitorum longus muscle from hind limbs of exercised and sedentary rabbits were available for this study. For this type of tendon, which is rather stiff and in which small bends occur during "melting," the isotonic methods are to be preferred compared to the isometric techniques.

In this part of the study the discriminatory power of three isotonic methods were analyzed. (a) Thermal: Ringer's solution at 62 °C, (b) 40% solution of potassium iodide, and (c) 8 M solution of urea; (b) and (c) at 37 °C, all three solutions buffered to pH 7.0. The experiments were carried out in a parallel-walled plastic chamber immersed into a large water bath, the temperature of which was controlled to achieve appropriate temperature in the chamber. The tendons were clamped to the top of the chamber and weights were attached to attain isotonic tension during testing. The lengths of the tendons were recorded photographically and read to the nearest 0.25 mm (against a grid engraved on the back wall of the chamber, the horizontal lines spaced 1.00 mm apart). The length changes were calculated as length (L) in units of original length.

Tendons from 45-day-old and 12-month-old white male rabbits were used. Tendons were dissected out immediately after sacrifice, rinsed first in a Ringer's solution and then in distilled water. They were straightened out, mounted on a cork board; lengths and weights were recorded after drying at 30 °C overnight. The tendons were equilibrated in Sorensen's buffer for 1 to 4 hr before immersion into an experimental solution. The weights attached were 0.5 and 1.0 g for tendons from young and adult animals respectively.

The mean shrinkage-time curves for the tendons from the young rabbits are shown in Figure 1 and the mean curves for young and mature rabbits from the potassium iodide series in Figure 2. The weights and maximum contraction values are given in Table 1 together with the results of a one-way analysis of variance. All three methods were able to discriminate between the two groups at the 5% level; the potassium iodide method had the best discriminative power and was thus selected for the main experiment. There were not significant correlations between maximum contraction and weight per unit length nor between maximum contraction and original length.

Influence of Physical Exercise

Seven rabbits were trained for 40 weeks from the age of 3 months according to Viidik (1969). They were trained three times a day, 5 days a week. Initially each training session in an encased treadmill was at 35 m min^{-1} for 3 min and increased with improvement of the physical fitness of the animals to ultimately 55 m min^{-1} for 5 min. Nine rabbits were kept "sedentary" in standard cages for the same period of time. There were no significant differences between the body weights in the two groups, though the mean curve for the trained animals was above that for the sedentary ones from the 4th week.

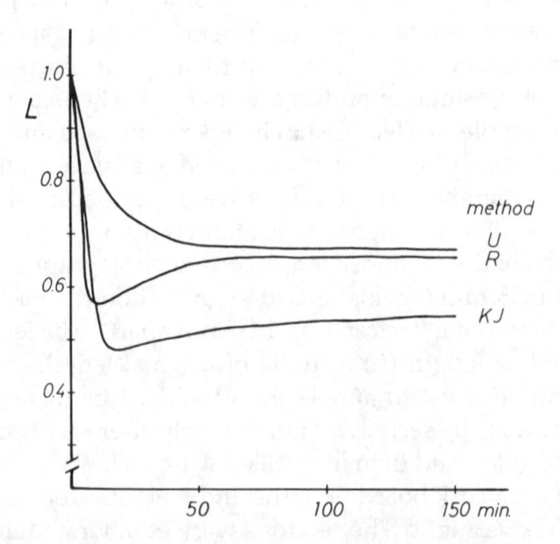

Figure 1 Mean length-time curves for tendons from 45-day-old rabbits tested in 8 M urea (U), 40% potassium iodide (KJ), both at 37 °C, and Ringer's solution at 62 °C (R).

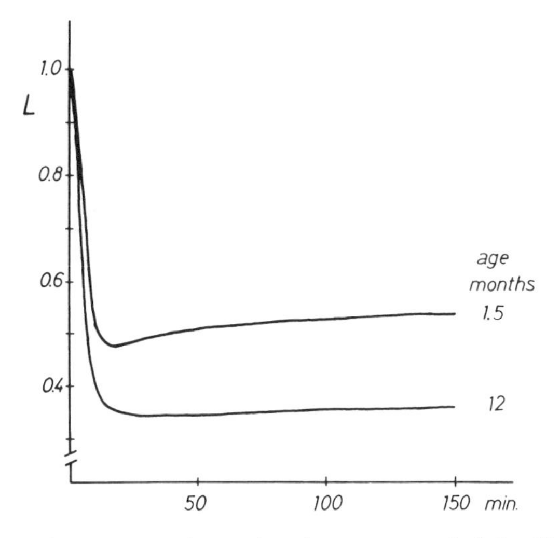

Figure 2 Mean length-time curves for tendons from young and adult rabbits tested in 40% potassium iodide.

Table 1 Tendons Tested Isotonically With Different Methods. Tendon Lengths in Units or Original Length at Maximum Contraction and Weights in mg/cm (After Overnight Drying). (Mean Values ± S.E.M.)

Method	Young	Adult
Thermal		
Maximum contraction	0.564 ± 0.023	0.387 ± 0.009 [a]
Weight	0.76 ± 0.04	3.06 ± 0.11
Potassium iodide		
Maximum contraction	0.466 + 0.013	0.340 ± 0.006 [b]
Weight	0.71 ± 0.05	3.57 ± 0.24
Urea		
Maximum contraction	0.654 ± 0.012	0.567 ± 0.035 [c]
Weight	0.68 ± 0.04	3.18 ± 0.30

[a] $n = 20 + 8$, $S^2 = 78.40$, $F = 22.79$
[b] $n = 12 + 8$, $S^2 = 14.51$, $F = 52.34$
[c] $n = 12 + 8$, $S^2 = 49.12$, $F = 7.38$

The tendons were handled as described above and tested in the 40% potassium iodide solution at 37 °C. The maximum contraction was significantly less for the tendons from the trained animals, while there was no significant difference in tendon weight between the two groups (Table 2). Although the collagen in the tendons from the trained animals

Table 2 Tendons From Trained and Sedentary Rabbits Tested Isotonically at a 40% Potassium Iodide Solution. Tendon Lengths in Units of Original Length at Maximum Contraction and Weights in mg/cm (After Overnight Drying). (Mean Values ± S.E.M.)

Measurements	Trained	Sedentary
Maximum contraction	0.408 ± 0.022	0.350 ± 0.019 [a]
Weight	3.04 ± 0.11	3.27 ± 0.13

[a] $n = 43 + 24$, $S^2 = 64.60$, $F = 4.20$

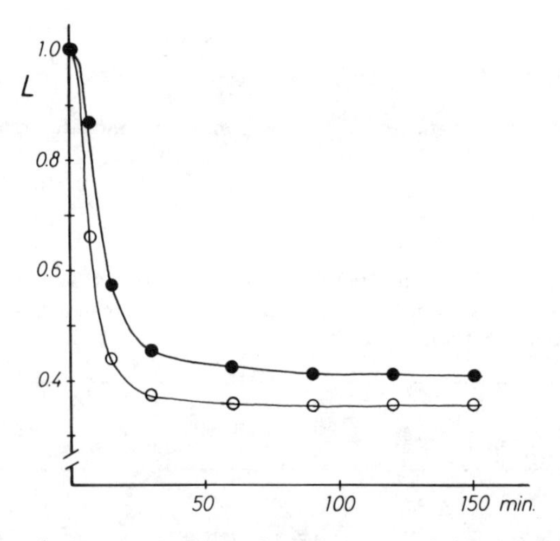

Figure 3 Mean length-time curves for tendons from trained (filled circles) and sedentary (open circles) rabbits tested in 40% potassium iodide.

thus was less stable, the length-time curve (Figure 3) shows that the relaxation following maximum contraction seen for young tendons (cf. curve KJ in Figure 1) was not retained.

These results indicate that the "aging" cross-linking pattern of collagen is delayed by physical training, because there is no weight increase in the tendons nor any change in collagen content and concentration (Viidik, 1967), probably attained by an increased turnover. To induce an increase of collagen mass in rabbit tendons the training probably should be started earlier than at 3 months of age (cf. Ingelmark, 1945, 1948).

MECHANICAL PROPERTIES OF COLLAGEN

A large number of biomechanical investigations have focused on the tensile strength of tendons and ligaments. The most informative approach is to record the complete stress-strain curve from the relaxed state to the point of failure (Figure 4). The primarily recorded load-deformation curve, which is valid only for the specimen tested (or group of specimens, provided there is reasonable geometric congruence within it), is transformed to a stress-strain curve; that is, is "generalized" to represent material properties. This is achieved by expressing load values in units of cross-sectional area and deformation in units of original length (for review see (Viidik, 1979a, 1980c). The parameters usually evaluated are the ultimate tensile strength (σ_{MAX}) and the strain at that point, the inclination of the linear part of the curve (tan α), "elastic stiffness" and failure energy (W_f, calculated as the area between the curve and the strain axis).

It is more interesting from a physiological point of view to evaluate the mechanical properties within the range of normal functioning; that is,

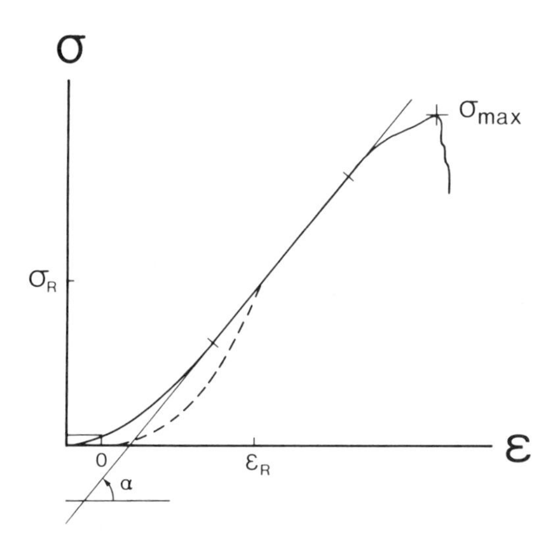

Figure 4 Stress (σ) - strain (ϵ) curve for parallel-fibered collagenous tissue until failure (solid line). Tan α is "elastic stiffness." The beginning and end of the linear segment are marked with bars. The dashed curve is for unloading, if the cycle is reversed at the point (σ_R, ϵ_R). From "Elastimechanik biologischer Gewebe" by A. Viidik, 1980, in H. Cotta, H. Krahl, and K. Steinbrüch (Eds.), *Belastungtoleranz des Bewegeapparates*, p. 127. Stuttgart: George Thieme Verlag. Copyright 1980 by Georg Thieme Verlag. Reprinted by permission.

the stress level that a maximum tetanic contraction of the muscle can produce. Available data suggest that this level is about one third of the ultimate strength (the range up to σ_R, $\in^{\epsilon}_R$ in Figure 4) (Elliott & Crawford, 1965; Hirsch, 1974; for review see Viidik, 1980a). This leaves under statical conditions a ''safety margin'' of about 200% under normal functioning. Some data suggest that half of this safety margin, which thus has been calculated from statical experiments, is used under dynamic conditions; for example, when a dog jumps over an obstacle (Alexander, 1981) and during ordinary running push-offs in humans (Barfred, 1971). Barfred (1971) also reported calculations showing that the safety margin can be exceeded when suddenly altering running direction; partial rupture of the Achilles tendon occurred. Some data, however, suggest that this safety margin is increased under dynamic loading, due to ''locking'' of the viscous components of the viscoelastic properties of the tissue. Haut (1983) found that the ultimate tensile strength increased by a factor of two and energy absorption by a factor of three, when the strain rate was increased from 0.036 to 7.2 s^{-1}.

This viscoelastic behavior of parallel-fibered collagenous tissue is evident also under quasi-static testing (Figure 5). When deformation is halted and kept constant, when the stress level σ_0 has been reached, the stress decreases symptotically towards σ_A (stress-relaxation). On the other hand, if the stress is kept constant at the same level, the strain approaches $\in_A$ asymptotically (creep phenomenon). Figure 5c shows that the elastic stiffness increases with increasing strain rate. (For review see Viidik, 1979a, 1980a.)

The reported changes in biomechanical properties elicited by changes in physical activity present a mixed pattern. Increased strength in junctions between bone and tendon or ligament have been found in rabbits (Viidik, 1968) and male (Tipton, Matthes, & Sandage, 1974) but not female (Booth & Tipton, 1969) rats. The strength of isolated tendons increases in rabbits (Viidik, 1967) but not in mice (Kiiskinen, 1977). Some of these discrepancies can be explained by species and/or specimen type differences. Woo et al. (1982) demonstrated in an extensive series of experiments on trained and sedentary pigs that initially stiffer flexor tendons did not increase their stiffness, while the less stiff extensor tendons did, reaching after training the same stiffness as the flexor tendons. These results should be correlated to the observation of Elliott and Crawford (1965) that the maximum tetanic contraction in flexor muscles is higher than in extensor muscles. The flexor tendons also have a higher collagen content per unit length, which suggests that the level of the tensile forces acting on them during development is higher. It should be noted that the analysis of Woo et al. (1982) showed qualitative differences; that is, the flexor tendons not only have a larger mass of collagen but also have qualitatively different collagen from a mechanical point of view.

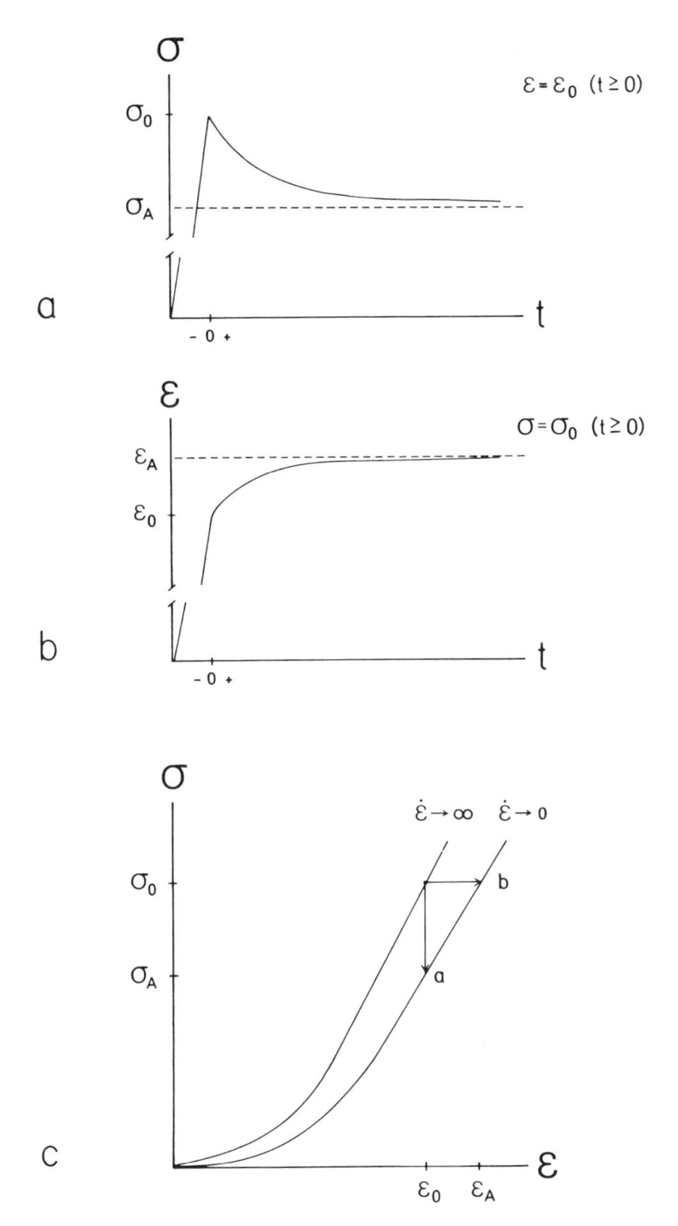

Figure 5 Stress-relaxation and creep. The loading is halted at time t=0 at the point ($0\sigma_0$, $\in_0$): (a) shows stress-relaxation towards a symptote, σ_A and (b) creep towards $\in_A$; (c) shows stress-strain curves for very high ($\in\rightarrow\infty$) and very low ($\in\rightarrow 0$) strain rates, with arrows indicating stress-relaxation and creep that would occur if the deformation and stress respectively would be kept constant (cf. Viidik, 1980 [b] and [c]. From "Elastimechanik biologischer Gewebe" by A. Viidik, 1980, in H. Cotta, H. Krahl, and K. Steinbrüch (Eds.), *Belastungtoleranz des Bewegeapparates*, p. 132. Stuttgart: George Thieme Verlag. Copyright 1980 by Georg Thieme Verlag. Reprinted by permission.

Not much is known about the effect of training on the viscoelastic properties of tendons and ligaments. Viidik (1968) found that stress-relaxation in rabbit knee joint ligaments increased after exercise. This would suggest that the dynamic safety margin is increased by physical activity. No dynamic testing has, however, been performed on trained animals.

A number of studies have been conducted on the effects of immobilization. Most recently Woo et al. (1982) showed that immobilization of medial collateral ligaments in rabbits for 9 weeks reduces their strength to one fourth and their stiffness correspondingly.

CONCLUSIONS

The formation of tendons and ligaments during development is dependent on information belonging to the genome. Later, however, their functional characteristics develop, or degenerate, dependent on the nature of the tensile forces acting on them throughout the lifespan of the organism: While it is possible to enhance the quantity of collagen mass only during early postnatal development, the qualitative properties can be influenced also in the mature and aging organism. How the mechanical stimuli are translated into information "readable" by the cells is not known. There are no known chemical stimuli. The studies on the influence of exercise on connective tissues outside the musculoskeletal system suggest that there is a systetic effect. Piezoelectricity has mostly been studied in bone, and the information available on soft connective tissues is inconclusive.

The information available on the adaptability of connective tissues when subjected to physical exercise is mostly related to tensile strength parameters, derived for statical and at times quasi-statical tests. An obvious avenue for further research is to focus on dynamic testing and on the viscoelastic properties of these tissues. Another important direction is to correlate the mechanical properties and especially exercise-elicited changes in them to the molecular characteristics of collagen and to the interaction between collagen and the ground substance.

REFERENCES

Alexander, R. McN. (1981). Factors of safety in the structure of animals. *Science Progress* (Oxford), **67**, 109-130.

Allain, J.-C., Le Lous, M., Bazin, S., Bailey, A.J., & Delaunay, A. (1978). Isometric tension development during heating of collagenous tissues—Relationships with collagen cross-linking. *Biochimica et Biophysica Acta,* **533**, 147-155.

Andreassen, T.T. (1976). Rate of collagen maturation in relation to thyroxin and caloric intake. *Aktuelle Gerontologie,* **6**, 19-22.

Andreassen, T.T., Seyer-Hansen, K., & Bailey, A.J. (1981). Thermal stability, mechanical properties and reducible cross-links of rat tail tendon in experimental diabetes. *Biochimica et Biophysica Acta,* **667**, 313-317.

Banga, I., Balo, J., & Szabo, D. (1954). Contraction and relaxation of collagen fibres. *Nature,* **174**, 788-789.

Barfred, T. (1971). Experimental rupture of the Achilles tendon. *Acta Orthopaedica Scandinavica,* **42**, 406-428.

Booth, F.W., & Tipton, C.M. (1969). Effects of training and 17-B estradiol upon heart rates, organ weights, and ligamentous strength of female rats. *Internacionale Zeitschrift für angewandte Physiologie,* **27**, 187-197.

Boros-Farkas, M., & Everitt, A.V. (1967). Comparative studies of age tests on collagen fibers. *Gerontologia,* **13**, 37-49.

Elden, H.R., & Webb, G. (1961). Extendability of tendons undergoing contraction-relaxation. *Nature,* **192**, 742-744.

Elliott, D.H., & Crawford, G.N.C. (1965). The thickness and collagen content of tendon relative to the strength and cross-sectional area of muscle. *Proceedings of the Royal Society of London,* (Series B), **162**, 137-146.

Everitt, A.V. (1971). Food intake, growth and the aging of collagen in rat tail tendons. *Gerontologia,* **17**, 98-104.

Everitt, A.V. (1976). Hypophysectomy and aging in the rat. In A.V. Everitt & J.A. Burgess (Eds.), *Hypothalamus, pituitary and aging* (pp. 68-85). Springfield, IL: Charles C. Thomas.

Everitt, A.V., Giles, J.S., & Gal, A. (1969). The role of the thyroid and food intake in the aging of collagen fibres. II. In the old rat. *Gerontologia,* **15**, 366-373.

Giles, J.S., & Everitt, A.V. (1967). The role of the thyroid and food intake in the aging of collagen fibres. I. In the young rat. *Gerontologia,* **13**, 65-69.

Gotschlich, E. (1893). Über den Einfluss der Wärme auf Länge und Dehnbarkeit des elastischen Gewebes und des quergestreiften Muskels. *Pflügers Archiv,* **54**, 109-164.

Hansen, T.M. (1979). *Cyclophosphamide and collagen.* Copenhagen, Denmark: Laegeforeningens forlag.

Haut, R.C. (1983). Age-dependent influence of strain rate on the tensile failure of rat-tail tendon. *Journal of Biomechanical Engineering,* **105**, 296-299.

Heikkinen, E., & Vuori, I. (1972). Effect of physical activity on the metabolism of collagen in aged mice. *Acta Physiologica Scandinavica,* **84**, 543-549.

Heikkinen, E., Suominen, H., Vihersaari, M., Vuori, I., & Kiiskinen A. (1975). Effect of physical training on enzyme activities of bones, tendons and skeletal muscles in mice. In H. Howald & J.R. Poortmans (Eds.), *Metabolic adaption to prolonged physical exercise* (pp. 448-450). Basel, Switzerland: Birkhäuser Verlag.

Hirsch, G. (1974). Tensile properties during tendon healing. *Acta Orthopaedica Scandinavica,* (Suppl. 153).

Ingelmark, B.E. (1945). Über den Bau der Sehnen während verschiedener Altersperioden und unter verschiedenen funkionellen Bedingungen. *Uppsala Läkareförenings Förhandlingar,* **50**, 357-396.

Ingelmark, B.E. (1948). Der Bau der Sehnen während verschiedener Altersperioden und unter wechselendes funktionellen Bedingungen. I. Eine qualitative morphologische Untersuchung an den Achillessehnen weisser Ratten. *Acta Anatomica* (Basel), **6**, 113-140.

Kiiskinen, A. (1977). Physical training and connective tissues in young mice. Physical properties of Achilles tendons and long bones. *Growth,* **44**, 123-137.

Kiiskinen, A., & Heikkinen, E. (1976a). Physical training and connective tissues in young mice. Part II. *Biochemistry of Achilles tendons* (Publication No. 29). University of Jyväskylä Department of Public Health, Jyväskylä.

Kiiskinen, A., & Heikkinen, E. (1976b). Physical training and connective tissues in young mice. Biochemistry of skin. *British Journal of Dermatology,* **95**, 525-529.

Kühn, K., & Glanville, R.W. (1980). Molecular structure and higher organization of different collagen types. In A. Viidik & J. Vuust (Eds.), *Biology of collagen* (pp. 1-14). London: Academic Press.

Light, N.D., & Bailey, A.J. (1980). Molecular structure and stabilization of the collagen fibre. In A. Viidik & J. Vuust (Eds.), *Biology of collagen* (pp. 15-38). London: Academic Press.

Miller, A. (1980). Structural studies on connective tissues. In A. Viidik & J. Vuust (Eds.), *Biology of collagen* (pp. 39-52). London: Academic Press.

Nimni, M.E. (1983). Collagen: Structure, function and metabolism in normal and fibrotic tissues. *Seminars in Arthritis and Rheumatism,* **13**, 1-86.

Oxlund, H., Sims, T., & Light, N.D. (1982). Changes in mechanical properties, thermal stability, reducible cross-links and glycosyl-lysines in rat skin induced by corticosteroid treatment. *Acta Endocrinologica,* **101**, 312-320.

Rasmussen, D.M., Wakim, K.G., & Winkelmann, R.K. (1964). Isotonic and isometric thermal contraction of human dermis. II. Age-related changes. *Journal of Investigative Dermatology,* **43**, 341-348.

Rundgren, Å. (1974). Physical properties of connective tissue as influences by single and repeated pregnancies in the rat. *Acta Physiologica Scandinavica.* (Suppl. 417).

Segal, D.M. (1969). Polymers of tripeptides as collagen models. VII. Synthesis and solution properties of four collagen-like polyhexapeptides. *Journal of Molecular Biology*, **43**, 497-517.

Stucke, K. (1950). Über das elastische Verhalten der Achilles-sehne im Belastungsversuch. *Langenbecks Archiv und Deutsche Zeitschrift für Chirurgie*, **265**, 579-599.

Suominen, H., Heikkinen, E., Moisio, H., & Viljama, K. (1978). Physical and chemical properties of skin in habitually trained and sedentary 31- to 70-year-old men. *British Journal of Dermatology*, **99**, 147-154.

Suominen, H., Heikkinen, E., & Parkatti, T. (1977). Effect of eight weeks' physical training on muscle and connective tissue of the m. vastus lateralis in 69-year-old men and women. *Journal of Gerontology*, **32**, 33-37.

Tipton, C.M., James, S.L., Mergner, W., & Tcheng, T.-K. (1970). Influence of exercise on strength of medial collateral knee ligaments of dogs. *American Journal of Physiology*, **218**, 894-902.

Tipton, C.M., Martin, R.K., Matthes, R.D., & Carey, R.A. (1975). Hydroxyproline concentrations in ligaments from trained and nontrained dogs. In H. Howald & J.R. Poortmans (Eds.), *Metabolic adaption to prolonged physical exercise* (pp. 262-267). Basel, Switzerland: Birkhäuser Verlag.

Tipton, C.M., Matthes, R.D., & Sandage, D.S. (1974). In situ measurement of junction strength and ligament elongation in rats. *Journal of Applied Physiology*, **37**, 758-761.

Verzär, F. (1955). Veränderungen der thermoelastischen Eigenschaften von Sehnen-fasern beim Altern. *Experientia*, **11**, 230.

Verzär, F. (1964). Aging of the collagen fiber. In D.A. Hall (Ed.), *International Review of Connective Tissue Research* (Vol. 2, pp. 244-300). London: Academic Press.

Viidik, A. (1967). The effect of training on the tensile strength of isolated rabbit tendons. *Scandinavian Journal of Plastic and Reconstructive Surgery*, **1**, 141-147.

Viidik, A. (1968). Elasticity and tensile strength of the anterior cruciate ligament in rabbits as influenced by training. *Acta Physiologica Scandinavica*, **74**, 372-380.

Viidik, A. (1969). Tensile strength properties of Achilles tendon systems in trained and untrained rabbits. *Acta Orthopaedica Scandinavica*, **40**, 261-272.

Viidik, A. (1971). Influence of the termperature in different parts of the body on physical properties of collagen. In *Proceedings of the 2nd Nordic Meeting on Medical and Biological Engineering* (pp. 83-85). Oslo.

Viidik, A. (1979a). Biomechanical behavior of soft connective tissues. In N. Akkas (Ed.), *Progress in biomechanics* (pp. 75-113). Alphen aan den Rijn: Sijthoff & Nordhoff.

Viidik, A. (1979b). Connective tissues—Possible implications of the temporal changes for the aging process. *Mechanisms of Aging and Development*, **9**, 267-285.

Viidik, A. (1980a). Elastimechanik biologischer Gewebe. In H. Cotta, H. Krahl, & K. Steinbrück (Eds.), *Belastungstoleranz des Bewegeapparates* (pp. 124-136). Stuttgart: George Thieme Verlag.
Viidik, A. (1980b). Interdependence between structure and function in collagenous tissues. In A. Viidik & J. Vuust (Eds.), *Biology of collagen* (pp. 257-280). London: Academic Press.
Viidik, A. (1980c). Mechanical properties of parallel-fibred collagenous tissues. In A. Viidik & J. Vuust (Eds.), *Biology of collagen* (pp. 237-255). London: Academic Press.
Viidik, A. (1982). Age-related changes in connective tissues. In A. Viidik (Ed.), *Lectures on gerontology, Volume I: On biology of aging* (Part A, pp. 173-211). London: Academic Press.
Viidik, A., Danielsen, C.C., & Oxlund, H. (1982). On fundamental and phenomenological models, structure and mechanical properties of collagen, elastin and glycosaminoglycans. *Biorheology,* **19**, 437-451.
Viidik, A., Holm-Pedersen, P., & Rundgren, Å. (1972). Some observations on the distant collagen response to healing wounds. *Scandinavian Journal of Plastic and Reconstructive Surgery,* **6**, 114-122.
Vogel, H.G. (1969). Zur Wirkung von Hormonen auf physikalische und chemische Eigenschaften des Bindeund Stützgewebes. *Arzneimittelsforschung,* **19**, 1495-1503, 1723-1742, 1790-1801, 1981-1996.
Woo, S.L.Y., Gomez, M.A., Woo, Y.-K., & Akeson, W.H. (1982). Mechanical properties of tendons and ligaments. II. The relationship between immobilization and exercise on tissue remodeling. *Biorheology,* **19**, 397-408.
Yamada, H. (1970). In F.G. Evans (Ed.), *Strength of biological materials.* Baltimore, MD: William & Wilkins.

Discussion from the Session

Wasting and Growth of Skeletal Muscle

Jens Halkjaer-Kristensen
University of Copenhagen
Copenhagen, Denmark

Thorsten Ingemann-Hansen
University of Aarhus
Aarhus, Denmark

TOPICS FOR DISCUSSION

Gunnar Grimby (Gothenburg, Sweden) quickly reviewed the basic questions that he thought should be asked during this panel discussion: What are the mechanisms operative during adaptation to training and disuse? Why is there such controversy between the results of many studies? Is it due to differing methods, difference in species, external influence, type of muscle studied, etc.?

Adaptations of Muscle to Training

Philip D. Gollnick (Pullman, WA, U.S.A.) reviewed the classical question of adaptation in skeletal muscle fibers to strength training, starting with the Murporgo study from 1893 demonstrating hypertrophia to occur and then some studies from the 1960s and 1970s demonstrating fiber-splitting to occur during the training period.

All of these studies have been performed by analysis of cross-sections of muscle and thereafter calculation by extrapolation to the total number of fibers. Such calculations sometimes resulted in obviously wrong figures; for example, fiberlength exceeding the length of the whole muscle. Therefore, Gollnick directly counted all muscle fibers in the trained muscle, using the nitric acid digestion method. He reported a constant number of muscle fibers during physical training, and he also found many different shapes of fibers, some X, H, Y-shapes, which in studies using cross-sections of the muscle might appear as a result of fiber splitting. Since heavy training (e.g., overload of muscle in animal experiments) leads to some muscle damage, muscle hypertrophy in such experiments is accompanied by repair and regeneration processes. This will affect the interpretation of the single experiment. Recently an elaborate review on this topic has been published by H. Schmalbruck (1985).

Strength and Velocity

Robert A. Binkhorst (Nijmegen, The Netherlands) focused on the force-velocity diagram. A great number of experiments have been done concerning the relation between static strength and velocity. Using a simple apparatus his group was, in an elegant experiment, able to demonstrate a positive effect of static strength training on the maximal static force and the velocity of movement with high loads, while no effect was measured on the velocity at small loads (De Koning, Binkhorst, Vissers, & Vos, 1982). The model may prove useful in relating functional properties with intrinsic properties in human skeletal muscle.

Motor Nerves

V. Reggie Edgerton (Los Angeles, CA, U.S.A.) focused upon the relationship between motor control and neural drive, and contemplated our definitions in this area. He has used the glycogen-depletion method of muscle fibers supplied by a single motor neuron and has found a great variation in fiber size within the individual motor unit. Supposedly all muscle fibers in the same motor unit receive the same message from the motor nerve. What is then the regulatory system responsible for the great variation in fiber area within one single motor unit? Finally he discussed the definition of activity/inactivity/disuse; everybody speaks about it, but we have to be more precise in the definition: Using strain-gauge measurements on the Achilles tendon he demonstrated a great variability between subjects in power during, for example, walking and running.

Muscle Atrophy

J. Duncan MacDougall (Hamilton, Ontario, Canada) focused on atrophy during immobilization. In this session the importance of definition of experimental situations was stressed again, due to the different effects of immobilization in arm versus leg muscle. The usual finding is atrophy of type II fibers during immobilization of arm muscles opposite to type I fiber atrophy in leg muscle immobilization.

In their examination of the normal human triceps brachii they find the type II muscle fiber area larger than the type I area in contrast to a leg muscle, for example, the vastus lateralis where type II area equals type I area. This might be due to the difference in daily activity in the two muscles, and might explain the preferential atrophy of type II fibers of arm muscle during immobilization. Many immobilization studies in humans have been performed on injured knees or after leg fractures, but these models should be looked upon as models of *injury* plus *immobilization*. In the majority of human studies the biopsies are from a leg muscle after injury plus immobilization, whereas MacDougall's experiment is performed in arm muscle of healthy males without any injury.

Myosin Pattern Changes

Hans Howald (Magglingen, Switzerland) reviewed his investigations of single fiber myosin characteristics. A group of long distance runners were allocated to muscle strength training, and repeated biopsies from leg muscles demonstrated definite changes in the myosin-electrophoresis pattern of pooled type I fibers. Thus, modifications at subcellular levels can be elicited in human skeletal muscle by physical training.

Adaptations of Connective Tissue

Andrus Viidik (Aarhus, Denmark) drew the attention of the audience to the connective tissue and the ability of this organ to adapt to different levels of activity. The elasticity of arm skinfold is significantly changed due to leg endurance training, thus demonstrating effects of training on organs that apparently do not seem to be involved in the training process. These adaptations are modulated to different degrees depending upon such factors as animal models, aging, or several pharmacological treatments.

Muscle Strength

Archie Young (Oxford, England) went through the results of correlations between muscle cross-sectional area and muscle strength, where they have found a good correlation in both young and old women, whereas younger men showed a weaker relation. This demonstrates again the regulation of muscle strength to be a multifactorial function, as also found in many previous studies, including clinical models (Halkjaer-Kristensen & Ingemann-Hansen, 1985; Ingemann-Hansen & Halkjaer-Kristensen, 1985). The panel discussion was terminated by a contribution of *Bente Danneskiold-Samsøe* (Hvidore, Denmark), who reported results on muscle strength in patients with rheumatoid arthritis, some of which had been treated with corticosteroids. She found that corticosteroid treatment resulted in reduced isokinetic strength and a reduction in the areas of both type I and type II fibers compared to nonsteroid treated patients (Danneskiold-Samsøe, Grimby, Saltin, & Bach Andersen, 1985).

The discussion in the panel session revealed some new information, but raised even more questions about the regulatory mechanism in wasting and growth of skeletal muscle.

REFERENCES

Danneskiold-Samsøe, B., Grimby, G., Saltin, B., & Bach Andersen, R. (1985). Isokinetic strength and muscle morphology in patients with rheumatoid arthritis. *Clinical Physiology,* **5**(Suppl. 4). (Abstract 121)

De Koning, F.L., Binkhorst, R.A., Vissers, A.C.A., & Vos, J.A. (1982). Influence of static strength training on the force-velocity relationship of the arm flexors. *International Journal of Sports Medicine,* **3**, 25-28.

Halkjaer-Kristensen, J., & Ingemann-Hansen, T. (1985). Wasting of the human quadriceps muscle after knee ligament injuries. *Scandinavian Journal of Rehabilitation Medicine,* (Suppl. 13), 29-37.

Ingemann-Hansen, T., & Halkjaer-Kristensen, J. (1985). Physical training of the hypotrophic quadriceps muscle in man. *Scandinavian Journal of Rehabilitation Medicine,* (Suppl. 13), 45-49.

Schmalbruck, H. (1985). Skeletal muscle. *Handbuch der mikroskopischen Anatomie des Menschen.* Berlin-Heidelberg-New York: Springer.

Author Index